DICTIONARY OF LEATHER-WORKING TOOLS, *c.* 1700–1950

and the tools of allied trades

*To my wife Miriam, our children
and grandchildren*

DICTIONARY OF LEATHER-WORKING TOOLS, *c.* 1700–1950

and the tools of allied trades

R. A. Salaman

London
GEORGE ALLEN & UNWIN
Sydney

George Allen & Unwin (Publishers) Ltd,
40 Museum Street, London WC1A 1LU, UK

George Allen & Unwin (Publishers) Ltd,
Park Lane, Hemel Hempstead, Herts HP2 4TE, UK

Allen & Unwin Inc.,
9 Winchester Terrace, Winchester, Mass 01890, USA

George Allen & Unwin Australia Pty Ltd
8 Napier Street, North Sydney, NSW 2060, Australia

First published 1986

British Library Cataloguing in Publication Data

Salaman, R.A.
    Dictionary of leather-working tools, c. 1750–
1950: and the tools of allied trades.
1. Leather work—Equipment and supplies—
Dictionaries
I. Title
621.9′08′0321   TT290
ISBN 0-04-621030-X

Set in 9 on 10 Times by Mathematical Composition Setters Ltd., Salisbury, Wilts.
and printed in Great Britain by William Clowes Limited, Beccles and London

CONTENTS

INTRODUCTION

My aim, when compiling material for this Dictionary, has been to describe and illustrate every tool used in the leather-working trades in this country from about 1700 until the present time, and to explain its purpose. I have included tools belonging to certain allied trades (for example, the tools of the Furrier), and I have also included tools imported from abroad if commonly found in British leather-working shops.

The tools listed are grouped under the trade in which they are chiefly employed, and there is a general index to help find a particular tool, irrespective of the trade to which it belongs. The trade sections begin with a brief history, and a short account of the process involved.

Nomenclature and etymology of tool names

I have recorded all the names and alternative names known to me but without giving their source, beyond mentioning an apparent Scottish or American connection. If the etymology of a tool name is discussed in the text, the source of my information is usually the Oxford English Dictionary or the Scottish National Dictionary.

References and Bibliography

In the Bibliography I have included the names of books and other printed material that I have myself consulted and found useful.

Entries in this section serve a double purpose: they give the reader the particulars of the writer or publication that may be referred to in the text only by a name in parentheses; and, in addition, they serve as a token of my gratitude to the person or publication concerned.

NOTES ON USING THE DICTIONARY

How to look up a tool

If the name of a tool and the trade to which it belongs is known, the reader can find the entry in the trade section concerned. In case of difficulty, e.g. if the reader is not sure of the correct name, the index at the end of the book should be consulted.

If the name of the tool is not known, the reader is advised to make a guess at the trade to which the tool belongs, and then look at the illustrations in the trade section concerned.

Cross references

When a reader is referred to another entry (indicated by italics), it will be found in the same trade section in which this direction is given. If the entry referred to belongs to a different trade section, the reader will be informed which one.

Names in the text printed in parentheses refer to publications, trade catalogues or personal communications, of which particulars will be found in the References and Bibliography section.

Abbreviations

c.	circa (about)
OED	Oxford English Dictionary
SND	Scottish National Dictionary
'Diderot *c.* 1760'	Diderot and d'Alembert's Encyclopaedia

Dimensions

The illustrations are not to a uniform scale, but approximate dimensions are included in the text. Unless otherwise stated, it may be assumed that a 'hand tool' is *c.* $4\frac{1}{2}$–7 in. (11.5–17.8 cm) long. Metric equivalents are given in parentheses after Imperial measurements.

THE TOOL MAKERS

A list is given below of the names to be found stamped on tools used in leather-working shops in this country. The names of towns have been added as being those in which, so far as is known, these firms were operating.

Many of these tools are as ingenious, well made and good to look at as their rightly admired counterparts in the woodworking and metal-working trades; and it should be added that these virtues apply equally to tools imported from such makers as Blanchard (Paris), E. A. Berg (Sweden), and C. S. Osborne (USA).

So far as the present writer is aware – and unlike the situation in the woodworking and metal-working trades – very little seems to be known of the history of the firms who made tools for leather-working, or about the origin of their design. It is hoped that the list of firms given below will encourage future research; and for this purpose it should be noted that:

(*a*) though many of these firms will be found in the trade directories of the last two centuries (e.g. Pigot, Kelly or Post Office) they may have been founded many years before being included in a directory;

(*b*) that the tool on which a firm's name is stamped may have been 'factored' by the firm named rather than made by them; it should be remembered that many tool makers of the eighteenth and nineteenth centuries put out some of their work to the anonymous 'little masters' who forged hand tools in their own backyards. As late as the 1930s one could still hear the anvils ringing in the back streets of Sheffield.

Name of Firm	Tools made for
Adam, George (Birmingham)	B/S
Adams, John (London)	S/H
Adams, Thomas (London and Walsall)	H/S
Baker, William (London)	A/N
*Barnsley, George (Sheffield)	B/S and T/C
Bliss, Beauchamp and Bliss (London)	H/S
Brindley, H. (Birmingham)	H/S and B/S
Butler, W. or A. (London)	H/S
Cheney, Edward (Kettering)	B/S
Collins, Joseph (London)	A/N
Collins, Mrs Emma (Birmingham)	A/N
*Dixon, Joseph, Tool Co. (Walsall)	H/S
Dixon, Thomas, & Son (Walsall)	H/S
Garrard (London)	B/S
Haley, Thomas (Leeds)	D/B
Hampson & Scott (Walsall)	H/S
Jackson, Isaac (Glossop)	D/B
James, John, and Sons (Redditch)	A/N
Jupp, C. F. Formerly Jupp, John (London)	B/S
Moyns, Thomas (London)	B/S
Oxley, James (Sheffield)	B/S
Pasco, Henry (?)	B/S
Penton, Edward (London)	B/S
Richter, L. (Northampton)	B/S
Shuttock, Hunter (Bristol)	H/S
Shrimpton and Hooper (Studley)	A/N

Name of Firm	Tools made for
Shrimpton, Thomas (Redditch)	A/N
Stutter, J. W. (London)	B/S
Taylor & Co. (London)	Bag
Thornhill Bros	B/S
Timmins, Richard, & Sons (Birmingham)	B/S and H/S
Ullathorne & Co (London)	B/S
Wilson, Edward (Bootle)	T/C
Wing, Thos. (Sheffield)	B/S
Wright, B. & J. (Leeds)	T/C
Wynn, Timmins (Birmingham)	B/S and H/S

Imported Tools

*Berg, E. A. (Sweden)	B/S
*Blanchard, Simonin (France)	H/S
Goldenberg & Co. (France)	T/C etc.
Gomph, Henry G. (USA)	H/S
Joseph, Marcel (France)	B/S
Osborne, C. S. (USA)	H/S
Rampon (Paris)	Bag
Ross Moyer Mfg. Co. (USA)	B/S

Note: These firms were established during the late seventeenth or early eighteenth century and are today still making tools for the shoe or the harness and saddlery trade.

Abbreviations

A/N	Makers of awls and/or needles
Bag	Tools for bag makers and leather crafts
B/S	Tools for boot and shoe makers
D/B	Tools for driving-belt makers
H/S	Tools for harness makers and saddlers
T/C	Tools for tanners and curriers

ACKNOWLEDGEMENTS

I offer my warmest thanks to the many people who have helped me: the tradesmen in their workshops; the artists who made the illustrations; the friends who visited workshops and libraries on my behalf; the specialists who advised me and examined my manuscripts; the typists who prepared the text for the printers; the correspondents from abroad who answered my questions – and many others.

The names included in the References and Bibliography at the end of this book serve also as a token of my gratitude to the persons and publications named; but in the following paragraphs I have attempted to set out the various kinds of help I have enjoyed, and to whom I am particularly indebted.

The illustrations

The following are the artists who have contributed to this book.

All the line drawings except the few mentioned below are by the late Mr Norman Purnell. Mr Charles Haywood, who made the drawings for my previous book, kindly consented to do the same for the present work. But having completed the drawings for the shoemaking section, he asked me to look for a substitute since he was soon to leave the district.

I was fortunate in finding Mr Norman Purnell, a retired architect who, like Charles Haywood, had the combined gift of being both artist and technical draughtsman. During the subsequent seven years Norman Purnell completed most of the work until his sad and untimely death early in 1983.

Drawings of particular subjects are by the following artists: the drawings of horse harness are by Mr James Arnold, known for his remarkable illustrations of wagons; the drawings of eighteenth-century shoemaking are by Mr D. A. Saguto; drawings of some special tools, including glove-maker's, are by Mr Jim Channel; others are by Mr Dennis Griffiths, Mr Alan Jones and Mr Graham Hobbs. Drawings of certain bookbinding processes (i.e. *Figs* 1:2, 1:12, 1:16, 1:25, 1:26, 1:28, 1:34) are reproduced from those by Mr Alan J. Turvey which appeared in *Bookbinding* (1963), by Mr Jeff Clements.

Most of the engravings come from the catalogues of firms who, at the dates indicated below, were trading under the following names:

George Barnsley & Sons, Sheffield. Makers of shoemaking tools (1890)
Ward & Payne Ltd, Sheffield. General tool makers (*c.* 1900)
Richard Timmins, Birmingham. General tool makers (*c.* 1800)
Harrild & Sons, London. Makers of bookbinder's tools (1903)
Hampson & Scott, Walsall. Makers of saddler's tools (*c.* 1900)
G. Kremp, successors to George Lutz, Paris. Makers of saddler's tools (1905). The engravings in this catalogue (kindly lent by Mr Philip Walker) appear to be the same as those in the catalogue of Simonin Blanchard, the tool makers founded in 1823 and still working in Paris
C. S. Osborne, Newark, USA. Makers of saddler's tools (*c.* 1883)

Finally, there are some engravings which are taken from Charles Tomlinson's *Cyclopaedia of Useful Arts and Manufactures* (1853). In the section on bookbinding they are *Figs* 1:31, 1:36 and 1:37, and in the leather manufacturing section they are *Figs* 11:5, 11:13, 11:16, 11:17 and 11:24.

The workshops

Most of what I have learnt about tools and trades comes from talking to tradesmen and visiting them in their workshops or factories. Their names are given below; I am most grateful to all of them.

I became well acquainted with village workshops in my boyhood, but the visits recorded below were made between 1946 and the present time.

Bookbinders
Roger and Rita Powell, Bookbinders, Froxfield, Hampshire
The Campfield Press, St Albans, Hertfordshire

Boot and Shoe Makers and Repairers
Mr William Chalwin, London
Mr Percy Cook, Luton
Mr H. Dew, Middlesbrough
Mr W. Graysmark, London
Messrs John Lobb, London
Mr H. W. Marks, Enfield
Mr William Martin, cobbler and village barber, Barley, Hertfordshire (visited 1913–20)
Messrs Henry Maxwell and Co. Ltd, London
Mr G. Sheldrake, Hunstanton, Norfolk
Mr F. Stack, London
Mr W. Ward, Dover
Mr Jack Whitcher, Aldeburgh, Suffolk
   Shoe repairers and makers in Harpenden, Hertfordshire: Mr H. R. Bigg, Mr K. Botting, Mr A. Fellowes, Mr W. K. Gibbons and Mr K. S. Munt.

Clog Makers
Mr William Bradnell, Besses O'th Barn, Lancs
Mr H. Brierley, Rochdale
Mr Pickup, Burnley
*Mr C. Powell, Manchester
Walton Bros (Halifax) Ltd

Cricket Ball Makers
*Alfred Readers & Co., Maidstone

Driving-Belt Makers
Webb & Son (Combs) Ltd, Leather Manufacturers. Formerly makers of driving belts, leather buckets, hose, etc., of Stowmarket, Suffolk.
Barrow Hepburn Belting Ltd, London

Framed Handbag Makers
*S. Launer & Co., London
Taylor & Co. Tools Ltd, London (Bag-making tools)

Fur Manufacturers and Furriers
*Calman Links, London
*Hacker Furs Ltd, London
Martin-Rice Ltd, London
Wright & Sons (Furriers), St Albans, Hertfordshire

Glove Makers
*Dent-Fownes Ltd, Warminster
L. E. Clothier & Co. Ltd, Woodstock

Harness Makers and Saddlers
Messrs Basing and Mathews, Newbury, Hants
Champion and Wilton and their successors, W. & H. Gidden, London
Mr Alfred Clarke, Ipswich
Mr Herbert Cox, Chesham, Bucks
D. Gilbert & Sons, Newmarket

Mr G. F. Humphrey, Royston, Hertfordshire
*G. J. Huskisson & Son (also collar makers), Walsall
Mr J. G. Maddie, Harpenden, Hertfordshire
Mr A. H. Marshall, Kirton, Lincolnshire
J. Miles & Son, Dorchester (Mr R. Thomas)
Mr George Stace (Collar Maker), Birchington, Kent
Mr Martin Wilkinson, Redbourn, Hertfordshire

Hat Makers (Top Hats)
*S. Patey (London) Ltd

Last Makers
Messrs John Lobb, London

Leather Manufacturers
*J. & F. J. Baker & Co. Ltd, Colyton, Devon
Connolly Bros (Curriers) Ltd, London
Josiah Croggon & Sons, Grampound, Cornwall
W. J. Francis & Son, Falmouth, Cornwall
Handford Greatorex & Co. Ltd, Walsall
Elliot Hallas & Son, Huddersfield
The Liverpool Tanning Co., Liverpool
William R. Pangbourne & Son, London
G. W. Russel & Son, Hitchin, Hertfordshire
Webb & Son (Combs) Ltd, Stowmarket, Suffolk (see also *Driving-Belt Makers* above)

Parchment Makers
*H. Band & Co., London
William Cowley & Sons, Newport Pagnell

Pump and Ram-Leather Makers
Barrow Hepburn Belting Ltd, London

Table Liners and Gilders
*Murga Candler Ltd, London

Whip Makers
Wm. Crawley & Sons Ltd, Peterborough

Note: Workshops marked with a star were visited by one of the helpers listed under *Research* (below), and not by the author.

Specialist advice
When I started work on this book, I was fortunate in having the friendly guidance of that pioneer of modern leather-working studies, the late Mr John Waterer.

I want to give my thanks to the following experts who helped me in particular fields, and who in many cases undertook to read and criticise what I have written. Needless to say, the responsibility for any mistakes rests with me alone: had I not consulted these friends there might have been many more.

Bookbinding: Roger and Rita Powell gave me practical demonstrations and valuable advice on many aspects of their work,

Boot and Shoemaking: In coping with this longest section of the book and its rather complex subject matter, I had much advice and many kindnesses from four people with long experience in this field, namely: the late Mr John Thornton, formerly head of the Department of Boot and Shoe Manufacture in the

Northampton College of Technology; Mr William B. E. Glasow, a shoemaker of wide experience who, though retired, still works for his former employers Messrs John Lobb of London (both Mr Thornton and Mr Glasow gave me their own version of many processes and tools used in shoemaking; and before his sad death in 1983, John Thornton gave a long and critical look at everything I had myself written on this subject); Mr R. C. Pond, a surgical bootmaker who worked for several well-known firms in Norwich including Messrs J. Buckingham & Sons, and finally as Director in charge of shoemaking at Messrs W. H. H. Clarke & Co.; and Miss June Swann, Keeper of the Shoe Collection in the Northampton Central Museum, an authority on every aspect of boot and shoemaking both here and abroad.

I am also greatly indebted to: Mr D. A. Saguto of Kensington, USA, an authority on eighteenth-century shoemaking, and himself a maker of boots and shoes; Mr Raymond R. Townsend of Williamsburg, USA, who worked in the Boot Shop and Research Dept. of the Colonial Williamsburg Foundation; the late Mr George Barnsley, Director of George Barnsley & Sons, Sheffield: for notes on the shoemakers' tools made by his firm; and Mr H. W. J. Edwards (Trealaw) and Mr Ben Vincent (Radlett): for the background to the legends concerning the patron saints of the shoemakers.

Clog Making: Mr C. Powel, clogmaker of Swinton near Manchester: tools and methods of clogmaking; Miss Evelyn Vigeon, Keeper of the Ordsall Museum, Salford: history of the wooden-soled shoes.

Coach Trimming: Mr Sydney Stiff, formerly at Hoopers and Co., Coachbuilders, London: coach trimming for horse carriages and the early motor cars.

Decoration of Leather: On the complex processes of leather decoration and moulding, I have been greatly helped by Mr Neil MacGregor, himself a practitioner in this field working in Tetbury. He has also contributed generously from his wide knowledge of leather working in other fields.

Driving Belts: Mr Nicholas Portway, director of Messrs Webb & Son, Leather Manufacturers at Comb near Stowmarket in Suffolk, provided me with information on the little-known tools and equipment used for making driving belts, leather hose and leather buckets, all of which were formerly produced by his firm.

Fur Trades: Mr Francis Weiss (London), practitioner of these trades and writer on its history and its specialised processes.

Glove Making: Mr J. E. Troughton, a retired glove maker in Woodstock who has written about this trade (see Bibliography). He has checked my own writing and allowed me to make good use of his. I have also been helped by Mr John G. Rhodes, Keeper at the Woodstock Museum.

Gut String Making: Mr M. C. Meinel, Director, Bow Brand Ltd, Kings Lynn, has informed me about the methods and tools used in the process of making gut strings for industry, sport and surgery.

Harness Making and Saddlery: For this second longest section of the book, I was very fortunate to have advice and written contributions from Mr Edward Lawrence, a saddler and harness maker now working near Canterbury. He was formerly a member of the well-known London saddlers and harness makers, Messrs Champion and Wilton.

I am also grateful to Mr Russel Bigelow (Winchester, USA) for advice on American harness-making tools and methods.

Leather Manufacture: This section includes a description of the tools used by the tanner and currier, but I have only touched on the mammoth subject of leather manufacture itself. Instead, I asked Mr Roy S. Thomson to contribute an explanation in layman's language on how a raw skin is transformed into the incorruptible substance we call leather. Mr Thomson is a chemist at the Wellington Tannery at Raunds near Wellingborough, and a writer on the history of the trade.

For specialist information on tanner's and currier's tools I am grateful to the late Mr R. W. Bishop, formerly Works Manager of J. & F. J. Baker & Co., Tanners & Curriers of Colyton, Devon; and to the late Mr John Snell who worked as a beamsman in the same firm.

The Loriner: Mr William T. Stone, a retired Loriner in Walsall, one of the survivors from this highly skilled and specialised trade, has provided me with both descriptions and drawings of the different processes and tools for making horse bits, stirrups and harness buckles.

Taxidermy: Mr Graham S. Cowles, of the Natural History Museum, has informed and guided me on the little known methods and tools of this trade.

Other subjects: For their general assistance and advice I am also indebted to Mr David Archer (Powys); Mr W. L. Goodman (Bristol); Mr Michael A. Field (Acle); Mr Kenneth Hawley (Sheffield); Mr Chris Healey (Newark-on-Trent); Mr Tristan Jones (St Nicholas at Wade); Mr Colin Maughan (Crawley); Mr L. John Mayes (High Wycombe); Lord Miles (London); and Mr Philip Walker (Stowmarket).

For translating and interpreting the writings of French eighteenth-century Encyclopaedists, I am most grateful to Mrs Betty Nagelschmidt, Mr Nicholas Hobbs and Mr Michael Hatch.

For Scottish tool names I am indebted to Mr David Murison, formerly editor of the *Scottish National Dictionary*.

American tools

There are several leather-working tools used in North America that are seldom, if ever, seen over here. I sent questions about them to the Early American Industries Association, who published them in their Journal, and to Mr Kenneth Roberts (author and publisher of books on tools and trades) who put me in touch with experts in this field. Many responded with typical American generosity, sending me both explanations and printed material. I am most grateful to all of them:

Mr F. E. Abernethy; Mr A. M. Beitler; Mr Richard O. Byrne; Mr William A. Downes; Professor Richard S. Hartenburg; Mr A. Oris Jones; Mr John S. Kebabian; Mr Paul B. Kebabian; Mr Hugh W. Parker; Mr Charles Reichman; Mr Ivan C. Risley; Mr Elliot M. Sayward; Mr Robert Siegal; Mr Mark Sipson; Mr Richard Starr; and Mr Kenneth Wirtz. (See also Mr Bigelow, Mr Saguto, and Mr Townsend under *Specialist Advice* above.)

Permission to print

For permission to reproduce illustrations, I am grateful to:

Mr George Barnsley and Mr F. G. Barnsley for permission to reproduce engravings from the 1890 and 1927 catalogue of George Barnsley and Sons (Sheffield), makers of shoemaker's tools.

Messrs J. Stead & Co. Ltd, the Sheffield tool makers, for permission to reproduce engravings from the catalogue of Richard Timmins (Birmingham), *c.* 1800, makers of saddler's, shoemaker's and other tools.

Messrs W. L. Harrild and Partners (London), Engineers to the Printing Trade, for permission to reproduce engravings from their 1903 catalogue of bookbinder's tools.

Mr Jeff Clements, author of *Bookbinding* (London: Arco Publications, 1963), for permission to reproduce line drawings by Mr J. Alan Turvey.

For permission to print passages from their books, I am grateful to the following authors and their publishers: Mr George Ewart Evans, *The Farm and the Village* (Faber & Faber, 1969); Mr B. Eldred Ellis, *Gloves and the Glove Trade* (Pitman, 1921); Mrs I. F. Grant, *Highland Folk Ways* (Routledge & Kegan Paul, 1961); Miss Dorothy Hartley, *Made in England* (Methuen, 1939); Mr J. Geraint Jenkins, *Traditional Country Craftsmen* (Routledge, 1965); Mr E. M. Jope, *A History of Technology* (Oxford, 1954); Mr Andrew Lawson, *Handmade in London* (Cassell, 1978); Mr Frank Plucknett, *Boot and Shoe Manufacture* (Pitman, 1916-31); Mr Roy S. Thomson, Newcomen Society *Transactions* (1981-82); Mr John W. Waterer, *Leather Craftsmanship* (Bell, 1968); Mr Jack Hill, *Country Crafts* (David & Charles, 1979); Mr John H. Thornton (ed.), *Text Book of Footwear Manufacture* (London: Butterworth, 1970).

Research

I offer my grateful thanks to:

Mrs Moira Rey for visits to fur dressers and furriers, handbag makers, hatters, glove makers, table liners, and many reference libraries, and for recording the words of experienced workers in these specialised trades.

Mrs Thalia Polak for her wide-ranging investigation of the bookbinding trade and her descriptions and drawings of their tools; for her search among the directories for early makers of leather-working tools; and for investigating the tanning methods recorded by the French Encyclopaedists.

Mr Kenneth Kilby for visits to tanners, curriers, and a parchment maker: and for his fully illustrated reports on their work and hand tools which have been of great value to me.

Dr Richard Knight for his investigation of horse-collar making in Walsall, whipmaking in Birmingham, and for his inquiries among other trades.

The late Mr Norman Purnell (see under *Illustrations* above) for investigating and illustrating the work of cricket ball makers, gut string makers and makers of top hats.

Mr Michael Marr for investigating the history of harness-making, and for his critical examination of harness nomenclature.

Museums and Institutions

I am grateful for the help given to me by the following:

Beamish	North of England Open Air Museum (Mr Frank Atkinson)
Birmingham	Museum and Art Gallery (Mr Stephen Price)
Cambridge	East Asian History of Science Library (Dr Joseph Needham FRS)
	Cambridge County Folk Museum
Gressenhall	Norfolk Rural Life Museum (Miss Bridget Yates)
Halifax	West Yorkshire Folk Museum (Mr R. A. Innes and Miss P. F. Milward)
Hatfield	Old Mill House Museum (Miss Susan Agate)
Hertford	Hertford Museum (Mr A. S. Davies)
Hitchin	Hitchin Museum and Art Gallery (Mr Alan L. Fleck)
Huddersfield	Tolson Memorial Museum
	Colne Valley Museum (Mr H. G. Bamforth)
Kendal	Abbot Hall Museum
Leicester	Newarke Houses Museum (Mr J. A. Daniell)
London	The Guildhall Library
	Victoria & Albert Museum Library
	The Leather Institute (Mr R. D. Britter)
	Council for Small Industries in Rural Areas
	Cordwainers' College
	National Union of Boot & Shoe Operatives
	Society of Antiquaries (Mr J. H. Hopkins)
	Society of Master Saddlers
	The Leathersellers' Company
	The Science Museum and Library (Mr A. K. Corry)
	The Saddlers' Company
	Hackney Reference Library
Luton	Wardown Museum (Mrs Marion Nichols)
Northampton	British Leather Manufacturers' Research Assoc. (Mr A. W. Landman)
	Central Museum (Miss June Swann)
	Museum of Leathercraft (Miss Victoria Gabbitas)
Norwich	Bridewell Museum (Mr David Young)
Pitstone	Museum of Country Trades (Mr J. Hawkins)
Reading	Museum of English Rural Life
St Albans	City Museum (Miss Gillian Gregg)
Salford	Ordsall Hall Museum (Miss E. Vigeon)
Stockport	Vernon Park Museum (Mrs Gaby Porter)
Stowmarket	Museum of East Anglian Life
	Tool And Trades History Society
Street (Somerset)	Shoe Museum (C. & J. Clark Ltd)
Walsall	Museum & Library
Woodstock	Oxford County Museum (Mr John G. Rhodes)
York	The Castle Museum

Abroad

Australia (Melbourne)	Maritime Museum (Arthur E. Woodley)
Belgium (Liège)	Musée de la Vie Wallonne
Canada (Moncton)	Canadian Conservation Institute (Mr Richard O. Byrne)
France (Paris)	Musée National des Arts et Traditions Populaires

Germany (Offenbach)	Deutsches Ledermuseum
Holland (Arnhem)	Nederlands Openluchtmuseum
Israel (Tel-Aviv)	Man and His Work Museum (Prof. S. Avitsur)
United States *of America*	Early American Industries Association Smithsonian Institution, Washington Colonial Williamsburg Foundation The Cincinnati Public Library

Preparing the text

For six years I was fortunate in having my manuscript deciphered and typed out by Mrs Marilyn Mahaney. Before and after that period, I have been helped by Mrs Ann Lanchbery, Mrs Madeline Morris and Mrs Dawn Wells. I am most grateful to all of them.

I am indebted to Mr Graham Hobbs for collating and indexing the typescript, and for his critical examination of the final manuscript.

Finally, I want to thank the Leathersellers' Company, and my publishers, George Allen & Unwin, for their contributions towards the cost of the illustrations.

1

Bookbinder

Historical Note

The earliest books were rolls or sheets made from stems of the aquatic reed known as papyrus. This was the writing material of the ancients from about 3000 BC; the name papyrus is the origin of our word 'paper'. By the second century AD, parchment, prepared from the skins of sheep and other animals, began to be used as a writing material, and by the fourth century AD, had taken the place of papyrus. The skins were usually sewn together into scrolls which were wound on rollers − a method still used for the Scrolls of the Law that are read in the synagogues throughout the world.

By about the second century AD, the parchment was cut into separate leaves, gathered, folded over and stitched through the fold. Thus began the development of the codex, or hinged book, as we know it today. Protective wooden covers were provided, later to be replaced by pasteboard, sometimes covered in leather.

In his *History of English Craft Bookbinding Technique* (1963), Bernard Middleton writes that the earliest known use of paper in England was in 1308, and that the first English paper mill was set up at the end of the fifteenth century. From about this time paper gradually replaced parchment except for certain important documents.

The edges of parchment-leaved books tended to 'cockle' with changes in the weather, and had to be trimmed with a knife or shears. But when paper came into general use it became possible to trim the edges more smoothly and by the middle of the sixteenth century this was done with the *Plough*.

Tawing − an early mineral tannage using alum which produced a white leather − was used to cover the earliest leather bound books. Vegetable tanned goatskin, deerskin, sheepskin or calfskin were used from the fifteenth century onwards.

By the early years of the eighteenth century, the hand tools of the bookbinder, as illustrated in Diderot's Encyclopaedia (Paris, *c.* 1760), had reached a stage little different from that of today.

Note on decoration

A large number of the bookbinder's tools are used for the decoration of the edges, spine and cover.

The edges of books have been decorated in many ways since they began to be smoothly finished: these decorative finishes protected the edges of the leaves from dirt and dust. The earliest type of edge finish was solid colour, the dyes coming from indigo, brazil wood or various powdered earths. Sprinkling became popular in the sixteenth century, red being the favourite colour. The marbling of book edges (giving an appearance of variegated marble) began at the end of the seventeenth century and remained popular in the nineteenth; edge-gilding was practised in Flanders in the fifteenth century and reached England by the middle of the sixteenth.

The leather for covers was often dyed, grained or embossed, before being attached to the book. After being attached, the leather was decorated in many ways. One of these was blind tooling (i.e. without gold leaf) which was in use by the tenth century; heated tools (or stamps) were pressed into the leather on the boards or spine to produce indented designs. By the sixteenth century the patterned *Roll* was in use. Stamps or blocks date back to the thirteenth century and were impressed 'in the blind'; gold tooling and blocking began in England during the sixteenth century.

Many books had some sort of clasp or strap and buckle in medieval times, and some also had metal bosses to protect their corners. Later, the clasps were replaced by silk ties.

The use of jewels to embellish the covers of important books is said to have led to the destruction of many of them by thieves.

Commercial bookbinding

As commercial bookbinding developed in the eighteenth and nineteenth centuries, books became smaller, lighter, and cheaper. It is fortunate that in this field at least a good standard of design and workmanship, inherited from earlier hand-bound books, has been retained.

1

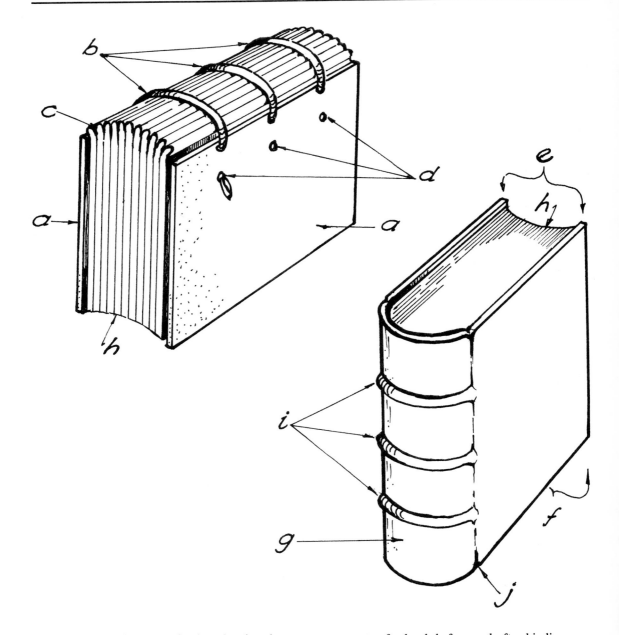

Fig. 1:1 Diagrammatic view showing the component parts of a book before and after binding

(a) Boards (or cover)
(b) Cords (or tapes)
(c) Sections
(d) Slips (ends or cords or tapes before and after trimming)
(e) Head
(f) Tail
(g) Spine
(h) Fore-edge
(i) Raised bands
(j) Joint or groove

Process Fig. 1:1

The purpose of the process is to protect the pages of the book, to enable the book to be held open conveniently, and to ensure that when standing on the shelf, the spine looks well, and proclaims the title.

SEE ENTRY:

(*a*) *Folding and Pressing*
The printed sheets of paper are folded into sections. these are flattened and compacted in a press or with a hammer.

Folder
Press I (Standing)
Hammer
Knocking-Down Iron

(*b*) *Sewing*
Grooves ('kerfs') are cut in the spine for the cords onto which the sections will be sewn.

Saw
Sewing Press

(*c*) *Forwarding* (Fitting the boards etc.)
The 'backswell' due to the sewing is reduced or flattened.

Press II (Lying)
Knocking-Down Iron
Hammer

The spine is glued.

Scratcher

Backing: the spine is rounded and backed.

Hammer, Backing
Press II (Lying)
Boards (Backing)

The edges are levelled.

Plough

The cover boards are cut.

Guillotine Shears
Plough
Press II (Lying)

Holes are made in the boards for the ends of the cords (slips) and the boards are laced on. The book is pressed and the spine is set with glue.

Bodkin
Press I (Standing)

(*d*) *Covering*
The leather is cut, pared if necessary, pasted and attached. The cover is shaped to the bands.

Knife (Paring)
Folder
Band Nipper
Band Stick

(*e*) *The decorative process*
Blind tooling: a pattern is pressed into the leather by tools, usually preheated.

Finishing Tools
Lettering Tools

Gold tooling: similar tools are used to press gold leaf into the impressions already made in the leather. The surplus gold is removed and collected.

Gilder's Tools
Finishing Stove

Block printing: this involves the pressing of a die engraved with a complete design onto the book cover.

Press III

Edge-decoration. Methods include:
(1) Sprinkling: By beating or shaking a brush full of colour so that the colour falls in small drops onto the edge. Later a Sprinkling Frame was used.

Sprinkling Frame

(2) Marbling: See the entry

Marbling Comb

(3) Gilding: The book edge is scraped smooth, treated with Glair etc. and the gold leaf applied. When dry the gilt edge is burnished.

Gilder's Tools
Polishing & Burnishing Tools

(4) Gauffering: The gilt edge is sometimes decorated with a pattern impressed with small (usually heated) tools. The term Gauffer comes from the French *gaufre* for honeycomb.

3

The Tools

Band Nippers (Lining Pliers) *Fig. 1:2*
A plier, usually sprung, with wide, flat jaws. It is used for squeezing leather on the spine against the sides of the bands. Unlike other types of plier, the jaws are smooth in order to avoid damaging the leather.

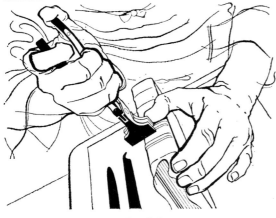

Fig. 1:2

Band Stick *Fig. 1:3*
Flat strips of polished hardwood, some with bevelled edges, others with a groove cut along the edge.

After using the *Band Nippers*, the band is rubbed with a Band Stick to give it a neat, sharp edge. The space between the bands can also be rubbed down with these sticks.

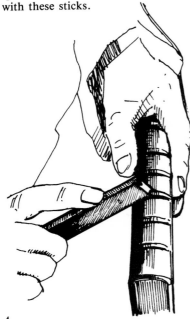

Fig. 1:3

Boards
A name given to a number of shaped wooden boards used in the bookbinding process. They are usually made of smooth hardwood. (*Note*: The term 'Boards' is also the name given to the stiff side covers of the book which were originally made of wood.)

Bookbinder's Boards include the following:

(*a*) *Pressing Boards*
Flat boards used to separate and protect the books when being pressed and flattened (see *Press*).

(*b*) *Cutting Boards* (Gilding Boards)
A pair of wedge-shaped boards with a horizontal top face used to hold a book in the Lying Press (see under *Press II*) while the edges are cut with the *Plough*. They are also used to hold the book while kerfs are being sawn in the spine, and when edge-gilding.

(*c*) *Backing Boards*
A pair of wedge-shaped boards used to hold a book in the Lying Press for the process of 'Backing'. When in position, the top face of the wedge is at an angle of about 60° to the horizontal. (See also *Hammer, Backing*.)

(*d*) *Tying-up Boards*
A pair of L-shaped boards used to protect the front edges of the book covers. This is necessary when tying cords round the whole book for holding the leather cover over the back of the spine while it is drying.

Diderot describes and illustrates a 'whipping board' for the same purpose. The worker wears a leather gauntlet on his hand to allow him to pull the cord very tight without hurting himself.

Bodkin or Awl (Binder's or Printer's Bodkins)
A plain, tapered, steel spike, round in cross-section set in a wooden handle. Two sizes are used: a small awl for making sewing holes and also for teasing out the ends of the cords when lacing boards to the book; and a longer Awl, usually known as a Bodkin, for holing the boards for lacing.

Two holes are made in the board for each slip, usually by punching the bodkin through the board onto a lead plate.

Cutting Tools
Cutting tools used by bookbinders are described under the following entries: *Gilder's Tools* (Gold Knife); *Guillotine Shears* (Bench Knife, Board Cutter etc.); *Knife* (Cutting-out, Paper, Paring etc.); *Plough*; *Shears* (Hand); *Spokeshave*.

Decorating Tools: see *Finishing Tools*; *Gilder's Tools*; *Marbling Comb*; *Polishers and Burnishers*; *Sprinkling Frame*.

Fillet: see Finishing Tools.

Finishing Stove *Fig. 1:4*
A heated centre-plate or hearth with a circular rim providing support for the handles of finishing tools which are placed radially with their metal heads resting on the heated centre. Today these stoves are heated by gas (as shown) or electricity.

Diderot illustrates a bowl-like fire box with a grill above it for the 'gilding tools'.

Finishing Tools for edge and cover decoration. *Figs 1:5–1:10*
(See also *Guilder's and Lettering Tools*; *Polishers and Burnishers*. Also notes on decorative processes under *Process and Tools* in the introductory pages.) The following tools are used in the finishing process which includes imprinting lines and decorative designs on the covers and spine of the book. Most of them have a brass head fitted into a wooden handle, *c.*6–8 in. (15.2–20.3 cm) long overall, or *c.*13 in. (33 cm) long if designed to be worked from the shoulder. In many cases the tools are heated before use: see *Finishing Stove*.

Fig. 1:4

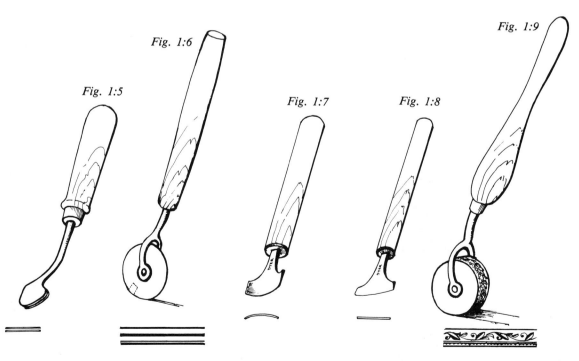

Fig. 1:9

Fig. 1:6

Fig. 1:5

Fig. 1:7

Fig. 1:8

5

(a) Crease (Creaser) *Fig. 1:5*
Used for imprinting lines, they are similar to those used by harness makers for making lines on straps etc. They may be Single or Double Creasers, or of the Shoulder Vein type. (See HARNESS MAKER AND SADDLER section.)

(b) Fillet Fig. 1:6
The term may be derived from the thread-like imprint made. (See also *Roll* below.)
A solid metal wheel, usually of brass, of $2-3\frac{1}{2}$ in. (5–8.8 cm) diameter, held on a forked or single-arm carriage which is set into a wooden handle, *c*.15 in. (38.1 cm) overall – long enough to be worked from the shoulder. A very small fillet, 'smaller than a silver threepenny piece', was introduced in the 1890s to produce designs with curved lines.

The edge of the wheel is cut to roll single, double or treble lines. A gap is often cut on the edge of the wheel, known as a mitre, so that the wheel can be stopped at a right-angled corner of the design without overlapping. Since the sides of the gap are cut at an angle of $45°$, the lines imprinted will meet as a mitred joint.

(c) Gouge Fig. 1:7
A handled 'stamp' with a curved head, made in sets to imprint a range of arcs of different radii. These arcs imprint plain or decorative lines.

(d) Pallet. (The simple Line Pallets are sometimes called Line Tools; those with $45°$ ends are known as Mitre Pallets.) *Fig. 1:8*
A handled tool with a brass head shaped to imprint a line or band (or in special cases, a set of letters) from $\frac{1}{4}$–3 in. (0.6–7.6 cm) long. The head is usually given a convex working face so that the tool can be rocked on the surface being tooled. They are used mainly for tooling the spines of a binding. The Mitred Pallet has ends cut at $45°$ to fit a corner.

(e) Roll (Pattern Roll) *Fig. 1:9*
This is similar to the *Fillet* except that the edge is wider and is engraved with a continuous design.
The early Rolls were $c.1\frac{3}{4}$ in. (4.4 cm) diameter and thus produced 5–6 in. (12.7–15.2 cm) of pattern. The modern Rolls can have a diameter of $3\frac{1}{2}$ in. (8.8 cm) and produce a pattern of *c*.11 in. (27.9 cm). Most early Rolls were intaglio-cut so that the design was raised and the background leather pressed in.

(f) Lettering Tools: see separate entry.

(g) Unit Stamps (Brass Tools; Corner Tools; Drop Tools; Hand Tools) *Fig. 1:10*
In general the stamps used for blind tooling (i.e. without gold leaf) are intaglio-cut to produce a raised pattern and a depressed background; those used for gold tooling have their design as an outline above the surface which produces a pattern of depressed gold lines.

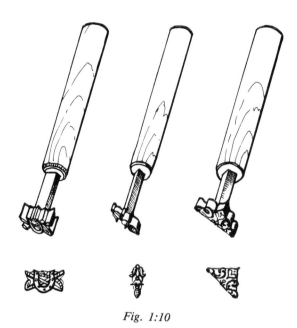

Fig. 1:10

There are two main kinds of stamp:

(1) Small individual brass stamps usually set in wooden handles and engraved in a great variety of different patterns, mostly geometric or floral devices.
(2) 'Corner Tools' made of right-angled patterns to be used as the corners or centre of a design which was often rather ornate. They were at one time much used in repetitive tooling, particularly in half-bound leather bindings.

Folder *Fig. 1:11*
A smooth polished piece of bone or ivory shaped like a paper knife, between 5 and 9 in. (12.7–22.8 cm) long. One end is rounded, and the other may be a soft point or hook-shaped.

Used when hand-folding the printed sheets into sections of a book; also to manipulate the leather cover when it is attached to the book so that it fits smoothly over the edges of the boards and into the grooves. The hooked point is used for dealing with awkward corners.

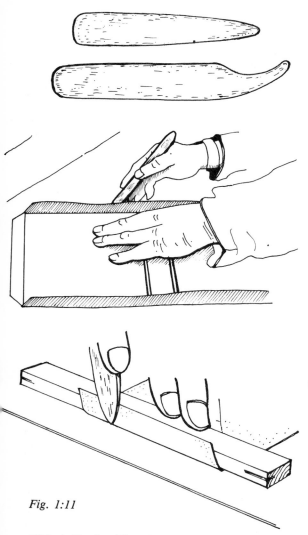

Fig. 1:11

Gilder's Tools *Figs. 1:12–1:14*

In the bookbinder's trade gilder's tools are used for applying gold leaf to book edges and to the decoration and lettering on the cover and spine. Gold leaf was being made 5,000 years ago in ancient Egypt; the method of cutting it, described below, was in use in Europe 500 years ago. Today it is made by gold beaters who supply it to the gilders in sheets of about $3\frac{1}{4}$ in. (8.2 cm) square lying between the pages of 'books' made specially for the purpose. The leaf is extremely thin – about 1/250,000 of an inch. It is so delicate that the gentlest breath directed at one side of it will lift it up, while a gentle puff from above will lay it flat. Gilder's tools include:

(a) The Cushion Fig. 1:12
This is made from a piece of wood about 12x6 in. (30.5 x 15.2 cm) in size, on which a small quantity of wadding is covered with a piece of calf-skin, with its flesh (rough) side uppermost and with its edges nailed down to the edges of the board. A screen of vellum or other material about 5 in. (12.7 cm) high is sometimes fitted on three sides of the cushion to prevent draughts from disturbing the leaf. The surface of the cushion is very slightly convex: this facilitates lifting the leaf by sliding the knife under it.

A pinch of dry powder such as bath brick or red ochre is sprinkled occasionally over the surface of the cushion to avoid adhesion if the leather becomes too smooth.

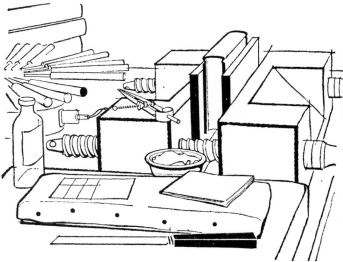

Fig. 1:12

(b) The Knife (Gold Knife) *Fig. 1:13*
This has a straight blade *c.*7 in. (17.7 cm) long. The edge is blunt but smooth – rather like an ordinary table knife. In use the knife is held horizontally and is applied with the blade at right angles to the leaf and cushion; it is drawn back and forth slowly but firmly, care being taken to keep the whole length of the blade in contact with the leaf and cushion – otherwise the leaf may 'ruck'.

The knife is also used for lifting the gold leaf: hence the need to keep the blade smooth and clean. Experienced gilders handle the leaf with apparent ease by a combination of lifting by knife and a gentle puff of their own breath: a light puff of breath in the centre of the leaf to lay it flat; a light puff near the edge to fold it over.

Fig. 1:13

Note on cutting gold leaf

It may be asked why gold leaf is cut on the soft surface of a cushion with a blunt knife, rather than cut on, say, a smooth piece of card with a razor blade. The answer is probably this: cutting with a sharp knife on a smooth surface needs great care to prevent the leaf from slipping about or, worse still, from dragging. The cushion method was probably developed to avoid this: the suede-like surface of the cushion holds the leaf still, but without the risk of adhesion; and it allows a blunt knife to form a groove in the leaf which parts the leaf in two by wearing through rather than by cutting.

(c) Burnisher

An agate or steel burnisher is used for polishing book edges after applying gold leaf: see *Polishing and Burnishing Tools*.

(d) Scraper (Gilder's scrape)

A steel scraper, of the type used by cabinetmakers, is used for smoothing book edges before gilding.

(e) Devil   Fig. 1:14

A tool often home-made, used to mix egg-white when making Glair – the traditional gold size used by bookbinders as an adhesive foundation for the gold leaf. The Devil consists of two short pieces of quill or wooden peg fastened to the end of a stick. This is inserted into the Glair and rolled between the palms of the hand like a domestic egg or cocktail whisk.

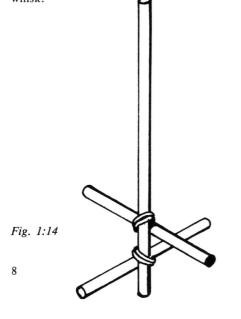

Fig. 1:14

(f) Gilder's Press

For holding books while edge-gilding (see under *Press* II).

(g) Gilder's Frame

A light wooden frame with a fine net or gauze stretched onto it. When lightly greased it will pick up a leaf of gold and release it with the help of a puff of air through the mesh. It is used mainly for applying gold leaf to book edges.

(h) Gilder's Tip

A type of brush consisting of long sable hairs fixed into a cardboard frame about $3\frac{1}{2}$ in. (8.8 cm) wide. Used to pick up gold leaf for edge-gilding or gold tooling.

(i)   Glair and Sealing Paste

As mentioned under *Devil* above, the traditional adhesive for gold leaf is Glair – a mixture of white-of-egg and water, with the addition in some cases of a little vinegar. A rather less homely mixture, known as Gilder's Sealing Paste or Surfacing Paste (used as a foundation), contains, according to Diderot, Armenian Bole (coloured earth), blood, blacklead or plumbago, tallow or soap, and sugar candy.

Guillotine Shears (Bench Knife; Board Cutter) *Figs. 1:15; 1:16*

(See also *Cutting Tools*; *Plough*.)

The term 'Guillotine Shear' is used by tool merchants for the whole group of Bench Knives and Guillotines designed for a wide variety of work. They are named after the French physician J. I. Guillotin who, in 1789, suggested the use of a heavy blade, falling by its own weight between guides, as more merciful than the headsman's axe.

These tools have a common ancestor in the Shear (a heavy version of the Scissor) in which two overlapping blades are moved across one another over the material to be cut. But whereas both blades of the Shear or Scissor close on the material being cut, only the upper blade of the Guillotine Shear moves as it is forced down on the work. The lower blade remains stationary, acting as a support for the work at the precise line where the material is to be 'sheared off' by the upper blade.

Diderot describes a handled iron tool (*Pointe*) about 20 in. (50.8 cm) long with a point 'chamferred and very sharp' for cutting boards. No guillotine-like tools are mentioned.

Guillotine Shears used for bookbinding are listed below; they are given the names used in the trade. Most of them incorporate a clamp on the worktable to hold the material being cut, and also some kind of

Fig. 1:15

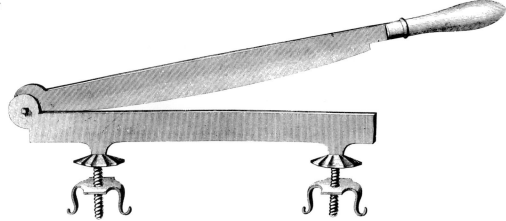

measuring and squaring device. In the smaller hand-operated tools, the knife is pivoted at one end like a Clogger's Knife.

(a) Bench Knife (Card Shears) *Fig. 1:15*
Fitted to its own base, or screwed to the bench, it has a 12–25 in. (30.5–63.5 cm) blade which is slightly convex along its cutting edge. Used for light trimming.

(b) Board Cutter (Board Chopper; Lever Cutter) *Fig. 1:16*
A heavier version of the Bench Knife, mounted on its own frame (often made in decorative cast iron) with a blade 25–40 in. (63.5 cm–1.01 m) long. The blade is sometimes fitted with a counterweight beyond its pivot to lift it ready for the next cut. Used for trimming covers and pages.

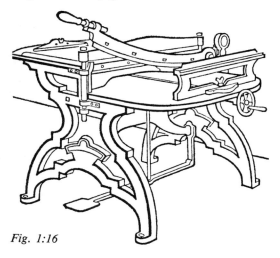
Fig. 1:16

(c) Guillotine (Lever Guillotine)
Bookbinders use this name for a machine or hand-operated Guillotine designed for heavy work including the cutting of book edges as a substitute for the *Plough*. Instead of the pivoted knife of (*a*) and (*b*) above, the blade descends vertically (or nearly so) often with a system of levers to increase the pressure exerted by the blade on the work.

Hammer *Figs. 1:17; 1:18*
The following hammers are used by bookbinders. In all cases the face of the hammer must be kept smooth and polished.

(a) Backing Hammer *Figs. 1:17; 1:26*
This is an ordinary shoemaker's hammer with its round mushroomed face and wedge-shaped pane.

It is used to give the spine a rounded shape. The book is held between Backing Boards in the Lying Press with the spine upwards. The spine is then given glancing blows with the hammer until it spreads sideways into a smooth curve, overhanging the backing boards to form the joint or groove.

Fig. 1:17

(b) *Beating Hammer* *Fig. 1:18*
A heavy hammer, weighing from 9 to 14 lb. (19.8–30.8 kg), with a short handle. It is made with a head in various shapes, all of which include the provision of a smooth-ground face of comparatively large area.

It is used (in the absence of a rolling machine) to flatten and compact the sections of a book. This is done on a stone or metal slab, sometimes bedded in a shallow box filled with sand. The hammer is held with fingers meeting on top, knuckles below, and allowed to drop vertically onto the work, from which it could bounce upwards ready for the next stroke. *Note*: The examples illustrated here are taken from the following publications: (1) Diderot's Encyclopaedia (c.1760). (2) A Dutch engraving of c.1849. (3) From the catalogue of Harrild & Sons (1903).

Knife *Figs. 1:19–1:25*
Knives used by bookbinders include the following:

(a) *Cutting-out Knife* *Fig. 1:19*
A general purpose type of knife used for cutting leather, card and paper.

Fig. 1:19

(b) *Gold Knife* (Gilder's Knife) *Fig. 1:20*
A knife with a blunt edge used for parting gold leaf: see under *Gilder's Tools.*

Fig. 1:20

(c) *Paper Knife* *Fig. 1:21*
A long, narrow knife, like a ham knife. Used for slitting a folded sheet of paper. (See also *Folder.*)

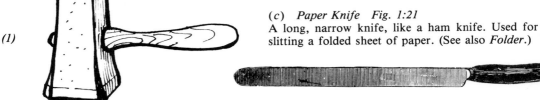

Fig. 1:21

(d) *Trimming Knife* *Fig. 1:22*
Rather like a large bread knife, with a blade *c.* 8–10 in. (20.3–25.4 cm) long, it was sometimes used for trimming the edges of a book as an alternative to the *Plough.*

Fig. 1:22

(e) *Paring Knife (French type)* *Fig. 1:23*
A wide-bladed, chisel-like tool used by bookbinders for paring down leather. It is described and illustrated under *Knife, Paring* in the BOOT AND SHOE MAKER section.

Fig. 1:23

(1)

(2)

(3)

Fig. 1:18

(*f*) *Paring Knife ('Spear' type) Fig. 1:24*
A knife with a spear-shaped blade illustrated in trade catalogues such as Harrild (1903) and Melhuish (1912). Used for paring down leather.

Fig. 1:24

(*g*) *Paring Knife ('German' type) Fig. 1:25*
This is an all-steel blade, described under *Knife, Shoe* in the BOOT AND SHOE MAKER section. Bookbinders use it mainly for paring down the edges of the leather.

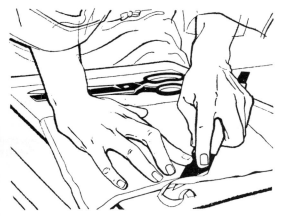

Fig. 1:25

Knocking-Down Iron *Fig. 1:26*
This is the bookbinder's anvil. It consists of a heavy iron plate, measuring $c.10 \times 4 \times \frac{3}{4}$ in. ($25.4 \times 10.1 \times 1.9$ cm) thick, with a central projecting bar on the underside. This bar is set in the Lying Press (see under *Press II*) to hold the plate in a horizontal position. It is used as an anvil on which, for example, to hammer out the backing from sections of a previously bound book, and to hammer down the cord slips and pierced boards after lacing on the book boards.

Fig. 1:26

Lettering Tools *Fig. 1:27*
Printing the name of the book and its author on the spine of the book is a vital part of the binding process, and requires skill and experience to accomplish successfully. The tools used include:

(*a*) *Handled Letters*
Brass stamps, with letters cut in relief, set in wooden handles.

(*b*) *Printer's Type*
These are separate letters which are used to make up words when placed in a *Type Holder*.

(*c*) *Type Holder* (Letter Holder) *Fig. 1:27*
A metal box-like compartment, 2–3 in. (5–7.6 cm) long set on the end of a short handle, for holding sufficient type to make up a few words. There is a thumb-screw for holding the letters securely in the box.

Fig. 1:27

(*d*) *Lettering Pallets*
Occasionally used when the same word is needed for a large number of books. (For Pallet see *Finishing Tools* for cover decoration.)

Marbling Comb
Marbling is a process of decorating paper used for lining book covers (including, traditionally, account books) and for decorating book edges. The variegated marble effect is carried out in a trough

11

containing special liquid gums on which pigments are sprinkled.

The Marbling Comb is one of the methods used for producing the fantastic but pleasing shapes made in the coloured surface of the gum, and which are transferred to a paper which is deftly placed in contact with it. The comb is rather like a painter's Graining Comb, but the teeth are of pin-wire cross-section.

Pallet: see *Finishing Tools*.

Plough (Bookbinder's Plane) *Figs. 1:28; 1:34*
A plane-like tool used by bookbinders for levelling book and board edges. Burdett remarks (1975, p.128): 'It may seem curious that even today, unless exceptionally heavy board guillotines are available, the best edge results from the use of the centuries old method of ploughing.'

The bookbinder's Plough has two wooden cheeks, one of which is guided by runners that are fitted along one beam of the *Cutting Press*. The cheeks are connected by two stems (fixed in one cheek and running freely through the other) and drawn together or moved apart by a central wooden screw. By turning this screw, the cutting knife is fed into the work.

The Cutting Knife is held in a dovetailed slot in a metal plate under one cheek, and is secured by a bolt that passes through the thickness of the cheek to its upper edge, where it is held by a large wing nut. There are two common forms of cutting knife. Both have spear-points sharpened only on their upper side: one type slides into its dovetailed slot, the other is held by the bolt and wing nut.

Diderot (Paris, 1760) illustrates a similar cutter, but certain eighteenth-century engravings illustrate a bookbinder's Plough with a circular knife which, like the Moon Knife once used by curriers and others, could be turned when blunt to expose a new part of the edge.

When levelling the edges, the book is held in a Cutting Press (see *Press II* and also *Trindle*) with the edges of the sheets projecting sufficiently for cutting. In use, the left hand holds the protruding end of the wooden screw, while the right hand holds its handle. The Plough is pushed forward and back while the cheek bearing the knife is screwed slowly into contact with the work. A few leaves are sliced off at each stroke until the whole edge has been planed flat.

Though outwardly resembling the woodworker's grooving plough, it differs in many ways, not least in its cutting iron, which is horizontal and knife-like, while the woodworker's Plough has the sloping chisel-like cutter of the Plane family. It is perhaps

nearer to a modern descendant, the machine tool called a Shaper, in which a cutter fixed to the head of a reciprocating ram is fed transversely across the work after each stroke.

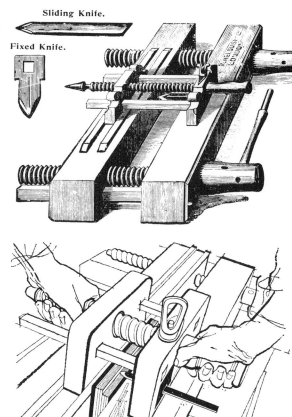

Sliding Knife.

Fixed Knife.

Fig. 1:28

Polishing and Burnishing Tools *Figs. 1:29–1:30*
Those used by bookbinders include the following:

(*a*) *Polishing Iron* (Glazing Iron; Goose) *Fig. 1:29*
A highly polished metal head mounted on a wooden handle, *c*.15 in. (38.1 cm) overall – long enough to be worked from the shoulder. There are two types of head: one, shaped as a short, horizontal cylinder; the other, wedge-shaped and known as a 'Goose'.

It is used for smoothing and polishing before tooling and lettering. The cylindrical head is used on the flat surface of the cover; the wedge-shaped head on the spine and for working close to the bands.

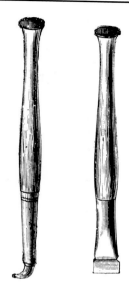

Fig. 1:30

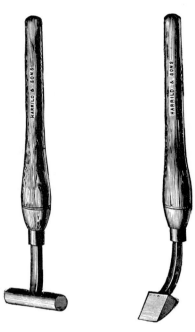

Fig. 1.29

(*b*) *Burnisher* (When used on gold leaf it is usually called a Gilder's Burnisher or Gilder's Agate.) *Fig. 1:30*
A piece of highly polished agate, bloodstone, steel, or occasionally flint, set into a metal collar and mounted on a wooden handle. The overall length of the tool is *c.*10 in. (25.4 cm), or *c.*15 in. (38.1 cm) when intended for working from the shoulder.

It is used for burnishing book edges after staining, marbling or gilding. It can also be used on leather covers.

There are two main types:

(1) Straight or 'flat', sometimes called an 'Edge Burnisher'. The head may be as wide as $1\frac{1}{2}$ in. (3.8 cm) when used for burnishing book edges after applying gold leaf.
(2) Curved, and known as 'Tooth or Dog Tooth', because of its shape. In Diderot's time (1760) these Burnishers were in fact made from the tooth of a dog or wolf. They are used on curved work, such as the fore-edge of a book.

Some Agates for delicate work are illustrated in the section: DECORATION OF LEATHER.

Press
Most of the presses used by bookbinders have been adapted from those used in other trades; but bookbinders have given their own names to some of them.

Accessories that go with the presses include metal protective sheets (known as Pressing Plates), and wooden spacing pieces – see *Boards*. The iron or wooden bar used for turning the screws is known as a Press Pin.

There are many variations, but the main types are described in the following entries:

Press I Vertical Presses for compacting and flattening. *Figs. 1:31; 1:32*

(*a*) *Standing Press Fig. 1:31*
A heavy vertical press, 5–8 ft (1.5–2.4 m) high, operated by a stout central screw. It is usually bolted to the floor and sometimes braced to an adjoining wall. Earlier examples are made in heavy timber, but in recent times they are mostly made in iron. When fully raised there is a gap of *c.*3 ft (91.4 cm) between the platten and the base.

It is used to flatten and compact the book sections before they are sewn; to set the spine of the book after it has been rounded and backed; to press the

---

book after the boards have been laced on; and to press the book after it has been covered.

The French Standing Press is usually made in wood except for the screw mechanism. The top platten is forced downwards by a horizontal iron wheel which looks rather like a ship's steering wheel with its handles turned at right angles to the plane of the wheel.

Fig. 1:31

(*b*) *Nipping Press* (Screw Press; Bench Press) *Fig. 1:32*

A vertical iron press; smaller and lighter than the Standing Press, made for mounting on a bench. The platten measures between 9 × 16 in. (22.8 × 40.6 cm) and 14 × 22 in. (35.5 × 50.8 cm) and the gap or 'daylight' measures from 7 to 15 in. (17.7 to 38.1 cm). The screw presses at one time used in offices for copying letters are often made to serve as Nipping Presses. It is used to press the books when a lighter pressure is required.

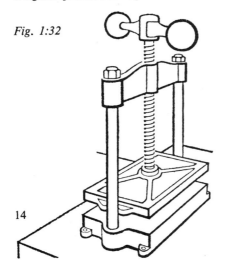

Fig. 1:32

Press II Horizontal Presses for holding *Figs. 1:33–1:35*

These are holding devices, made on similar lines to a carpenter's Bench Chop, and used for gripping a book while various processes are carried out including edge-cutting, gilding edges, and backing. The most important member of this group, the Lying Press, is described by Burdett (1975) as the bookbinder's 'most essential item of equipment ... with it the newcomer can dispense with a standing or bench press, and it may be used for any operation that calls for pressure'.

Variants include:

(*a*) *Lying Press* (Backing Press; Laying Press) *Fig. 1:33*

Two beams are connected by two screws which are traditionally of wood but can be of metal. The blocks are also connected by two stems, square in cross-section, fixed into one beam and running freely through the other. The screws are turned by *Press Pins* of iron or hardwood. The length of the press is about 30–40 in. (76.2 cm–1.01 m) giving 18–24 in. (45.7–60.9 cm) of space between the screws.

The press is placed on a stand still called a 'tub', on which the medieval binder rested his press, perhaps because it served to catch the paper edge shavings. Diderot (*c*.1760) calls this stand a 'donkey'.

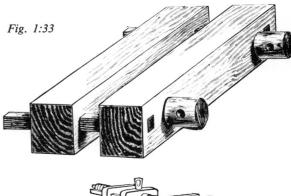

Fig. 1:33

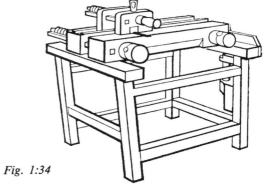

Fig. 1:34

(b) Cutting Press Figs. 1:28, 1:34
The same as the Lying Press (above) except that the top of one beam is fitted with two runners to act as a guide for the *Plough*. The runners may be fitted to the lower side of the Press so that it can be turned upside down when required for cutting.

(c) Finishing Press Fig. 1:35
Similar to the Lying Press but lighter and without the stem guides. The outside cheeks of the beams are often cut at a bevel to leave more room for the hand when the spine of the book is being tooled.

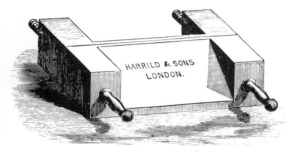

Fig. 1:35

(d) Gilder's Press
Similar to the Finishing Press but with longer screws to hold a number of books while the edges are gilded.

Press III Vertical Presses for lettering and blocking *Figs. 1:36, 1:37*
These are used to impress letters and designs on the cover and spine of the book.

(a) Blocking Press (Arming Press; Lettering Press) *Fig. 1:36*
The term 'Arming Press' originates from its use to impress the owner's heraldic arms on the cover of the book.

Fig. 1:36

A heavy vertical press, with a heated platten which can be forced downwards by a lever onto the bed. The head can be lowered or raised by a crank according to the thickness of the work in hand. The blocks or stamps which impress the design are usually made of brass. In early examples, the heat was provided by heated iron bars laid inside holes in the heater box; later the platten was heated by gas or electricity.

(b) Fly Press Fig. 1:37
A heavy vertical press with the central screw operated by a cross-handle fitted with fly-weights, which, like a fly-wheel, impart an additional impetus. Tomlinson's *Cyclopaedia of Useful Arts and Manufactures* (1853) describes the operation as follows:

'This man swings round the ponderous arm, furnished with two huge balls at its extremities, and by the weight as well as the centrifugal force of this arm, the upper bed is jerked down upon the lower one, and the leather, in an instant, takes the impression of the die.'

Fig. 1:37

Press Pin
Known as a tommy-bar in other trades, this is an iron or hardwood bar used to turn the screws of a press. It is put into holes bored through the boss at the head of the screw.

Press, Sewing
This is not a press, but a frame supporting cords on which the sections of the book are sewn. (See *Sewing Press*.)

15

Saw

A small saw such as a Tenon Saw is used to cut grooves (kerfs) across the spine of the book in which to sink the bands or cords upon which the sheets of the book are sewn. These cuts are made when the book is held in the Lying Press.

Scratcher (Scratching-up Tool; Grater)

A metal hand tool with a toothed working-edge. It is used to scratch a surface to provide a key for the paste or glue, or to increase its penetration, for example on the back. Diderot (*c*.1760) illustrates a double-ended scraper (*grattoir*) which he described as 'an iron tool, about 9 in. (22.8 cm) long, round in the middle part which serves as a handle … flat at the ends which are of different sizes for use with different sized books'.

Sewing Press (Sewing Frame) *Fig. 1:38*

Not a press in the modern sense, but a wooden frame on which the cords (or tapes) are held taut and correctly spaced while the sections of the book are sewn to them. Practically unchanged since the sixteenth century, the Sewing Press, made entirely of wood, consists of a base with screw threaded uprights fixed at each end. These uprights pass freely through holes in a horizontal crossbar, which is held up by wooden nuts, one on each upright. The top ends of the tapes or cords are attached to the crossbar; the lower ends are taken through a slot in the base-board and are attached to *Sewing Keys* (see below). These keys hold the cords firmly under the base, yet allowing adjustments sideways. The cords are drawn tight when the crossbar is raised: this is done by turning the wooden nuts which force the bar upwards.

Sewing Keys

These are flat pieces of metal about 3–4 in. (7.6–10.1 cm) long, made in two shapes:

(1) Forked-shaped, for use with cords.
(2) H-shaped, for use with tapes.

Shears, Hand (Millboard Shears)

Hand Shears are sometimes used instead of a *Guillotine Shear* for cutting thinner millboard. They range in size and power from a heavy scissor to the stout Hand Shears used by tailors or tinsmiths.

Spokeshave

A woodworker's Spokeshave is sometimes preferred to a Paring Knife (see under *Knife*) for paring larger surfaces of leather used for binding. The blade is often slightly modified by grinding away the sharp corners of the cutting edge to prevent 'digging in'. Burdett (1975) writes, 'The use of the spokeshave demands confidence born of experience – sometimes bitter.'

Sprinkling Frame

A sieve of interlaced copper wire with a long handle which rests under the arm of the user.

It is used to sprinkle a coloured powder for decorating the edges of a book. The powdered colour is taken up on the bristles of a brush which is rubbed across the wire mesh of the Sprinkling Frame.

Stone

A piece of flat stone, such as a discarded lithographic stone, or a piece of glass, is used as a base when paring (see *Knife*). A heavier piece of stone, or a slab of iron, is used when hammering the sections of a book (see Beating Hammer under *Hammer*).

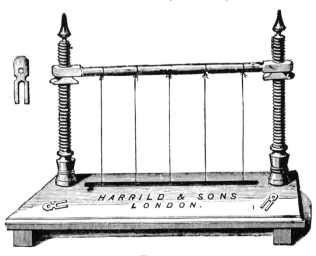

Fig. 1:38

Trindle *Fig. 1:39*
Trindle is the name given by bookbinders to a piece
of thin wood or metal, about 4–6 in. (10.1–15.2 cm)
long, shaped like a button-polishing guard. Its
pleasant-sounding name has connections with wheel-
making, but why the name should have been given to
this small tool has not been explained.

It is used when cutting the fore-edge of the book
– see *Plough*. Before doing this it is necessary to flatten the curved back of the book so that the fore-edge
becomes flat also. For this purpose, the cover boards
of the book are folded open, and two Trindles are
pushed between the boards and the back of the
pages. The protruding cords do not prevent this
operation because they sink into the slots along the
centre of the Trindle.

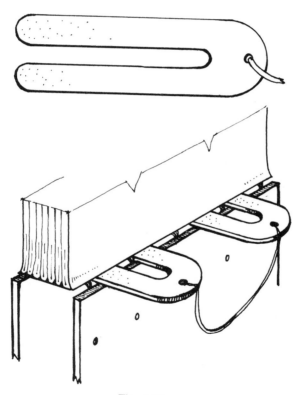

Fig. 1:39

17

——2——

Boot and Shoe Maker

The term 'cordwainer', for boot and shoemaker, is still used in the title of certain guilds and trade unions. From about AD 1100, the term implied a person working or dealing in leather of the type imported at that time from Cordova in Spain; later, and until the eighteenth century at least, the term was in general use as a name for the men who are today known simply as boot and shoe makers. (In France the shoemaker is still called *cordonnier*.)

In Scotland the form 'cordiner' was retained until recent years. The term 'souter' (or 'suter') is a Scottish and northern dialect word for shoemaker or cobbler, and is derived from the Latin word *sutor*, a shoemaker.

The name cobbler ('cobelere') was given in the fourteenth century to a mender of shoes, and is of uncertain orgin. 'Snob' is a slang name of unknown origin for a shoemaker or cobbler, and was originally applied to a man of low birth or breeding.

Historical Note   *Figs. 2:1; 2:6*

There seems no reason to doubt that while still living in the so-called stone ages, man learnt to protect his feet from sharp stones and thorns. Vegetable fibre may have been among the first materials used for covering the feet: some evidence for this comes from the discovery of a pair of sandals made from woven fibres found buried beneath volcanic ash in Oregon, USA; they have been dated at *c.* 7000 BC.

What appear to be 'foot-bags' made of animal skin are depicted in cave paintings of *c.* 8000 BC; some of the earliest known examples of leather sandals and shoes have come from ancient Egypt and

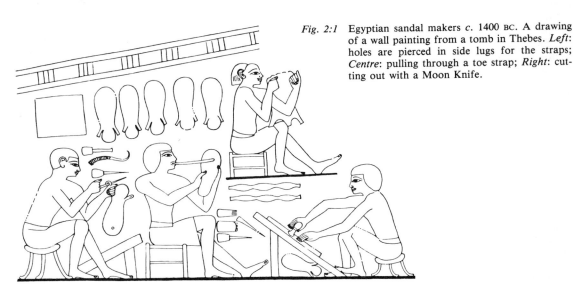

Fig. 2:1   Egyptian sandal makers *c.* 1400 BC. A drawing of a wall painting from a tomb in Thebes. *Left*: holes are pierced in side lugs for the straps; *Centre*: pulling through a toe strap; *Right*: cutting out with a Moon Knife.

have been dated at *c.* 5000 BC. Dry conditions have helped to preserve them.

The idea of wearing leather foot-bags survived in the Hebrides until recent times, as related by Mrs I. F. Grant in her *Highland Folk Ways* (1961, p. 207):

'According to a letter to Henry VIII by John Elder, a priest in the Highlands, the ancient Highlanders generally went barefoot, but if, in specially inclement weather, they required footgear, they simply cut a piece of undressed hide to fit their feet, punched holes round the edges so that it could be tied round their ankes and made additional holes to let the water out. Even within living memory, footgear almost as primitive and known as "rivelins" were occasionally still worn in Sutherland and the Hebrides. They were made of untanned calfskin worn hairy side out, roughly shaped to fit the feet, the edges of the toes and heels were drawn together by overcasting, holes were punched along the tops and laces threaded through. They are said to have given a better foothold on the slippery seaweed-covered rocks than any other kind of footwear.'

There has been no basic change in the design of boots and shoes since the Middle Ages. The chief improvements have been the development of the welt (q.v.), and improved tanning and currying methods. The penetration by water was, and remains, one of the unsolved problems of shoemaking. There is an old story that when King George IV (*c.*1830) was asked whether he considered water to be a wholesome beverage, he replied, 'I don't know what it does to my stomach, but I know it rots my boots.'

Much skill and effort was devoted to the design of boots and shoes by makers of the period *c.* 1800–1920. A look at their products in museums such as that at Northampton, or at Messrs Clark's Museum in Street (Somerset), or in the showrooms of London makers such as John Lobb or Henry Maxwell, immediately reveals an elegance of design and quality of workmanship comparable to the products of the best tradesmen in other fields – and this in spite of the humble position of shoemakers at that time and the harsh conditions under which most of them worked.

One of the driving forces behind their high attainment may have been the fierce competition for patronage that existed between the makers; but these products also exemplify the high standard of excellence in both design and execution that comes about almost spontaneously when traditional skills are applied to familiar objects over a long period.

Since the middle of the nineteenth century, machines, both power- and hand-driven, have gradually taken over every operation needed for making a pair of boots or shoes (see also *Machines for Shoemaking*). There are now only a few hand-sewn makers left at work, and the shoes they produce cost from ten to twelve times as much as those made in the factories. Yet handmade shoes are eagerly sought by those who can afford them, owing to their comfort, long life and good looks.

A remarkable and moving account of the boot and shoemakers of that time was written in *c.* 1850 by Henry Mayhew (1851). He gives the numbers employed in various ocupations in London, and he finds there were 28,574 boot and shoemakers, more than any other skilled trade. Today the number of handsewn makers in London might amount to fifty or sixty.

In the country the figures for two adjacent Hertfordshire villages (Wheathampstead and Harpenden), taken from the census of 1851, are probably fairly typical: their combined population at that time was 3,880, and there were twenty-eight shoemakers. At the present time, the population in the same area has risen to 29,300, and there are no shoemakers left.

It is interesting to see that the designers of machine-made shoes have taken considerable pains to preserve the traditional good looks of their handmade prototype: for instance, in the elegant shaping of the forepart and instep; and, where seams have been joined by adhesives, the simulation of stitches where appearance would suffer from their absence.

In the long search for a water-resistant shoe, the development of rubber had a profound effect. By the 1860s rubber was used not only for soles, but for the whole boot (see the entry *Wellington Boot*). An interesting development is the shoe made of a special plastic which has some of the 'breathing' qualities of leather. It is waterproof, durable, comfortable in a temperate climate, and relatively cheap to produce (see paragraph on Materials below).

Materials (See also the entry *Finishing Tools and Materials.*)

The skins of many different animals have been used for making boots and shoes: in general, soles are made from cattle hides and uppers are made from calf or other softer leathers, such as kid.

Among the qualities that make leather such a good material for footwear are its flexibility, and its permeability to air and water vapour which helps to keep the feet comfortable and cool; it 'lets the feet breathe'. It is this last quality that the makers of synthetic substitutes find so difficult to imitate (see below).

Another valuable property of leather is its ability

19

to grip the waxed thread that is used to sew the parts of a shoe together. If exposed stitches attaching the sole are worn through, the sole remains in place, at least for a time, held by the remaining short lengths of thread that are embedded in the leather 'substance' of each separate part. This attribute contributed towards the water-tightness of the leather-covered ship *Brendan* that made its epic voyage across the Atlantic in 1976 (T. Severin, 1978).

Threads used for sewing are made from hemp or flax, the several plies twisted together with beeswax and a pig's bristle (now usually nylon) acting as points or tags to the threads (see *Sewing and Stitching*).

The reputation of makers depends not only on their skill but also on their ability to buy the best leather. Thus Leno (1895, p. 45) expects a maker to be equally skilled in choosing the best materials:

'Select hides that have an agreeable smell, a healthy hue, and are moderately clean. Avoid those that are coarse on the offal, and remember that unusually heavy necks are a pretty sure index to the poor loins. Firmness in the flank, lightness in the neck, levelness in the shoulder, and substance in the butt are the characteristics of a good hide. In selecting shoulders for welting, see that they are neither too open nor too horny, inasmuch as it is difficult to get a firm edge from the former, and the latter is liable to break in sewing ... there is only one method of judging tannage that we know of, and that is by cutting through the prime of the butt. If when cut it is found to be even in colour throughout, the tannage may be safely taken to be good; but if the cut edge is found to possess a dark green shade in its centre it may be safely assumed that the leather has not been properly tanned, and will discredit its user.'

The search for a water-resistant yet inexpensive boot or shoe has led recently to the making of shoes from synthetic material. The most outstanding development in this field has been the production of man-made material which has many of the properties of leather. Rubber or plastic soles have been used successfully for many years, but with the development of a polyurethane-type sheet which has some of the 'breathing' quality (i.e. permeability) of natural leather, it appears most likely that the non-leather shoe has come to stay, at least in countries of temperate climate. And though this new material may not feel as cool as leather, it can claim to be comfortable and entirely waterproof; and it is easily and quickly cleaned with a damp rag instead of the inconvenience of polish and brush. The cost to the customer is, at the time of writing, about one third of the price of an ordinary all-leather shoe.

Process

The making of a handmade shoe is a skilled operation involving not only the use of leather with its variable qualities and peculiarities, but also the covering of the asymmetrical human foot, which is even more variable than the leather. After 3,000 years of trial and improvement, the humble shoe has attained a high standard of design and workmanship. Much could be written about the production of the handmade shoe: here only a note of the main processes is given without listing the many separate operations included under each. If the reader wishes to learn more, there are several good textbooks on the subject, including those listed in the Bibliography under the following authors: J. Devlin (1839); J. B. Leno (1895); F. Plucknett (1916); J. C. Swaysland (1905); J. H. Thornton (1970).

When reading about, or looking at, the process of shoemaking, it should be remembered that there are often differences in methods between one maker and another, and between the methods of the early eighteenth century and those of today. Almost every process described under the tool entries that follow could be contradicted by some shoemaker who does the job in another way. As a young West End maker remarked (1977), 'When I left technical college I thought there was only one way to make a pair of shoes; but when I'd spent three months in the workshop I learnt that there are a dozen.'

Division of Labour

The traditional idea of a shoemaker is that of a solitary man who works alone making a shoe right through from the cutting up of the leather to the final finishing off. This is a true picture — indeed, it remains largely true of the few handsewn makers still at work today. But from the eighteenth century (and possibly before) a few shoemakers would gather together in workshops where each concentrated on a specific operation, or on several closely linked operations. Pictures of shoemakers' workshops of that time often show one man standing at a bench cutting up the leather, while others sit on stools stitching the shoe together. The main divisions of labour which have evolved in more recent years are indicated in the table below.

Factory production went even further; as Leno, writing in 1895 (p. 209), comments:

'The divisions of labour in a modern bootmaking establishment are enough to drive the great art critic, John Ruskin, mad. There is undoubtedly a deal of truth in what he has written with regard to the evil effects of keeping a man continually engaged on one simple operation.'

Leno goes on to explain that manufacturers cannot be expected to listen, for the divisions of labour, both in America and England, have effectively 'cheapened the labour cost of production'.

Division of Labour	*Process*
1. *The Last-Maker*, who makes a model of the foot. An essential first step in shoemaking; but since the eighteenth century, last-making is usually carried on as a separate business.	After measuring the foot, an approximate model is made of it with certain essential modifications to meet current fashion and the manufacturing process, and to increase foot comfort. This model — the 'last' — is made in wood or plastic and will serve as a mould on which the shoe is subsequently built (see *Last and Boot Tree Maker* under MISCELLANEOUS TRADES AND TOOLS section.
2. *The Designer* Today, when fashion is important, some large firms employ separate designers and pattern cutters; but traditionally, one person, perhaps the master, carried out both functions.	Given the basic dimensions of the last, the designer produces a sketch or painting of a shoe design for it, either on a fabric or plastic cover for the top of the last itself, or on a flat paper representation of the side of the last. Sometimes a mock-up of the shoe is also made.
3. *The Pattern Cutter*, who makes working patterns for the clicker.	The design is then converted into working patterns made of paper or other material from which the upper may be cut. If necessary, bottom patterns may also be made. From the average size used as a starting point, these are graded up and down to produce a range of sizes and possibly width fittings (see Pattern-Cutting and Grading under *Measuring Tools*).
4. *The Clicker*, who cuts out the component parts of the upper. Since leather was very expensive this operation was often done by the master who also probably measured the feet of his more important customers.	The cutting of the leather and other material for the upper sections of the shoe. When, in more recent times, 'off-the-peg' shoes were introduced, a suitable last would be selected and if necessary modified. Then, using stock patterns, or modified ones, the various sections would be cut out. (For tools and methods see *Clicker*.)
5. *The Closer*, who prepares, fits and stitches together the various parts of the shoe upper.	The component parts of the upper are prepared by skiving (i.e. bevelling the edges) after which they are stitched together. In the nineteenth century, with the arrival of sewing machines, female labour began to be employed for closing, and still is. (For tools see *Closer*.)

6. *The Bottom Stock* or *Rough Stuff Cutter*, who cuts out the heavier leather for soles, welts and heels.

In earlier times the soles and other bottoming components were cut out by the clicker or by the maker (the man who stitched them on). But during the last century, at least, the cutting and preparation of these components has constituted a separate division within the trade.

When hand cutting, the hide is held down on the bench with heavy weights, and is cut with a special knife with the point held downwards (see *Knife, Butt*).

7. *The Maker Fig 2:2.* The man who assembles and actually joins together the upper, sole, insole, the heel (if any), and all minor components. In Devlin's time (1839) a maker was classified as either a 'boot-man', who made men's boots, or a 'woman's-man', who made ladies'.

Note: *Fig. 2:2* The operations mentioned under 'sole attaching' (7*b*) are carried out while the shoe is on the last and held by a *Stirrup* upside-down on the maker's knee. Since the inside of the shoe is now filled by the *Last* the sewing together of the upper, insole and welt is done externally with the stitches running sideways through the part of the insole known as the hold-fast. The joining of the outer sole to the welt is done subsequently with vertical stitches.

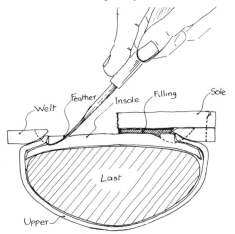

Fig. 2:2 Attaching the sole (diagrammatic section) while the lasted shoe is held upside down on the maker's knee. See Note under para (7) above.

8. *Final Cleaning and Dressing.*
This has gradually evolved as a separate department of shoe manufacture during the present century. It involves general inspection of the finished shoe, making minor repairs, removal of stains, insertion of laces, general polishing and final wrapping and boxing.

The major stages are:

(*a*) Lasting: the stretching and moulding of the upper over the last. In some constructions it is tacked or stuck to an insole already fixed to the last bottom (see *Lasting Pincers*).

(*b*) Sole attaching: the fixing on of the sole, traditionally by thread either direct to the lasted upper, as in a turnshoe, or by means of a welt as in a welted shoe. In the turnshoe the shoe is made inside-out with a single seam and then turned the right way round; in the welted shoe there are two seams: (i) uniting welt, upper and insole; (ii) uniting welt and sole.

There are several variations of these methods and heavier boots may have their soles nailed, screwed or pegged on, or a combination of methods.

In recent years leather soles have been largely replaced by stuck-on or moulded-on rubber or synthetic ones (see *Turnshoe Tools*; *Welt*; *Welt Tools*; *Sewing and Stitching*).

(*c*) Heel attaching: since their introduction (*c.* 1600) heels have been of two types: (1) built ('stacked'), i.e. made of separate lifts; or (2) solid from a block of wood (recently, plastic), sometimes covered with leather or other material. With built heels the first lift was sometimes stitched to the heel-seat of the shoe, and the remainder (including the top piece next to the ground) held on by wooden pegs or nails. Wooden heels could be nailed on from inside, but sometimes had no attaching nails and were kept in position by their leather covers which were stitched to the shoe seat (see *Heel*).

(*d*) Finishing: trimming, colouring and burnishing the edges of soles and heels; scouring, colouring and polishing the surfaces of sole and heel top pieces (see *Finishing Tools and Materials*).

The Workshops and Conditions of Work

During the earlier part of the last century, when most boots and shoes were still being made by hand, the many smaller workshops were often situated in an upper floor garret, or in a dismal basement lit only by a pavement light, augmented, when the master allowed, by a candle or oil lamp.

The chief furniture of these workshops was a low bench and stool for the closers and makers; a higher stand-up bench for the clickers; a pail, or tub, in which to soften leather; and sometimes a small chest of drawers for nails and fittings. (See the entries *Bench and Seat; Equipment and Furniture.*) And judging by the few surviving workshops of this sort, the floor was littered with leather cuttings and other rubbish.

Many authors have written about the appalling conditions suffered by working people during the nineteenth century; of the grinding poverty of men who competed with one another to make a bare living; of the indifference of some masters. That such conditions persisted into recent times is exemplified by a retired maker of riding boots in London, a man who reached the top of his profession, who, when speaking to the author about his employers of fifty years ago, exclaimed: 'They treated us like pigs.'

But at least the employment of young children as cheap labour was stopped during the later years of the nineteenth century. V. A. Hartley wrote in the *Journal of the British Boot and Shoe Institution* (Sept. 1961) as follows:

'The child closers worked long hours, anything from ten to fourteen daily. They [earned] pitifully small sums of money; after a wageless apprenticeship of six months, children were paid one shilling weekly, rising gradually to one shilling and sixpence, and for the most skilful, half-a-crown. The closing rooms were often overcrowded, the occupants sitting hunched on stools. No attention was paid to hygiene and ventilation, and the incentives used by the masters were harsh words, the withholding of wages, and, it may be suspected, blows.'

Shoemaking was often a lonely occupation and, as Miss June Swann of the Northampton Museum has pointed out, there is a long tradition of keeping birds for company: caged birds appear in two paintings exhibited in the Museum, 'The Shoemaker' by H. Walton (*c.*1770) and a similar subject by David Teniers (Antwerp *c.*1650). Mr R. C. Pond, a retired Norwich shoemaker, speaking of his life in the workshop of about fifty years ago, told the author that 'hammering leather on the lapstone was strictly forbidden when young birds were hatching'.

Devlin, writing in 1839, was well aware of the hard life of the shoemaker, but in his 'few parting words to the journeyman' he allows a chink of sunshine to penetrate the general gloom:

'... even as a journeyman much happiness is still within your reach. Do you love to change? Are you desirous, as the saying is, of seeing the world? Then, as a journeyman shoemaker, no artisan can do so better. Reared in the country, you make your way up to London; or, pent up in London till your apprenticeship expires, you can put a kit on your back, and, for the first time in your life, get out into the high roads and open fields, and, like all uneducated children of the city, discover what a large place is the country, and how beautiful and exhilarating it is, and how novel! How different the lark looks, freely ascending up to the heavens, to hanging out of a murky garret window, in its dark and wire-barred confinement!'

The Cobbler or Shoe Repairer

The cobbler, a mender of boots and shoes, survives in many small towns, but nowadays more often in a small modern workshop, with power-driven sewing and finishing machines, and, perhaps, one or two helpers. One rarely sees a cobbler working in the villages where, sixty years ago, it would have been difficult to find a village without one.

In the towns, the cobbler's working conditions were often as grim as those suffered by the makers. But the village cobblers often worked in a room or hut that opened onto the street, and some air and light was admitted through the open door. Such was the case of Mr Bill Martin, a cobbler in the village of Barley in Hertfordshire, in the pre-1914 years and after. He was the son of a local brick maker and a brother of the village hurdle maker. The present writer, as a boy, spent happy hours watching him at work and listening to him talk. In his little shop opposite the church, two steps above the level of the road, he also shaved and cut the hair of his customers on request.

Up till fifty years ago, in the days when it was worth having extensive repairs carried out on a torn shoe (rather than scrap it and buy another), a cobbler needed the same skill, and many of the same tools, as a maker.

Devlin describes the cobbler's work in his day (1839, p. 106):

'The cobbler must have good abilities. Being accustomed to the strong work, he will think nothing of the great awls and the large threads he must use; but in his mending, he will have such out of the way holes and fractures to put in order, that considerable practical skill will be necessary to gain him a reputation ... a carter's old shoe is in his hand, gaping like an oyster between sole and upper leather, and with a rent in the upper-leather stretching half-way across the vamp, and running into various sinuosities. What is he to do? He himself wants his 9d. or his 1s. for the job, and the carter wants his shoe, and will call for it at his dinner hour.'

Fifty years later, Leno (1895, p. 112) writes sorrowfully:

'It is not so with the latest class of shoe menders. With them the awl and thread are things of secondary importance, and nail and file having the preference. This class of mending is evidently attracting a considerable share of custom. Cheapness and rapidity are held out to the public as enticements ... It is in too many instances a mere covering up of old wounds. It requires real talent to mend shoes as they were formerly mended, and are still mended in respectable bespoke establishments, but all that is required of the newest operator is to be able to cut and skive, drive a nail or rivet and ink the edges.'

Cobbler's Tools

The most essential tools for repair work are the Cobbler's Foot, Knife, Awl, Hammer, Pincers and Rasp; and for finishing he needs a few Edge Irons and Polishing Bones, a Glazer, and a Heating Lamp.

Folklore (see also *St Hugh's Bones*)

Many trades have their legends — and even patron saints — but anyone who reads the history of the shoemakers will be struck by the number of legends they have acquired. And the student will also notice that most of the stories have an aristocratic flavour. For example, their ancestral saints were men of rank who renounced their status and took to shoemaking in order to support themselves while teaching the Gospel. Such was St Crispin, the patron saint of the shoemakers, who was born into a noble Roman family; and St Hugh, remembered in *St Hugh's Bones*, who was a 'Prince of Britain'. Both were martyred in the third century AD.

In an anonymous pamphlet, 'The History of the Gentle Craft' published in 1676, St Crispin is depicted as fitting a princess with a shoe. (According to the legend, the two fell in love and eventually married.) The following lines are printed below the picture:

A *Gentle Craft* that hath the Art,
To steal soon into a LADIES Heart;
Here you may see, what Youth and Love can
    do,
The Crown doth stoop to th' Maker of a
    Shooe.

On the same note the shoemaker's trade was known in some of the writings and songs of the Middle Ages as 'the gentle craft' — a term that gives them the status of gentlemen. According to one of the popular legends of the sixteenth century, Edward IV, in disguise, once drank with a gathering of shoemakers, and gave them a toast:

You shall no more be called shoemakers
But you and yours to the world's end
Shall be called the trade of the gentle craft.

St Crispin's Day was celebrated on 25 October up until recent times. The festival must have been well known to theatre audiences in 1599, when Shakespeare's 'King Henry V' first appeared, for the name Crispin is spoken five times in a single speech by Henry V before the victory at Agincourt, ending with the famous lines:

And gentlemen in England now a-bed
Shall think themselves accursed they were not
    here,
And hold their manhoods cheap whiles any
    speaks
That fought with us upon Saint Crispin's day.
                (King Henry V, Act IV, scene 3)

Perhaps these legends provided some compensation for the shoemaker's lowly position in society, and gave a feeling of pride to a body of men who were forced to live on very low wages. But it is noticeable that certain other leather-workers, for instance the tanners, or harness-makers, do not have much folklore connected with their trades, although their social status may have been similar. This question was put to Professor Warren E. Roberts of the Folklore Department of Indiana University, USA. In a letter to the author (1979) he wrote:

'The only explanation I can suggest is as follows: Thomas Deloney (c.1543–1600) wrote *The Gentle Craft*; Thomas Dekker (c. 1570–1641) wrote *The Shoemakers' Holiday*. Deloney's book especially contains a great deal of folklore because it was written at a time when the craft was really flourishing, and when a fair amount of medieval oral lore was still alive. I would suppose that the Puritan period would have put an end to any active use of such terms as St Crispin and St Hugh's Bones. Had similar works been written on the harness and saddler's trades at comparably early dates, it is possible that large amounts of similar oral material would have been included.'

It appears that another characteristic of shoemakers is their habit of telling funny stories ostensibly against themselves, some of which are

24

really telling the listener what clever fellows they are. One of these stories, about a shoemaker trying to convince a customer that his shoes don't hurt his feet, is related in Vanburgh's play 'The Relapse' (1697). (See the entry *Measuring Tools*.) Another was a bit of music-hall humour related to the author by a retired London maker, Mr W. B. Glasow (1976):

'A customer takes a pair of riding boots back to the shoemaker.

> *Customer*: I was just walking in these boots when the soles came off.
> *Shoemaker*: Ah Sir! you have been walking in them! You know Sir, these are Riding Boots, they are made for riding, not for walking.'

There is a tradition of thoughtfulness and contemplation among shoemakers. (It will be remembered that Leo Tolstoy took to shoemaking in order to regain some peace of mind.) Richard Mayhew, that remarkable social investigator of the mid-nineteenth century, wrote:

'The boot and shoemakers are certainly far from being an unintellectual body of men. They appear to be a stern, uncompromising and reflecting race. This, perhaps, is to be accounted for by the solitude of their employment developing their own internal resources, and producing that particular form of mental temperament which is generally accompanied with austerity of manner.' (Quoted by Yeo and Thompson in *The Unknown Mayhew*, 1971.)

'Concealed Shoes'

Until recent times old shoes were sometimes concealed in the wall, floor, or roof of a new house. Examples, dating from the fourteenth century onwards, have been found in many parts of Europe (including Britain), America, Australia, and in other countries. It is thought that this custom may have served originally as a substitute for the human or animal sacrifices made in remote times, perhaps to propitiate the spirits of the forest from whom the timber for constructing the house had been taken. Miss June Swann (Northampton Museum Shoe Collection, 1983) relates that some concealed shoes are found to have been deliberately and hideously damaged (killed) on burial.

There is a pleasanter interpretation of the happy custom of throwing an old shoe at the departing couple after a wedding. Whatever may have been its primeval purpose, the custom has served for several centuries as a symbol of good luck. John Heywood wrote in the sixteenth century: 'And home again hitherwards quicke as a bee. Now for good luck cast an old shoe after me.'

Shoemaker's Kit

The table below shows how the size of a shoemaker's kit has increased from the indispensable Knife, Hammer and Awl, to the comprehensive kit of the nineteenth century.

Since modern tool makers offer such an enormous range of tools, it is not suprising that if questioned about the use of a particular tool, an experienced maker will often say that in his day they got along quite nicely without it. One retired maker (Mr Glasgow, 1975) wrote to the author: 'I remember an old shoemaker saying to me when I was an apprentice "My boy! A good shoemaker can make a pair of shoes with a knife and fork."'

However, even as far back as 1839, when James Devlin drew up his list of shoemaker's tools (reproduced below), 125 tools were considered necessary to produce the well-finished boots and shoes being made at that time.

Date and origin (approx.)	Evidence	No. of tools shown or listed
1800 BC (Egypt)	Mural of shoemakers at Beni Hassan	4
550 BC (Greece)	Vase in Ashmolean Museum	3
AD 1568 (Germany)	Engraving of a shoemaker by Jost Amman	4
1636 (England)	T. Deloney's poem (see *St Hugh's Bones*)	16
1650 (Belgium)	Paintings of a shoemaker by G. D. Teniers	6
1760 (France)	Diderot's Encyclopaedia	20
1839 (England)	Devlin's *Guide to the Trade*	125
1920 (England)	Catalogue from George Barnsley & Sons	200*

* Of which several tools are offered in many different sizes.

List of Shoemaker's Tools in 1839. (From *The Guide to Trade. The Shoemaker* by James Devlin, London, 1839, pp. 112–15.)

In a preliminary paragraph, Devlin writes that his list was made 'from a personal inspection of some of the best sets of *kit* of some of the best workmen in London...; and as to all the inferior classes of workman, these on every occasion just do with as few as they can help, the knife, the awl, and hammer, being their great reliance.'

Author's note: The following text has been slightly altered for the sake of clarity.

Boot-closer's kit
3 awls for flat closing @ 3 for 1d.
2 awls for lining @ 3 for 1d.
2 awls for stabbing @ 3 for 1d.
2 awls for side closing of Wellingtons @ 3 for 1d.
2 prs. of seam setters 1/6d.
2 welt setters 9d.
2 stabbing setters 6d.
2 top and golosh setters 6d.
bone setter for welts of inside top closing 4d.
punch 6d.
set of files 2/0d.
petty-boy or seam slicking stick 3d. [see Wooden Sticks under *Bones and Sticks*].
bit of rule 2d. [see *Measuring Tools*].
marker 2d.
set of prickers (6) 9/0d.
compasses 1/0d.
knives 3d.
knife rubber 6d.
cutting board 1/6d.
closing blocks (2) 1/6d.
setting board generally lignum-vitae or some other hard wood 3/0d.
clams 2/6d.
stirrup 3d.
groove for tops 1/0d.
welt runner 6d.
rag stones for pointing awls 3d.
piece of pumice stone for hairs 1d.

... in all between 50–60 different pieces amounting in their total shop value to about thirty shillings.

Kit of the boot-man
large hammer 1/6d.
smaller or waist hammer 1/0d.
2 pr. pincers, large and small 3/0d.
nippers 1/0d.
3 knives 4d.–5d. ea.
welt fitter 6d.

rand fitter 2d.
2 rasps 1/3d.
12 files 4/6d.
jiggers (6) 9d.–1/0d. ea.
shoulder or fore-part irons (6–10) 6d.–9d. ea.
2–3 breakers 1/4d. ea.
1 rand iron, a tool for setting up the rand before stitching 1/0d.
3 boot irons, tools for setting and finishing the rands after stitching 3/6d.
1 rand wheel 4/6d. [see *Rand Tools*].
same for french seats 2/6d.
glazing iron, tool for burnishing the heel 1/0d.
seat file 6d.
2 stamps 1/6d.
joint iron and peg fitter 9d.
crooked knife, or knife for taking pegs out of the inside after the boot is made 9d.
prickstitch 3d.
stitch-bone 6d.
rule 3d.
long-stick 9d.
colt 6d. [see *Colt*].
dull knife 2d.
fore-part brush 6d.
buffing and edge knives (3–4) 6d.
knife sharpening strop 8d.
paste horn 3d.
bottles for gums and ink bottles (3) 2d. ea.
compasses 8d.
3 sewing awls 3d.
6 stitching awls 6d.
rand awl 1d.
2 heel awls 2d.
6 pegging, holding, pin-point and sprigging awls 6d.
joint awl 1d.
tacks for lasting 3d.
stirrup 6d.
waist-strap 2d.
hand-leather 2d.
shop-pan or tub for wetting the stuff 6d.
last-hook 6d.
apron 1/6d.
skiving board 3d.
rag-stone 3d.
paring-horn 2d.
channel-cleaner 1d.
lap-iron 4d.

... Upwards of a hundred different pieces, costing in their shop value about £3 0s. 0d ...

Kit of the woman's man

3 knives 4d.—5d. ea.

a crooked and a bevel knife for seating and dressing wood heels or cork seats 8d. ea.

a wrinkled knife (1/6d), the name coming from the use it is put to in dispersing and making smooth the wrinkles on the inside of pump boots [see *Knife, Lining*].

4 shoulder sticks, generally made of cocoa or box-wood 6d. ea.

2 pr. pump irons for same purposes as the shoulder-sticks but are used for strong work 8d. ea.

channel-iron 8d.

seat-file 6d.

long-stick 9d.

2 stamps 1/0d.

pincers 1/4d.

scissors 1/0d.

sharpening strop 8d.

rasp 6d.

bottom-file 6d.

files for cutting the kit 2/0d.

6 instep leathers, leathers used by the English work-man to lift the instep of the woman's shoe; the French workmen using what is called the *block-last*, the same as the man's boot or shoe is made of 9d. ea.

2—3 scrapers or buffing knives 3d.

paring-horn 2d.

fitting board 4d.

12 awls in haft 1/0d.

Besides these there are many other pieces of kit now falling into disuse in consequence of the work going out of fashion, such, for instance, as the long-necked cramping hammer once necessary to the cramping in the sole at the heel of the high-heeled woman's shoe, the purpose of which is scarcely known to the majority of the present race of workmen.

Diagrams of a Boot and Shoe *Figs. 2:3, 2:4, 2:5*

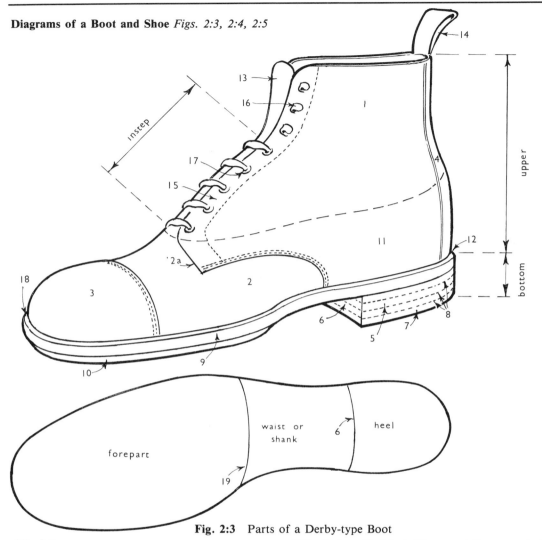

Fig. 2:3 Parts of a Derby-type Boot

(*1*) Leg
(*2*) Vamp
(*2a*) Throat of vamp
(*3*) Toe-cap
(*4*) Back-strap. If much broader this part is called a counter – see diagram of shoe below.
(*5*) Heel
(*6*) Heel breast
(*7*) Top piece or face
(*8*) Lifts (indicated by dotted lines). Layers of leather or other material making up the heel.
(*9*) Sole
(*10*) Clump. A half sole added if required, to resist wear.
(*11*) Galosh. If the part shown below the dotted line, including the area of the vamp (2) is made in one piece, this part is called the 'galosh'.

(*12*) Seat, or Heel Seat. The area at the rear end of the sole (and/or insole) on which the foot heel rests.
(*13*) Tongue
(*14*) Loop
(*15*) Facing or tab. This type of opening is called 'open tab'.
(*16*) Hooks
(*17*) Tie holes fitted with eyelets
(*18*) Welt. The upper surface of the sole-edge, where it protrudes beyond the upper, is covered by the welt. The joint between the sole and upper is sometimes called the welt or feather.
(*19*) A bevel-edged join (sometimes called a 'graft') between two sections of the sole, made in repair work.

28

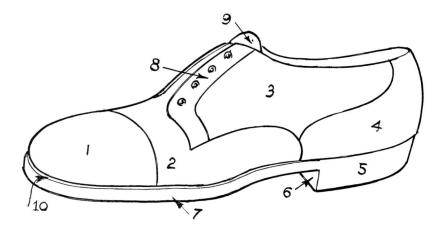

Fig. 2:4 Parts of a Derby-type shoe

(1)	Toe-cap	(6)	Heel breast
(2)	Vamp	(7)	Sole
(3)	Quarter	(8)	Facing or tab
(4)	Counter	(9)	Tongue or tab
(5)	Heel	(10)	If welted, the edge of the welt shows here

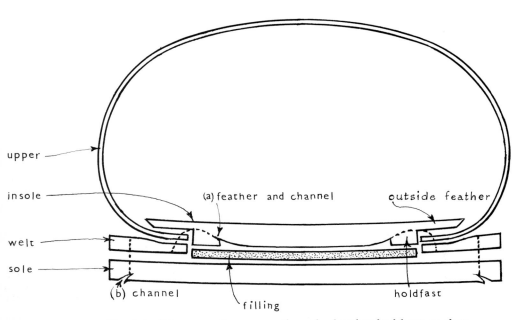

Fig. 2:5 Diagrammatic cross-section of a hand-welted boot or shoe

(a) Channel for the stitching that joins together the insole, upper and welt.

(b) Channel for the stitching that joins the sole to the welt.

French Boot and Shoe Maker's Tools of the Eighteenth Century. From the Encyclopaedia of Diderot and D'Alembert, Plates I and II *Cordonnier et Bottier*, Paris *c*. 1760. See the entry *Eighteenth-Century Methods*. *Figs. 2:6, 2:6a.*

Key to the plates: a slightly abridged translation.
(The words in brackets are explanatory notes and are not in the original).

Fig. 2:6 Plate I
The vignette above the plate shows a shoemaker's shop
- *Fig. (1)* Shoemaker taking measurements
- *(2)* Worker looking for the appropriate last
- *(3)* Worker stitching on a sole
- *(4)* Worker lasting a boot
- *(5) & (6)* Two fellow workers
- *(7)* A cobbler at his stall
  - *a,b,c* rows of different lasts
  - *d* boot lasts
  - *e* finished boots
  - *f* tape measures
  - *g* pattern for an upper or vamp
  - *h* table laden with various tools

Lower part of the Plate
- *(1)* Pliers (Lasting Pliers)
- *(2)* Pincers
- *(3)* Shoe-lift (for pulling on boots or shoes)
- *(4)* Welt set
- *(5)* Sleeking tool in boxwood (an Edge Tool)
- *(6)* Shoemaker's knives
- *(7)* Boot – see Plate II, 48
- *(8)* Polishing stick in boxwood
- *(8)(2)* Round knife
- *(9)* Polishing bone
- *(10)–(13)* Various nails
- *(14)* Size stick
- *(15)* Curved needle
- *(16)* Hammer
- *(17)* Man's clog
- *(18)* Woman's clog
- *(19)* Seam-sett or liner
- *(20)* Tranchet knife (paring)
- *(21)* Star punch
- *(22)–(27)* *A–F* Awls in the English style
- *(28)* Single-block last
- *(28)(2)* 'Broken' last
- *(28)(3)* Another 'broken' last

Fig. 2:6a Plate II
- *Fig. (29)(1)* Boot tree
- *(29)(2)* Key for boot tree or last
- *(30)* Boots
- *(31)* Shoemaker's stirrup
- *(32)* Gipon (Bundle of rags used for applying blacking to tools)
- *(33)* Sole-forming block
- *(34)* A stretching device in operation (probably for pushing a last into a turnshoe)
- *(35)* Thread holder
- *(36)* Section through 35 showing ball of thread
- *(37)* Small Awl used by shoemakers
- *(38)* Bowl for soaking soles
- *(39)* Sole beating block
- *(40)* Upper
- *(41)* Sole
- *(42)* Quarter
- *(43)* Shoe: *A* uppers, *B* quarter, *C* tongue, *D* heel
- *(44)* Hand-leather
- *(45)–(51)* Various spurs and boots
- *(52)* Blacking pot (see also 32)
- *(53)* Apron

English Boot and Shoe Maker's Tools: see page 83

Pl. 1.

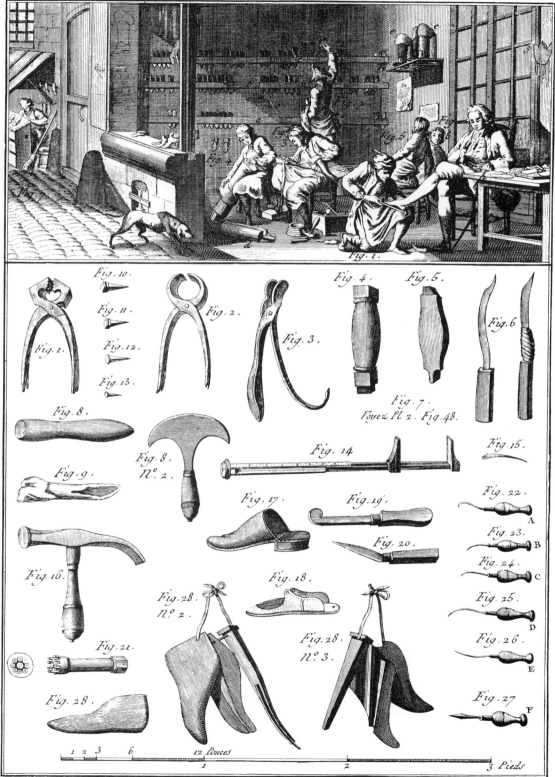

Benard Direxit.

Fig. 2:6 From the Encyclopaedia of Diderot and D'Alembert, Paris *c.* 1760.

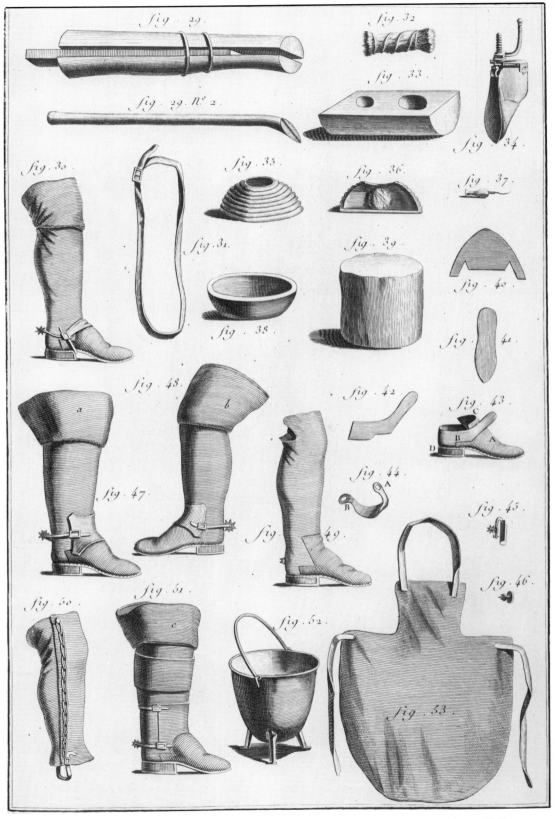

Fig. 2:6a From the Encyclopaedia of Diderot and D'Alembert, Paris, *c*. 1760.

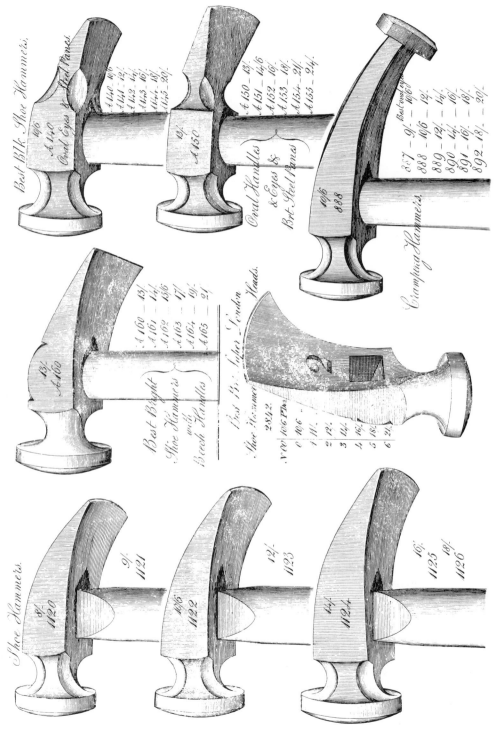

Best Blk. Shoe Hammers.

4/6
A.140

Oval Eyes & Steel Panes.

A.140 — 4/6
A.141 — 12/-
A.142 — 14/-
A.143 — 16/-
A.144 — 18/-
A.145 — 20/-

4/-
A.150

A.150 — 4/-
A.151 — 14/6
A.152 — 16/-
A.153 — 18/-
A.154 — 2/-
A.155 — 24/-

Oval Handles & Eyes & Brt. Steel Panes.

4/6
888

Cramping Hammers.

Belt'oval eyes
887 — 9/-   10/6
888 — 10/6   12/-
889 — 12/-   14/-
890 — 14/-   16/-
891 — 16/-   18/-
892 — 18/-   20/-

4/-
A.160

A.160 — 4/-
A.161 — 14/-
A.162 — 156
A.163 — 17/-
A.164 — 19/-
A.165 — 21/-

Best Bright Shoe Hammers with Beech Handles.

Best Brt. Liver London Heads.

Shoe Hammers.
2842
New 106 Pdn.
0   10/6   . .
1   11/.   . .
2   12/.   . .
3   14/.   . .
4   16/.   . .
5   18/.   . .
6   21/.   . .

Shoe Hammers.

8/-
1120

9/-
1121

10/6
1122

12/-
1123

14/-
M.8M

16/-
1125

18/-
1126

Fig. 2:7

Shoemaker's Tools (Richard Timmins' Catalogue, Birmingham c. 1800).

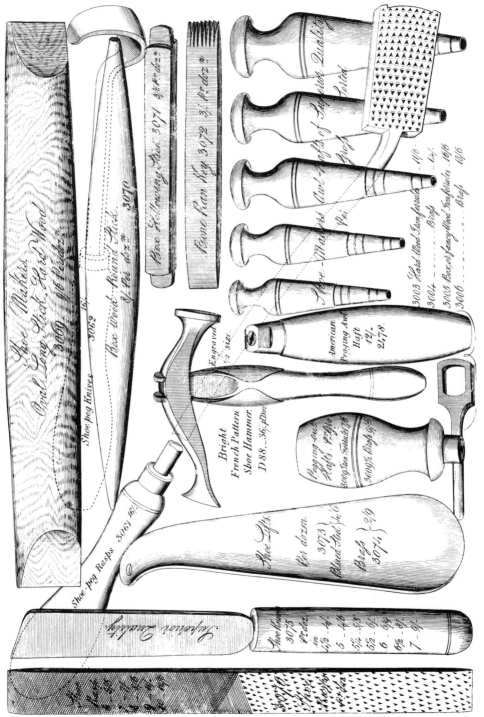

Shoemaker's Tools (Richard Timmins' Catalogue, Birmingham c. 1800).

Fig. 2:8

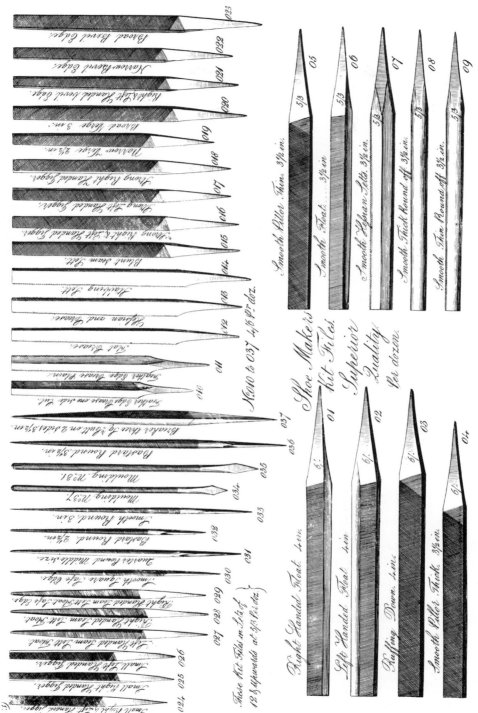

Fig. 2:9

Shoemaker's Tools (Richard Timmins' Catalogue, Birmingham c. 1800).

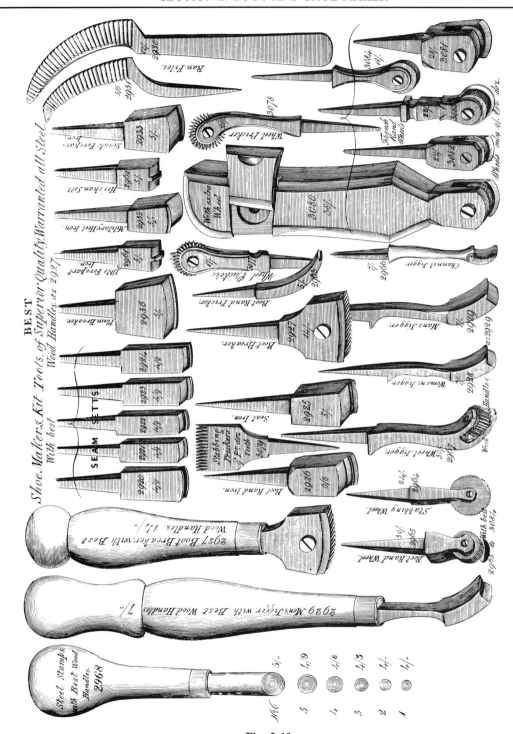

Fig. 2:10

Shoemaker's Tools (Richard Timmins' Catalogue, Birmingham c. 1800).

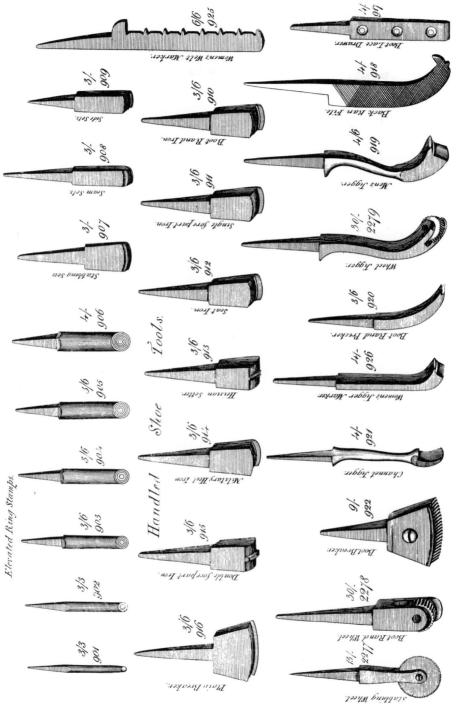

Women's Welt Marker. 926 925

Boot Lace Drawer. 907

Side Sets. 909 3/-

Boot Rand Iron. 910 3/6

Back Ran File. 918 4/-

Seam Sets. 908 3/-

Single Forepart Iron. 911 3/6

Men's Jigger. 919 9/6

Stabbing Sets. 907 3/-

Seat Iron. 912 3/6

Wheel Jigger. 926-9 10/-

Elevated Ring Stamps.

906 4/-

Hessian Setter. 913 3/6

Boot Rand Pricker. 920 3/6

905 3/6

Military Heel Iron. 914 3/6

Women's Jigger Marker. 926 4/-

904 3/6

Double Forepart Iron. 915 3/6

Channel Jigger. 926 4/-

903 3/6

Boot Breaker. 922 9/-

902 3/3

Plain Breaker. 916 3/6

Boot Rand Wheel. 927-8 30/-

901 3/3

Stabbing Wheel. 927-11 15/-

Tools. Shoe Handled

Shoemaker's Tools (Richard Timmins' Catalogue, Birmingham c. 1800).

Fig. 2:11

37

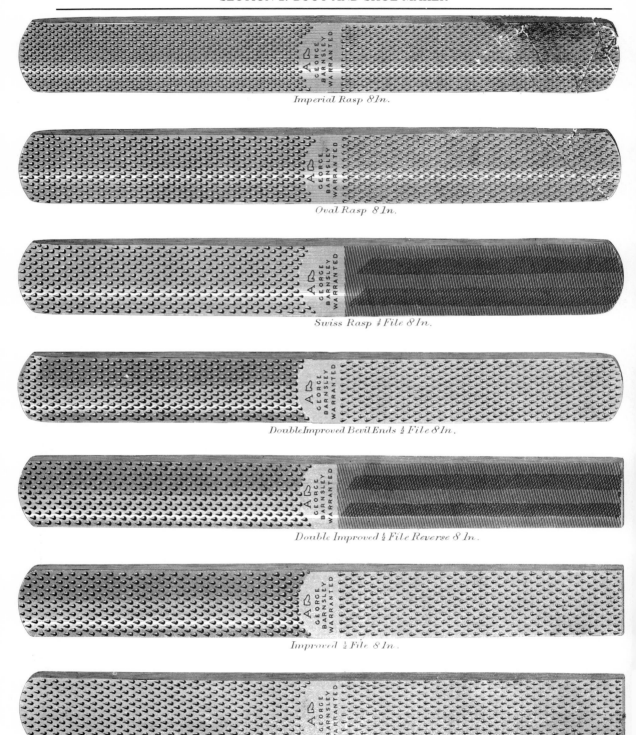

Imperial Rasp 8 In.

Oval Rasp 8 In.

Swiss Rasp ¼ File 8 In.

Double Improved Bevil Ends ½ File 8 In.

Double Improved ½ File Reverse 8 In.

Improved ½ File 8 In.

Plain ½ File 8 In.

Fig. 2:12   Shoemaker's Tools (George Barnsley and Son's Catalogue, Sheffield 1898).

4.4½ Inch
ad Point

Nº 4 4½ Inch
Spear Point

Nº 4 4½ Inch
Clip Point

Nº 4 4½ Inch
Sheep Foot Point

Nº 17.4 Inch
Broad Point
Brass Ferruled

Nº 17.4 Inch
Spear Point
Brass Ferruled

Nº 101 3½ Inch
Broad Pt Brass Ferruled
Nº 101 Spear Point

Fig. 2:13 Shoemaker's Tools (George Barnsley and Son's Catalogue, Sheffield 1898).

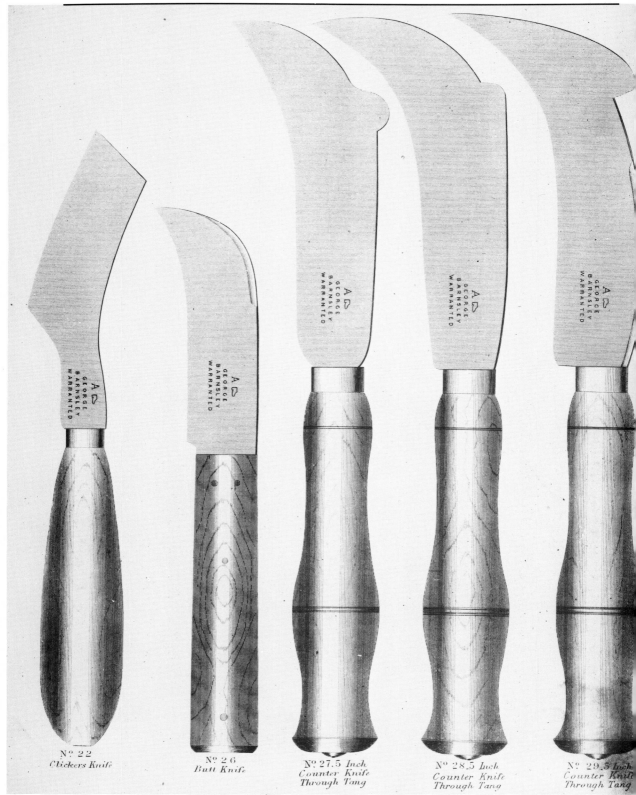

Nº 22
Clickers Knife

Nº 26
Butt Knife

Nº 27.5 *Inch*
Counter Knife
Through Tang

Nº 28.5 *Inch*
Counter Knife
Through Tang

Nº 29.5 *Inch*
Counter Knife
Through Tang

Fig. 2:14 Shoemaker's Tools (George Barnsley and Son's Catalogue, Sheffield 1898).

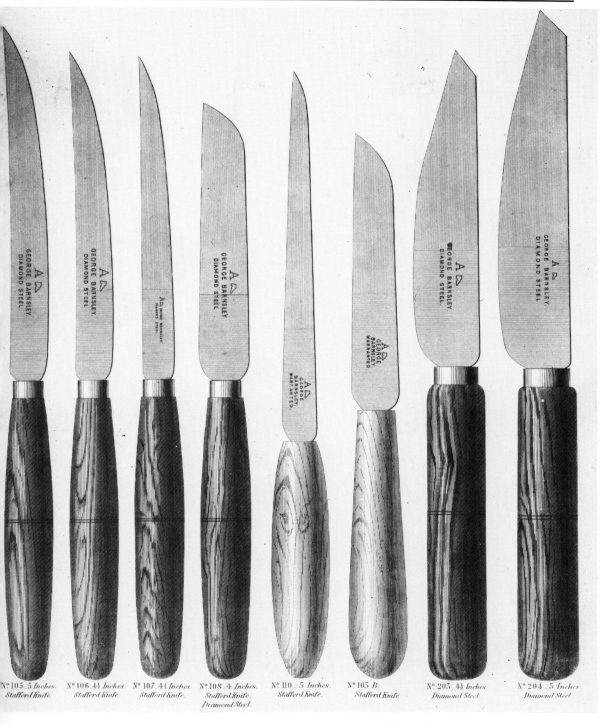

Nº 105. 5 Inches.
Stafford Knife.

Nº 106. 4½ Inches.
Stafford Knife.

Nº 107. 4½ Inches.
Stafford Knife.

Nº 108. 4 Inches.
Stafford Knife.
Diamond Steel.

Nº 110. 5 Inches.
Stafford Knife.

Nº 105 B.
Stafford Knife.

Nº 203. 4½ Inches.
Diamond Steel.

Nº 204. 5 Inches.
Diamond Steel.

Fig. 2:15 Shoemaker's Tools (George Barnsley and Son's Catalogue, Sheffield 1898).

41

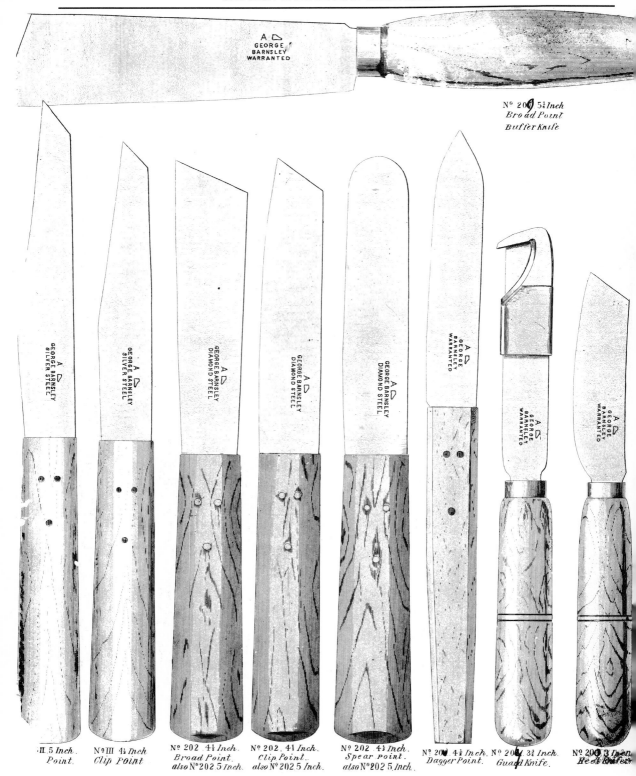

Nº 200 5½ Inch.
Broad Point
Buffer Knife.

II.5 Inch.
Point.

Nº III 4½ Inch.
Clip Point

Nº 202 4½ Inch.
Broad Point.
also Nº 202 5 Inch.

Nº 202 4½ Inch.
Clip Point.
also Nº 202 5 Inch.

Nº 202 4½ Inch.
Spear point.
also Nº 202 5 Inch.

Nº 200 4½ Inch.
Dagger Point.

Nº 200 3½ Inch.
Guard Knife.

Nº 200 3 Inch.
Heel Knife.

Fig. 2:16   Shoemaker's Tools (George Barnsley and Son's Catalogue, Sheffield 1898).

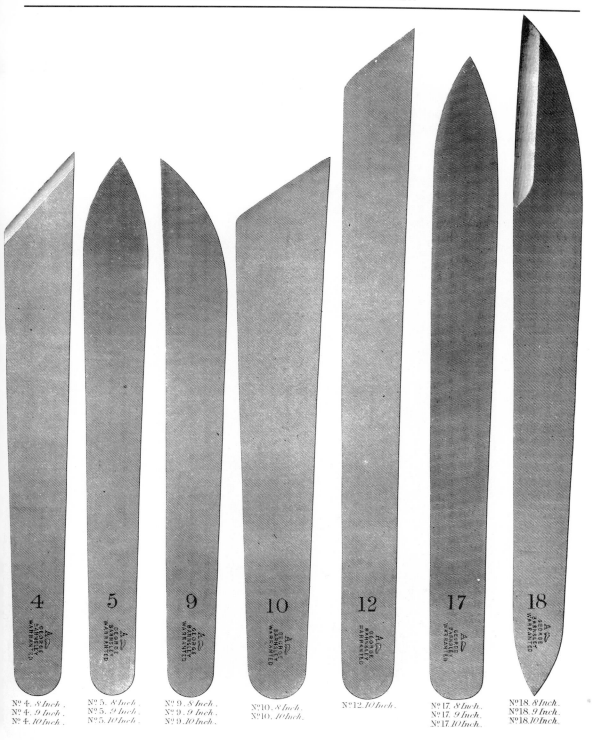

Fig. 2:17 Shoemaker's Tools (George Barnsley and Son's Catalogue, Sheffield 1898).

French Knives, (Tranchets.)

Butchers Steels.

Shoemakers Steels.

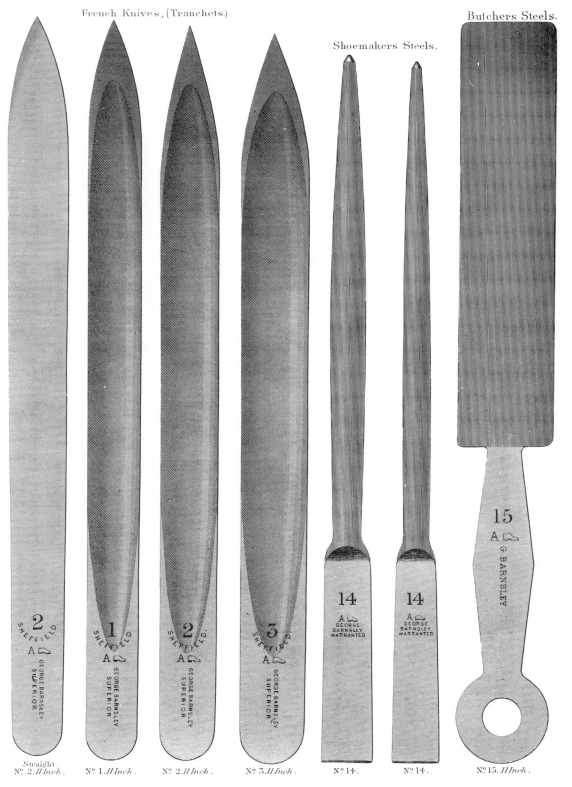

Straight.
Nº 2. 11 Inch.   Nº 1. 11 Inch.   Nº 2. 11 Inch.   Nº 3. 11 Inch.   Nº 14.   Nº 14.   Nº 15. 11 Inch.

Fig. 2:18 Shoemaker's Tools (George Barnsley and Son's Catalogue, Sheffield 1898).

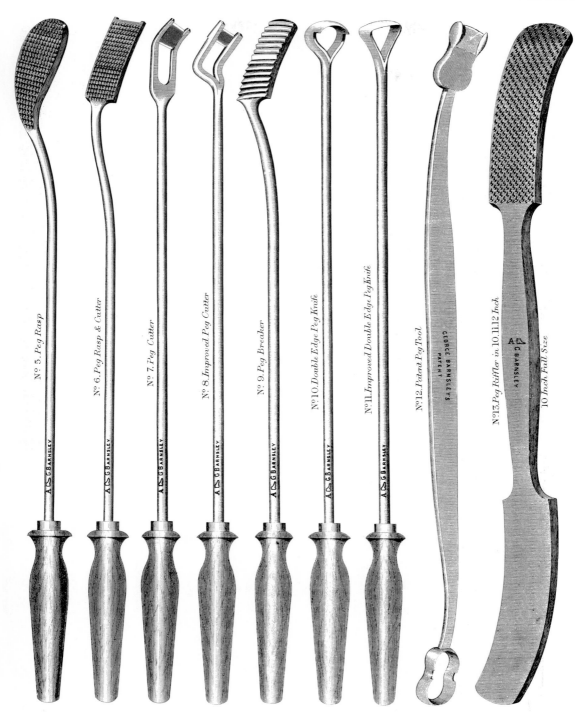

Nº 5. Peg Rasp

Nº 6. Peg Rasp & Cutter

Nº 7. Peg Cutter

Nº 8. Improved Peg Cutter

Nº 9. Peg Breaker

Nº 10. Double Edge Peg Knife

Nº 11. Improved Double Edge Peg Knife

Nº 12. Patent Peg Tool

Nº 13. Peg Riffler in 10, 11, 12 Inch

10 Inch Full Size

Fig. 2:19 Shoemaker's Tools (George Barnsley and Son's Catalogue, Sheffield 1898).

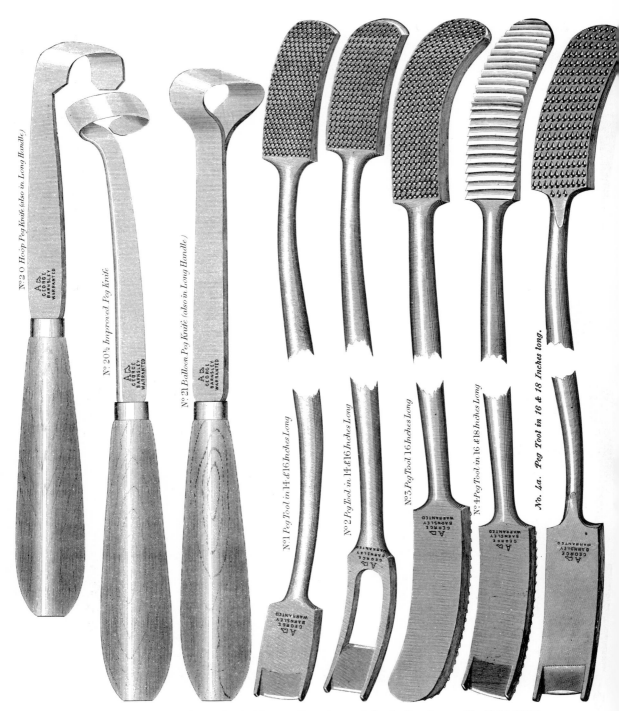

Fig. 2:20 Shoemaker's Tools (George Barnsley and Son's Catalogue, Sheffield 1898).

Nº 1 Forepart Iron

Nº 2 Seat Iron

Nº 3 Double Iron

Nº 4 Bevil Edge Iron

Nº 5 Shank Iron

Nº 6 Single Pump Iron

Nº 7 Double Pump Iron

Nº 8 Double Forepart Iron

Nº 9 Double Double Iron

Nº 10 Jigger

Nº 11 Boot Iron

A   B   C   D   E   F   G

Forepart, Seat, Bevil, Shank and Double Irons made in Substance from A to G

Nº 12 Scratch Bone

Nº 13 Channel Jigger

Nº 14 Glazing Iron
1, 2, 3 Sizes

Nº 15 Single Top Sett

Nº 16 Binding Sett

Nº 17 Double Top Sett

Nº 18 Welt Sett

Nº 19 Seam Sett

Nº 20 Breaker
1, 2, 3 Sizes

Nº 21 Brass Flowered
Stamp Assorted Patterns

Nº 22 Band File

Nº 23 Stitch Bone

Fig. 2:21 Shoemaker's Tools (George Barnsley and Son's Catalogue, Sheffield 1898).

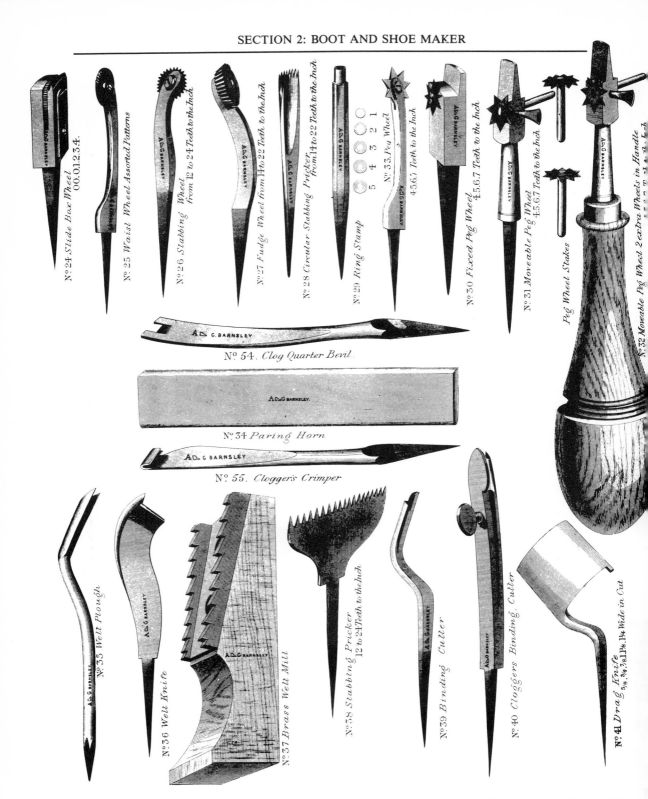

Nº 24. Slide Box Wheel OO.O.1.2.3.4.

Nº 25. Waist Wheel Assorted Patterns

Nº 26. Stabbing Wheel from 12 to 24 Teeth to the Inch

Nº 27. Fudge Wheel from 14 to 22 Teeth to the Inch

Nº 28. Circular Stabbing Pricker from 14 to 22 Teeth to the Inch

Nº 29. Ring Stamp 5 4 3 2 1

Nº 33. Pea Wheel 4.5.6.7. Teeth to the Inch

Nº 30. Fixed Peg Wheel 4.5.6.7. Teeth to the Inch

Nº 31. Moveable Peg Wheel 4.5.6.7 Teeth to the Inch

Peg Wheel Stakes

Nº 32. Moveable Peg Wheel 2 extra Wheels in Handle

Nº 54. Clog Quarter Bevil.

Nº 34. Paring Horn

Nº 55. Clogger's Crimper

Nº 35. Welt Plough

Nº 36. Welt Knife

Nº 37. Brass Welt Mill

Nº 38. Stabbing Pricker 12 to 24 Teeth to the Inch

Nº 39. Binding Cutter

Nº 40. Cloggers Binding Cutter

Nº 41. Drag Knife 5/8, 3/4, 7/8, 1 1/8, 1 1/4 Wide in Cut

Fig. 2:22 Shoemaker's Tools (George Barnsley and Son's Catalogue, Sheffield 1898).

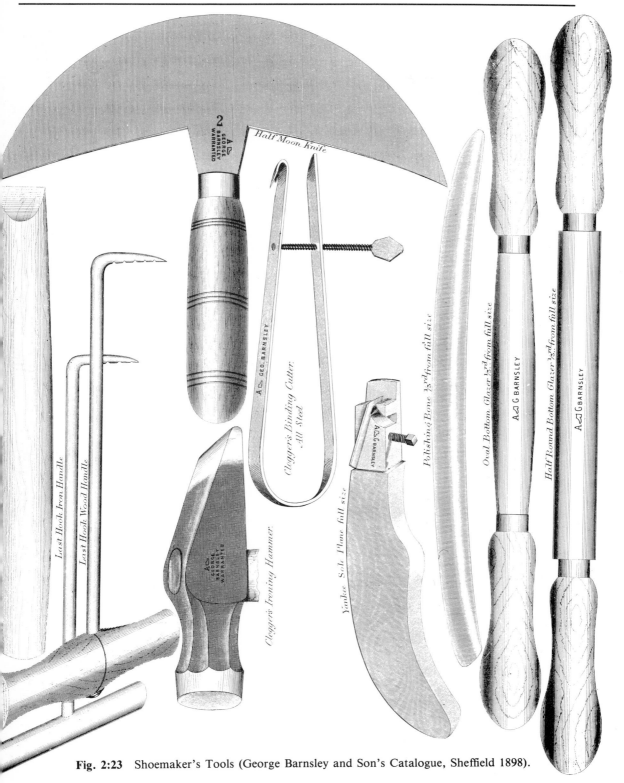

Fig. 2:23 Shoemaker's Tools (George Barnsley and Son's Catalogue, Sheffield 1898).

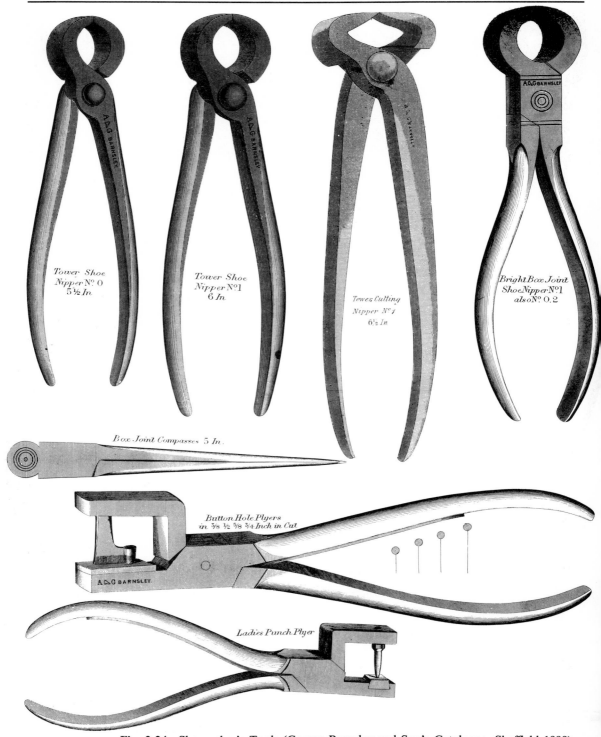

Fig. 2:24 Shoemaker's Tools (George Barnsley and Son's Catalogue, Sheffield 1898).

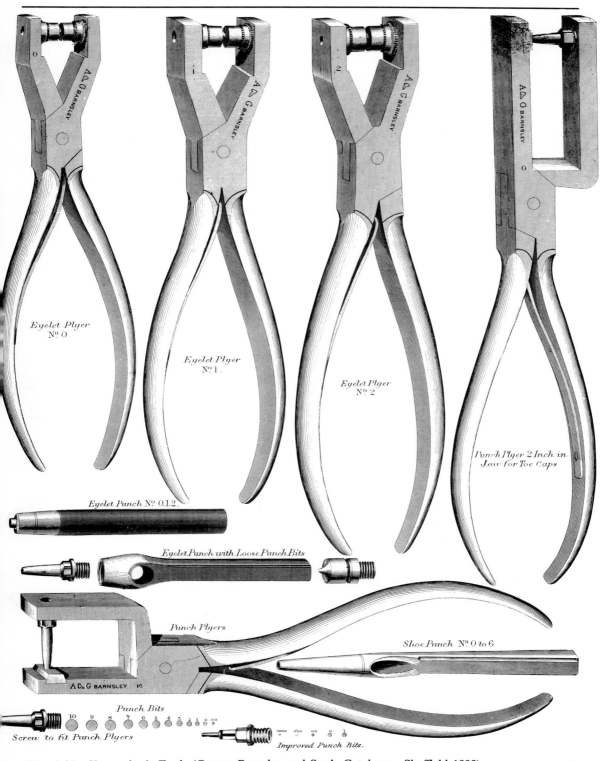

Fig. 2:25 Shoemaker's Tools (George Barnsley and Son's Catalogue, Sheffield 1898).

51

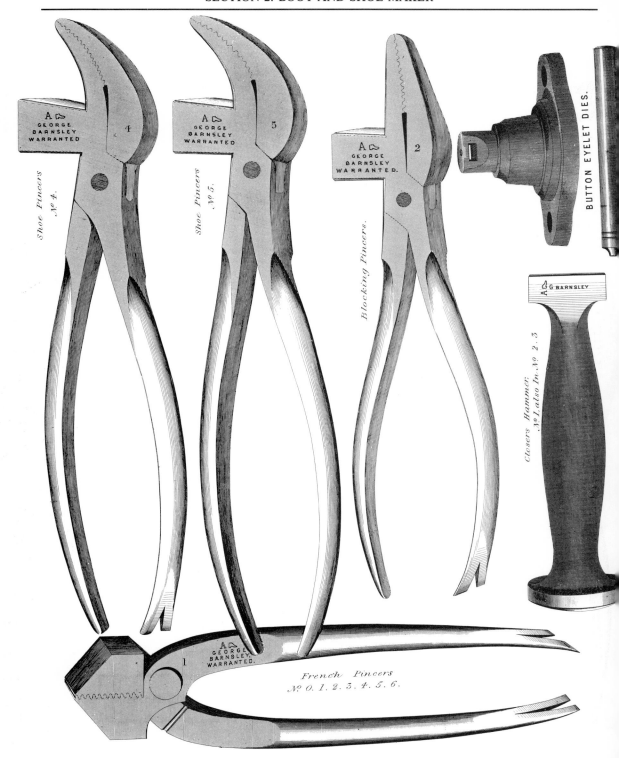

Fig. 2:26 Shoemaker's Tools (George Barnsley and Son's Catalogue, Sheffield 1898).

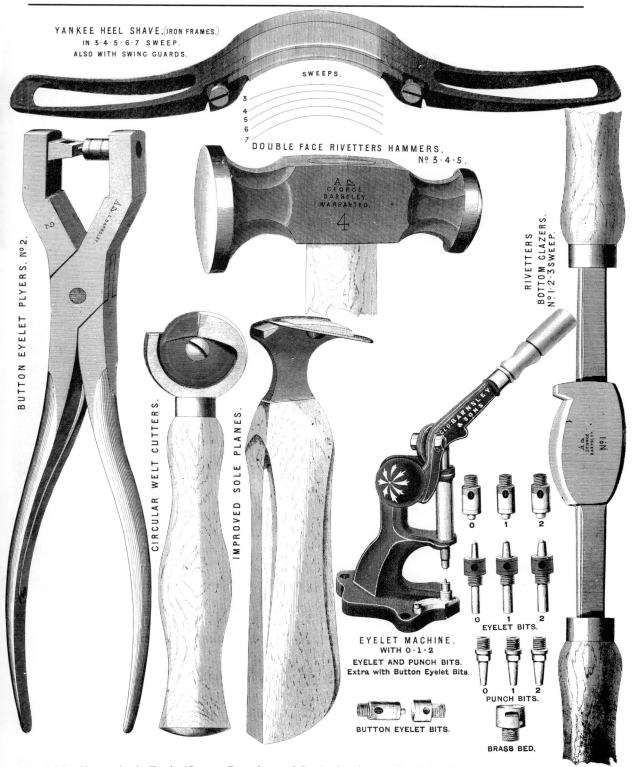

YANKEE HEEL SHAVE. (IRON FRAMES.)
IN 3·4·5·6·7 SWEEP.
ALSO WITH SWING GUARDS.

SWEEPS.

DOUBLE FACE RIVETTERS HAMMERS,
Nº 3·4·5.

BUTTON EYELET PLYERS, Nº 2.

CIRCULAR WELT CUTTERS.

IMPROVED SOLE PLANES.

EYELET MACHINE.
WITH 0·1·2
EYELET AND PUNCH BITS.
Extra with Button Eyelet Bits.

EYELET BITS.

PUNCH BITS.

BUTTON EYELET BITS.

BRASS BED.

RIVETTERS BOTTOM GLAZERS. Nº1·2·3 SWEEP.

Fig. 2:27 Shoemaker's Tools (George Barnsley and Son's Catalogue, Sheffield 1898).

SHOE TOOLS & KIT TOOLS.

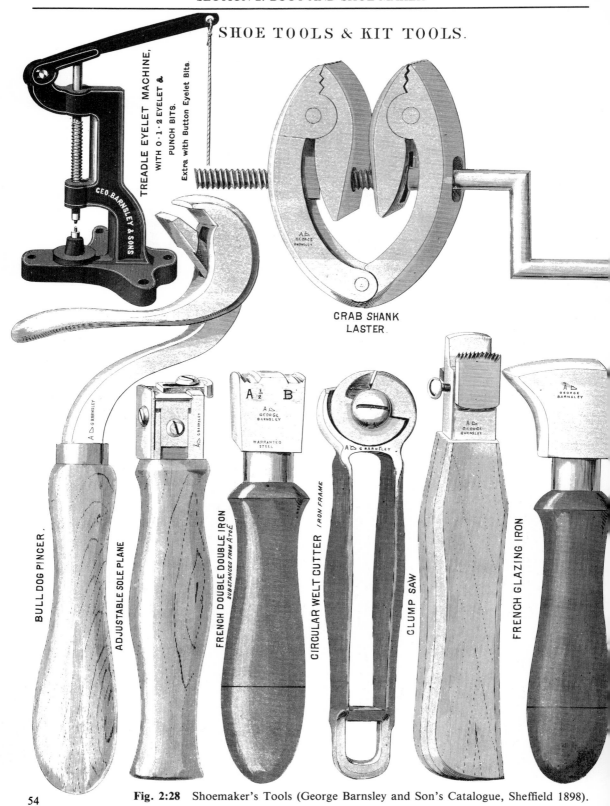

TREADLE EYELET MACHINE,
WITH 0·1·2 EYELET &
PUNCH BITS.
Extra with Button Eyelet Bits.

CRAB SHANK
LASTER.

BULL DOG PINCER.

ADJUSTABLE SOLE PLANE

FRENCH DOUBLE DOUBLE IRON
SUBSTANCES FROM A TO E

CIRCULAR WELT CUTTER IRON FRAME

CLUMP SAW

FRENCH GLAZING IRON

Fig. 2:28 Shoemaker's Tools (George Barnsley and Son's Catalogue, Sheffield 1898).

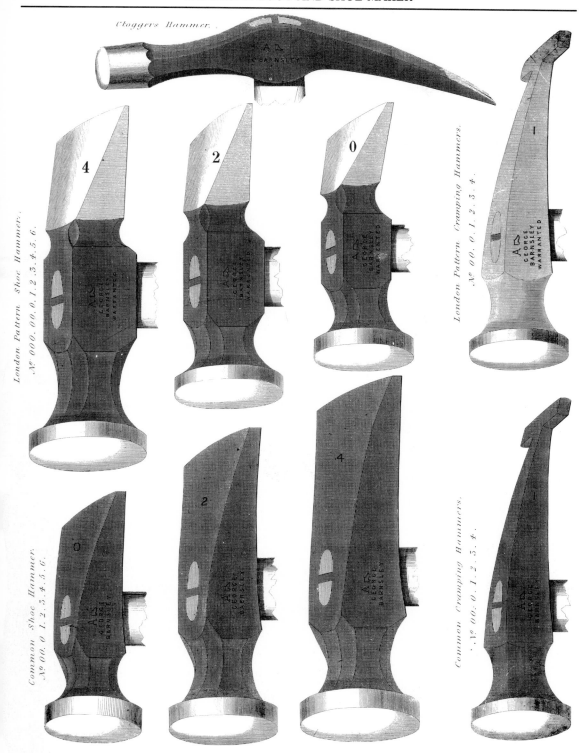

Fig. 2:29 Shoemaker's Tools (George Barnsley and Son's Catalogue, Sheffield 1898).

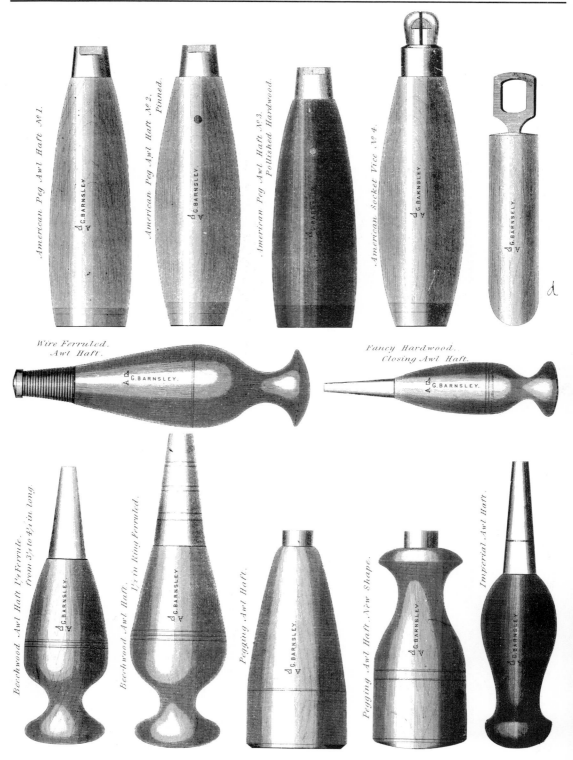

American Peg Awl Haft No 1.

American Peg Awl Haft No 2. Pinned.

American Peg Awl Haft No 3. Polished Hardwood.

American Socket Vice No 4.

Wire Ferruled. Awl Haft.

Fancy Hardwood. Closing Awl Haft.

Beechwood Awl Haft 1½ Ferrule. from 3¼ to 4½ in. long.

Beechwood Awl Haft. 1½ in Ring Ferruled.

Pegging Awl Haft.

Pegging Awl Haft. New Shape.

Imperial Awl Haft.

Fig. 2:30 Shoemaker's Tools (George Barnsley and Son's Catalogue, Sheffield 1898).

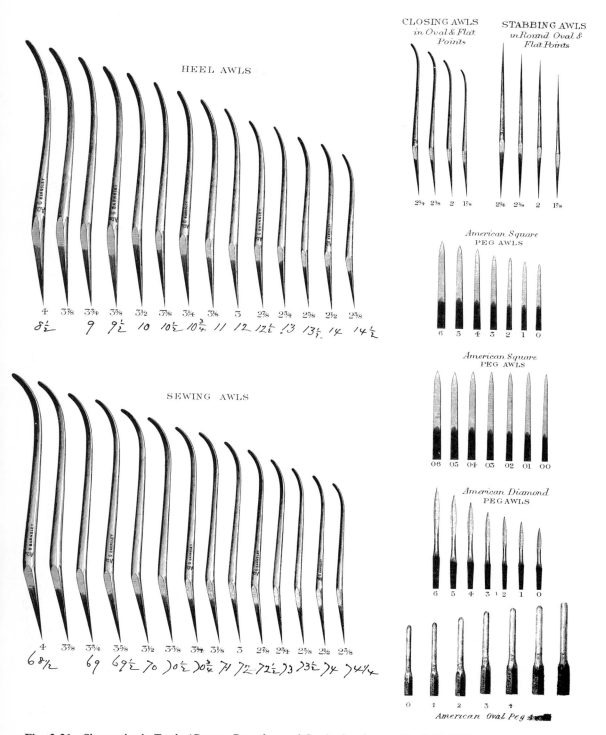

Fig. 2:31 Shoemaker's Tools (George Barnsley and Son's Catalogue, Sheffield 1898).

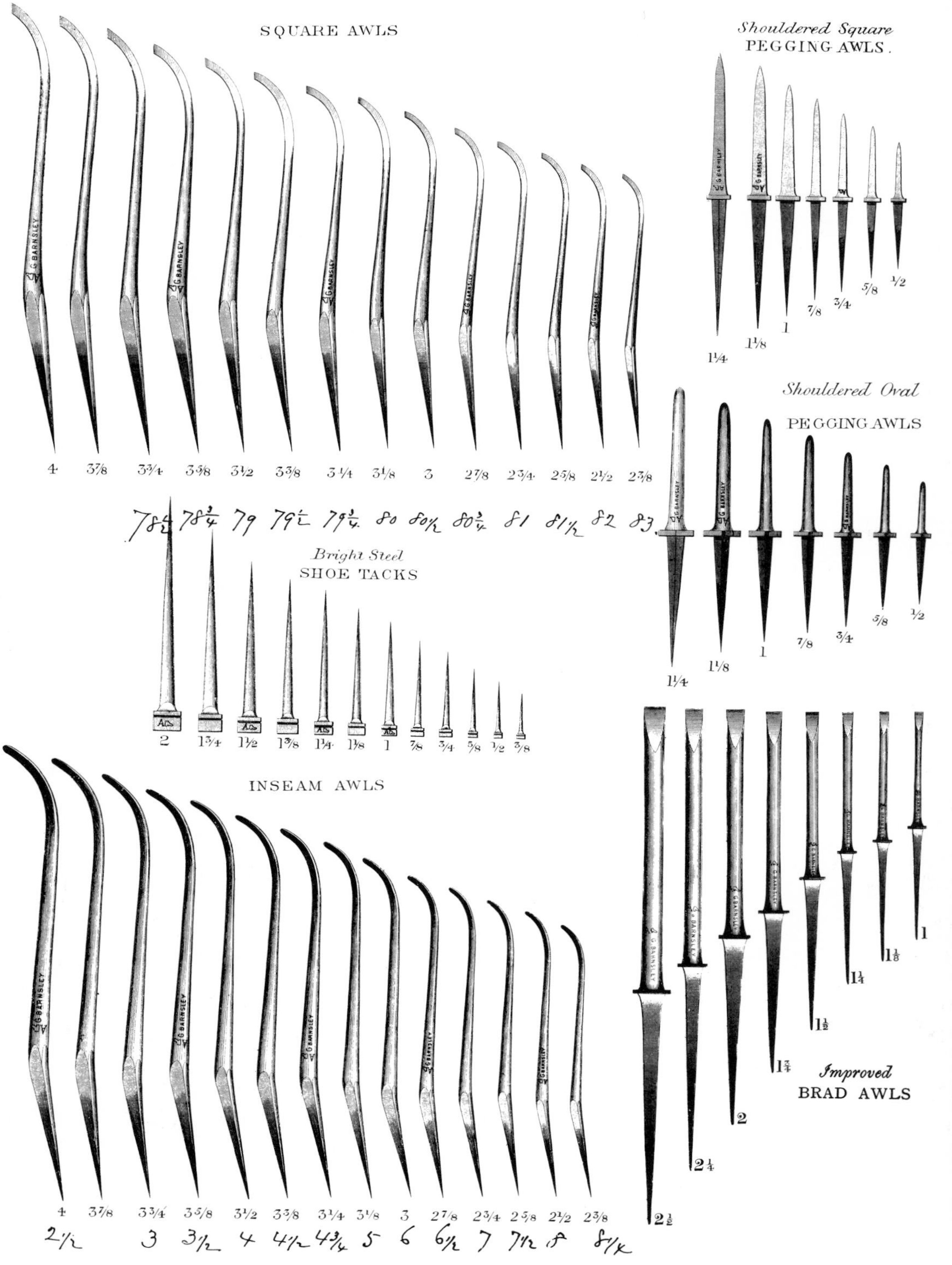
SQUARE AWLS
4 3⅞ 3¾ 3⅝ 3½ 3⅜ 3¼ 3⅛ 3 2⅞ 2¾ 2⅝ 2½ 2⅜
Shouldered Square
PEGGING AWLS.
1¼ 1⅛ 1 ⅞ ¾ ⅝ ½
Shouldered Oval
PEGGING AWLS
1¼ 1⅛ 1 ⅞ ¾ ⅝ ½
Bright Steel
SHOE TACKS
2 1¾ 1½ 1⅜ 1¼ 1⅛ 1 ⅞ ¾ ⅝ ½ ⅜
INSEAM AWLS
4 3⅞ 3¾ 3⅝ 3½ 3⅜ 3¼ 3⅛ 3 2⅞ 2¾ 2⅝ 2½ 2⅜
Improved
BRAD AWLS
1 1⅛ 1¼ 1½ 1¾ 2 2¼ 2½
G BARNSLEY

Fig. 2:32 Shoemaker's Tools (George Barnsley and Son's Catalogue, Sheffield 1898).

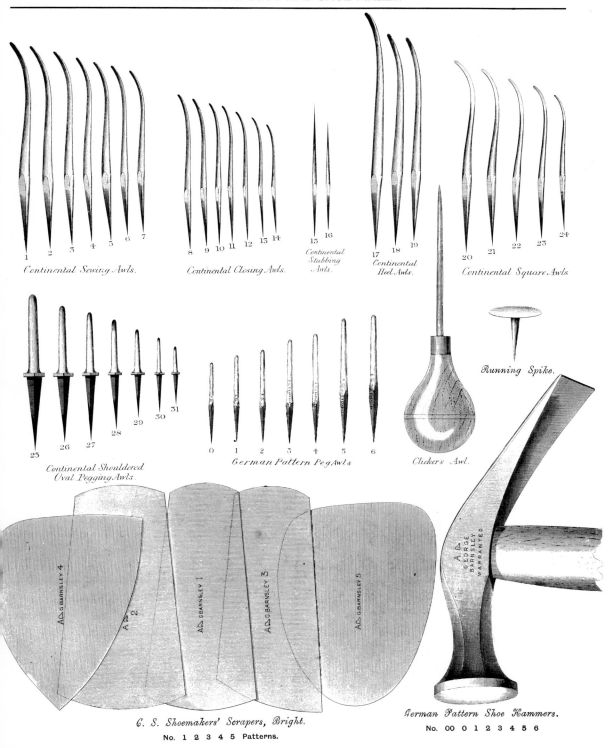

Continental Sewing Awls.

Continental Closing Awls.

Continental Stabbing Awls.

Continental Heel Awls.

Continental Square Awls

Continental Shouldered Oval Pegging Awls.

German Pattern Peg Awls.

Running Spike.

Clickers Awl.

C. S. Shoemakers' Scrapers, Bright.
No. 1 2 3 4 5 Patterns.

German Pattern Shoe Hammers.
No. 00 0 1 2 3 4 5 6

Fig. 2:33 Shoemaker's Tools (George Barnsley and Son's Catalogue, Sheffield 1898).

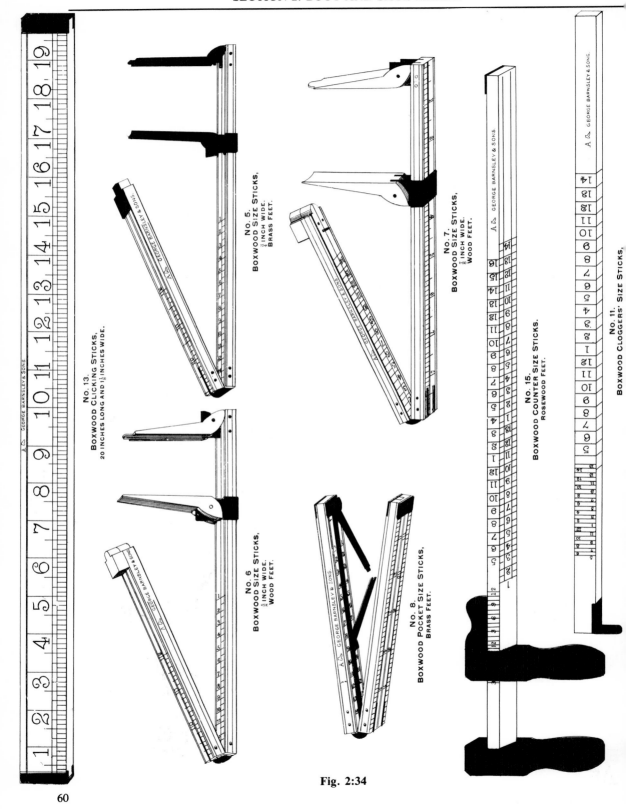

NO. 13.
BOXWOOD CLICKING STICKS,
20 INCHES LONG AND 1⅜ INCHES WIDE.

NO. 5.
BOXWOOD SIZE STICKS,
⅞ INCH WIDE.
BRASS FEET.

NO. 7.
BOXWOOD SIZE STICKS,
⅞ INCH WIDE.
WOOD FEET.

NO. 6.
BOXWOOD SIZE STICKS,
⅝ INCH WIDE.
WOOD FEET.

NO. 8.
BOXWOOD POCKET SIZE STICKS,
BRASS FEET.

NO. 15.
BOXWOOD COUNTER SIZE STICKS.
ROSEWOOD FEET.

NO. 11.
BOXWOOD CLOGGERS' SIZE STICKS.

Fig. 2:34

SHOE KNIVES.

THESE illustrations show **only** the various shapes of blades. All knives on page 6 can be supplied with these shapes. Shapes "C," "S," "B" and "P" apply to all knives on page 7, but "C," "S" and "B" only apply to the first five patterns on page 8. The letter given at the side of the following designs if placed **after** the pattern number is sufficient to obtain the proper pattern, thus **401.C.**

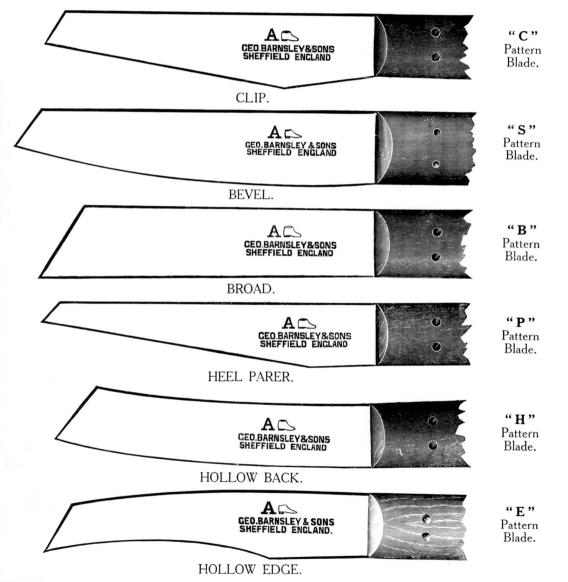

CLIP.
"C" Pattern Blade.

BEVEL.
"S" Pattern Blade.

BROAD.
"B" Pattern Blade.

HEEL PARER.
"P" Pattern Blade.

HOLLOW BACK.
"H" Pattern Blade.

HOLLOW EDGE.
"E" Pattern Blade.

CORNISH WORKS · SHEFFIELD · ENGLAND

Fig. 2:35 Shoemaker's Tools (George Barnsley and Son's Catalogue, Sheffield 1927).

CLICKERS' KNIVES.

Code No.	Patt. No.	
2300	22	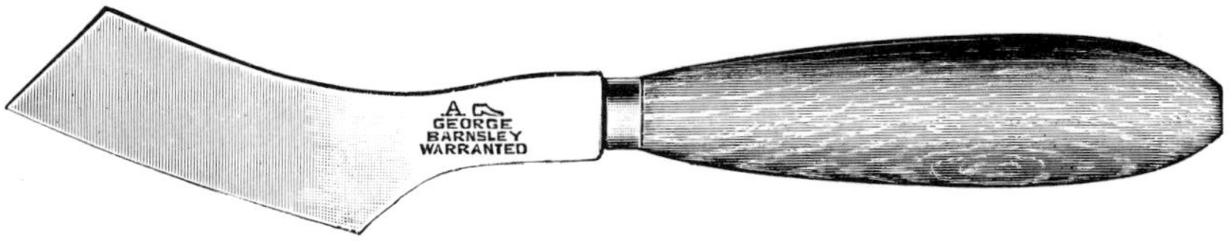 Warranted Steel, yellow handle, brass ferrule.
2302	103	 Warranted Steel, white handle.
2306	105	 Diamond Steel, rosewood handle, brass ferrule.
2312	112	 Beechwood handle.
2314	113	 Skiving Knife, Diamond Steel, rosewood handle, brass ferrule, sheep foot point.
2316	109	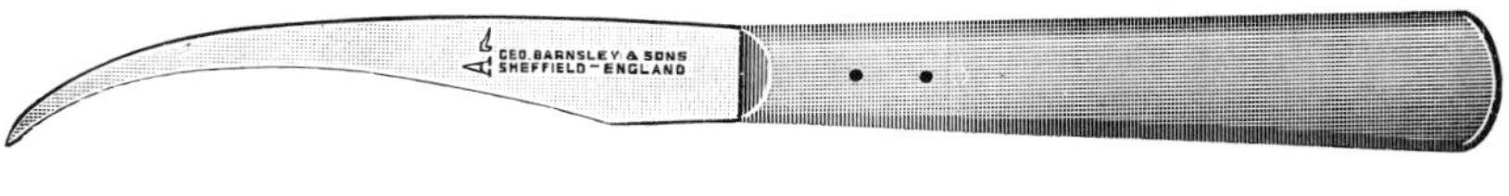 Warranted Steel, beechwood handle.
2318	109½	 Warranted Steel, white handle, bright steel ferrule.
2320	120	 Polished beechwood handle, brass ferrule.

A CORNISH WORKS · SHEFFIELD · ENGLAND A

Fig. 2:36   Shoemaker's Tools (George Barnsley and Son's Catalogue, Sheffield 1927).

CLICKERS' KNIVES.

Code No.	Patt. No.	
2322	A80	

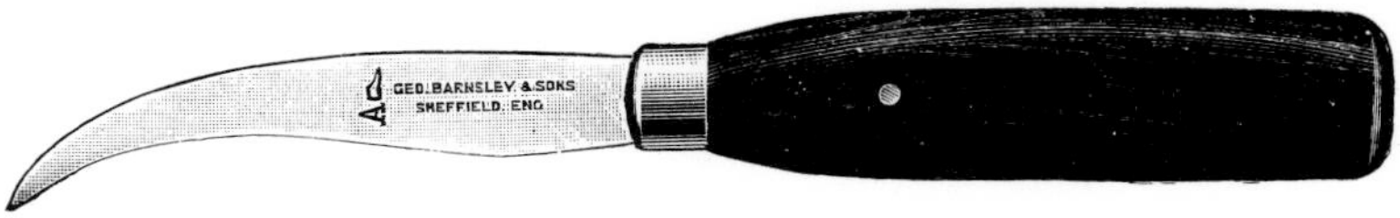

Paris curve, brown pinned handle, nickel ferrule.

2324	122	

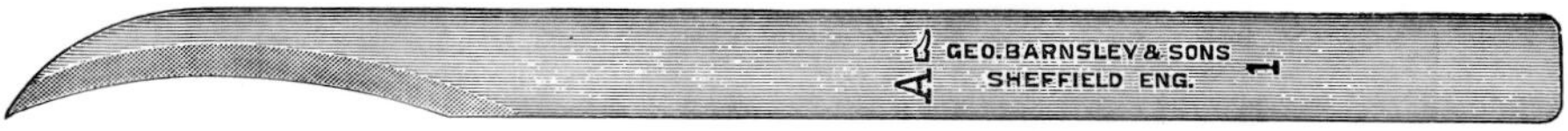

Extension Clicker Blade, ordinary curve.

2326	122	

Extension Clicker Blade, short curve.

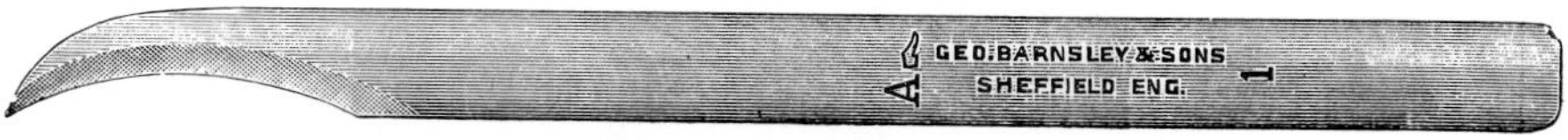

2328	122	

Extension Clicker Blade, bevel point.

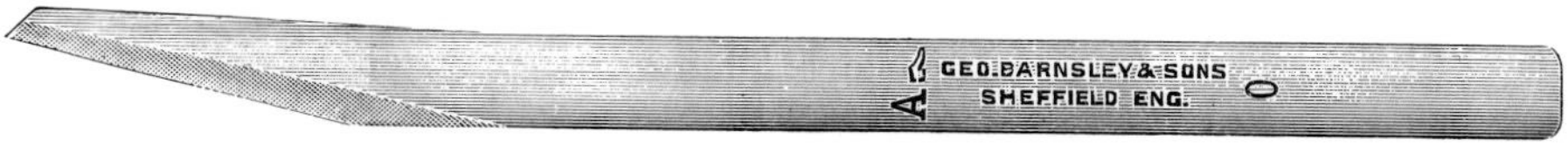

2330	122	

Extension Clicker Blade, lance point.

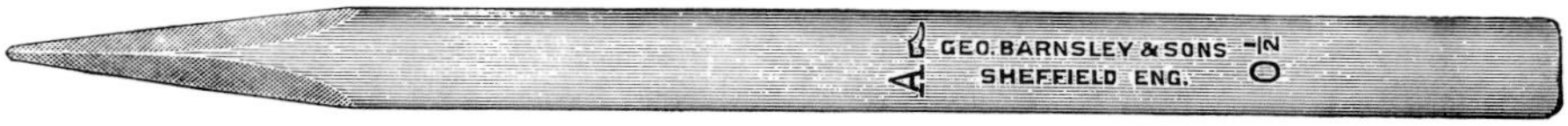

2332	122	

Extension Clicker Blade, sharp point.

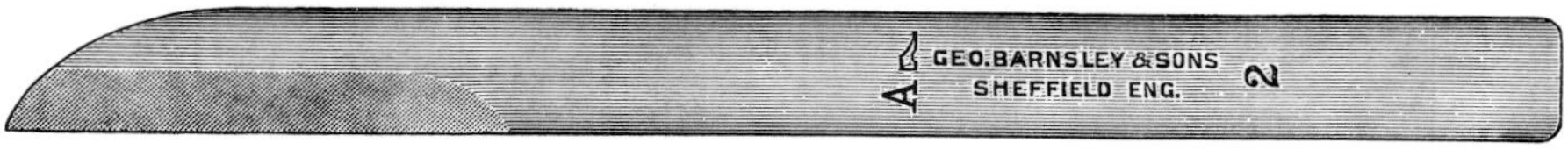

2334		

Extension Clicker Blade Handle.

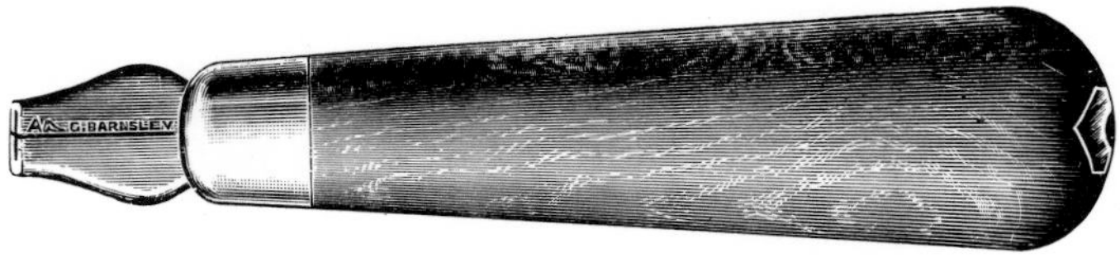

A🥾 CORNISH WORKS · SHEFFIELD · ENGLAND A🥾

Fig. 2:37 Shoemaker's Tools (George Barnsley and Son's Catalogue, Sheffield 1927).

SHOE KNIVES.

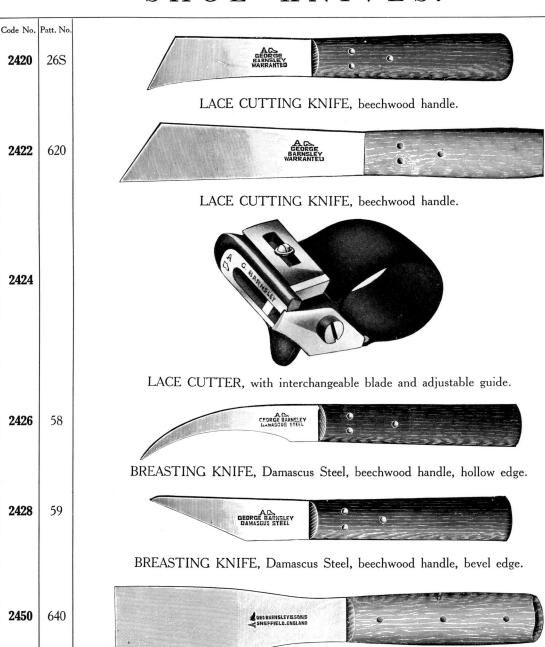

Code No.	Patt. No.
2420	26S
2422	620
2424	
2426	58
2428	59
2450	640

LACE CUTTING KNIFE, beechwood handle.

LACE CUTTING KNIFE, beechwood handle.

LACE CUTTER, with interchangeable blade and adjustable guide.

BREASTING KNIFE, Damascus Steel, beechwood handle, hollow edge.

BREASTING KNIFE, Damascus Steel, beechwood handle, bevel edge.

BOTTOM FILLING KNIFE, beechwood handle.

 CORNISH WORKS · SHEFFIELD · ENGLAND

Fig. 2:38 Shoemaker's Tools (George Barnsley and Son's Catalogue, Sheffield 1927).

SHOE KNIVES.

Code No.	Patt. No.	
2500	641	

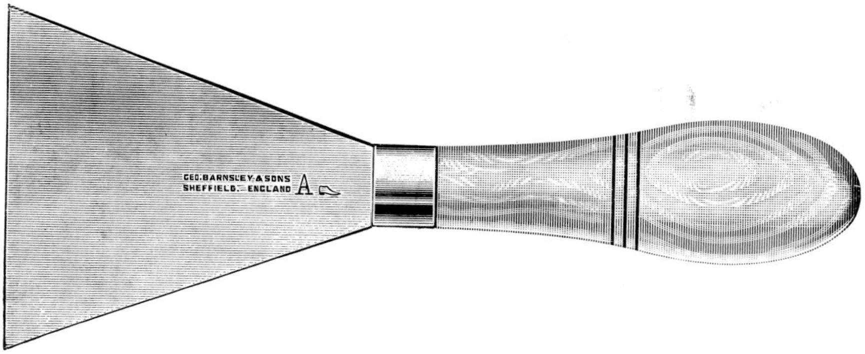

TRIANGULAR SHOE KNIFE, polished beechwood handle, brass ferrule.

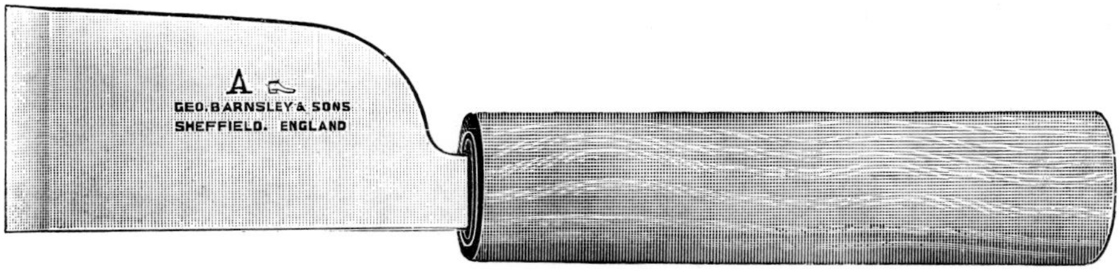

2520	642	

PARING KNIFE "CHOP" PATTERN, white handle.

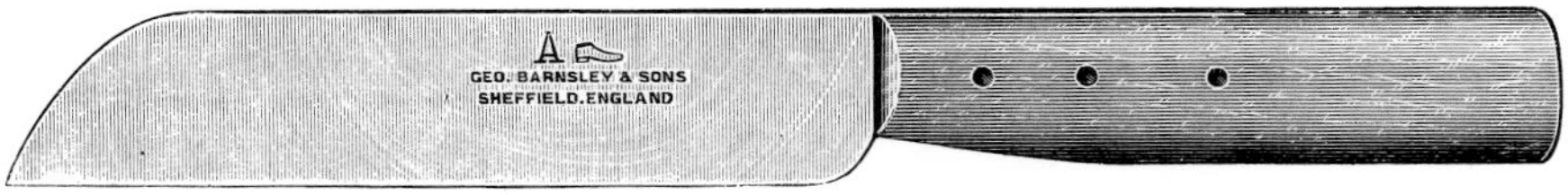

2214		

BROWN HANDLE, scale tang.

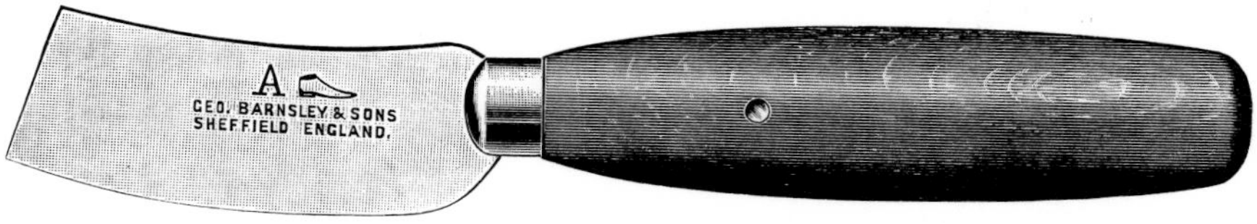

2210	A85	

ROUND EDGE HEEL KNIFE, brown pinned handle, nickel ferrule.

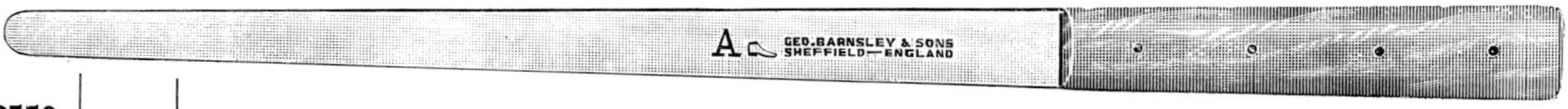

2550		

LINING KNIFE, flexible blade, beechwood handle, through tang rivetted.

A CORNISH WORKS · SHEFFIELD · ENGLAND A

Fig. 2:39 Shoemaker's Tools (George Barnsley and Son's Catalogue, Sheffield 1927).

SHOE HAMMERS.

Code No.	Patt. No.		
3000	B50	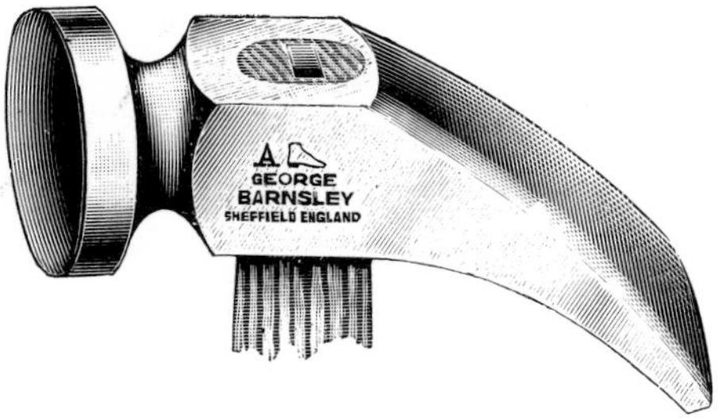	ALL BRIGHT, Forged Steel, oval shaft.
3002	B51	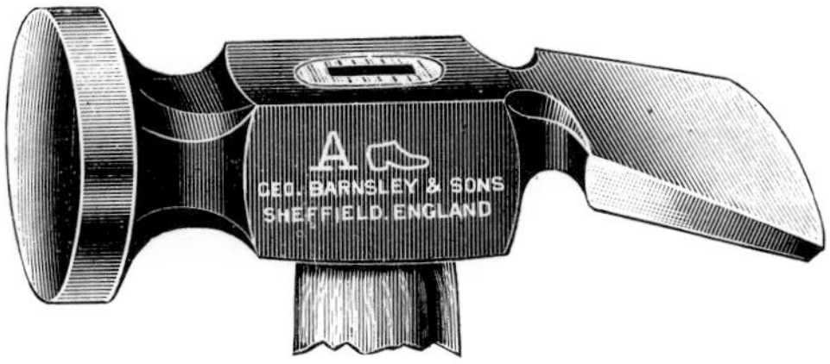	LONDON PATTERN, Forged Steel, Bright Pein, polished oval shaft.
3004	B52	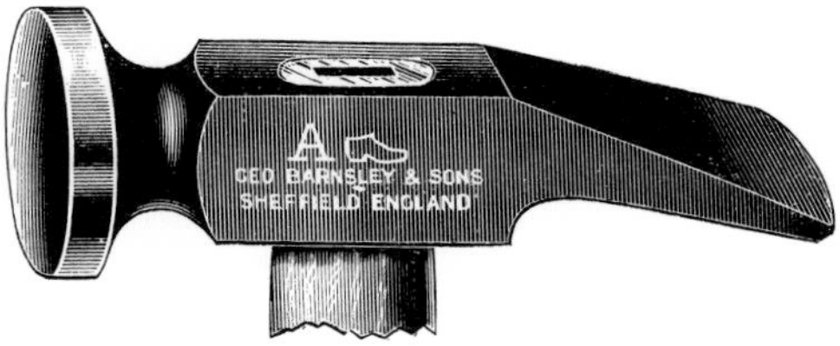	COMMON PATTERN, Forged Steel, Bright Face, polished round shaft.
3006	B53	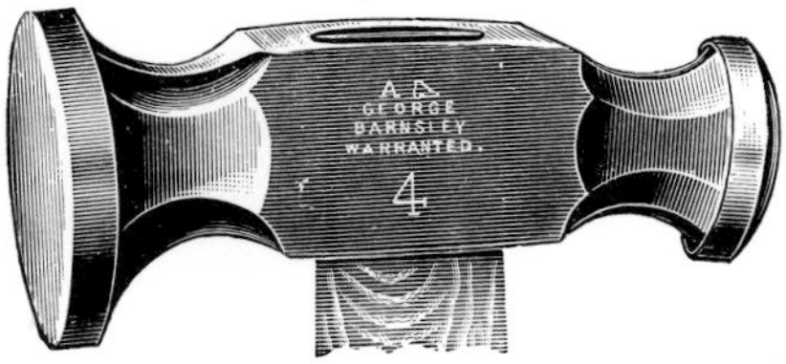	DOUBLE FACED RIVETTER'S PATTERN, Forged Steel, polished oval shaft.
3008	B54	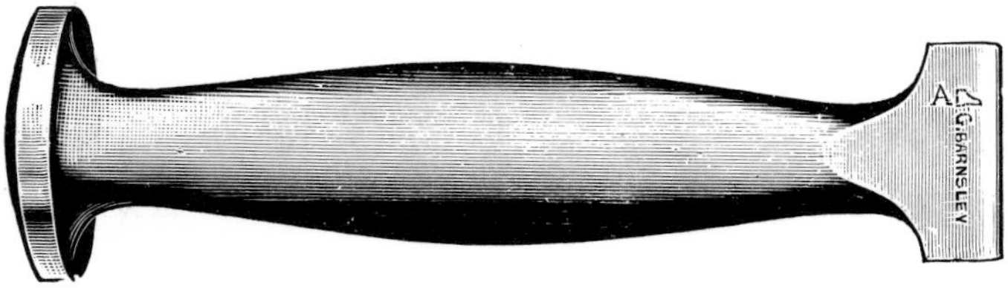	CLOSER'S or PASTE FITTER'S PATTERN, Forged Steel, hardened and tempered, bright all over.
3012	B56	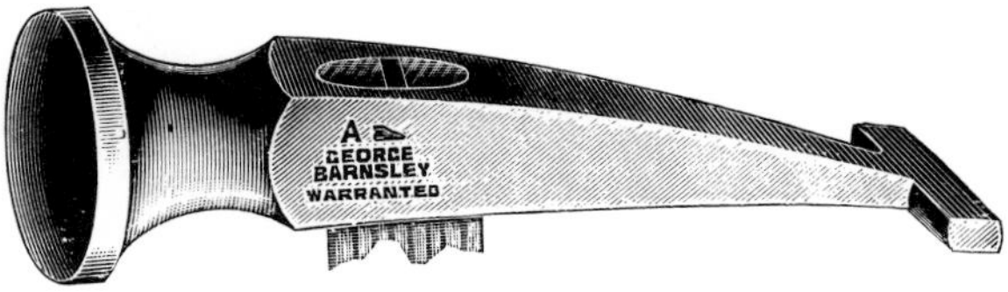	LONDON PATTERN CRAMPING, Forged Steel, bright all over, polished oval shaft.

Fig. 2:40 Shoemaker's Tools (George Barnsley and Son's Catalogue, Sheffield 1927).

SHOE HAMMERS.

Code No	Patt. No.		
3014	B58	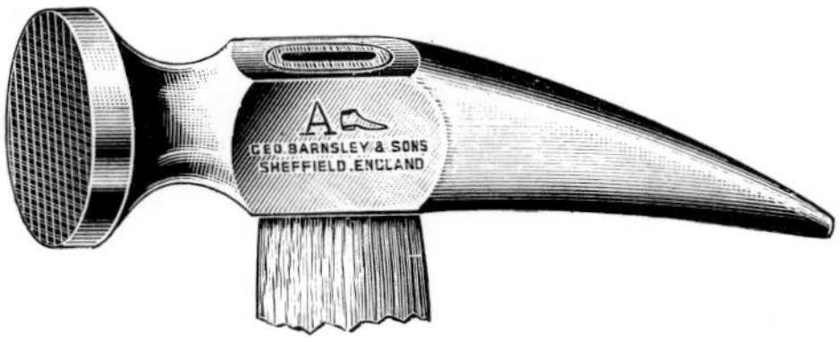	**RIVETTING,** Forged Steel, bright all over, magnetised pein, polished oval shaft.
3016	B59		**CRISPIN,** Forged Steel, bright all over, knurled face, polished oval shaft.
3018	B60		**WOOD HEEL,** Forged Steel, bright all over, polished oval shaft.
3020	B61	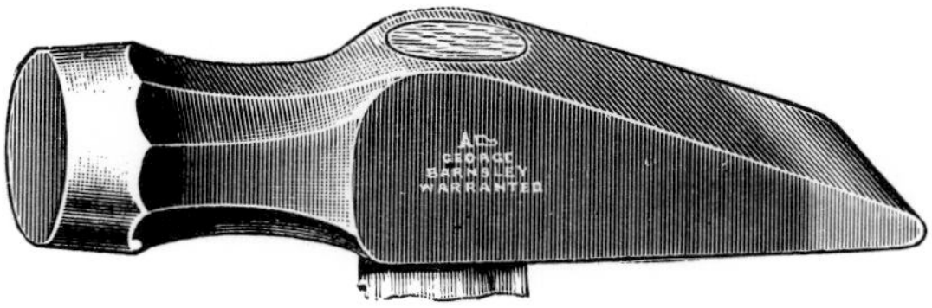	**CLOGGER'S IRONING,** Forged Steel, polished oval shaft.
3022	B62		**CLOGGER'S TACKING,** Forged Steel, oval shaft.

A🞔 CORNISH WORKS · SHEFFIELD · ENGLAND A🞔

Fig. 2:41 Shoemaker's Tools (George Barnsley and Son's Catalogue, Sheffield 1927).

SHOE HAMMERS.

Code No.	Patt. No.		
3024	B63	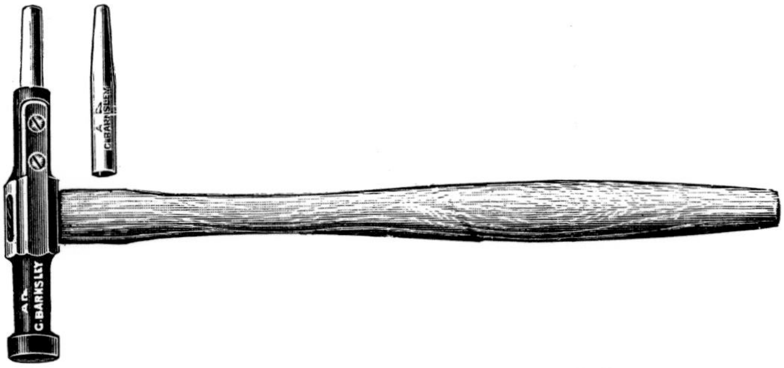	MAGNETISED TACK, with loose magnets.
3028	B64	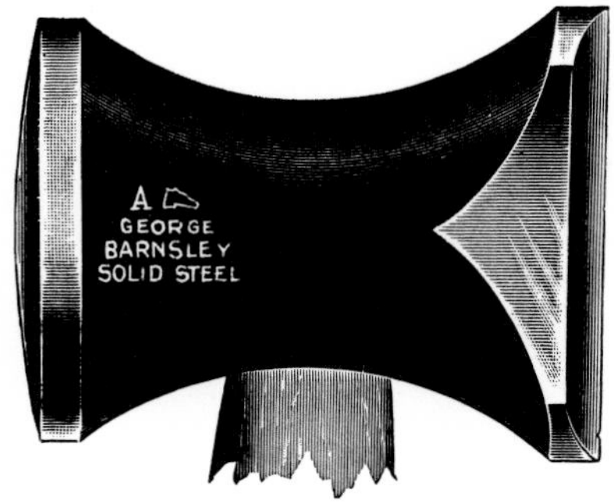	BEATING, Forged Steel, polished oval shaft.
3030	B65	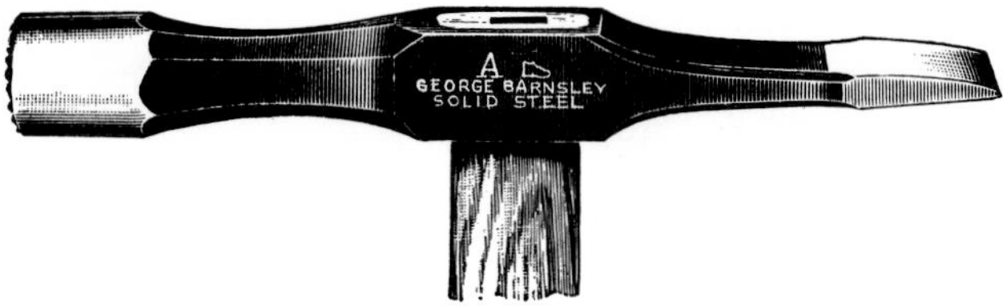	PRESS, Forged Steel, knurled face, chisel end, oval shaft.
3032	B66	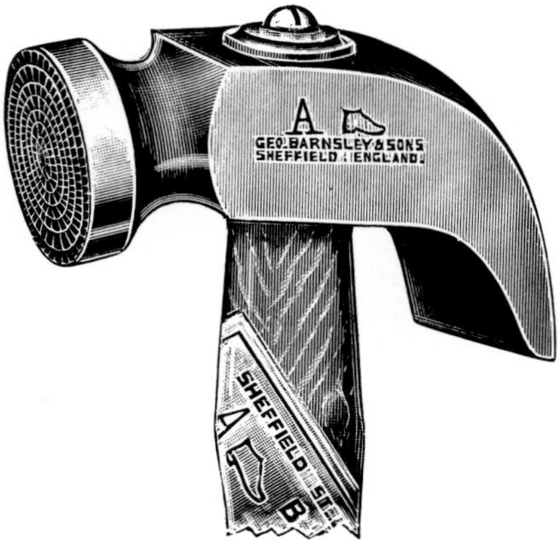	CORDWAINER'S PATTERN, Forged Steel, bright all over, knurled face, oval shaft.

A CORNISH WORKS · SHEFFIELD · ENGLAND A

Fig. 2:42 Shoemaker's Tools (George Barnsley and Son's Catalogue, Sheffield 1927).

SHOE HAMMERS.

Code No.

3036

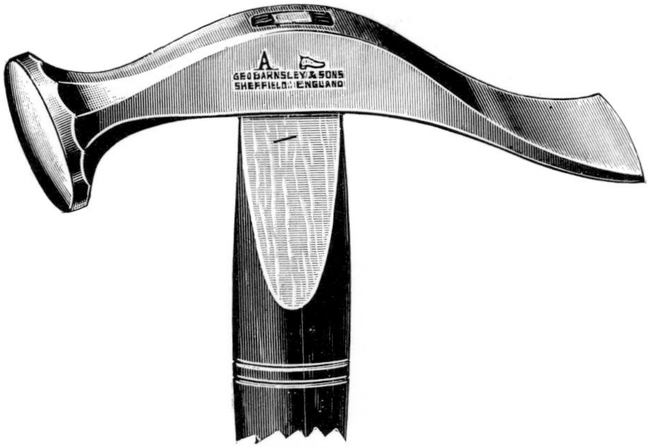

FRFNCH PATTERN,
Forged Steel,
bright all over,
round red shaft.

3038

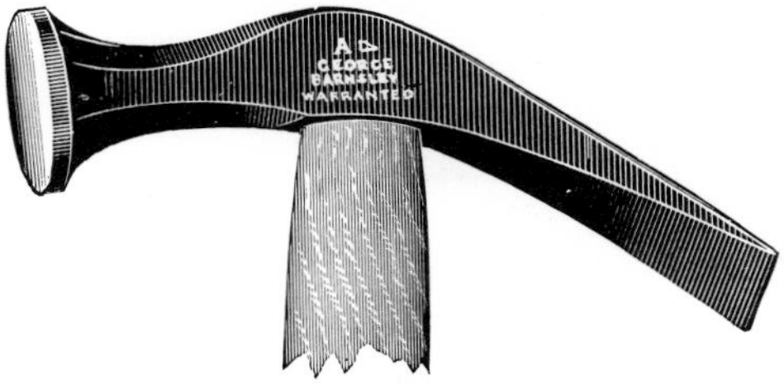

GERMAN PATTERN,
Forged Steel,
polished oval shaft.

3500

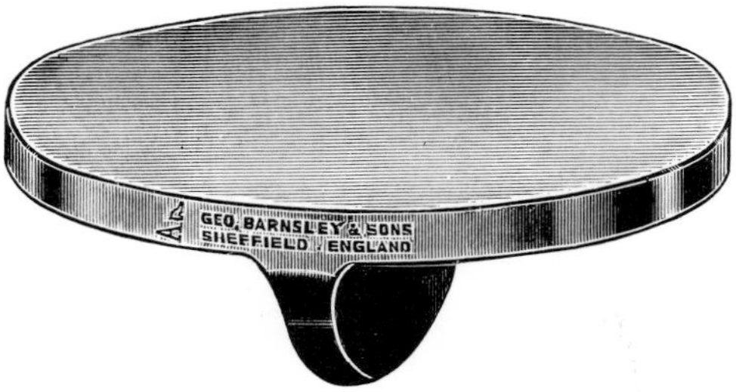

LAP IRON,
polished face.

HEEL CAP
FOR MEN'S
BOOT

CHILD'S
FOOT

LADIES'
FOOT

LADIES'
FOOT.

3600

ADJUSTED TO FIT
CHILD'S SIZE BOOT

ADJUSTED FOR
MEN'S SIZE
BOOTS

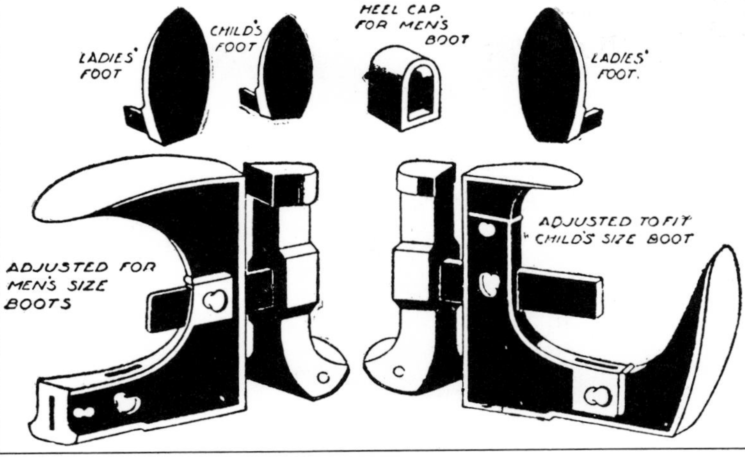

**PATENT
ADJUSTABLE
LAST.**

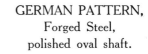 CORNISH WORKS · SHEFFIELD · ENGLAND

Fig. 2:43 Shoemaker's Tools (George Barnsley and Son's Catalogue, Sheffield 1927).

CUTTING & TOWER NIPPERS.

Code No.		
4200		**BLACK CUTTING NIPPER.** Machined joint.
4210		**TOWER SHOE NIPPER** (black).
4180		**LINING PLYER.**
4220		**MANCHESTER NIPPER,** bright all over.
4204		**HEAVY RIVET CUTTING NIPPER,** with screw stop.
4240		**SIDE CUTTING NIPPER.**

Fig. 2:44 Shoemaker's Tools (George Barnsley and Son's Catalogue, Sheffield 1927).

PUNCH PLYERS & PUNCHES.

Code No.

4300

PUNCH PLYER.

4304

PUNCH BITS.

4306

IMPROVED PUNCH BITS
for Toe Caps.

4308. PUNCH BIT, SIDE SLOT.   **4309.** SPECIAL PUNCH BITS.

4310

SOLID REVOLVING
PUNCH PLYER,
Six Bits.

4312

SOLID REVOLVING
PUNCH PLYER,
Four Bits.

A🥾 CORNISH WORKS · SHEFFIELD · ENGLAND A🥾

Fig. 2:45 Shoemaker's Tools (George Barnsley and Son's Catalogue, Sheffield 1927).

PUNCH PLYERS & PUNCHES.

Code No.	
4314	**TOECAP PUNCH PLYER,** Jaw 2 inches long.
4320	**FANCY PUNCH PLYER** for Toe Caps, &c., with adjustable guide.
4322	A L — B M — C N — D O — E P — F Q — G R — H S — I T — J U — K V **PATTERNS OF FANCY PUNCH PLYER BITS.**

 CORNISH WORKS · SHEFFIELD · ENGLAND

72   **Fig. 2:46**   Shoemaker's Tools (George Barnsley and Son's Catalogue, Sheffield 1927).

PUNCH PLYERS & PUNCHES.

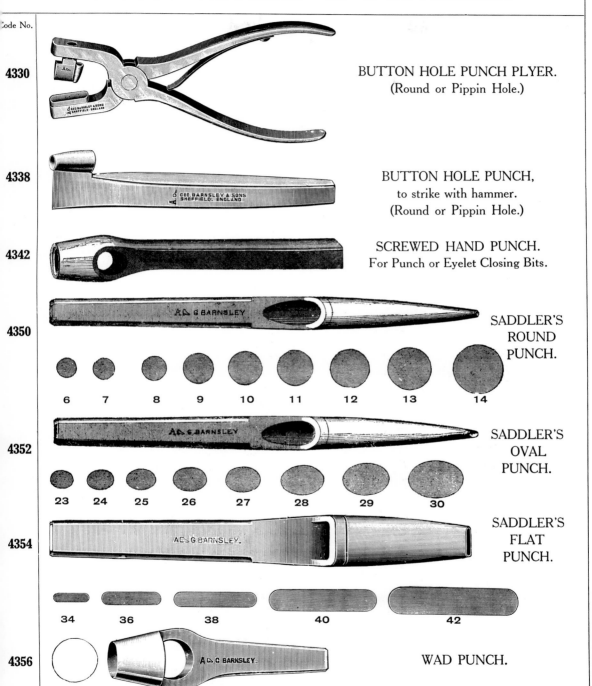

Code No.

4330 — BUTTON HOLE PUNCH PLYER.
(Round or Pippin Hole.)

4338 — BUTTON HOLE PUNCH,
to strike with hammer.
(Round or Pippin Hole.)

4342 — SCREWED HAND PUNCH.
For Punch or Eyelet Closing Bits.

4350 — SADDLER'S ROUND PUNCH.

6   7   8   9   10   11   12   13   14

4352 — SADDLER'S OVAL PUNCH.

23   24   25   26   27   28   29   30

4354 — SADDLER'S FLAT PUNCH.

34   36   38   40   42

4356 — WAD PUNCH.

CORNISH WORKS · SHEFFIELD · ENGLAND

Fig. 2:47 Shoemaker's Tools (George Barnsley and Son's Catalogue, Sheffield 1927).

EYELET CLOSING PLYERS & DIES.

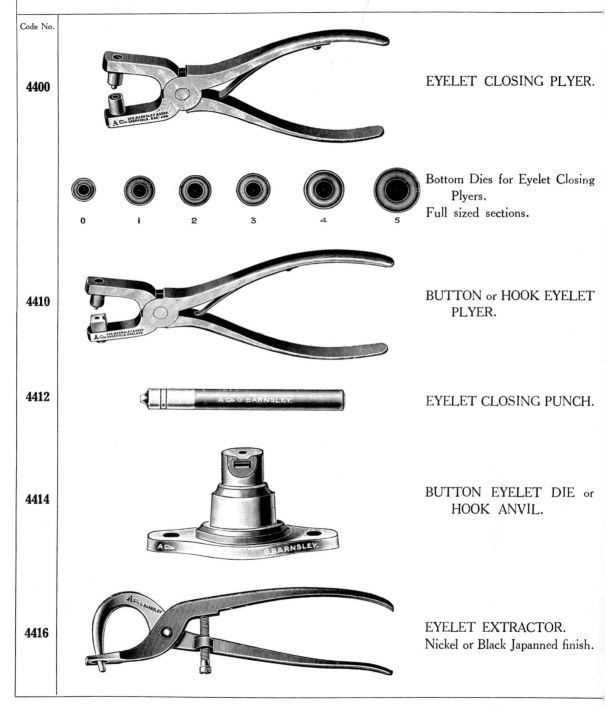

Code No.	
4400	EYELET CLOSING PLYER.
	Bottom Dies for Eyelet Closing Plyers. Full sized sections.
	0 1 2 3 4 5
4410	BUTTON or HOOK EYELET PLYER.
4412	EYELET CLOSING PUNCH.
4414	BUTTON EYELET DIE or HOOK ANVIL.
4416	EYELET EXTRACTOR. Nickel or Black Japanned finish.

CORNISH WORKS · SHEFFIELD · ENGLAND

74 Fig. 2:48 Shoemaker's Tools (George Barnsley and Son's Catalogue, Sheffield 1927).

PUNCHING & EYELETTING MACHINES.

Code **4420.** Pattern No. 0.
HAND POWER MACHINE,
with 0, 1, and 2 Punch and
Eyelet Closing Bits.

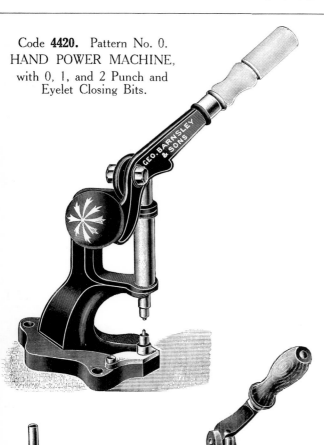

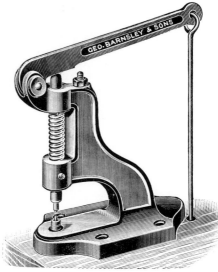

Code **4422.** Pattern No. 1.
FOOT POWER MACHINE
with 0, 1, and 2 Punch and
Eyelet Closing Bits.

Code **4426.** Pattern No. 3.
SMALL SPRING HOOK
EYELET MACHINE,
to strike with hammer.

Code **4424.** Pattern No. 2.
SMALL
HAND POWER MACHINE,
for ordinary or celluloid eyelets,
dies not interchangeable.

Code **4428.** Pattern No. 4.
HAND LEVER MACHINE,
for eyelet hooks or lacing studs,
dies not interchangeable.

A CORNISH WORKS · SHEFFIELD · ENGLAND A

Fig. 2:49 Shoemaker's Tools (George Barnsley and Son's Catalogue, Sheffield 1927).

ORDINARY SHOE TOOLS.

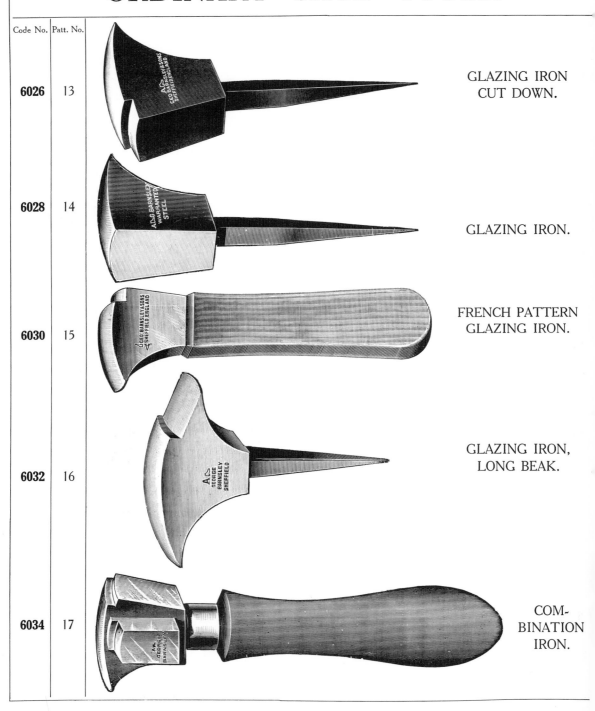

Code No.	Patt. No.		
6026	13		GLAZING IRON CUT DOWN.
6028	14		GLAZING IRON.
6030	15		FRENCH PATTERN GLAZING IRON.
6032	16		GLAZING IRON, LONG BEAK.
6034	17		COM-BINATION IRON.

CORNISH WORKS · SHEFFIELD · ENGLAND

Fig. 2:50   Shoemaker's Tools (George Barnsley and Son's Catalogue, Sheffield 1927).

ORDINARY SHOE TOOLS.

Code No.	Patt. No.
6148 or **6150**	68 or 69

HALF ROUND or OVAL BOTTOM GLAZER.

6152	70

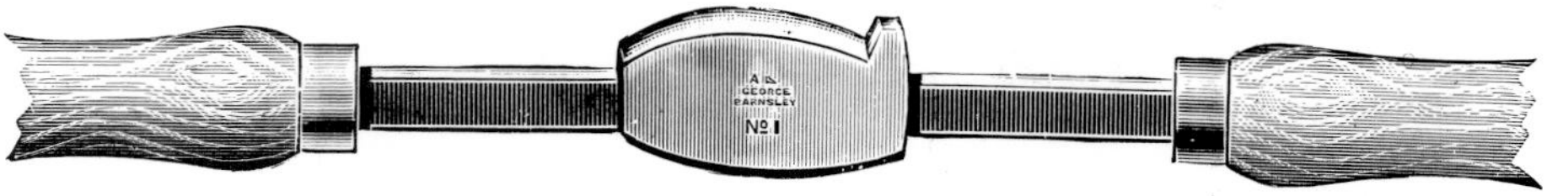

DUMMY or HEEL GLAZER.

6154	71

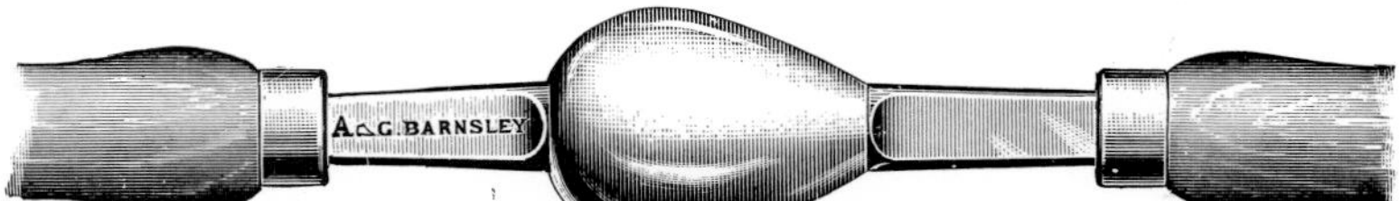

EGG SHAPED BOTTOM GLAZER.

6156	72

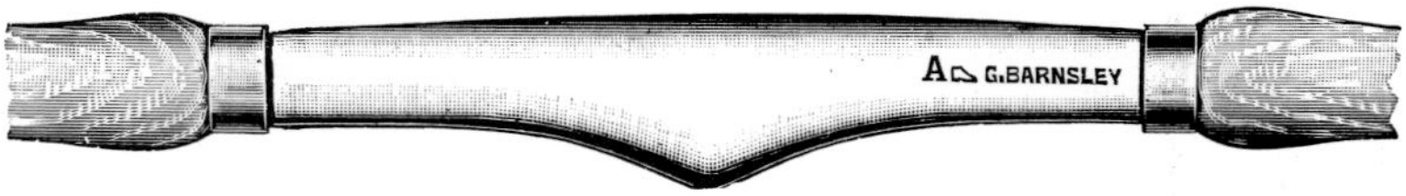

FISH TAIL BOTTOM GLAZER.

6136	62

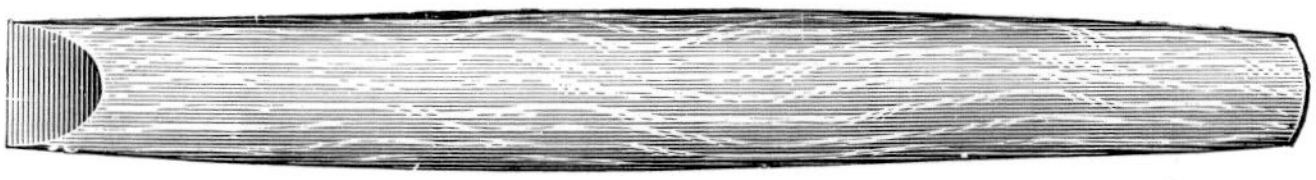

BOXWOOD LONG STICK.

6158	73

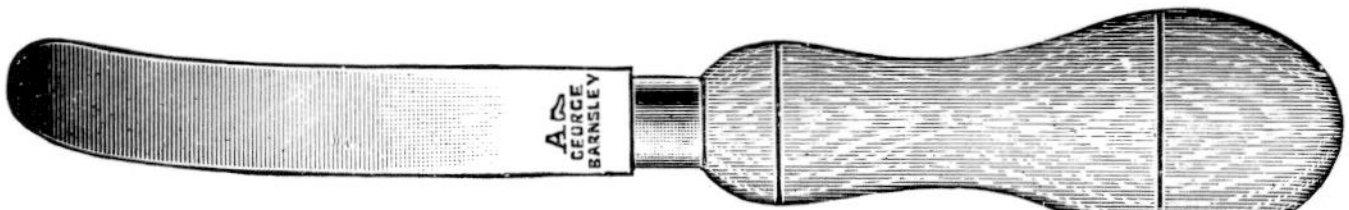

FIDDLER or WAIST BURNISHER.

6128	58

POLISHING BONE.

A🥾 CORNISH WORKS · SHEFFIELD · ENGLAND A🥾

Fig. 2:51 Shoemaker's Tools (George Barnsley and Son's Catalogue, Sheffield 1927).

ORDINARY SHOE TOOLS.

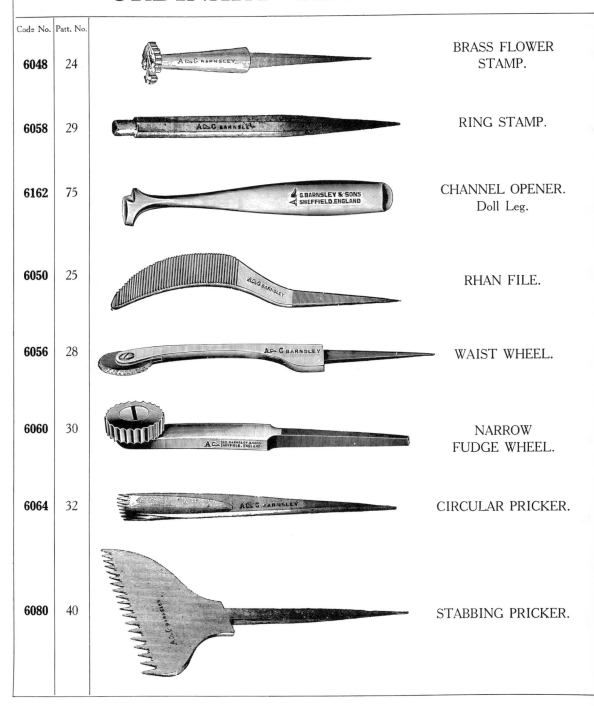

Code No.	Patt. No.		
6048	24		BRASS FLOWER STAMP.
6058	29		RING STAMP.
6162	75		CHANNEL OPENER. Doll Leg.
6050	25		RHAN FILE.
6056	28		WAIST WHEEL.
6060	30		NARROW FUDGE WHEEL.
6064	32		CIRCULAR PRICKER.
6080	40		STABBING PRICKER.

A🥾 CORNISH WORKS · SHEFFIELD · ENGLAND A👞

Fig. 2:52 Shoemaker's Tools (George Barnsley and Son's Catalogue, Sheffield 1927).

ORDINARY SHOE TOOLS.

Code No.	Patt. No.		
6100	44	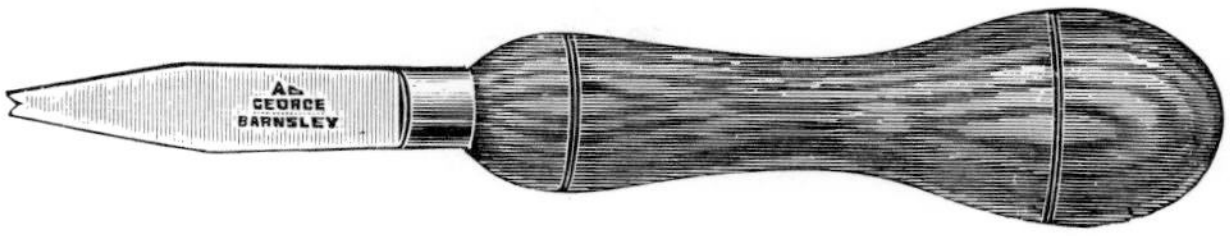	STITCH PRICKER. Double.
6102	45	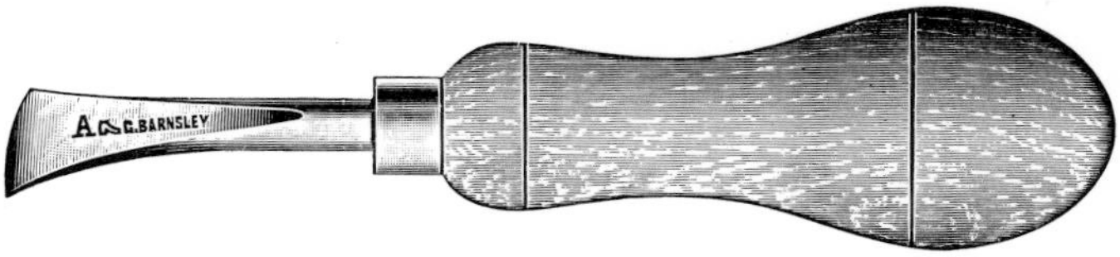	STITCH MARKER. Single.
6104	46	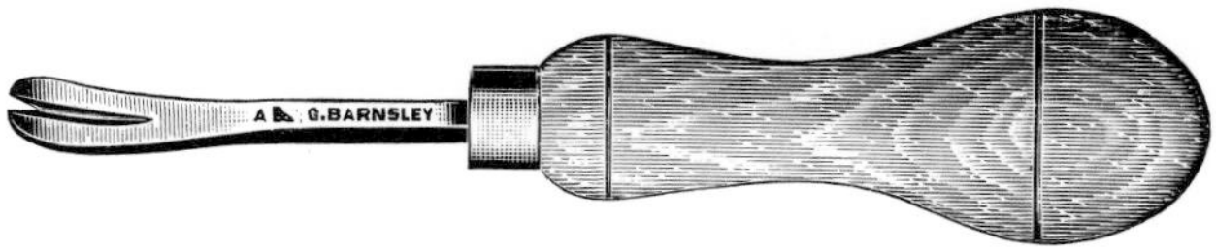	FITTER'S PLOUGH or STRIP AWL.
6106	47		WELT PLOUGH.
6108	48	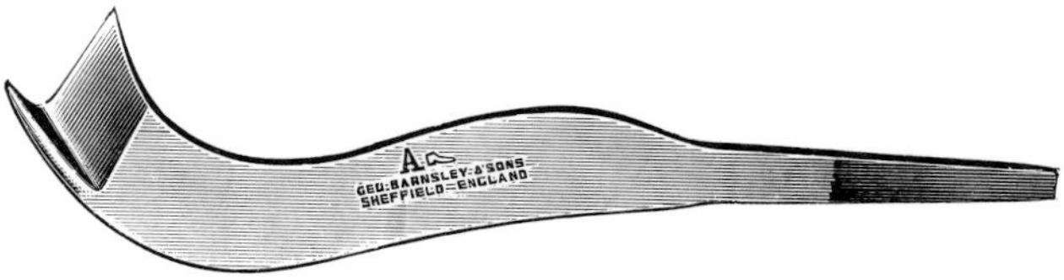	WELT KNIFE.
6110	49		SAFETY WELT KNIFE.
6112	50	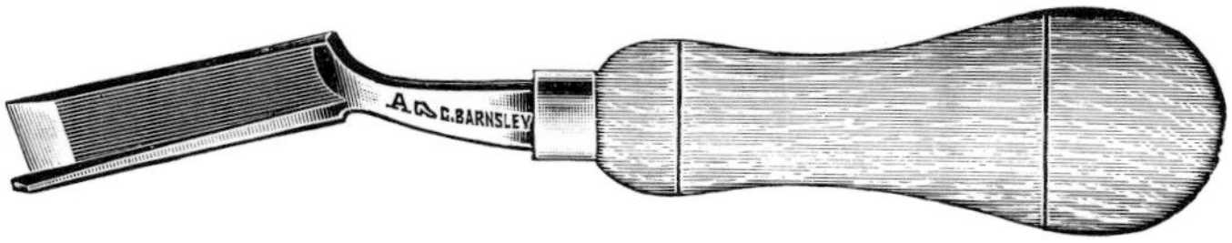	FEATHERING KNIFE.
6116	52	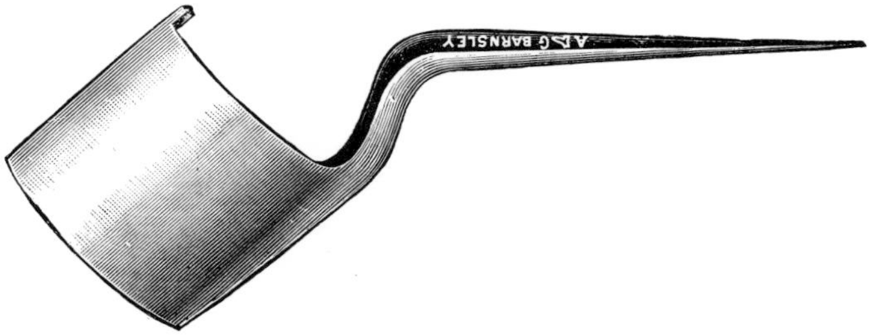	DRAG KNIFE.

A CORNISH WORKS · SHEFFIELD · ENGLAND A

Fig. 2:53 Shoemaker's Tools (George Barnsley and Son's Catalogue, Sheffield 1927).

ORDINARY SHOE TOOLS.

Code No.	Patt. No.		
6140	64	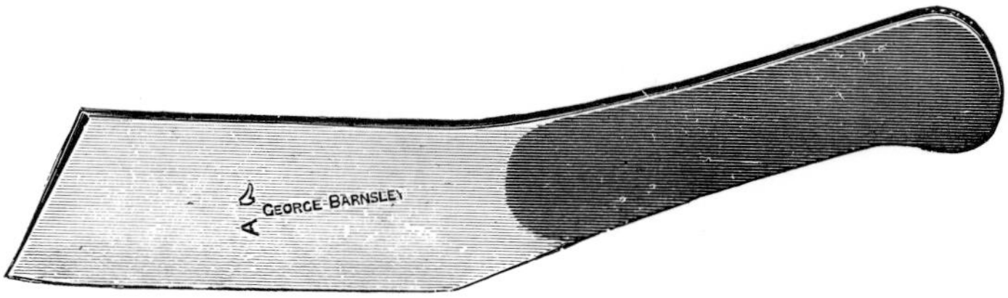	HACKING KNIFE. All Steel.
6142	65	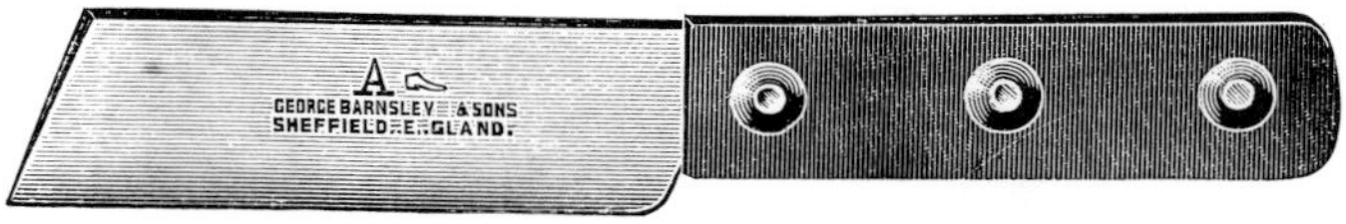	HACKING KNIFE. Leather Handle.
6146	67		HALF-ROUND RIVET DRIVER.
6166	77	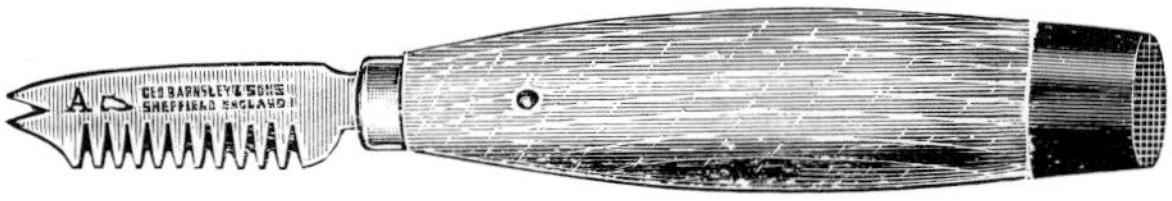	SAW TOOTH TACK LIFTER.
6170	78	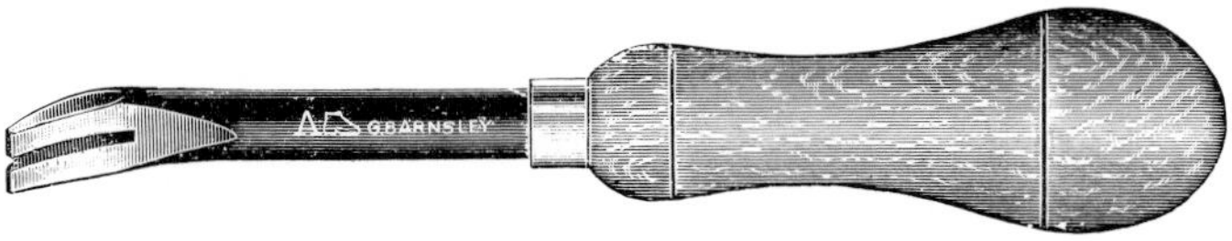	ORDINARY TACK LIFTER. Beech Handle.
6164		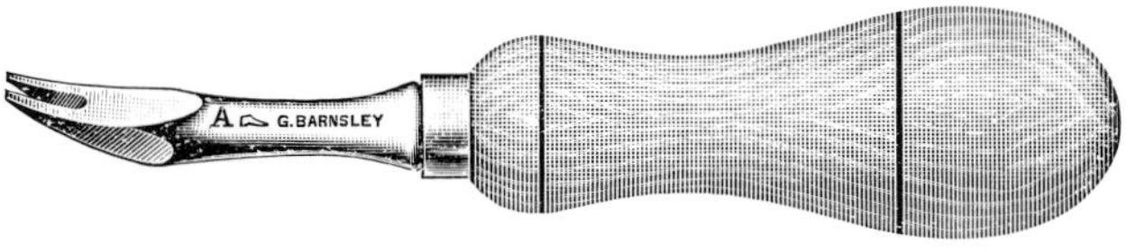	SPRIG LIFTER.
6192		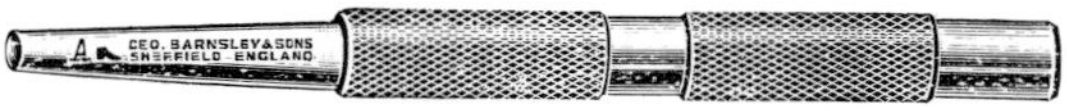	NAIL SETT. Knurled handle, cupped end.
6194			BRAD PUNCH. Round end, file cut.
6195			BRAD PUNCH. Square end, file cut.

A CORNISH WORKS · SHEFFIELD · ENGLAND A

Fig. 2:54 Shoemaker's Tools (George Barnsley and Son's Catalogue, Sheffield 1927).

ORDINARY SHOE TOOLS.

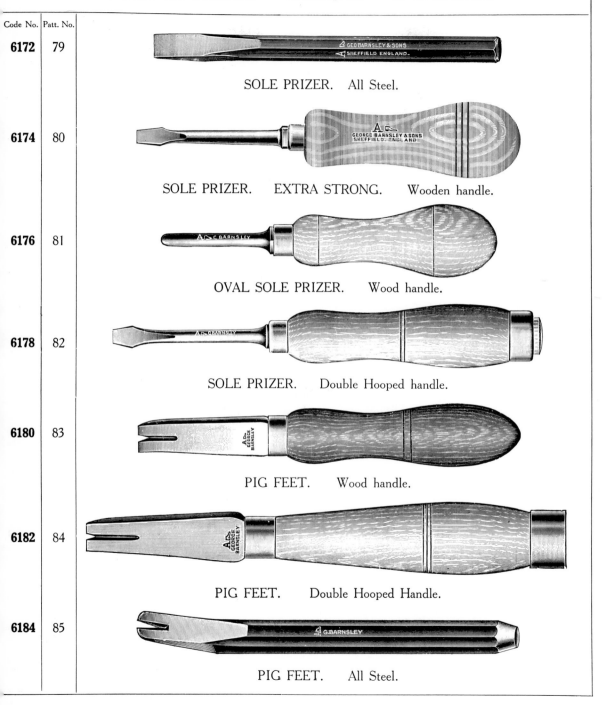

Code No.	Patt. No.
6172	79
6174	80
6176	81
6178	82
6180	83
6182	84
6184	85

SOLE PRIZER.   All Steel.

SOLE PRIZER.   EXTRA STRONG.   Wooden handle.

OVAL SOLE PRIZER.   Wood handle.

SOLE PRIZER.   Double Hooped handle.

PIG FEET.   Wood handle.

PIG FEET.   Double Hooped Handle.

PIG FEET.   All Steel.

A CORNISH WORKS · SHEFFIELD · ENGLAND A

Fig. 2:55   Shoemaker's Tools (George Barnsley and Son's Catalogue, Sheffield 1927).

ORDINARY SHOE TOOLS.

Code No.	Patt. No.		
6126	57		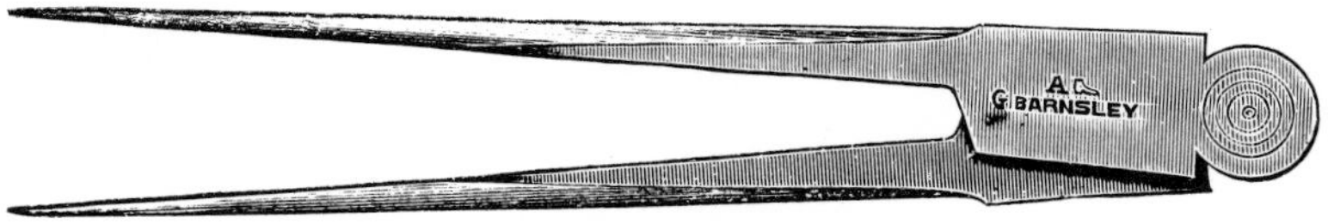 BOX JOINT COMPASSES.
6214			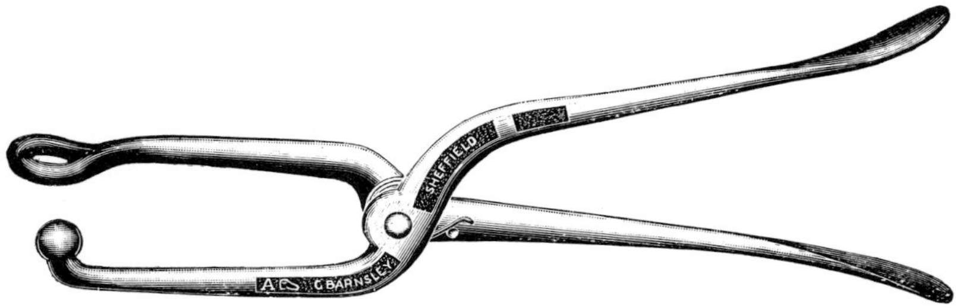 BOOT STRETCHING PLYER.
6200			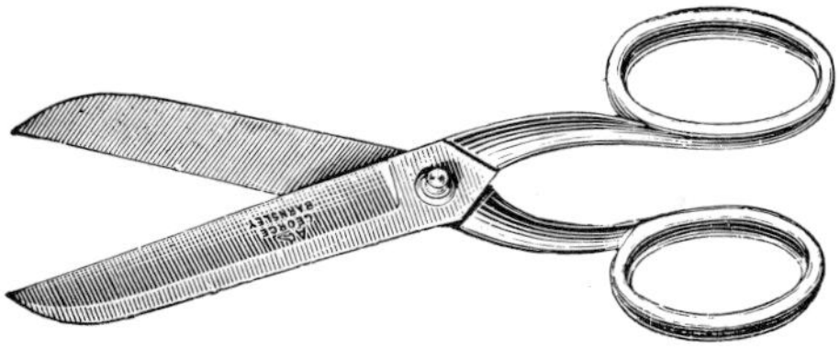 TAILOR'S SCISSORS.
6198			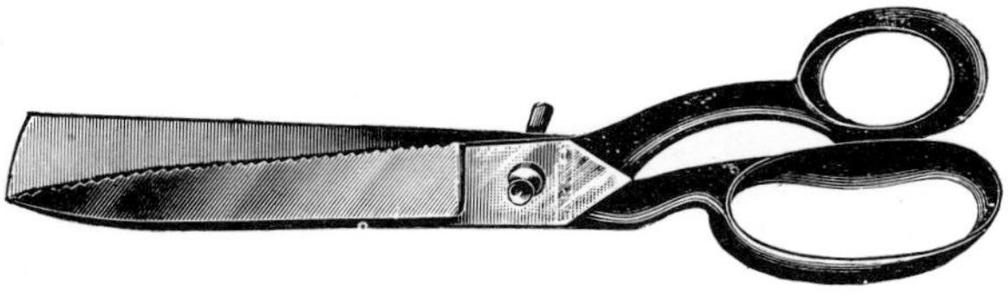 LEATHER SHEARS, serrated edges.
6216			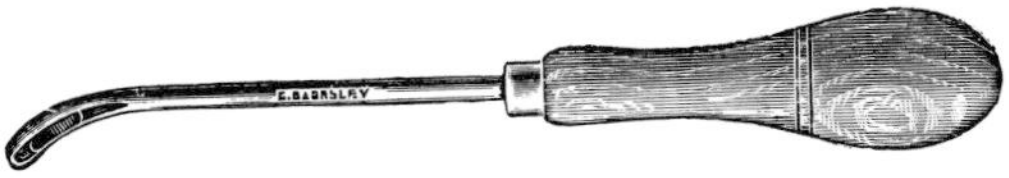 FOOTBALL LACING AWL, wood handle, pinned.
6218			 FOOTBALL LACING AWL, all steel.
6138	63		 LOOP or PUFF STICK.

CORNISH WORKS · SHEFFIELD · ENGLAND

Fig. 2:56 Shoemaker's Tools (George Barnsley and Son's Catalogue, Sheffield 1927).

The Tools

Abrasives

Abrasive substances used in shoemaking – particularly in finishing operations – include carborundum (silicon carbide), garnet and red flint, spread on a backing of paper or cloth.

To avoid clogging, these abrasive cloths or papers are specially made with a sparser than usual layer of particles on the glue, so leaving larger spaces between the particles. (See also *Sandstick*.)

Apron

These are made in leather or cloth, often white linen or cotton. Shoulder tapes are sewn to the top; waist tapes are attached to each side.

Armour

A term for metal 'tips' fitted to shoe heels and toes to resist wear. The heavier tips are horseshoe-shaped, the lighter ones are plates or 'quarter tips'. Now mostly replaced by rubber. (See also *Nails*.)

Awl (Alishin or Elsin in some northern counties and in Scotland.) *Figs. 2:31; 2:32; 2:33 (pp. 57–59)*

(See also *Awl Handles*; *Sewing and Stitching*; diagram under *Welt*; *Awl* in the HARNESS MAKER AND SADDLER section; and *Sewing Tools* in the GLOVE MAKER section.)

The Awl is a pointed instrument designed for piercing holes. It is one of the earliest tools used by man. Originally made of stone, bone, or antler, awls (and needles) of more slender build followed the development of metals.

In the shoemaking trades, the Awl is used for piercing a hole in the leather to prepare the way for the thread. After piercing, the thread is taken through the hole by means of a hog's bristle (now made of nylon) which, serving as a needle, is attached to the end of the thread.

The length of shoemaker's awls, including the tang, but excluding the haft, varies from c. $2\frac{3}{8}$–4 in. (6–10.1 cm).

In the language of the trade the term sewing relates mainly to the horizontal threads that join together the insole, upper and welt; the term stitching is applied to the vertical threads that join the welt to the sole.

Most of these awls are made in the form of a very shallow letter S – a graceful shape which is helpful when thrusting the Awl through leather in a curved path. There are variations in the amount of bend towards the point: generally, the closer the work the greater the bend.

An important feature is that the thickness of the blade must be less than that of the thread, so that the thread will fit tightly in the substance of the leather. It is this tightness which enables a seam to hold even when exposed stitches are worn through; and it also helps the seam to remain watertight.

Slender awls are easily snapped in two. Devlin (1839) gives a characteristically humane injunction when the apprentices suffer this misfortune – see *Awl, Stitching*, below.

Note: Awls belonging to other trades are often found in shoemaking workshops. For example, a cobbler may have a few saddler's awls, perhaps because he may be asked to repair harness to oblige a customer. These have a diamond-shaped cross-section.

Similarly, sail maker's needles (which have a triangular cross-section) are sometimes used by shoemakers for repairs to canvas. They are sometimes found mounted in handles to serve as awls.

(a) The Blade

Awl blades vary in cross-section according to their purpose.

The following are examples:

See entry under	Cross-section of the Awl blade (approx.)	Used when
Awl, Sewing	A flat oval (long axis horizontal)	Sewing together the insole, upper and welt
Awl, Stitching	A flat rectangle (long axis vertical)	Stitching the sole to the welt
Awl, Closing	Usually flat oval	Joining together (closing) the parts of the upper
Awl, Stabbing	Usually round	Patching etc.

(b) The Point

Plucknett, in his book on shoemaking (1916), discusses the design of awls, especially the position of the curved point which, he says, should be true with a line running through the centre of the haft. 'A poor craftsman', he writes, 'may say I never trouble about that, but it is this kind of thing that prevents his being more than a poor craftsman.'

(c) Haft

Variants are described under *Awl Handles*. Most of them have the characteristic neck round which one end of the thread can be given a turn for pulling tight.

Awl, Bradding

A name given to an awl made like a short wood-worker's Bradawl with a chisel-like point. It is probably intended for making preliminary holes in the heel and sole to take heavy nails or brads.

Awl, Clicker's   *Fig. 2:33 (p. 59)*

A straight, tapered blade, round in cross-section, mounted in a short handle. The size, as illustrated by Barnsley (1890), is $2\frac{1}{4}$ in. (5.7 cm) from point to ferrule and 4 in. (10.1 cm) overall.

This is a general purpose awl used by clickers for marking out and for occasional stabbing. The clicker pricks guide-points for the closer using the marked pattern as a guide. (Sometimes the Clicker's Knife has a steel point inserted in the butt of the handle for this purpose.)

There is some evidence that this awl was also used by the clicker to mark faults in the leather by pricking the flesh side. This shows up on the grain side, and tells the closer which parts of the upper-leather should remain hidden, or used where the faults will do no harm. A wax crayon is also used for this purpose. (See also *Clicker*.)

Awl, Closing   *Fig. 2:31 (p. 57)*

(See also *Awl, Stabbing*.)

A curved blade, oval in cross-section, similar to the Sewing Awl, but smaller and much slighter in build. Barnsley (1890) lists both oval and flat points in sizes *c.* $1\frac{7}{8}$–$2\frac{1}{4}$ in. (4.8–5.7 cm), including the tang.

A curved awl is needed by closers when making a flat or butted seam in high-class work. For this purpose the edges to be joined are skived (bevelled) and fitted so as to overlap precisely; the awl is then passed through the substance of the leather without penetrating the outer surface which thus shows no sign of a stitch.

Awl, Dart (Prick Awl; Pricker)

A name given to a short pointed awl, round in cross-section, used for marking out patterns etc., and as an alternative to the closer's Stabbing Awl.

Awl, Dull

A name given to an awl with a blunted (dull) point which could be used for marking out the surface of the leather without scratching it.

Awl Handles (Awl Hafts)   *Fig. 2:30 (p. 56)*

Size: The length of the hafts vary from 3–$4\frac{1}{2}$ in. (7.6–11.4 cm).

The most usual types are shown in Fig. 2:30 which is taken from the 1890 catalogue of George Barnsley. The material is usually beech. Variants include:

(a) Necked Sewing-awl Haft

This haft has a long conical ferrule, and a mushroom-shaped top (designed for pushing), separated from the body of the haft by a narrow neck. When sewing, a turn or two of thread can be wound round the neck, and then pulled tight. Sometimes the ferrule is replaced by a coil of wire.

Awl handles of very similar shape are illustrated by Diderot (*c.* 1760). The chief difference is that the handles appear to be 'reeded', i.e. turned with a series of shallow grooves, presumably to give a firmer grip (*Fig. 2:6*).

(b) Pegging Awl Haft

A bottle-shaped haft (known also as 'peg-top' shape) with a plain round ferrule into which a Peg Awl blade with a pointed tang is driven.

(c) 'American' Peg Awl Haft   *Fig. 2:30 (p. 56)*

Shaped more like a conventional chisel handle, this popular design was made in rosewood or hickory as well as in beech. A split-nosed screw chuck (or 'vice') is provided for holding square-shanked Peg Awls. The conical nut used for compressing the jaws of the chuck is operated by a special key or wrench, illustrated in *Fig. 2:30*. A cap on the heel of the handle made of hard leather protects both haft and hand from the shock of hammer blows. (Peg Awls are mostly driven by hammer.)

Note: Awl hafts of this kind are listed in Barnsley's catalogue of 1890 as 'American' and are designed to hold only awl blades with square tangs. More recently, so-called 'patent' awl hafts have come onto the market provided with sockets designed to hold awl blades of all types.

Other shapes of Awl Handles include:

(d) A bellows-shaped Sewing Awl handle, shaped

like pear-shaped blacksmith's bellows, with a long conical ferrule.

(*e*)   A Peg Awl with a neck just above the ferrule.

(*f*)   Awl handles are sometimes given a flat on one side to prevent their rolling off the bench.

Awl, Heel   *Fig. 2:31 (p. 57)*

Similar to the Sewing Awl except that it is less sharply curved at the tip. And, because it has to penetrate some $\frac{3}{4}$ in (1.9 cm) or more of leather, there is less difference in girth throughout its length. The length of the blade rises in eighths (0.4 cm) from $2\frac{5}{8}$–4 in. (6.7–10.1 cm).

Heel Awls are used when joining the sole at the back of the shoe to the body of the heel. Among the different methods of doing this is the usual practice of pushing the Awl in at the seat, passing it through the stitches which join the upper to the insole and thereby interlocking with them, then penetrating the 'lifts' of the heel, and finally emerging in the channel on the heel surface.

After the sewing is complete, the projecting part of the sole is beaten down to cover up the stitches. This is subsequently trimmed and 'broken' (see *Seat Breaker*).

Sewing on the heel is heavy work, and in order to ease the path of the Awl the leather is first moistened, and the Awl is dipped in soap (see *Heel*).

Awl, Holing

A name sometimes given to a straight awl such as the Stabbing or Dart Awl.

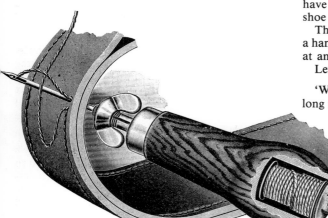

Fig. 2:57

Awl, Inseam   *Fig. 2:32 (p. 58)*

Similar in shape and size to the larger versions of the Stitching Awl, it was probably used for piercing the 'inseam' of the insole when attaching it to the upper and welt.

Awl, Lining

This awl is described by Devlin (1839) as a tool used for sewing linings into Wellington boots: '...it has not any thickness behind, but is as small there as immediately above the point, has no keenness of side, is shortly hooked, and entering on the upper in preference to the lining, the stitches can be taken firmer, securer, and more abundant.'

The term 'Lining Awl' is not included in the catalogue of any tool maker known to us.

Awl, Magazine   *Fig. 2:57*

A strong awl in which the thread is held on a reel in a magazine inside the wooden handle. The needle is eyed, and is used like that of a sewing machine to produce a lock-stitch. It was designed for amateur users for repairs to boots, harness, sacks, tents, carpets, suit-cases, leggings, dog collars, and the like.

Awl, Patent Patching

An awl described by Leno (1895, p. 120) and intended to overcome the difficulty of blind stabbing within a shoe by someone whose hands are too large to go inside. It is claimed that this instrument is capable of producing a lock-stitch similar to that made by a Sewing Machine. Whether it became popular among shoemakers we do not know; we have not found an example in the workshops, though shoe repairers speak of it.

This awl has a long eye-pointed needle mounted in a handle, and a straight Stabbing-type Awl sticks out at an angle of 45° from the side of the handle.

Leno describes its operation as follows:

'When it is desired to put in a row of stitches the long needle is threaded with a thread, the ends being brought through a hole in the handle, at the lower end of which a small cork is fitted that impedes the ready passage of the thread, and thus forms a tension. The stabbing awl is then thrust through the leather in the required direction, is withdrawn, and the needle carrying the thread thrust through as far as it will go. The thread carried by it can now easily be reached; and as the withdrawal of the needle, to a small extent, causes a slackness of the carried thread, it thus becomes easy to pass between it and the needle a second thread. The needle is now withdrawn, and a lock-stitch is thus formed, which can be repeated as many times as is necessary.'

Awl, Peg (Pegging Awls) *Figs. 2:32; 2:33 (pp. 58–9)*
(See also *Peg Tools* and *Awl Handles*.)
Length of blade including the tang, from $1-2\frac{1}{2}$ in. (2.5–6.3 cm).

Peg Awl blades are straight, short and stubby. Their cross-section is either square, oval or diamond-shaped. They are used for boring holes in the sole and heel to take wooden pegs inserted as a means of attachment – usually as an alternative to sewing or rivets. (Pegs are also used for special footwear, e.g. sea boots – see *Peg Tools*.)

In addition to English-made awl blades, Barnsley's. list of 1890 illustrates awl blades of similar appearance which are described as American, Continental, or German. These foreign sources do not appear in Barnsley's 1927 catalogue, but they add a 'Scotch Pattern' which appears to be identical to those called 'American Square Peg Awls' in the earlier ·edition.

Knight (USA, 1877, p. 193) describes a Pegging Awl in which 'the socket gripping the awl is surrounded by a sleeve, which is projected by a spiral spring within the handle, so as to assist in extracting the awl by pressing upon the leather'.

Awl, Sewing *Figs. 2:58; 2:31 (p. 57)*
Size of blade $2\frac{3}{8}-4$ in.(6–10.1 cm), including the tang, rising in eighths (0.4 cm).

The blade has a shallow curve, sometimes S-shaped, and is tapered towards the point. The point is a flat-oval in cross-section, and in use produces an oval hole whose long axis is in line with the sewing.

This flat-oval cross-section enables the user to make a horizontal slit-like hole through the substance of the leather: for example, when piercing the 'holdfast' (the ridge round the edge of an insole) before sewing it to the upper and welt. When piercing, the awl follows a curved path in what one writer calls a 'half-circle or swing-boat motion' (Thornton, 1970, p. 291). To ease its path the user works the

point into the leather with a sinuous or wobbling motion.

The number of holes made varies from four to the inch (2.5 cm) for men's work, to six to the inch (2.5 cm) for ladies.

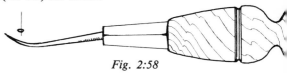

Fig. 2:58

Awl, Stabbing *Fig. 2:31 (p. 57)*
(See also *Awl, Closing*; *Awl, Patent Patching*.)
A straight slender blade, tapering to a fine point. It is listed by Barnsley (1890) as having 'Round, Oval, and Flat Points'. The size of blade varies from $1\frac{7}{8}-2\frac{1}{4}$ in.(4.7–5.7 cm) including the tang.

Used by cobblers when patching, but also sometimes by closers when sewing together parts of the upper.

Awl, Stitching (French Awl; Square Awl) *Fig. 2:58A* and see Square Awl *Fig. 2:32 (p. 58)*
Size of blade: $2\frac{3}{8}-4$ in. (6–10.1 cm) including the tang, rising in eighths (0.4 cm).

Note: Devlin (1839, p. 37) wrote that this awl, with its flattened sides, was 'formerly called the French blade, though, strange to say, in France it is now called the *alêne Anglais*, or *English awl*. I believe, however, the fashion came originally from our neighbours, though afterwards Collins, at one time a celebrated awl maker at Liverpool, improved the make of the awl so much, that the stitching awls of his manufacture not only won a British but an European reputation, and are yet sought for by the name *alêne Anglais*.'

The Stitching Awl blade is shaped to a shallow S-curve, but it has flat sides, and consequently its cross-section is a flat rectangle. The object of the curve in the blade is to enable the user to stitch close to the upper without damaging it with the awl haft. The terminal half-inch (1.2 cm) of the blade is ground thin to enable the user to force through a thick substance of leather more easily, and for close stitching.

Its main use is in joining the sole to the welt. The slot-shaped hole made has its long side at right angles to the line of stitching, and being very narrow, a greater number of stitches per inch (2.5 cm) can be made with this awl, than with the Sewing Awl with its oval cross-section. The actual number of stitches varies from seven to the inch for coarse work, to sixteen (or even twenty) to the inch in fine work.

Mr W. B. Glasow (1974) writes that the awl should be 'introduced into the leather with one effort, taking into consideration the "bend"of the awl. This is skill (or knack) which the apprentice has to master without of course snapping the Awl.' Devlin (1839) makes the same point, with an addition which is typical of his consideration for the learner:

'The awl, besides its square or flattened character on each side, is also more curved than the round or common awl, and therefore the greater danger of snapping in being thrust through the leather. The apprentice, no doubt, will break many in his first trials; he must, however, go on; and if the master be wise, he will take as little notice in an angry way of these misfortunes as possible, for thereby the apprentice will feel himself safer, and thus, not having so much terror on his mind, he will make the fewer breaks, and do better in all.

'Stitching, when performed with ease and certainty, is a handsome operation, and especially when the work is light; the performance, too, is rapid, the adept workman going round the entire welt of a thin-edged shoe or boot in something about an hour, though it is said the well-known "ready Moyle" has stitched many a boot for Hoby, for whom he wrought, even in half this time.'

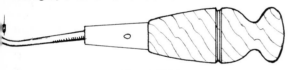

Fig. 2:58(a)

Awl, Strip. Not an Awl: see *Fitter's Plough.*

Bat (or **Buff**): see *Sharpening Bat.*

Beater (Beating Iron)
An iron bar about 7 in. (17.7 cm) long, often made from an old Shoe Rasp or File,and used with a Hammer for shaping certain parts of the shoe. Beaters vary in shape according to their purpose, as follows:

(a) *Corner Beater*
Similar to the *Welt Beater* (below) but the edges of the rasp are beaten square at one end. The sharp edge of the tool is placed in the angle between the heel breast and the waist and then hammered until a sharp corner is formed at that point.

(b) *Toe Beater* (Jigger; Seat Beater; Upper Beater) *Fig. 2:59*
An old rasp, forged into a shallow S-shape. One end is held against the upper and hammered lightly to

smooth out and set the upper against the last, all round the shoe.

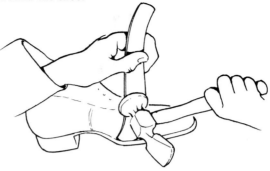

Fig. 2:59

(c) *Welt Beater* (Bent Iron; Crook Rasp) *Fig. 2:60*
An old rasp or file with a half-inch (1.2 cm) turned over at right angles at one end. Before the sole is stitched on, this end of the iron is pressed into the joint between upper and welt to serve as a 'table' on which the welt can be beaten lightly with a hammer. This is done to make the welt stand out at right angles to the last, and clear of the upper.

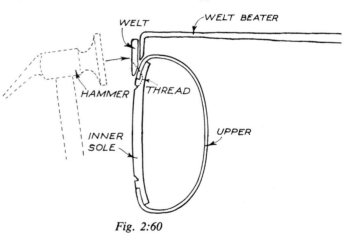

Fig. 2:60

(d) See also Turnshoe Mallet under *Turnshoe Tools.*

Bench and Seat
In general, cobblers, shoemakers, and closers, sit at their work on low stools or benches; clickers, makers of riveted boots, and some cobblers work standing at the bench. (See also the paragraph on the *Workshop and Conditions of Work* in the introduction to this section.)

Fig. 2:61

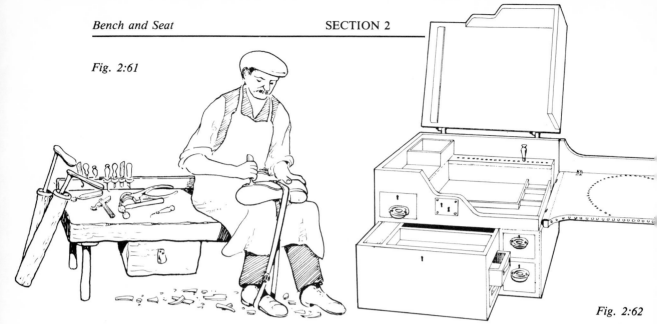

Fig. 2:62

The above statement is subject to many exceptions. For instance, a closer, who usually sits at his work, does his skiving (paring the edges) while standing at the bench; the cobbler either works with a Cobbler's Foot mounted on the bench at which he stands, or he may work seated with a Cobbler's Foot mounted on a stake held between his legs. Though hardly relevant to present day practice, it appears that in ancient Egypt and Greece even clicking was done while seated. Reproductions of paintings of shoemakers in Egypt of *c.* 1450 BC, and in Greece *c.* 500 BC (Northampton Museum, 1975) show them cutting leather while sitting. In the Egyptian painting, the cutting is done at knee height on a low board sloping away from the shoemaker's feet; in the Greek painting, cutting is done on a low bench in front of the seated worker (see *Fig. 2:1*).

Seats and benches used by shoemakers and cobblers include the following:

(a) Combined Seat and Bench   Fig. 2:61
These are purpose-made to provide both a seat for the worker and a bench-top for his tools. They are thus described by Randle Holme (1688):

'On this seat upon the right hand of the Workman, is made several Divisions, whereof one is for his Wax and Thread, another for his Awls, and another for the rest of his Tools, so that what he wants he can easily put his hand to without confusion or tumbling of the rest' – and so it is today.

(b) Portable Seat and Bench   Fig. 2:62
The portable, folding seat and bench illustrated below was used in the USA in the nineteenth century.

It was presumably used for shoe-repairing rather than shoemaking.

(c) Separate Seat and Bench   Figs. 2:63; 2:64
Many seventeenth- and eighteenth-century paintings and engravings show shoemakers sitting on a separate stool, with their lasts and tools on a separate bench nearby, or on the ground. They do not appear to sit as low as is done nowadays, with the result that the foot in the stirrup is often shown propped up on a block of wood to bring the knee higher (see *Stirrup*).

Miss Swann (1977) has pointed out in a private communication: 'shoemakers (handsewn, that is) normally sit low in order to make a lap to work on. They also need to soak the leather in a tub, which is more conveniently placed on the floor than on a bench: it prevents the water getting where you don't want it.'

Today, most shoemakers doing handsewn work sit on a backless chair with legs cut down to bring the seat about 14 in. (35.5 cm) off the ground; low enough to grasp things from the floor without bending; and nearby, a low bench, old box, or one of the standardised types of chest illustrated here, on which to lay their tools.

Though very occasionally one sees a shoemaker using a chair with a back, most of them will tell you that a back interferes with the free movement of the arms. (The cross-legged tailor will tell you the same.) It is true that much of the work is done leaning forward, in order to bring pressure to bear on the tool; but it is nonetheless strange that the uncomfortable backless chair survives. Perhaps it is just part of the

Fig. 2:63

Fig. 2:64

tradition that condemns shoemakers to work in ill-lit, poverty-stricken workshops which few other tradesmen would tolerate.

(d) Standing Bench Fig. 2:65

Waist-height benches used by clickers, makers of riveted boots, and cobblers are of the ordinary kind. But there have been several attempts at designing a Standing Bench, sometimes on grounds of health, for handsewn makers. Miss June Swann (in a private communication 1977) writes:

'The earliest record I have for a bench at which the shoemaker stands (other than clickers' benches, of course, which occur from at least medieval times) is 1804, when Thomas Parker explained his invention at a meeting of the Society of Arts, designed for anyone incapable of working in a sitting position (cripples, including wounded soldiers, were frequently put to the trade). There was another produced in 1806, about the time when Brunel was starting making riveted boots, which would require a standing bench. His bootmaking survived to 1816, and riveted boots were not made again in any quantity until Crick's patent in 1853. In 1856 J. Sparkes Hall printed his pamphlet on "Upright Shoemaking. An Address to Working Shoemakers &

Others on the Advantages of the Upright Bench". It claimed to be more healthy standing, instead of constricting the chest: TB was, of course, a common disease in the industry.'

A Standing Bench of the type illustrated may be seen at Messrs C. & J. Clark's Shoe Museum in Street, and labelled 'John Bright Clark's workbench, 1886'. It contains a built-in foot-strap (stirrup) to hold a shoe securely on the bench top. The strap is enclosed in a wooden casing, and is tightened by depressing an adjustable foot pedal. The shoe is held down on a circular pad fixed to the bench top.

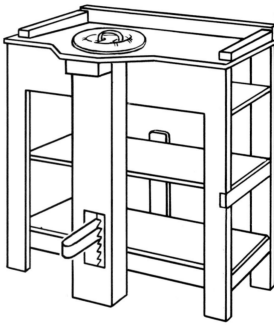

Fig. 2:65

Bespoke Work (Bespeak; Bespoken)
In the boot and shoe trade the word 'bespoke' has come to mean more than 'ordered'. The term is used to describe the making of boots and shoes to the requirements of a particular person. This includes taking measurements and making a last for each customer. A 'bespoke shoemaker' is now one who only makes to order.

Billet
Term for an oblong piece of leather, usually in the rough form of a sole.

Binding and the Binder

Binding the edges of shoe uppers is defined by Thornton (1970, p. 171) as 'the treatment of an edge by the use of a fabric tape or leather strip, stitched and turned in several differing methods'. He describes and illustrates six of these methods.

The term 'Binder' is applied by Devlin (1839, p. 98) to the individual who prepares the whole of the upper parts of a woman's shoe for the maker – not just the binding. The clogger applies the term 'Binding' to the groove made round the edge of the uppers which imitates the stitched binding of a shoe. (See *Lace Cutting Tools* and *Binding Cutter* in the CLOG MAKER section.)

Birse

Scots term for *Bristle*.

Block: see *Blocking Tools*; *Sewing Block*; *Sole-Forming Block*.

Blocking Tools (Crimping Tools)

The tools described below are designed to shape the front of a boot to fit over the instep, and to smooth out wrinkles resulting from this operation. The term 'blocking' is also applied to certain other shaping operations, such as the blocking of insoles, which, according to Devlin (1839, p. 23), was the task of the boy apprentices.

The tools used in blocking boot fronts include the following:

(a) Boot Block (Crimper) *Fig. 2:66*

In its simplest form the Boot Block is a piece of wood shaped in outline like a boot, over which a previously dampened upper can be stretched. This is done to mould the upper into the required shape, and to smooth out wrinkles that tend to gather at the bend of the instep. Its operation is described by Leno (1895, p.148) as follows:

'The old style of blocking a Wellington front was by using a piece of wood fashioned to the shape of the front when cut and ready for the closer ... After the unblocked front had been wetted and rubbed, the bottom part of the leg was placed over the curve of the block, its front made free of every sign of a wrinkle. The heel part corners were then forced with the fingers on both sides as far back as possible, pulled with the pincers and tacked down to the block.'

(b) Blocking Pincer Fig. 2:26 (p. 52)

A pincer similar to the *Lasting Pincer*, but with a straight nose instead of a curved one. The size overall is $c.8\frac{1}{2}$ in. (21.5 cm).

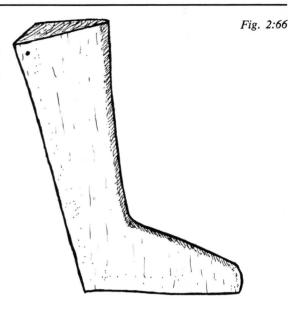

Fig. 2:66

It is used for pulling the front of the boot over the Boot Block. This work usually involves a straight pull (unlike lasting) and consequently the nose is straight.

(c) Wooden Rasp

A term used both by Devlin (1840, Vol. II, p. 55) and by Leno (1895, p. 149) for a wooden tool used for forcing out 'every ridge and wrinkle'. It is described by Devlin as follows:

'The instruments or tools to be used are, besides the pincers, only two: one is a sort of wooden rasp, with rounded back, made often by the workman himself, the teeth blunt, and standing at about a quarter of an inch from each other; the wood of a fine, smooth, and hard description, and the length of the tool altogether being from fourteen to sixteen inches, the rasp portion extending to about ten inches in the middle, and the two untoothed ends used as the handles. Sometimes, also, a circular notched stick, made by the turner, is preferred by certain blockers, though I believe the other kind is thought the best by the best workmen, the top portion serving occasionally as a sleeking, or what in the trade is technically called a *long-stick*. [See *Bones and Sticks*.] The front being temporarily secured, the wrinkles ... are next to be conquered. Now it is that the rasp is brought into efficient operation; being taken between the two hands, and pressed downwards and crossways on each side of the block, bruising, confining and flattening the wrinkles into smaller dimensions, the higher portion of the stick, where there are no notches, to be occasionally rubbed over or along the block at its front angle, to keep the leather here level and clear.'

(d) Blocking Iron (Blocking Knife)
This is described by Devlin (1840, p. 56) as follows:

'The other tool or instrument, is the blocking-iron or *blocking knife*, with a heavy deep handle ... the whole width of the hand, and cased at each end with a plate of steel, to serve as a hammer in striking in the tacks, it being no matter how the tool in the hurry of work may be taken up, each end equally serving the purpose; the *knife* or under part is of a blunt edge, and in depth about two inches, and near upon four inches wide, with rounded corners.'

(e) Flounder (Flounder's Hammer)
The following extracts mention a Flounder as a tool used in blocking. None of the authors describe its appearance but it may be a version of the Blocking Iron described above:

Leno (1895, p. 149): 'The instruments used by the blocker consisted of pincers, a round wooden rasp, a short round stick made of hard wood and perfectly smooth and a Flounder's Hammer.'

Andrew Ure's *A Dictionary of Arts, Manufacture and Mines* (1874, III, p. 100) states that: 'After this, the fronts are regularly placed on a block, being forced into position by an instrument called a flounder, and tacked to their place.'

Knight (USA, 1877) describes a Flounder as a 'slicking-tool whose edge is used to stretch leather for a boot front in a blocking or crimping board'.

Miss June Swann (1978) suggested that the Flounder may be a tool from which the Closer's Hammer derived. This view is supported by a London closer (W. Graysmark, 1977) who uses a Closer's Hammer when blocking top boots and thinks he had once heard it called a Flounder. It may be added that though the Closer's Hammer has a fish-like shape, it is by no means 'as flat as a flounder'.

(f) Long Stick
An ordinary Rubbing or Long Stick is also used in the blocking process. These are described under *Bones and Sticks*.

(g) Crimping Screw and Board   Figs. 2:67; 2:68
A special clamp known as a Crimping Screw is sometimes used to help in the process of blocking. Mr A. L. Saguto (USA, 1980) writes as follows about its use:

'Sometime, probably late in the first quarter of the 19th century, the idea of the "crimping screw" was born. The early crimping boards are plain "L" shapes, but later on, the instep becomes more pronounced and rounded, and a notch appears at the back, made into the corner. This notch usually has a small hole at its bottom, bored at a 45° angle to the juncture of the "L". This hole is meant to receive the tip of the crimping screw shaft. The screw itself was usually a separate piece of hardware, and my board is one which has the screw permanently mounted. The crimping screw is a three piece affair, consisting of: a threaded shaft, inner shouldered block, and outer "U"-shaped toothed block. The inner shouldered block is threaded, and works on the threaded shaft the same as a nut and bolt. The inner block fits down into the "U"-shaped toothed block, which is slightly tapered so that the inner block's shoulders rest quite flush against the "float cut" teeth of the "U"-shaped block. The tip of the threaded shaft rests in the small hole at the base of the above-mentioned notch in the crimping board, and the bulk of the "U" block fits freely within the notch.

'In crimping the front of the boot, it is crucial to make the bend smooth from wrinkles, which inevitably form there. Therefore the greatest strain is brought to bear at this point. Removing these wrinkles, and pulling the front down tight, is where the crimping screw comes into play. The front is placed over the board, and secured at the toe end, and the top of leg, with tacks. The front is worked down with the pincers and hands as much as possible, working from both directions towards the notch. The two extreme corners of the front are now

Fig. 2:67

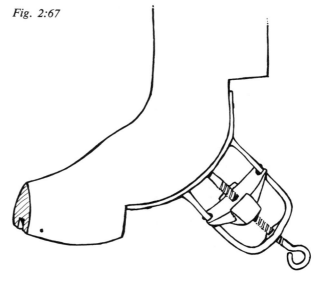

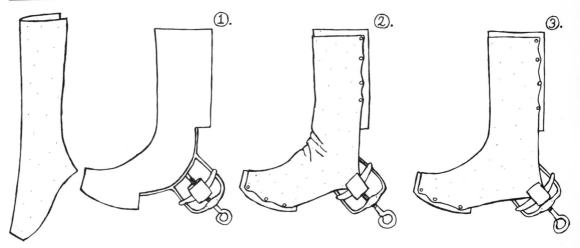

Fig. 2.68 The Crimping Screw: Diagram showing how a typical riding boot is blocked on a Crimping Board with a Crimping Screw.
(*1*) The folded boot front and the Crimping Board before the operation begins.
(*2*) The front has been tacked partially into place upon the board, and the two lower corners of the front have been inserted into the jaws of the Crimping Screw.
(*3*) The Crimping Screw has been rotated, tightening the jaws on the leather and drawing it backwards, so removing the wrinkles at the bend.

inserted between the inner, and outer blocks of the screw, the shaft resting in its hole. By tightening the threaded shaft, the inner block moves away from the board, pinching the leather between it, and the teeth of the "U" block, which can be moved freely along the shaft. As one continues to tighten the shaft, the whole apparatus is pulled back away from the board with tremendous force. This crimps the front "like a hot knife cuts butter"! A great improvement over hand blocking.'

(*h*) *Machines for Blocking or Crimping*
Attempts to expedite the laborious work of blocking the fronts of top boots resulted in many devices, both hand- and power-operated. For example, Knight (USA, 1877) describes, under Crimper, a hand-operated device which is mounted on a bench. It consists essentially of a metal former which forces the boot front over the Boot Block by means of a powerful screw. The front is held in place during this operation by the Crimping Screw described above. And in the 1884 Supplement (p.231) he describes one of the blocking machines or 'brakes' as follows:

'The Jamison machine has a pair of descending cheeks which slip over the sharp edge of the bent

former, crowding the leather over the latter and pressing it at all points, to prevent wrinkles, and to produce regular thickness.'

Blucher Boot
(See also Blucher Pliers under *Pincers and Pliers* in the HARNESS MAKER AND SADDLER section.)
The so-called Blucher boot might be classed as an institution of the British Army (as indeed of many armies of the world), for it was the basis for the design of army ankle boots in two world wars. It also became a regular working-man's boot. Based on earlier designs, it is distinguished by being made with an open *tab*, and with only four pieces in the upper (the vamp and tongue are cut in one piece), which makes it very serviceable; and having no facings or toe-caps, is smooth and comfortable inside.

Whether it was invented by Field Marshal Prince Gerhard Leberecht von Blücher (1742–1819), whose arrival on the field of Waterloo completed Wellington's victory, or only named in his honour, is not certain. He was a man of great energy and originality, and may well have turned his hand and mind to the development of a soldier's most important article of clothing.

In his *Dictionary of Military Uniforms* (1977), W. Y. Carman writes:

'British infantrymen adopted half boots in 1823 when shoes were discontinued. These boots were expected to be worn alternately on either foot to give even wear. Eyelet holes had to be made to take laces. In 1838 the Cossack boot replaced these but in turn gave place to a new pattern in 1873. The handsewn boot called the Blucher was worn until 1913 when the new pattern Army ankle boot with machine-made seams was issued. Light-weight ankle boots appeared in 1932.'

Miss June Swann (1975) in a letter to the author wrote as follows:

'The first reference I have to the use of the name Blucher is 1817, a Northampton price list: "Blucher, 14s. Short ditto 12s." – apart from something which we would not recognise as a Blucher: 2 Sep. 1815, Ackermann's Repository on Berlin fashions of the court and fashionables: "Pair of Blucher demy-boots military (or half boots) of royal purple or dark blue morocco and kid leather, also of purple satin, a small scarlet star embroidered on the instep." Like Wellington, Blücher had a lot of things named after him!'

Bones and Sticks used for polishing and rubbing-down. (Burnishing Stick or Bone; Hollin, Hollen, or Hollowing Stock; Long Stick; Petty Boy: see section 2(*d*) below; Polishing Stick or Bone; Roundstick; Rubbing Down Stick; St Hugh's Bones; Shoulder Stick; Sleeking Stick or Bone; Stitching Stick; Scots: Langstick, Yickie-Yeckie, or Patie Bowie; USA: Rub Stick.)
(See also: *Blocking Tools*; *Edge Iron*; *Glazer and Sleeking Iron*; *Puff Stick*; *St Hugh's Bones*; *Seam Sett*; *Turnshoe Tools*.)

Most of these tools consist of short lengths of smooth bone or hardwood, varying in size from about 5–7 in. (12.7–17.7 cm), with the exception of the Long Sticks which may be as long as *c*. $13\frac{1}{2}$ in. (34.2 cm).

The most common uses of these tools are for levelling, smoothing and polishing, removing wrinkles, rubbing down stitches and seams, and for closing stitch channels.

For convenience these tools are listed in two groups: (1) Bone Tools and (2) Wooden Sticks. But it should be understood that for most purposes these materials are interchangeable. Some of them were later made in steel.

1. BONE TOOLS
(See also *Paring Horn*.)
Bones were used in shoemaking for all kinds of smoothing, flattening and polishing. Indeed, to read some of the oldest authorities, one might suppose that a bone was the shoemaker's principal tool (see *St Hugh's Bones*). According to Wright (1922) some of the old Northampton shoemaking hands used to go to the forest to find boxwood for rubbing sticks, and also to search for bones of the deer for rubbing the welt. Shoemakers say that bones of the deer are

best, presumably because they are hard and take a high polish.

Bone tools commonly to be found in the workshops include:

(*a*) *Polishing Bones Figs. 2:69; 2:23 (p. 49)*
These vary in size and type from small straight bones of *c*. 5 in. (12.7 cm) long to larger and stronger bones used in the same way as the *Long Stick* described under (2) below. The shorter bones are mostly oval in cross-section (*c*. $\frac{1}{2}$ in. (1.2 cm) wide), with one end round, and the other a blunt flattish point used for opening a stitch-channel.

A curious feature of these bones is that a few serrations are often to be found at one end. In some instances these serrations may have been intended to serve as *Scratch Bones* (see below). But another explanation was given to us by Mr W. Ward, a shoemaker in Dover (1954). He worked, with assistants, in an old, poorly lit workshop (which also contained two beds). Some of his tools and equipment appeared to have been made at least before *c*. 1850. He explained the serrations in this way: 'We used to talk as we worked in those days, so we roughened the end of the bone so we could feel or hear which end was in use.'

Fig. 2:69

(*b*) *Stitch and Scratch Bones* (Stitch Flattener; Richard Timmins *c*. 1800: Ran Key; Devlin 1839: Notched Bone, Rand Bone.) *Figs. 2:70; 2:21, No. 12; 2:8 (pp. 94, 47, 34)*
Though these bones are often home-made, Stitch and Scratch Bones have become standardised in the catalogues of tool makers. They appear as flat pieces of bone *c*. $6\frac{1}{2}$ in. (16.5 cm) long, *c*. $1\frac{1}{4}$ in. (3.1 cm) wide, and tapering from $\frac{1}{4}$ in. (0.6 cm) in thickness at one end, down to a blunt edge at the other. The thicker edge is smooth, with a low guard or fence in the case of the Stitch Bone, but serrated in the case of the Scratch Bone.

The smooth end of the bone is used to level out and smooth down the damp welt after it has been sewn in. The narrow fence on the factory-made tool may be intended to prevent the bone slipping off the welt.

The serrated end of the bone is used to rub down the stitches on the welt and to clean off any surplus wax, after which they can be 'pricked up' (i.e. separated) with the *Stitch Prick*, and finished by 'running on' the warmed *Fudge Wheel*. Another use of the Scratch Bone is the removal of old stitches in repair work.

A caption 'Bone Rand Key' appears in Richard Timmins' catalogue (*c.* 1800) across an illustration of a Stitch Bone. The tool does not appear in the same firm's catalogues of *c.* 1860 and 1890. The term Rand Bone is used by Devlin (1839, p. 90) who, when describing the stitched rand, writes of the stitches 'being cleaned off from wax, first with the rand-bone and soap, and then with clear gum'. (See *Rand Tools*.)

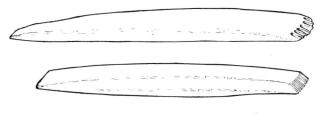

Fig. 2:70

(*c*) *Whalebone Inking Stick*
According to Devlin (1839, p. 42) the sole edge and heel were 'blacked by the application of a small bit of whalebone, or other stick, dipped in ink as the colouring matter'.

(*d*) *St Hugh's Bones*: see that entry.

2. WOODEN STICKS
(See also Wooden Edge Tools under *Edge Irons*.)

(*a*) *Hollin Sticks* (Hollen Stock)
A term for holly stick mentioned in the following quotation from Randle Holme's *Armoury* (1688, III, p. 349/2): 'Hollin Sticks used by Cordwainers; not that they are made of Hollin Wood, but a peculiar name so given them, with them they burnish and polish the upper Leather, and sides of the Sole Leather; also by the sharp ends they run Riggets, and score the Leather with what devises they please.' In chapter III, p. 99/1, Holme explains that a rigget is a channel 'in the outer sole for the Wax thread to ly in'. It would seem unlikely that such a channel could be cut with a 'sharp end' of hardwood; but it would have been used for producing 'scores' or 'devises' like the decorative lines impressed on harness with a saddle maker's Crease.

(*b*) *Hollowing Stick* Fig. 2:8 (p. 34)
This term is used in Richard Timmins' catalogue of *c.* 1800. A caption reads 'Box Hollowing Stick 3071 3/6 per dozen'. The picture shows an Edge Tool of the Double Forepart-Iron type. Since there is no hollowing operation that we know of, we presume that the term is derived from the Hollin Stick (see (*a*) above).

(*c*) *Long Stick* (Polishing Stick; Round Stick; Stitching Stick. Scots: Lang Stick or Yickie-Yeckie. Also, see list under the entry *Bones and Sticks* above.) *Figs. 2:71; 2:8, No. 3069 (pp. 95, 34).*
A name given to almost any polishing stick or bone over *c.* 10 in. (25.4 cm) in length. The most usual form is a rounded highly polished stick of hardwood, often boxwood or beech, but sometimes ebony or other hardwood. The length varies from *c.* 9–14 in. (22.8–35.5 cm).

The shape varies a good deal, but all are well rounded in cross-section, sometimes cylindrical, but more often a rough oval, or a rectangle with rounded corners. In longitudinal section, some are parallel (as Holme, 1688); some have a slight waist (presumably to help when polishing top boots over a block); and one, illustrated in Richard Timmins' catalogue (*c.* 1800) is 9 in. (22.8 cm) long, round in cross-section but of a marked fusiform shape in its length – for what purpose is not clear.

Many Long Sticks have one or both ends bevelled to a blunt wedge shape, presumably for rubbing down the welt or similar work. Some are provided with a step or shoulder at one end, or in the centre, which acts as a fence for bearing on the sole edge. (See also *Colted Long Stick* below.)

Long Sticks have two principal uses:

(1) For closing the stitch channel on the sole.
(2) For polishing soles and uppers.

Many writers have described its use, for example, Hasluck. (1898, p. 97):

'The sole is then slightly damped all over and rubbed down with a long-stick made from a piece of round boxwood, about a foot long, smoothed by rubbing with fine sandpaper. The sole is worked down by well rubbing all round the seam, and then the centre. The long-stick must be passed over the leather briskly, but not so as to generate heat and thus injure the grain. For this process the boot has to be held firmly between the knees, the long-stick is used as the file was, one end in each hand. The stick must form a right angle with the channel, and the rubbing must be done with the centre of it.'

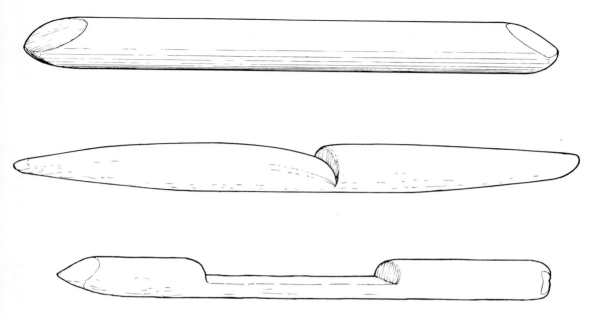

Fig. 2:71

Devlin (1839, p. 38):

'The channel . . . having some paste rubbed into it, is closed; after which . . . the sole to be layed hard and smooth with hammer and long stick.'

Amateur Mechanic (*c.* 1910, Vol. II, p. 591):

After scraping, staining etc. 'Grasp the ends of this stick firmly, press hard down on the sole bottom, and rub quickly from the waist to the toe. The leather will thus burnish up brightly.'

Tomlinson (1860, p. 44):

'The fine polish on the upper leather is produced by straining the shoe on a last and rubbing it with the polishing stick, a good kind of blacking being previously applied.'

(This work is now done with a steel Sleeker − see *Glazer and Sleeker*.)

Leno (1895, p. 67):

[of the Light Wellington]: 'The small strip of leather that forms the welt is then placed between the front and back, and the whole being placed in the clams, the sides are closed up. The closer's block is then inserted and the seam, slightly wetted, is rubbed smoothly down with the long stick.'

(*d*) *Petty Boy* (Scots: Patie Bowie)
This early term is used by the following writers:

Randle Holme (1688, III, p. 292/1).

'A Petty Boy, or a Shoemaker's Petty Boy . . . Instruments belonging to the *Cordwiner's* occupation: and are used generally for their burnishing and smoothing down the *Stitches*, and to pair pieces of Leather upon.'

Devlin (1839, p. 112), in a list of tools for the Boot-closer's Kit, includes a 'petty-boy or seam slicking stick (3d)'.

Mr David Murison (editor of the *Scottish National Dictionary*) agrees that the term almost certainly comes from the French *petit-bois*, a wooden sash or glazing bar. (Glazing bars often have a roughly oval cross-section, and have bevelled ends which make them rather similar in appearance to a shoemaker's sleeking or rubbing stick.) Mr Murison informed us (1974−5) that '*Patie Bowie* in Scots is a personal name (*Patie* for Peter, *Bowie* a not uncommon surname in West Scotland from the Gaelic for yellow-haired, flaxen) and that it is undoubtedly a jocular adaptation in this form of *petty boy*'.

We do not know what the Petty Boy looked like, nor its precise use, but Devlin, and Randle Holme before him, indicates that it was used for rubbing

95

down a seam. Priced by Devlin (1839) at 3d. it must have been a simpler form of stick than his 'Long Stick' priced at 9d. As to its purpose, it would not be a Seam Setter, for in the same list there appears the item '2 prs. of seam setters 1/6d'. It is presumed therefore that it was a simple polishing stick used for smoothing and, as Holme adds, to 'pair pieces of leather upon'. Assuming Holme was correct in mentioning this added use, the stick must have been flat, at least on one side, and wide enough to pare leather upon, or at least to skive down edges.

(*e*) *Shoulder Stick* (Fore Part Stick) See Wooden Edge Tools under *Edge Iron*.

(*f*) *Colted Long Stick*   *Fig. 2:72*
A cigar-shaped Stick with a piece of abrasive stone fitted to one side of the stick in the centre (see *Colt* for the origin of the word).

Illustrations of this tool have been found only in the following American trade catalogues: Ross Moyer (1884); Henry Arthur (1874); and Hirth and Krause (1890).

A. L. Saguto (USA, 1981) writes:

'As far as I know, the "colt" was added to the "long stick" around the time "pegged boots" became popular (*c.* 1840s in the US). Since the square peg-ends showed all around the border of the outsole, burnishing the bottoms required the prior smoothing of these peg-ends. With the "long stick", held with the "colt" downwards, the peg-ends were abraided smooth and the grain of the outsole buffed off. By simply flipping the stick over, the plain wooden side could be brought to bear as the burnisher.'

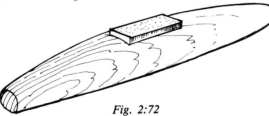

Fig. 2:72

Boot Holder
Apart from the *Foot Strap*, there are various devices designed for holding a shoe during manufacture or when cleaning. They commonly consist of two arms pivoted at their centres, which, when pressed together at one end, expand at the other to hold the shoe, and can be fixed in position by a catch or pawl bearing on a racked quadrant.

Boot Hooks (Boot Lift)   *Fig. 2:76*
A pair of strong metal hooks 4—9 in. (10.1—22.8 cm) long, with a cross-handle made in hardwood or

bone, or occasionally in metal. The lower turn of the hook is flat, so that the side straps of the boot do not become wrinkled. Richard Timmins' catalogue of *c.* 1850 illustrates fourteen varieties, some with a decorated shank, some made to fold, and some with knobs on the points of the hooks to prevent them from slipping out of the straps when in use.

Used for pulling on top boots. After inserting a hook into each loop of the side straps, the foot is thrust into the boot and then pulled on.

Boot Jack
A contrivance for helping the wearer to take off a boot, and in particular, a riding boot. It was used in the fitting room of a shoemaker's shop and in the home. There are two types:

(*a*) *Folding Boot Jack*   *Fig. 2:73*
A wooden foot-board with a forked end to hold the heel of the boot while the wearer pulls his foot out. The board is hinged down the middle so that it can be folded for travelling. Some were cleverly shaped so that, when folded, they looked like a shoe, complete with inscribed eyelets and heel. Another model contained a recess to hold a small brush and a box of blacking; of which Knight (USA, 1877, p. 336) notes that 'cases are made to contain all three, being nattily arranged to suit the fastidious'.

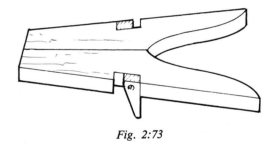

Fig. 2:73

(*b*) *'Fancy' Boot Jack*   *Fig. 2:74*
A curiously fashioned Boot Jack from the catalogue of Hirth and Krause (USA, 1890).

Fig. 2:74

(c) Standing Boot Jack Fig. 2:75

In use the wearer stands with one toe on the rear of the foot-board, while he eases the boot off the other foot by wedging its heel in the crotch provided. This type of jack gives the user a handle to hold onto whilst standing on one leg. Some are provided with a loose hanging tongue to press on the toe of the boot to ease its removal.

A retired London clicker (H. Marks, 1978) wrote in a letter to.the author, 'when riding boots are very tight and a Boot Jack is not available, the person wearing the boots sits down and someone stands in front of him, with his back towards the sitter, and

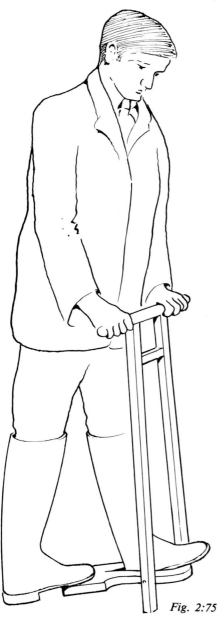

Fig. 2:75

with one boot held between his legs. The sitter pushes him in the back with his other boot. It is very effective.'

Boot Jockey *Fig. 2:76 (p. 98)*
This is a curved metal plate which can be hung over the top of a long boot next to the shin to prevent the breeches from rucking-up when pulling the boot on. The illustration, which also shows the use of a *Boot Hook*, comes from the catalogue of Pocock Brothers (*c.* 1920).

Boot Tree (Boot Last; Shoe Tree) *Fig. 2:77 (p. 98)*
Note: For process of manufacture see *Last and Boot Tree Maker* in the section MISCELLANEOUS TRADES AND TOOLS.
Wooden 'feet', known as trees, are used by the customer to keep boots or shoes in shape. The best trees are made in three parts, with the central piece slightly wedge-shaped, designed to be forced in after the toe and heel pieces are already in place.
Boot Trees are also made for stretching a boot or shoe (see *Stretcher*).
A simpler tree, used only for shoes, consists of a toe and heel piece separated by a wooden screw which forces the two pieces apart. More recently this type is made in metal, with an adjustable lever action instead of a screw.
The term 'Boot Tree' is also applied to a foot-operated machine in which shaped wooden parts are forced into a boot or shoe in order to smooth out wrinkles.

Bosher: see *Glazer and Sleeker*; and also under CLOG MAKER section.

Bottom
The underpart of a shoe, including the sole, insole and heel. It is confusing that the part of the sole that actually rests on the ground is often referred to by shoemakers as the 'top', and when speaking of the heel, the 'top piece'. This is because the shoe is held upside down, usually strapped down on the shoemaker's knee, while being made.

Bottom Filling Tool (Bottom Filling Knife) *Fig. 2:38, No. 2450 (p. 64)*
A square-ended blade, rather like a painter's Chisel Knife, used for spreading a compound of paste and granulated cork, or other malleable materials, known as 'bottom fillers'. These fillers are intended to level up the space between the edges of the inseam (between the insole and outer sole) in a welted shoe: see the diagram under *Edge Iron* or *Welt*. (See also *Knife, Hot*.)

97

Military
Pattern.

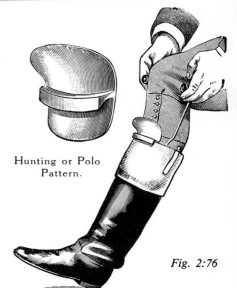

Hunting or Polo
Pattern.

Fig. 2:76

Long Boot Jockeys.

ART. No. PF.72.

The picture on the left shows the difficulty of pulling on a long boot without one of our Jockeys, whilst that on the right shows how easily it can be done with one.

per **36/-** doz.

Box Lodger

A term used by Devlin (1839, p. 114) for a bootmaker who carries his kit and his clothes in the same box:

'... though the kit of the boot-man is much easier packed and carried than that of the other; the heavy blocks, and setting board, and long awkward clams of the boot-closer being too bulky for any sort of knapsack. Yet there are boot-closers who, by certain contrivances of hollow blocks and jointed clams, can make all into a bundle, and are as fit for the road as the other. It were better, however, for both parties to put all into a box, a box too that holds something more than the tools – a little decent wearing apparel; and a *box-lodger*, as is well known, always gets better treated in the places of his stopping than the mere kit-lodger, and the reason is obvious.'

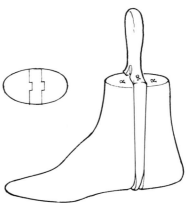

Fig. 2:77

Breaker: see *Seat Breaker*.

Bristle: see *Sewing and Stitching*.

Brogue

A lace shoe characterised by being made in several sections, each punched and serrated (gimped) round the edges. Brogue is an Irish word for a rough shoe made of untanned hide, worn at one time by the inhabitants of the wilder parts of Ireland and the Scottish Highlands. See Fancy Punch Plier under *Punches*.

Buffing Knife (and **Scrapers**): see *Knife, Buffing*.

Bunking Tools (Janking Tools)
Note: There is some confusion in the use of the terms 'Bunking' and 'Janking', as will be noted below. The words do not appear in the OED in relation to shoemaking. But the term 'Bunker' is included in *A Dictionary of Occupational Terms* (1927) as a person who 'sets, i.e. closes down, lip of channel (in sole of boot) after sole is fastened to welt, by pressing channel, by hand, [or] with ornamented edge of a wheel'. Both terms relate to operations done on the sole in connection with 'stitching aloft', that is stitching on the top of the sole without a channel — a practice confined mostly to heavy work — see *Sewing and Stitching*.

Tools used for the above purposes include:

(*a*) *Bunking Iron* (Bunker Iron; Chopper) *Fig. 2:78*
A short length of iron with one end turned at right angles to the handle, ending in a wedge-shaped blade. The tool is placed between stitches and struck with a hammer in the same way as a *Stitch Prick* is used on the welt stitches. The object is to tighten the stitches on the sole when stitched aloft, and to improve their appearance.

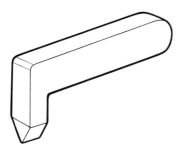

Fig. 2:78

(*b*) *Bunking Wheel* (Bunk or Bunker Wheel: Chopping-up or Chopper Wheel; Mock Stitch Wheel) *Fig. 2:79*
A special wheel set in a wooden handle, about $6\frac{1}{2}$ in. (16.5 cm) long overall. The wheel is cut to print serrations of eight, ten or twelve teeth per inch (2.5 cm).

This tool is similar to a *Fudge Wheel*, except that the cylindrical wheel runs on a spindle set at right angles to the head of the tool. The shank on which the wheel is fitted is provided with a guard. In later models, the wheel can be fixed (by means of a set-screw) at different positions in relation to the guard, so that the bunking print can be applied at different distances from the edge of the sole. The side of the fence which bears on the edge of the sole has a smooth, convex face to avoid scraping.

The wheel is heated and then run round the top of the sole. The original purpose was to enhance the appearance of the stitching, in which case the heated wheel was 'run-on' with Heel Ball — see *Finishing Tools & Materials*. This process also tended to consolidate and tighten the stitching for which purpose it was quicker, though probably less effective, than the *Bunking Iron* (*a*) above. But later, the wheel was used only to imprint an ornamental pattern which simulates stitching aloft. Gresham (1920, III, 244) asserts that the purpose of the bunking operation is to give machine-stitched boots the appearance of being handsewn, and to give a firm line of indents parallel to the edge of the sole and waist called the 'bunk'.

Fig. 2:79

(*c*) *Janking Wheel* (Jank Wheel; Chopping Up Wheel)
This term is used by Thornton (1970, p. 472) who writes that the Bunking Wheel is used for making a 'fancy pattern' on the sole and the Janking Wheel for stitch separation on the sole. The term is not mentioned by either Swaysland (1905) or Plucknett (1916).

Button Hook

A steel hook, set in a handle made of wood, steel, silver, mother-of-pearl, or ivory. It is designed to grasp a button below the head and draw it through the button hole.

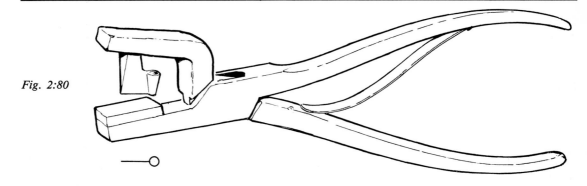

Fig. 2:80

In length they vary from almost 12 in. (30.4 cm) for a heavy instrument used for buttoning-up heavy boots and gaiters, to smaller sizes for ordinary boots and shoes, and miniature sizes, sometimes folding, for ladies' gloves. The variety of designs is endless and includes collectors' pieces with silver handles, much chased or embossed, sometimes in designs of considerable beauty. Others were made with a shoehorn serving as the handle.

Millions of these button hooks were made in the last century for use in both shoe-fitting shops and at home. A large proportion came from the Birmingham area, where they were one of the many small objects known in the trade as 'steel toys'. They were made, for the most part, by 'little masters' (i.e. outworkers) who made small tools etc. in their own homes, delivering up the finished or partly finished products to the larger firms who marketed them under their own names. One of the firms who bought their wares and sold them to the public, along with tools belonging to many other trades, was Richard Timmins of Birmingham, *c.* 1800, well known later as Wynn, Timmins & Co.

Button Tools

The button-boot was fastened with buttons instead of laces. Although buttons were used to fasten sandals in ancient Greece, and to fasten high boots and gaiters in medieval England, their heyday came with the button-boot introduced in the mid-nineteenth century and still common in the early years of the twentieth century. As one writer put it (Gresham, 1920), 'when buttoned, those boots and shoes present a very elegant appearance, the fastening being warm and close. Ladies favour this style of boot.'

Today, the button survives on the single-strap children's shoe, but this is giving way to the buckle which adjusts more conveniently to different sizes of foot.

The tools used include:

(*a*) *Button-Hole Plier   Figs 2:80; 2:24 (p. 50)*
Made as a strong plier, usually with spring handles, *c.* $7\frac{1}{2}$ in. (19 cm) overall. The punch itself is made to cut a slit in sizes from $\frac{3}{8}$ to $\frac{3}{4}$ in. (1–1.9 cm) long, with a hole at one end. The holes were described as 'Round or Pippin', which means round or pear-shaped. The jaw of the plier on which the punch bears is faced with brass to avoid blunting it.

(*b*) *Button-Hole Punch Fig. 2:47, No. 4338 (p. 73)*
Designed to do the same work as (*a*) above, but made in the form of an iron punch for striking with a hammer.

(*c*) *Button-Fasteners* (Button Clippers)
When fitting buttons to the best work, shoemakers prefer stitching, but there are a great many devices for attaching them with staples. These include Hand-Punches, hand – or foot – operated Machine Punches, and Button Pliers.

The plier grips the button and staple in one jaw, while the other jaw clenches the points of the staple after they have pierced the leather. One popular type called the 'Peninsular Button-Fastener' is provided with a magazine for holding a supply of buttons.

(*d*) *Button Eyelet Plier and Button Eyelet Punch and Die*
The word 'button' in the name of these tools relates to Push-Buttons (popularly known as 'poppers' when fitted to clothing) and not to boot-buttons. Similar tools were used for fastening lace eyelets and lace hooks (see *Eyelet Tools*).

Cabriolet

A device described by Garsault (1767) for holding a shoe on the knee when sewing (see Cabriolet under *Stirrup*).

100

Caliper Socket (Leg Iron Socket)
A piece of iron tube about 2 in. (5 cm) long, with flanges for attachment under the waist of a surgical boot, to hold a caliper or leg iron.

Calk (Ice-Creeper)
A sharp metal projection fitted and secured under the heel (or sole) of a boot, shoe, or clog, which digs into the ice or frosty surface, to prevent slipping. The 'Calkin' on a horseshoe serves the same purpose.

Candleblock (Dandiprat)
A heavy stool, about 3 ft (91.4 cm) high, with a hole in the middle into which was inserted a candle holder that could be raised or lowered as occasion required.

According to Wright (1922) this candle was called a 'Dandiprat', the term for a coin worth three halfpence, current in England in the sixteenth century; and he quotes the following nursery rhyme:

Little Jack Dandiprat, in a white petticoat,
The longer he lives the shorter he grows.

Like the lace makers, shoemakers sometimes used this device for lighting.

Cashal
Scots term for *Stirrup*.

Channel Shoes (Channel Galoche; Channel Pump)
These are shoes, mostly of the slipper type, made without a welt. The sole is sewn directly to the insole through the lasting-margin of the upper, which is sandwiched between them. The stitches lie in a channel cut along the sole margin.

Channel Tools
Shoemakers use channel tools to cut grooves into which stitches can be sunk below the surface of the leather. Two kinds of groove or channel are made: (*a*) those that are cut at an angle, with a knife, leaving a closable flap under which the stitching is sunk; and (*b*), those that are made by removing a thin string from the surface of the leather, leaving an open channel into which to sink the stitches.

1. THE 'CLOSABLE' CHANNEL IN THE SOLE
The channel is cut with a knife at an angle slanting inwards, to a depth of about half the substance of the sole, so that when the cut is opened (with one of the channel-opening tools described below) a flap is formed which, when closed, will cover the stitches. After wear the flap may be worn away, and indeed the stitches themselves may be broken, but they still hold for a considerable time because the threads are tightly held in the substance of the sole and welt.

The following quotation from Devlin (1839, pp. 36–7) about channel-cutting is typical of his campaign for good workmanship:

'After the sole is properly rounded, the *channel* is to be cut, running, in the first place, a tool to mark the distance of the same from the edge, though many only use the guiding of the finger for this purpose. The channel is always to have an inward inclination on the sole; and is better to be cut so shallow that the stitches may be partially seen, than so deep as to injure the value of the article to the consumer; a straight down, deep cut channel being one of the most disreputable things in the trade, rubbing off in the wear, and looking very unslightly.'

The tools used include:

(*a*) *Knife for cutting the channel   Fig. 2:81*
Experienced shoemakers and repairers use the sharp, round end of a Shoe Knife (see under *Knife, Shoe*). In more recent times, a special tool has been developed for cutting the channel (though older shoemakers insist that the Shoe Knife does the work better). This modern tool consists essentially of a metal handle into which is mounted (under a holding-screw) a short pointed knife-blade. A fence is provided to guide the tool along the edge of the sole; the butt of the handle is tapered to be used as a channel-opener.

Fig. 2:81

(*b*) *Home-made tools for opening the channel   Fig. 2:82*
After cutting the channel, the lip is opened with any handy implement, for instance, the blade of a screwdriver or *Stitch Prick* or, as has been noted more than once in a shoemaker's kit, and illustrated here, the blade of an old table fork which has been cut off at the shoulder.

Fig. 2:82

101

(c)   Factory-made tools for opening the channel Figs 2:83; 2:52, No. 6162 (p. 78)
These include the implements illustrated; one with chisel-like point, and the other with doll-like shank and toeless foot.

Fig. 2:83

(d)   'Channel File'
A name given by Devlin (1839, p. 38) to a tool probably used for both opening and removing loose material from the channel to make room for the thread, so that the lip, when closed, will bed properly. He writes: 'The forepart as it is called, being now stitched, the channel is to be cleared out with the channel file, and then, having some paste rubbed in it, is closed.'

(e)   Tools for closing the channel
After sewing, the stitches that lie in the channel are rubbed and bedded in' with the thin end of a bone, and a little paste is applied with a piece of rag.

The lip of the channel is then closed with the smooth side of an old file or any other convenient implement, then damped and rubbed down with a stick or bone. Finally, the sole is hammered all over until it is perfectly even. (See Long Stick under *Bones and Sticks*.)

There is a tool called a Channel Jigger which may have been intended for channel closing. Illustrated by Richard Timmins (Birmingham *c.* 1800) and Barnsley (Sheffield *c.* 1890), it is shaped like the ordinary Edge Jigger Iron, but the lips are wide enough apart for one of them to smooth down the channel on the bottom edge of the sole, while the other acts as a guide or fence by bearing on the edge of the sole. (See Channel Jigger under *Edge Tools*.)

2.   THE OPEN CHANNEL
These are plain grooves made without a flap to close over. They are used by leather workers for decoration, or to facilitate a bend or fold, or for sinking stitches below the surface. (Those made by harness makers and ·saddlers are described in that section under *Channeller* and *Race Tools*.)

Shoemakers cut open grooves on top of the sole when 'stitching aloft'. The tools used include the following:

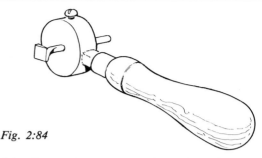

Fig. 2:84

(a)   Race Grooving Tools (Channel Gouge; Drag) *Fig. 2:84*
A small U-shaped blade bent round to form a sharp gouge-like cutter, similar to the Timber Scribe used by joiners and coopers, or the Race Compass used by harness makers. A modern version consists of a race-type blade mounted on an adjustable stem which is fitted at right angles through a circular guide or fence.

(b)   Punch-bit Groover Fig. 2:85
A short steel shank fitted with an interchangeable round punch-bit. This cuts a string of leather which emerges through a hole in the shank. The tool can also be used for deepening a channel previously cut. A modern version of this tool is fitted with an adjustable guide or fence intended to bear on the edge of the sole.

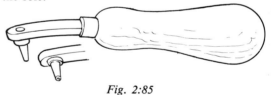

Fig. 2:85

(c)   'Top Groove' Tool
A tool mentioned by Devlin (1839, p. 68) intended to cut a groove to ease a bend in the leather. From the following description of the process it is probable that it was a Race tool:

'The *top* is now to be got ready . . . the distance or depth of the fold is to be marked off, that is, that part which is to be turned to the inside of the boot where the leg and top are joined. Along this mark the tool called the *top-groove* is to be run, striking out a portion of the flesh side of the leather, so that the top may bend or fold to the necessary thinness at that particular place.'

Chopper
A name given to a rough knife for cutting off worn parts of heel etc. (see *Knife, Hacking*).

Clamp

A pair of wooden jaws, held between the knees, for holding work near the seam when sewing, e.g. when closing the upper.

Description, illustrations, recent history and nomenclature will be found under *Clamp* in the HARNESS MAKER AND SADDLER section.

Clicker

The term 'clicker' is popularly supposed to originate from the sound made when the knife is used. It is true that there is a slight 'click' when the point of the knife leaves the edge of the leather and hits the board beneath, or when the user gives a slight turn of the wrist at the end of the cut. But, according to the OED, the term 'clicker' was applied in the seventeenth century to a shoemaker's tout, as described in the following passage quoted from *A new dictionary of the terms ancient and modern of the canting crew c. 1690*: 'the Shoemaker's Journeyman or Servant, that cuts out all the work, and stands at or walks before the door, and saies "What d'ye lack, sir? What d'ye buy, madam?"'

The clicker prepares and cuts the separate sections of the leather for making the uppers of boots and shoes. (See also in the introduction to this section for other *Divisions of Labour* within the trade.) His left hand presses the pattern down on the leather, while his right hand holds the knife, with the forefinger outstretched along the back of the knife in order to put pressure on it.

Leno (1895, p. 50) comments on the process as follows:

'As many pages as this volume contains, and one hundred diagrams to boot, would not suffice for a full and detailed explanation of the cutter's art ... In bespoke cutting, where big prices are asked for and obtained, economic cutting becomes a matter of secondary importance. In that department of the trade, fitness and excellence are the chief things to be considered. Taking a skin, the bespoke clicker critically scans it, not to resolve how he is to make the most out of it, but to learn whether it is of sufficient excellence for his purposes, and if so, he proceeds to cut his parts after a fashion that the manufacturer would stand aghast at.'

Today, although press knives frequently replace hand-held ones, the art of the clicker still remains. It is the ability not so much to manipulate the knife but rather to assess the leather and put the pattern or die in the right place and correctly oriented. Skins from the same type of animal are variable in quality from one to another according to age and living conditions, and from place to place in the same skin, the best quality being in the butt and the worst in the shanks. A clicker has to take into account variability in appearance (colour, grain pattern), thickness, 'handle' (resilience), freedom from blemishes (e.g. warble holes, barbed wire scratches, flay cuts), direction of 'tightness' and, very important, economy in the placing and interlocking of patterns to obtain the minimum of waste between them. Although the principles of good clicking can be taught, the skill comes only from experience. And, consequently, even today, the clicker regards himself, quite properly, as a rather special person.

For particulars of tools and methods, see the following entries: *Awl, Clicker's*; *Cutting Board*; *Knife, Clicker's*; *Measuring Tools*; *Plane, Clicker's Block*.

Clicker's Grader

A name given by Richter (c. 1890) to a *Pattern Cutter's* Fixed Allowance Divider. (See under *Measuring Tools*.)

Clogger's Tools: see the CLOG MAKER section.

Clooes

Scots term for 'a grip used by cobbler when hand-stitching two pieces together' (SND). Presumably a *Clamp*.

Closer (Boot-closer; Shoe-closer; Top-maker)

(See *Process* and *Division of Labour* at the beginning of this section.)

After the component sections of the upper have been cut to shape by the clicker, the closer sews them together to form the upper, which is later put on the last for the attachment of the sole.

The first occurrence in print of the term 'closer' (cited by the OED) is from the London Gazette of 1724; clicker appears a few years earlier in 1690.

No doubt the operation of clicking and closing were often performed by the same person, but when this was not the case they were expected to understand each other's work. Devlin (1839, p. 63) writes forcibly of this requirement:

'In commencing the top-boot, the closer should be also a *clicker*: that is, he should know how the work ought to lie, so that the boot when finished be what it ought to be, and not an offensive assemblage of ill-put-together pieces of spoiled leather. He must therefore be very skilful in his fitting ... in short, if a clicker cannot be a closer, a closer should always understand the business of the clicker; and if he does not, his ignorance may spoil the very best cutting. It will hence be seen that the perfection of the *mere* stitches is not the first essential in completing the leg of the top-boot but, on the contrary, that it is the fitting – for spoil or neglect this, and all is spoiled; the whole beauty of the boot is gone, be its leather and other workmanship as superior as they may.'

There are several methods for making the seams. All aim at strength, good appearance, and the absence of ridges on the underside that would cause discomfort. The seam most often used is the lapped seam. In this method one or both edges are pared down (skived) to avoid any thickening at the joint, and are then overlapped and stitched together.

The skiving is often done on a slab of marble or glass (see also *Cutting Board*). And after sewing the seam is rubbed down with a stick or bone.

Where a very strong seam is required, a strip, known as a welt, is first inserted between the two pieces to be stitched. After stitching, the surplus welt is removed with a *Closer's Welt Plough*, and smoothed with a *Seam Sett*. Further smoothing is done with a bone – see *Bones and Sticks*.

Note: Adhesives are sometimes used in the factories for holding the component parts of the upper together before stitching; and more recently some parts of the shoe – even the whole of it – are closed by adhesives without any stitching at all.

Closer's Tools

Those in present use include the following: *Awls*; *Bones and Sticks*; *Clamp*; *Closer's Block*: see *Sewing Block*; *Closer's Awl*: see *Awl, Closing*; *Closer's Hammer*; *Closer's Welt Plough*; *Seam Sett*; *Welt Setter*.

Devlin (1839, p. 26) writes as follows about the Closer's Tools:

'This person needs little kit; a slip of board to *fit* or prepare her work upon; a pair of clams; a block; a knife; about three awls, two differently sized closing awls, and one stabbing awl; two seam-sets, or it may be three – one for the stabbed sides; a stirrup; a case of needles – short blunts; and a thimble. And in the grindery, she requires that sort of rather hard twisted silk, formerly known under the name of *barber's twist*.'

Closer's Hammer (Fitter's Hammer; Paste Fitter's Hammer) *Figs 2:85a; 2:26 (p.52)*

Note: Not to be confused with a heavy hammer of the same name used in the engineering trades for riveting. (See also *Flounder*.)

Not a hammer of ordinary shape, but an all-iron baluster-shaped tool which is held by its swollen centre. One face is round, the other wedge-shaped. It

is made in three sizes: small (5 in. (12.7 cm) long), medium and large.

Hardwood versions of this hammer are seen occasionally in the workshops, but can be confused with a small size of the collar-maker's Smasher (see under HARNESS MAKER AND SADDLER section).

The Closer's Hammer is used after sewing to level down and flatten the seams by tapping with one end of the tool and rubbing with the other. It can also be used for 'tapping out' wrinkles when lasting the upper, and for 'tapping up' a patch or a lining after pasting: this is very necessary to ensure that there is no bumpiness. Sometimes the hammering is done on the flat, but more often on a *Last, Boot Tree*, or over a *Block*.

This tool is not illustrated by Diderot. The first illustration we have seen appears in Wynn, Timmins list of 1892. It is not in their list of *c*. 1800.

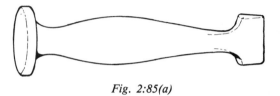

Fig. 2:85(a)

Closer's Welt Plough (Welt Cutter; Welt Runner) *Figs 2:86; 2:87; 2:22, No. 35 (p. 48)*

Note: This tool is used for trimming a welted seam; it should not be confused with the tools used for trimming the welt proper, described under *Welt Tools*.

A cranked trowel-type shank set in a wooden handle, *c*. 6 in. (15.2 cm) overall. The blade is V-shaped in cross-section, and bevel-ground on the cutting end; this provides a cleft in which the edge of the leather being cut is guided. The blade is ground off on the underside leaving a narrow flat in which there is a shallow groove.

It is used by closers to trim off the surplus leather from the edge of a welted seam (Fig. 2:87). Welted seams are chiefly used when closing the uppers of high boots for which a very strong seam is required. The narrow strip of leather that forms the welt is

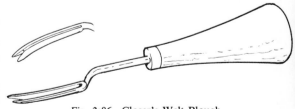

Fig. 2:86   Closer's Welt Plough

placed between the two edges of the boot leg and the three parts are held in the Clamp while being closed. The Block is then inserted and the seam, slightly wetted, is rubbed smoothly down with the Long Stick. Devlin (1839, p. 60) describes the next step: '... the welts ... will now be seen lying loosely on the outside. To cut these welts off close above the stitch, with the utmost evenness, a pretty instrument is used called the *welt-runner*, which striking in at the beginning (holding it in the right hand and the welt in the left) cuts off the welt to the greatest nicety.'

A different use of this tool was seen at Messrs Lobb, the London shoemakers (1975): it was used for trimming the edges of the upper itself. It should be added that one of their closers used a saddler's Edge Shave for the same purpose.

There is a difference of opinion among closers on the use of the groove under the blade of the Closer's Plough. One told us that it was used for setting a bead (half round) on the welt after it had been pared down; another that it was used to guide the tool along the edge being cut.

There is some evidence from the trade catalogues that this specialised tool was invented during the mid-nineteenth century. It does not appear in the catalogue of Richard Timmins of Birmingham of *c.* 1800, but appears in later catalogues of that firm, and also in the catalogues of George Barnsley of Sheffield in 1895 and 1927.

maker's list in which we have seen one illustrated. (The example illustrated has a maker's name T. King/Northampton.) However, the tool is mentioned by one of the well-known writers on boot and shoe manufacture – Edward Swaysland (1905, p. 199) – from whom it appears that it is used only as a means of improving appearance:

'This edge [of the sole] is divided into two parts. The parts are separated with a clump saw, which saws a groove all round the forepart. The saw has a lip which goes over the top of the forepart that acts as a guard, and a movable saw that can be set so that it makes the division in the edge of the forepart. These divisions are set with different irons and, as a rule, are finished different colours; the top part, brown, and the part of the edge nearest the welt, black. The top part of the edge is shaved under, which makes the extra substance of the forepart less apparent. Sometimes the whole of the edge is finished black, and when this is the case, the iron called a double-bevel clump iron can be used with advantage. This iron is cut so that it sets the whole of the edge at once.'

Another method of improving the appearance of a clumped shoe was by bevelling the clump edge and finishing it in brown. 'By this means the customer gets a really stout, good winter boot with the external appearance of a summer boot.' (Gresham, 1920.)

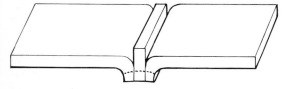

Fig. 2:87 Diagrammatic view of a welted seam

Clump Saw   *Figs 2:88; 2:28 (p. 54)*
A small saw-toothed blade fixed on its side to a short stem which can be set at distances varying from about $\frac{1}{8}$ to $\frac{3}{8}$ in. (0.4–1 cm) from the guard. The wooden handle is square, with a thumb-grip top. Size $6\frac{1}{2}$ in. (16.5 cm) overall.

A clump is a thick extra half-sole added to a shoe, usually as a repair, but also in order to thicken the sole during the winter. The word is derived from the early Dutch or North German word *Klamp* or *Klumpe* for a wooden shoe.

None of the elderly shoemakers and repairers we have spoken to have ever seen this tool or know what it is. The same may be said of Mr George Barnsley whose firm's catalogue of 1890 is the only tool

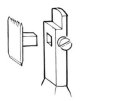

Fig. 2:88

Cobbler: see **Cobbler or Shoe Repairer** at the beginning of this section.

Cobbler's Foot (Cobbler's Last; Cobb-Iron; Foot Iron; Iron Foot; Knee Stock; Repairing Foot; Repairing Last; Shoe Boy; Tom Boy. From its use for holding a boot while hobnails are driven in: Hobbing Foot; Hobbling Foot; Hob Stob. Scots:

Fig. 2:89

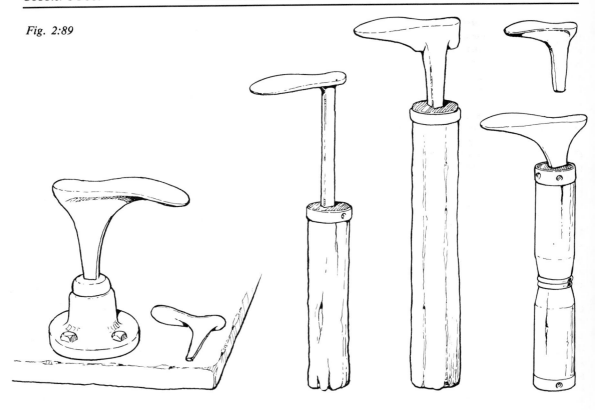

Deevil or Divel. USA: Stand. The modern all-iron Cobbler's Foot, made for mounting on a bench, is known as a Bench Foot.)   *Fig. 2:89*

This essential piece of cobbler's and maker's equipment consists of an iron 'foot' on which a boot or shoe can be held with its sole uppermost, during repair, or when driving nails. The stem is either fitted into a wooden stake, which is held between the legs for use while sitting; or is fitted into a metal socket which is screwed to the bench for use when standing.

An important purpose of the iron foot is to turn over the points of the nails and to clench them on the insole. In a letter to the author (1979) Mr J. H. Thornton writes:

'Over 20 years ago when I was examining Romano-British shoes in the Guildhall Museum, London (as it then was) I found nails with turned-over points and realised that an iron (or stone) last must have been used. ... Incidentally a few years ago I examined a Romano-British shoe from Ickham near Canterbury and there were 100 nails in it! 200 per pair – how many for a legion? And what do we know about the Roman nail-making industry?'

When fitted to the bench, the boot or shoe can be held steady with a Foot Strap (see *Stirrup*).

When designed for use while seated, the foot is driven into a stake about 26–30 in. (66–76.2 cm) high overall, sometimes made from an old table leg, with an iron hoop driven over the top to prevent splitting. If the cobbler wishes to work standing, and does not use a bench-fitted foot, the stake is often held in a small cask which is filled with rubble to hold the stake securely.

Home-made examples are often flat pieces of iron roughly forged to the shape of a foot. Others, more foot-like, were made from built-up forgings or from cast iron. Smaller sizes were made for children's shoes. In more recent times a full range of cast-iron feet are kept so that one can be selected to fit the boot or shoe under repair. These have rectangular stems which fit into a socket that can be screwed to a bench.

A variant is a double-ended foot with a toe of different size at each end. It could be used on the lap, or the end not in use could be pushed into a cavity on the side of the bench, leaving the other end ready to take the shoe under repair.

The Cobbler's Foot has been used since early times. One found at Sandy in Bedfordshire, and thought to date from the fourth century, is described by Rupert Cook (1977) as being of iron, about $15\frac{1}{2}$ in. (39.3 cm) high, with a 'foot' *c*. 6 in. (15.2 cm) long. At the bottom of the stem there is the usual tang and stop-ridge for sinking into a wooden base. Other examples have been found at the Roman site at Silchester, and elsewhere throughout Europe.

The Cobbler's Foot is not illustrated by Diderot (1760), nor by Tomlinson (1860), perhaps because these writers were describing the work of makers rather than menders. Yet it is difficult to imagine how a maker could drive heavy nails into a sole or heel without one.

Collice (Collish)
An American term for *Edge Iron*. The origin of this word is unknown but it has been suggested that there may be a connection with the French verb *coller*, to stick, paste or press, or with *coulisse*, a groove.

Colt
James Devlin (1839) includes this term in a list on p. 113 headed 'Kit of the boot-man'. The term is also described in the Supplement to Wright's *English Dialect Dictionary*, as an Antrim word meaning 'A piece of gritstone set in wood, used by shoemakers to rub the soles and heels to make them take the black stain.' The word does not appear in the Oxford English Dictionary nor in the Scottish National Dictionary but see Colted Long Stick under *Bones and Sticks*.

Compass (Dividers) *Fig. 2:24 (p. 50)*
Small compasses are often found in a shoemaker's kit. The usual type used are known in the tool-making trade as 'plain'; they are about 5 in. (12.7 cm) long, finished bright, have long tapering legs, and a boxed joint. (See also *Compass* in the HARNESS MAKER AND SADDLER section.)

Though seldom mentioned in the textbooks, they were in general use by shoemakers for measuring and marking out, e.g. for putting a fixed allowance round a pattern edge for folding over. Devlin (1839) includes a Compass among the tools for making men's boots (but curiously, not women's). Gresham (1920) mentions the use of a Proportional Compass for grading – the process whereby a range of shoe sizes can be marked out (see *Measuring Tools*).

Cordwainer and Cordovan (Corviser; Scots: Cordiner)
An early term for shoemaker: see the introduction to this section.

Counter (Back-strap) *Figs 2:3, 2:4*
The piece of leather, usually stiffened, forming the back of the shoe, running from the heel upwards. According to the OED the term derives from counterfort, a projecting piece of masonry to support or strengthen a wall. (See diagram of boot in the introduction to this section.)

Covers
Cloth covers were made to keep the shoe upper clean when working on the sole or heel. They are still used in the factories for white and suede shoes.

Cozer: see Bottom Glazers under *Glazer and Sleeker*.

Cramp
Term used occasionally for the piece of wood or 'block' forming the upper part (instep) of the last, on which the upper leather is stretched (see *Last*).

Cran
A word not recorded by the OED but explained by Devlin (1839, p. 81) as follows: 'These secrets, some valuable, others but very so-so, are among shoemakers called *crans*, probably from the word *cranny*, and are looked upon by the would-be knowing in such matters as of great importance, and the key is uniformly turned in the door when any such job is going forward.'

Crimper: see *Blocking Tools*.

Crow Wheel (Bottom Wheel; Fancy Wheel; Jim Crow Wheel; Waist Wheel) *Figs 2:90; 2:22, No. 25 (p. 48)*
A small metal wheel mounted in a forked carriage, set in a wooden handle, *c*. $5\frac{1}{2}$ in. (13.9 cm) long overall.

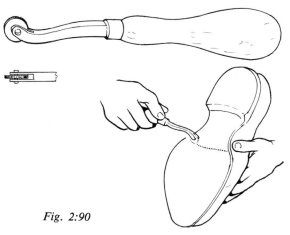

Fig. 2:90

After warming, the tool is used for printing a narrow decorative pattern across the waist of the sole – an operation known as 'crowing'. It is also used occasionally to cover a channel in which stitches have been sunk.

The pattern imprinted is frequently a series of V's known as herringbone or crow's foot – which may have given the tool its name. But there are other designs, described in one manufacturer's list as 'dot and fancy'. Joseph (*c.* 1900) illustrates twelve different imprints under *Roulettes à Fleurs*, including a variety of dots and dashes, a 'key' pattern, and wreaths of leaves and flowers. Only one of the twelve is of crow's foot design.

Cutting Board (Clicker's board or block; Devlin: Fitting Board. A heavier block catalogued by Ross Moyer (USA, 1884) is described as a Dinking Block.) A board or block used by clickers and closers on which to cut out the leather. (See also *Plane, Clicker's Block*.)

At one time made of limewood, but more recently made up of hardwood blocks stuck together like a miniature butcher's block, with the grain of the wood vertical to the operator. Using the end grain in this way avoids losing control over the knife, which tends to happen when the knife follows the long grain of a wooden board.

When worn, Cutting Boards are scraped ('buffed') with a scraper (see *Knife, Buffing*). After this smoothing process, the board is dressed with linseed oil. This makes the wood swell, thus closing the knife cuts that were too deep to be buffed out.

The cutting work is usually done standing at a bench, but Devlin (1839, p. 57) writes that the closer (who in those days was also the clicker) 'takes his cutting or fitting board on his knees, and fits his side linings, cutting and skiving them to a proper form and thinness at the edge'. Today, skiving is often done on a slab of hard material such as glass or marble.

The circular Cutting Board illustrated by Garsault (1767) may have been intended for use on the knees.

A Cutting Board made to withstand the impact of a hammer or power-operated Press Knife consists of separate grain-vertical pieces bound together with an adjustable iron band to form a rectangular block. Circular one-piece grain-up boards, bound in iron, are also used.

A plane was developed in America to take out the knife cuts, instead of using a Buffing Knife (see *Plane, Clicker's Block*).

Deevil
Scots term for *Last* and *Cobbler's Foot*.

Digging Shoe (Boot Plate; Digging Plate; Foot Plate) *Fig. 2:90a*
A piece of metal or leather with side lugs intended for strapping (or lacing) to the underside of the boot. Its purpose is to prevent the top edge of a spade or fork from damaging the sole of a boot when digging in heavy land.

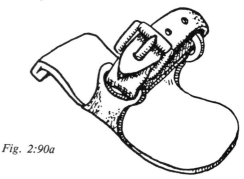

Fig. 2:90a

Dippin
Scots term for *Dubbing*.

Dividers: see *Compass*.

Drag
A name given to certain tools which cut on the pull stroke, such as the *Drag Knife*. The term is also applied to one of the race-like knives (*Binding Cutters*) used by clog makers for cutting grooves in the leather uppers (see CLOG MAKER section).

Dubbing (Dubbin; Scots: Dippin; USA: Daubing. The verb 'dub' means, among other things, to smear with fat or grease.)
(See also LEATHER MANUFACTURE.)

Dubbing is a mixture of tallow with neat's-foot, cod-liver, or sperm oil. It is used mainly by curriers, but it is also rubbed into the leather uppers of boots and shoes to keep out the wet and to render stiff leather more supple. (It was formerly used for the same purpose on leather fire hoses.)

Dummy: see *Glazer and Sleeking Iron*.

Edge Iron (Edge Burnishing Iron; Edge Setter; Irons; Kit Tool. USA: Collice or Collish.)
Note: For names of individual Edge Irons see list below. See also Shoulder Stick etc. under *Bones and Sticks*; *Seam Sett*.

The Edge Iron family is a large one – indeed the largest in the shoemaker's kit. If, about seventy years ago, a shoemaker acquired one of each kind offered by the tool makers of that time, he would find he had twenty different types of irons, each made in at least seven sizes – about 140 irons in all. In practice, however, like the few remaining bespoke makers today, he managed very well with about five to ten different irons each in three to four sizes.

Edge Irons are used to set the edge of the sole and improve its appearance. In the eighteenth century and before, tools for this purpose were made of bone, hardwood or even stone. They are illustrated by Randle Holme (1688), by Diderot (1760) and by Garsault (1767). Later, many different Edge Irons were developed to produce that elegance and finish that may still be seen in the showcases of the bespoke makers.

In the workshop, Edge Irons are usually kept in a box with honeycomb divisions or hung in rows by means of leather tabs nailed to the top of each handle.

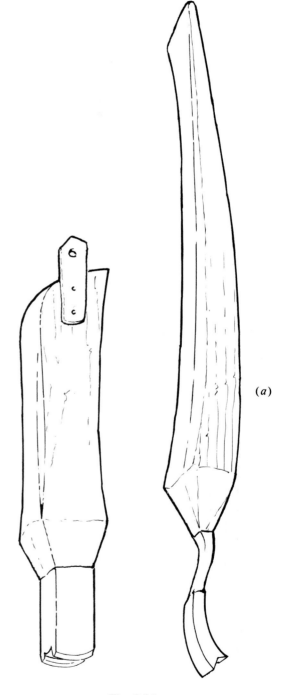

Contents of this entry

1. Description: *(a)* Typical Edge Iron types and sizes
                (b) The head or 'forge'
                (c) Edge Iron handles
2. Purpose
3. Parts of Edge Iron's head
4. Operation
5. Varieties of Edge Iron:

Used mainly on Forepart and Waist
(a)   Single Forepart Iron
(b)   Double Forepart Iron
(c)   Jigger Iron
(d)   Double Iron
(e)   Double-Double Iron
(f)   Bevel Iron
(g)   Pump Iron
(h)   Double Pump Iron
(i)   Welt Iron
(j)   Wooden Edge Tools
(k)   Waist Iron

Used on the Heel
(l)   Seat Iron
(m)   Top Piece Iron
(n)   Military Heel Iron

Use in doubt
(o)   Boot Iron or Boot Rand Iron
(p)   Clump Iron
(q)   Channel Jigger
(r)   Dress Bevel Iron
(s)   American Edge Irons

6. Cutting Edge Irons to shape (see under *Files*).

(a)

Fig. 2:91

1. DESCRIPTION

(*a*) *Typical Edge Iron types and sizes* *Fig. 2:91*
The Edge Iron has a steel head, rectangular in cross-section, set in a wooden handle by means of a short tang. Most Edge Irons measure *c.* 6–7 in. (15.2–17.7 cm) overall, but the handles of Jigger Irons and Waist Irons are often longer, resulting in a tool *c.* 8–10 in. (20.3–25.4 cm) overall. Some Edge Iron heads were made of wood or bone.

Each of the main types of Edge Iron was usually made in seven widths (sixteen for Waist Irons). Barnsley (1890) lists Irons which vary in width from $\frac{1}{4}$ to $\frac{5}{8}$ in. (0.6–1.6 cm), rising in sixteenths (2 mm), and are marked A to G. Richter (*c.* 1910) and others numbered their Edge Irons to correspond with the number on a Substance Gauge which is calibrated in 'irons'. (An iron = 1/48 in. – see Substance Gauge under *Measuring Tools*.) Ross Moyer (USA, 1884) lists a Double (Forepart) Iron in twenty sizes.

(*b*) *The head or 'forge'* See diagram *Fig. 2:92*
There are two main shapes of head. The most common one is made from straight, squared steel bar; but the head fitted to the longer Jigger and Waist Irons is 'bent', i.e. gracefully curved so as to lie close to the upper when in use without damaging it. In some older catalogues, e.g. Richard Timmins (Sheffield, *c.* 1800), most of the heads taper from the face towards the handle. This was most likely done for the sake of appearance, but was discontinued, probably for the good reason that when the face became worn and required re-cutting, the width of the head would gradually decrease.

The face of the Iron is shaped according to the contours required to be imprinted on the edge of the sole (see diagram). For this purpose, the forge of Forepart and Waist Irons was often cut to produce a bead along the edge of the sole, and a narrow shoulder (or 'step') along the edge of the welt.

These refinements, now abandoned except by a few bespoke makers, were carried out to improve the appearance of the sole edge; and there is no doubt they succeeded in doing so – at least while the shoes were still on display. The shoulder on the welt was said to make the sole 'look lighter', and the crease on the sole edge was supposed to define the edge more sharply. But the origin and purpose of the crease is explained rather differently by Devlin (1839, p. 41) who, when describing the rasping down of the stitch channel towards the sole edge, remarks that:

'...the leather will turn over a little, and make what is called the *crease*. The tool next used, named the *shoulder*, or *fore-part .iron*, has a very delicate hollow cut in it at the extreme angle, to receive this leather so filed over from the channel, and to gather and press it into a hard and beautiful wire, the appearance it ultimately takes. This tool also effects a still better purpose for through it the edge altogether derives that firm, even, and glossy character it commonly has: while, by the lip that runs along the top of the sole, the channel is hardened and polished.'

Note: Devlin's 'delicate hollow' is the crease, and the 'beautiful wire' is the bead. The 'channel' (in the last sentence) is the stitch channel.

The face of these Irons is usually made slightly convex in the lateral plane so that in use it makes a tangential contact with the edge of the sole and so avoids scraping. The face of the Forepart Iron is sometimes made 'round-both-ways' to give a slightly concave surface to the edge.

(*c*) *Edge Iron Handles*
(1) Round and square types. *Figs 2:91; 2:91a; 2:93*
During the early nineteenth century the handles of Edge Irons and other 'kit' tools appear in the catalogues as round in cross-section and often rather bulbous at the top. A handle of rectangular cross-section is illustrated by Diderot (1760) but it was not until about 1850 that the so-called 'square' handle, with or without a rounded thumb-rest at the top, became almost universal in this country. In cross-section, it is rectangular (*c.* $1\frac{1}{8} \times \frac{3}{4}$ in.; 2.9 × 1.9 cm) but with chamfered or rounded corners. This shape gives several advantages, for example:

It gives a good grip so that the tool can be held steady in the desired position without twisting.

If the head or blade of the tool is correctly mounted in the handle, a right-handed user can be certain that, if he holds the handle with his thumb over the rounded top corner, the tool will bear correctly on the work. For example, in the case of Edge Irons, the guard of the tool will come on the correct side to bear on the welt. This is important in a badly lit workshop – as so many of them were.

The square-shaped handle prevents the tool rolling off the heating appliance or the bench. This is important for tools that are heated before use.

(2) Long or shoulder types. *Fig. 2:91*
Jigger Irons and Waist Irons were mostly fitted with longer handles so that the user could exert greater pressure by leaning over the handle with his hand near his chin or shoulder. These longer handles are

gracefully curved, with a flat-oval cross-section, tapering towards the butt. The shank of the forge is often curved ('bent'), so as to lie towards the work.

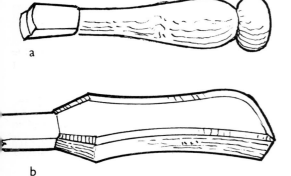
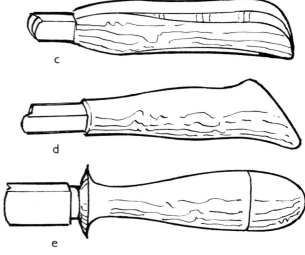

Fig. 2:91(a) Edge Iron handles
     (a)   Round (Birmingham *c.* 1800)
     (b)   Square (Birmingham *c.* 1850)
     (c)   Square (Sheffield *c.* 1900)
     (d)   Round (USA 1884)
     (e)   Round (France *c.* 1930)

2. PURPOSE

The chief purpose of the Edge Iron is to 'set' the edge of the sole, i.e. to smooth it and to imprint a desired shape upon it. This is done by running the heated tool, under pressure, along the edge of the leather. Thornton (1970) writes, 'Edge setting, like burnishing, has the useful purpose of sealing the fibres against water and so preserving the shape and appearance of the bottom. Wet leather is very plastic and the edge would become quite shapeless if exposed to the wet for even a short time, especially if knocked as well.

'Apart from the useful function of sealing the edge, the operation also enhances the appearance of the shoe by giving increased shine and greater definition to the style of the edge.'

Fig. 2:92 Diagrammatic cross-section of an Edge Iron, and its imprint on the sole edge.

3. PARTS OF THE EDGE IRON'S HEAD, and its nomenclature. *Fig. 2:92*

Note 1: A Double Iron is a combination of the Forepart Iron, used for setting the top edge of the sole, and its companion tool, the Jigger Iron, which is used to set the welt.

Note 2: In the language of shoemaking, 'top of the sole' relates to what an ordinary person would call the bottom of the sole, i.e. that part of the sole that

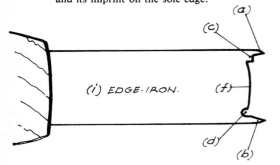
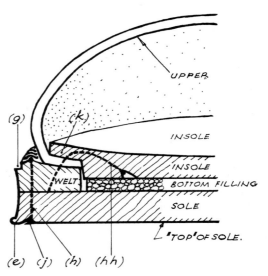

is in contact with the ground. The term 'top' is used because boots and shoes are held upside down on the last while the sole and heel are being worked upon.

(*a*)   *Welt Guard* (Front Lip) which runs on the welt.

(*b*)   *Sole Guard* (Sole Lip or Back Lip) which runs on the top edge of the sole.

(*c*)   *Jigger or Jigger-step* (Wire)
This produces the shoulder or step (*g*) on the top edge of the welt. The shoulder is intended to face up the stitches on the welt and give them a neat and solid appearance. It can also help to remedy any irregularities made by the Stitch Prick or Fudge Wheel. Irons made without the jigger-step are known as 'plain' or 'blind'. (See also Jigger Iron under *Edge Iron*.)

(*d*)   *Crease*
This forms the bead (*e*) along the edge of the sole. Sometimes another crease, known as a Jigger Crease, is cut instead of the Jigger (*c*) to form a bead on the top edge of the welt.
Note: Textbooks sometimes confuse the terms 'jigger' and 'crease'; but the most usual interpretation is that the crease is the depression (*d*) which produces the fine line of beading (*e*) that runs round the edge of the forepart of the sole top; while the jigger is the protruding step (*c*) at the foot of the welt guard which produces the narrow shoulder (*g*) that shows on the edge of the welt. The term 'crease' relates to the crease formed in the iron; its imprint on the edge of the sole, though sometimes referred to as a crease (or even a 'wire'!), is in fact a bead.

(*e*)   *Bead*
The moulding which is formed by the crease in the Iron (*d*).

(*f*)   *Face* (Bed; Belly; Bow)
This surface is made convex to form a slightly hollow edge to the sole, or made flat to produce a square edge.

(*g*)   *Shoulder* (or 'step')
This is formed on the edge of the welt by the jigger-step on the Iron.

(*h*)   *Stitching*
The threads that join welt to sole, and which show on the surface of the welt.

(*hh*)   *Sewing*
Threads joining together the insole, upper and welt.

(*i*)   *Head* (or Forge)
The head of the Edge Iron. The side of the head nearest to the welt is called the jigger or guard side; the lower side of the head, which runs on the top of the sole, is called the forepart, sole or lip side.

(*j*)   *Channel* in which the stitches joining the sole to welt are sunk.

(*k*)   *Outside Feather* of insole.

4.   OPERATION   *Fig. 2:93*
Before applying Edge Irons, the sole edge is first knifed to size, then rasped all round, scraped with steel or glass, sand papered, and finally dampened with water or with water coloured by ink. Heel Ball wax is then applied with a warmed iron to give a polish, and finally the work is brushed and rubbed off with a cloth. (See also *Finishing Tools and Materials*.)
     When using the Edge Iron, the boot or shoe is usually held on the left knee on its edge, with the toe towards the left, and with the upper nearest the worker. After warming, the Iron is held in the right hand, and the guard placed on the welt (i.e. in the joint between upper and welt). The Iron is then moved in the direction of the toe. As mentioned under (*c*) *Edge Iron Handles* above, if the forge is correctly mounted in the handle, the user can be certain that if he holds the handle with the rounded top corner towards him, the guard of the tool will bear on the welt.
     Mr R. C. Pond, a retired Norwich shoemaker, related (1975) that he was taught the following rhyme as a guide to the use of Edge Irons:

> Wet it,
> Sweat it,
> Set it.

which he interpreted as follows:

     'Wet it' – wet the leather with water, or with water coloured with ink.
     'Sweat it' – rub with a half-warmed iron to form the edge.
     'Set it' – rub with a hotter iron, with Heel Ball wax, for a final setting and burnishing of the edge.

     The warming of the iron is often done over a piece of candle stuck between three nails on the bench. A special spirit lamp made for the same purpose is illustrated. The Irons are heated to about 100°C, sufficient to make the Heel Ball melt and run under the iron (see *Heater*).

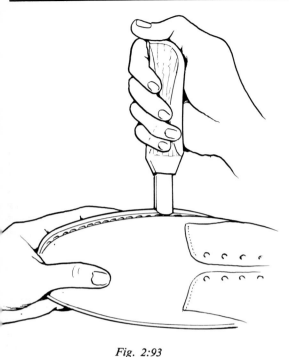

Fig. 2:93

5. VARIETIES OF EDGE IRON (see diagram *Fig. 2:92*)

There is some confusion in the nomenclature employed when describing the heads of Edge Irons. The terms 'jigger' and 'crease', which are explained by the diagram above, are given different names by different writers. For example, in the quotation under *Jigger Iron* below, Leno (1895) calls the jigger-step a 'wire'; yet elsewhere in his book he uses the same word for the bead produced on the sole edge by the crease.

The terms 'blind' or 'plain' are found in the trade catalogues. This indicates that the face of the Iron has neither jigger nor crease.

Edge Irons used mainly on the forepart and waist

(*a*) *Single Forepart Iron* (Forepart Iron; Shoulder Iron) *Fig. 2:21, No. 1 (p. 47)*
Devlin (1839, p. 41) writes that the term 'Shoulder Iron' originates from the 'practice of pressing upon the tool with the shoulder as it runs on guided by the hand'. The face is rounded both ways, and there is a crease at the foot of the guard which produces a bead on the top edge of the sole. Leno (1895) writes that the bed should slope slightly upward from the

foot of the guard, so helping the user to hold the Iron on the top of the sole ('clip the edge') without slipping off.

The single Forepart Iron is used for setting the top edge of the sole (i.e. the edge nearest to the ground), mainly for repair work or when a Double Iron of suitable size is not available.

(*b*) *Double Forepart Iron Fig. 2:21, No. 8 (p. 47)*
This is a combination of two Single Forepart Irons of different size in one head. There is a central guard between them.

(*c*) *Jigger Iron* (Men's Jigger; Women's Jigger) *Figs 2:10, Nos 2928/9; 2:11, Nos 919, 926*
The head of this tool is similar to the Forepart Iron except that there is a jigger-step at the foot of the guard (instead of a crease). This jigger-step produces a small shoulder on the edge of the welt which is intended to 'lighten' its appearance. The tool is made in two sizes, the smaller for women's shoes and the larger for men's.

Since considerable pressure is needed to press the edge close to the upper, these Irons are often given a longer handle, and have a bent forge (see *Fig. 2:91*).

Leno (1895), in his chapter on kit-cutting, writes: 'The wire [jigger-step] must be cut to suit the kind of boot on which it is intended to operate, that for a shooting-boot requiring to be very stout, the stitch being farther from the edge than in ordinary boots. The jigger crease [shoulder on the welt] on all work should take up the entire space from stitch to edge, one side of the wire facing up the stitch and giving it a neat, straight and solid appearance. If the wire be too stout it will bruise the stitch and destroy the look of the boot.'

(*d*) *Double Iron   Fig. 2:21, No. 3 (p. 47)*
The use of the term 'double' in relation to Edge Irons is confusing. The Double Iron illustrated here combines the duty of two *different* Irons in one head: in this case a single Forepart Iron and a Jigger Iron. When the term 'double' (or double-double) is applied to other Irons (e.g. the Pump Iron) it implies a head which combines the duty of two similar Irons but each of a different width.

Double Irons are designed to 'clip' a sole up to about $\frac{3}{8}$ in. (1 cm) in thickness. When the sole is thicker, two separate Irons are used.

Evidence from the tool makers' catalogues suggests that these combined Irons were not made before *c.* 1850.

(*e*) *Double-Double Iron   Fig. 2:21, No. 9 (p. 47)*
This strange name is not as queer as it sounds, for it

correctly describes a head containing two Double Irons, each of a different width.

(f) Bevel Iron Fig. 2:21, No. 4 (p. 47)
Similar to the Double Iron, but provided with a longer and heavier guard on the sole side. This guard is designed to bevel the top of the sole in order to make a heavy sole look lighter. In its narrowest sizes the Bevel Iron is used on pumps and ladies' shoes where there is no visible welt. It is intended to make a thin sole look even thinner.

(g) Pump Iron Fig. 2:21, No. 6 (p. 47)
Pumps are slippers or turnshoes of light weight. Having virtually no joint between upper and welt to act as a guide for the Iron, a single, long guard is provided which bears on the top of the sole, while the face of the Iron is run along the edge of the sole to burnish it. It is run along the whole of the edge — without the use of a different Iron for the waist.

(h) Double Pump Iron Fig. 2:21, No. 7 (p. 47)
Faces of two different widths, one on each side of a guard.

(i) Welt Iron (Welt Rubber)
A plain face with no guards. Probably used for rubbing down the welt of heavy boots or shoes.

(j) Wooden Edge Tools (Forepart Stick; Shoulder Stick) *Fig 2:94*
Note: The alternate names given under the entry *Bones and Sticks* are sometimes applied to some of the wooden Edge Tools.

Wooden versions of the Edge Iron are 6–7 in. (15.2–17.7 cm) long, usually with both ends shaped for edge-polishing, and often swollen at the centre for holding. Though mostly made of hardwood, examples made in bone, or even stone, are occasionally found.

When Devlin was writing his *Guide to the Trade* (1839), many of the Edge Irons were still made of wood. Even today, some makers use a shaped and shouldered wooden stick (still known as a Shoulder Stick) for burnishing sole edges; they say that it gives a pleasant natural finish, and is easier to cut to any required design or size. Devlin, writing about the finishing of pump soles (p. 53), declares: 'iron tools are at present in common use, though formerly the tools were made of wood. The shoulder-stick then in all cases set the edge, but now it is set with the edge-iron, and it is much better, readier, presses harder, and gives a more perfect gloss.'

(k) Waist Iron (Shank Iron; the names Channel Waist Iron or Round Waist Iron are given to the same or very similar tools). *Figs 2:21, No. 5; 2:91 (pp. 47, 109)*

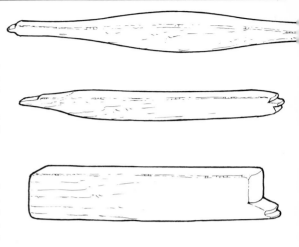

Fig. 2:94

An Iron for setting the edge of the waist, i.e. the narrow part of the sole under the arch of the foot. Very short guards clip the welt and sole, and the face slopes downwards between the two. Today, the commonest shape forms a slightly rounded edge on the waist, but other Irons were cut to form a square or hollow edge. A crease of jigger-step was often added.

Since considerable pressure is needed to press the edge close to the upper, these Irons are usually provided with the longer curved handle, and have a bent forge (see *Fig. 2:91*). The process is described by Gresham (1920, Vol. IV, p. 57) as follows:

'The edge is pared, scraped, and fitted to the size of the waist iron to be used. The edges are damped and the waist iron run cold. In running the waist iron, care should be taken that the pressure is applied in such a manner as to press the edge of the waist close and firm to the upper and not to bulge the sole from it.'

Edge Irons used on the Heel

(l) Seat Iron   Figs 2:21, No. 2; 2:11, No. 912 (pp. 47, 37)
A short guard which runs on the seat of the heel with a jigger-step at its base, and a flat face. It resembles the Single Forepart Iron, except that a jigger-step is provided instead of a crease.

Used for setting and hardening the edge of the heel at the seat. It also smooths that part of the heel to prepare for the *Seat Wheel*. When describing the cutting of this Iron, Leno writes (1895, p.137): 'This once popular piece of kit has been partially superseded by the seat wheel; but many of the best work-men still employ it to set the seat when putting the boot in colour, in other words before using the seat wheel.'

(m) Top Piece Iron (Top Iron) *Fig. similar to 2:10, No. 2932 (p. 36)*
Similar to the Military Heel Iron, with a pronounced jigger-step and, for women's shoes, a sloping face. Used for setting the edge of the top piece as an alternative to using the guard of the Dummy (*Glazer and Sleeking Iron*). The jigger throws a narrow step on the edge. It can also be used to set the edges on each side of the heel breast. (*Note*: 'top piece' is the surface of the heel that touches the ground.)

(n) Military Heel Iron Fig. 2:10, No. 2932 (p. 36)
Illustrated by Richard Timmins (*c.* 1800), it resembles a heavy Top Piece Iron and was probably used for the same purpose.

Use in doubt

(o) Boot Iron, or Boot Rand Iron Figs 2:21, No. 11; 2:10, No. 2926 (pp. 47, 36)
Illustrated by Richard Timmins (*c.* 1800), this heavy Iron with single guard and jigger appears to have a step or shoulder across the face, but for what purpose it is not clear. Devlin (1839, p. 113) lists what are presumed to be the same Irons under 'Kit of the boot-man' on p. 113, as follows:

'1 – rand iron, a tool for setting up the rand before stitching (1/-)
3 – boot irons, tools for setting and finishing the rands after stitching (3/6).'

A retired London maker (W. B. Glasow, 1978) suggested that if the rand referred to by Devlin is a form of storm welt, the Boot Rand Iron may have been intended to iron-up both the rand and the edge of the welt proper in one operation. (See also *Rand Tools*.)

(p) Clump Iron
According to Swaysland (1905, p. 218) this Iron has a 'wire down the centre of the bed dividing the edge into two; the two sides may be quite different in character; the guard side may be hollow-faced, with crease and jigger wire; the lip side may be bevelled off with any combination of wire and crease'.

Probably used for setting the edge of a clump sole which was sometimes divided into two parts (see *Clump Saw*).

(q) Channel Jigger   Figs 2:21, No. 13; 2:11, No. 921 (pp. 47, 37)
Illustrated by Richard Timmins (*c.* 1800), this Iron

differs from the other Irons: its forge is rounded, and the claw-like head has an almost vertical face. A version illustrated by Barnsley (1890 & 1927) is very similar to a Waist Iron.
The Channel Jigger could have been used to set up a bevelled waist, i.e. bevel the part between the forepart and the breast of the heel; or it may have been used for closing a channel (see *Channel Tools*).

(r) Dress Bevel Iron
This Iron is included in Leno's chapter on kit-cutting (1895, p. 136). Judging by the instructions given for cutting, it has a very narrow face and a crease. Probably used on very light shoes or slippers.

(s) American Edge Irons
An American term for Edge Iron is *Collice*. In the 1884 edition of the catalogue of shoe tools issued by the Ross Moyer Manufacturing Co. (USA) there are two Edge Irons whose purpose is not clear:

Catalogue entry	Suggested English equivalent
No. 384 Men's Kip Collice	Double (Forepart) Iron with two creases.
No. 395 Men's Peg Collice	Double (Forepart) Iron with Jigger and crease.

6. CUTTING EDGE IRONS TO SHAPE (see *File, Shoemaker's*).

Edge Plane (Edge Shave; Edge Trimmer, Forepart Shave; Sole Plane; Superseder. According to Mr George Barnsley (1974) of the Sheffield tool makers, the term 'Superseder' was applied to a later model of Edge Plane because it superseded the others).
The term 'Edge (or Sole) Plane' is given to at least three different tools, of which one is described under *Edge Scraper Plane* and the others under the variants listed below.
In all except the non-adjustable models, the iron is thin, slightly curved, and mounted horizontally, like that of a spokeshave. The curved blade enables the tool to be used in the waist of the shoe. Size: 6–7 in. (15.2–17.7 cm) overall.
Edge Planes are used for trimming the edge of the sole. They appear in the lists towards the end of the nineteenth century. Leno (1895, p. 208) describes them as an American invention and declares that 'there is little doubt of their superiority over the knife, rasp etc.' – a statement that would not be endorsed by the many bespoke shoemakers who prefer to use a knife; but they might agree with Hasluck (1898, p. 125) when he suggests that it is a good tool for the novice 'as with it he cannot do

much damage, whereas with a knife he can soon spoil a boot'. Some makers use this tool for trimming heels (see *Heel Shave*). Variants include:

(a) Edge Planes without adjustable fence Figs 2:95; 2:27 (p. 53)
In the older version the iron is set horizontally, or nearly so. But a later version (Barnsley, 1927) has an iron set at almost 45° to the face. In using the iron, the hand is best placed well down near the head of the tool: in some early models the wooden handle is broadened at the top to form a hand-rest; in later models, a brass plate set at right angles to the handle is added for the same purpose.

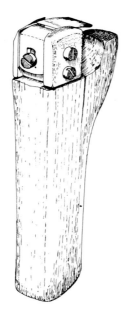

Fig. 2:95

(b) Edge Planes with adjustable fence Fig. 2:28 (p. 54)
The adjustable fence bears on the sole. There is usually an adjustable mouth below the cutter.

(c) Edge Plane with 'spokeshave' handles Fig. 2:96
The same type of cutting-head as (b), but provided with handles on each side like a spokeshave. One of the handles is offset to clear the upper. A specimen in the author's collection is inscribed 'Patd July 30 1867. No. 1 Oxford Mass'.

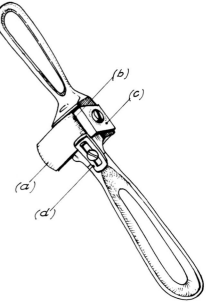

Fig. 2:96   Edge Plane with adjustable fence: diagram of cutter assembly
(a) Cutter
(b) Cutting edge
(c) 'Face' of plane adjustable to control depth of cut.
(d) Fence which bears on the sole of the shoe. Adjustable to control the width of cutter exposed to the edge of the sole.

(d) Edge Plane and Edge Iron combined Fig. 2:97
Richter's catalogue of *c.* 1910 states: 'These Edge Planes Are a Great improvement. The knife is made like a Forepart Iron cut in two. It pares edges, sets jigger, and creases at same time, and takes the welt out clean and even.' The idea of trimming and setting the iron with one tool may have originated in America, for it is illustrated by Ross Moyer (USA, 1884) and inscribed 'Hazard's Patent Edge Plane'. As Richter remarks, the head is shaped like an Edge Iron, but where cut across, the edge acts as a cutter which is intended to trim the face and cut the Jigger and Bead and set up the edge all in one go. Whether this tool was a success is to be doubted.

Fig. 2:97

(*e*) *Scraper pattern Edge Plane*: see below *Edge Scraper – Plane*.

Edge Scraper – Plane (USA Edge Buffer)   *Fig 2:23 (p. 49)*   Size *c.* 5½ in (13.9 cm) long.

Though sometimes called an Edge Plane, this tool has a cutting iron set at an angle of nearly 90° to the face, and is really a scraper. That illustrated by Barnsley (1890) is listed as a 'Yankee Sole Plane'; the same tool listed by Ross Moyer (USA, 1884) is called an 'Edge Buffer'. Both are mounted on a curved wooden handle, the American version resembling the horn handle of a carving knife. (See also *Knife, Buffing (and Scrapers*).)

Edge Shave   *Fig. 9:38*

A harness-maker's tool sometimes found in a shoemaker's kit. The forked blade is taper-ground underneath to give the end a cutting edge. In shoemaking it is occasionally used for cutting a fine bevel along the edge of a sole or welt. It can also be used for cutting off unwanted edges close to a seam. (See also *Closer's Welt Plough* in this section; *Quarter Bevel* in the CLOG MAKER section; *Edge Trimming Tools* in the HARNESS MAKER AND SADDLER section.)

Edge Trimming Machine

Knight (1877) describes a hand-operated machine which pares the edges of the sole as a substitute for a knife or Edge Plane. The shoe is revolved against a cutting knife, while a 'feeler' runs between sole and upper to guide the knife and prevent it from cutting the upper.

Eighteenth-Century Methods   *Figs 2:6; 2:6a (pp. 31, 32)*

Some of the methods of this period, mostly taken from Diderot (*c.* 1760) and Garsault (*c.* 1767), are noted under the following entries: *Blocking Tools; Edge Irons* (wood); *Knife, Heel; Lasting Pincers and Dogs; Rand Tools; Seat Breaker; Shoehorn; Sole Forming Block; Stirrup* (Cabriolet); *Thread Holder;* and introduction to this section.

Elshin

Scots term for *Awl*.

Equipment, Furniture etc: see *Bench and Seat; Boot Jack; Boot Holder; Clamp; Cobbler's Foot; Cutting Board; Heater; Machines for shoemakers; Nail Holder and Nail Chest; The Workshop and Conditions of Work* in introductory section.

Eyelet Tools

In the leather-working trades, an eyelet is a tubular metal bush which is inserted in a previously punched hole. In shoemaking the eyelet provides a smooth lining for the lace holes, and it prevents the leather (or fabric) from tearing. The eyelets have a narrow rim which lies on the front surface, and a tail which is clenched by the Eyelet Tool on the inside surface.

The tools used for the above process include:

(*a*)   *Hole Punching Tools*: see under *Punch*.

(*b*)   *Closing Punch and Die*   *Fig. 2:48, Nos 4412, 4414 (p. 74)*

A cast-iron base which carries the anvil or die, and a short metal punch for clenching the tail of the eyelet. A variant has a die and punch mounted in a single C-shaped casting in which the punch is spring-loaded to withdraw ready for fixing the next eyelet.

These punches are also made with a recessed die to take Lace hooks – see (*d*) below.

(*c*)   *Eyelet Closing Plier* (Eyelet Pliers; Eyelet Setter)   *Figs 2:98, 2:48, No. 4400 (p. 74)*

These pliers are fitted with a die on one jaw and a closing-bit on the other, both shaped like those of the Punch and Die sets described above. The pliers are made from 7–9 in. (17.7–22.8 cm) long, rising in ½ inches (1.2 cm).

Fig. 2:98

(*d*)   *Hook Eyelet Plier Fig. 2:48, No. 4410 (p. 74)*

Boot-lace hooks are fixed to the facing of boots by means of an eyelet which is clenched by this tool. It resembles the Eyelet Closing Plier, except that the die is recessed on one side to accommodate the hook.

(*e*)   *Press-Stud Plier* (Push Button Plier; Snap-Fastener Plier) These fittings, popularly known as 'poppers', are sometimes fixed by means of an eyelet. In such cases, an Eyelet Closing Plier is used to secure them.

(*f*)   *'Patent' Eyelet Pliers*   *Fig. 2:99*

Two of these ingeniously designed tools are illustrated: one has spring-loaded jaws for closing the eyelet: the other has a punch and eyelet-closer combined in the same plier.

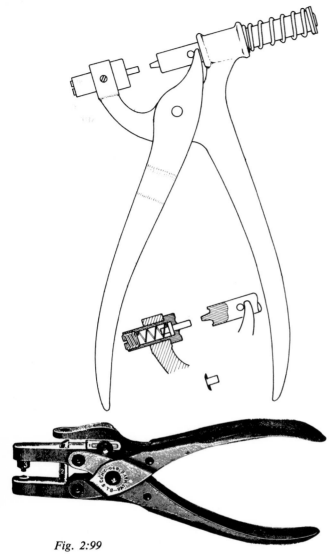

Fig. 2:99

is forced into the tail of the eyelet. When the handles of the plier are compressed, the eyelet is pushed out. An adjustable screw stop in the handle prevents the curved jaw from penetrating too far and distorting the leather.

Facing
Front edges of shoe quarters or boot legs on which the fastenings for laces or buttons are fixed. (See diagram of a boot in the introduction.)

Fasteners
Ever since shoes or sandals were first made, different means have been provided for opening the upper to let the foot pass easily into the shoe, and closing it again afterwards to hold the foot firmly and comfortably. These include laces, buckles, buttons, hooks, and in modern times, zip fasteners (see *Button Tools*; *Eyelet Tools*; *Lace Making Tools*).

In discussing the relative merits of fastenings J. H. Thornton (1970, p. 57) writes:

'There are, of course, other ways of fastening shoes such as hooks and eyes, press-studs, interlaced loops and zip-fasteners, all of which are capable of utility . . . Their drawback generally is that they have no latitude, that is to say they can only be fixed in a predetermined position and cannot be adapted easily for different size feet; buttons suffer from the same defect. Laces and buckles, therefore, retain their popularity for sound utilitarian reasons just as screw-down water taps and simple wooden lever latches on gates survive in spite of numerous "improved" inventions intended to replace them.'

Feather *Fig. 2:5 (p. 29)*
The verb 'to feather-edge' means to pare down a piece of wood or other material to a thin edge. In shoemaking the verb 'skive' is used for this operation: see *Skive*. The term 'feather' is used for the shoulder (or rebate) that is cut on the edge of the insole; the term is also used rather loosely for the boundary between the upper and the welt.

Fiddler: see under *Glazer and Sleeking Iron*.

File, Shoemaker's
Files are one of the abrading tools used in the process of trimming and finishing. They vary in length from 3–12 in. (7.6–30.5 cm). Other abrading tools will be found under: *Knife, Buffing (and Scrapers)*; *Peg-Fitting Tools*; *Rasp*; *Seat Breaker*.

(a) Shoe Files
Most of these are taken from the ordinary range of metal-working files. A possible exception is the

(g) Hand-operated machine for fitting Eyelets and Press Buttons Figs 2:27, 2:49 (pp. 53, 75)
There are many of these lever-operated machines. Some of them are fitted with revolving turrets that carry several sizes of eyelet bits and dies. Buck and Hickman (1935) illustrated nine varieties of this machine, all operated by hand-lever or treadle.

(h) Eyelet Extractor Fig. 2:48, No. 4416 (p. 74)
A plier designed for removing an eyelet. One jaw has a round hole at its tip which fits over the front of the eyelet; the other jaw, which is a tapered 'hawks-bill',

Waist File (or Waist Float) half round or flat, and up to 10 in. (25.4 cm) long; but, according to a London shoemaker, it is not used on the sole at the waist, but for shaping and finishing wooden heels for ladies' shoes. One use for the smooth, flat files is to polish the flush nail heads in the heel. A long double-cut file is used to roughen the sole before applying an adhesive.

(*b*) *Kit-Cutting Files Fig. 2:9 (p. 35)*
These are small files intended for shaping the Irons used in setting the edges of sole and heel, and for setting the seams of the uppers (see *Edge Irons* and *Seam Sett*).

This work is known as 'kit-cutting'. Leno (1895, p. 130) devotes five pages to this subject. We can judge the importance attached to the art by quoting his preliminary remarks on the subject:

'The art of kit-cutting is difficult to acquire, and necessitates, in those who practise it, a knowledge of the use of the tools to be operated upon. Tools cut by an incompetent person are practically of little or no value, and per contra, those set by a person who has mastered the art are positive treasures. Who that has ever worked on a shoemaker's bench will fail to confess the heart-burnings and disappointments resulting from ill-set kit? The kit itself may be all that kit need to be, well tempered, shaped, and having its proper bearing; but all these go for little if they are improperly cut. . . . To be a first-class workman it is necessary that he who aims so high should be able to cut his own kit.'

(*c*) *Rand File* (R. Timmins, *c.* 1800: Ran File; Hasluck, 1898: Welt File; Ross Moyer, USA, 1884, and Barnsley, 1927: Rhan File.) *Figs 2:100; 2:10, No. 2930/31; 2:21, No. 22 (pp. 36, 47)*
A curved, knife-shaped file *c.* 7½ in. (19 cm) overall including the handle, with float-cut or file-cut teeth on one side, but 'safe' (i.e. uncut) on the other. It is used for the trimming and levelling-up of the edge of the sole around the seat of the heel. The safe edge prevents damage to the upper.

For the sequence of operations see *Seat Breaker* and also *Rand Tools*.

A Rand File combined with a Welt-Trimming Knife is described under *Knife Welt*.

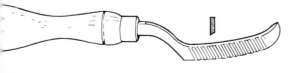

Fig. 2:100

(*d*) *Back Rand File* (Devlin, 1890: Back File) *Fig. 2:11, No. 918 (p. 37)*
Illustrated by Richard Timmins (*c.* 1800), this appears similar to the Rand File except that it is file-cut instead of float-cut, and the tip of the tool is slightly hooked. In the catalogue of Ross Moyer (USA, 1884, p. 181, fig. 379) this hook is more pronounced and the caption reads 'Rhan File, with Hooks, cast steel'. The purpose of this hook is not known.

The significance of the word Back in this context is uncertain, but the operation as described by Devlin (1890, p. 53) appears to give it the same purpose as the Rand File: 'In preparing the seat for the iron [i.e. Edge Iron] the back-file is run along behind against the upper and seat stitch, the leather then pared square, next rasped, and then glassed and scraped.' A London shoemaker (Glasow, 1978) thinks it may have been used also for levelling and cleaning up the breast of the heel.

(*e*) *Seat File Fig. 2:101*
An oval-shaped blade, file-cut on both sides, but with a safe bevel on the edge; *c.* 8 in. (20.3 cm) long overall. Its purpose is the same as that of the Rand Files.

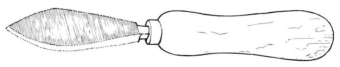

Fig. 2:101

Finger Leather: see *Hand and Finger Protectors.*

Finishing Tools and Materials

(*a*) *Tools*
Great importance was attached to the finishing in the making of boots and shoes (see introduction to this section). A high proportion of the shoemaker's tools are devoted to finishing; they include the following: *Bones and Sticks; Bunking Tools; Closer's Welt Plough; Crow Wheel; Dummy: see Glazer and Sleeking Iron; Edge Irons; Edge Plane; Files, shoemaker's; Forepart Fudge-Wheel Iron; Fudge Wheel; Glazer and Sleeking Iron; Heel Shave; Knives, including: Knife, Breasting; Knife, Buffing (and Scrapers); Knife, Drag; Knife, Welt; Peg-Fitting Tools; Stitch Prick; Rasp; Scraper: see Knife, Buffing; Seat Breaker; Seat Wheel; Striper; Welt Tools.*

(b) Finishing materials

Today the finishing process is mechanised and ready-mixed finishing materials are used. But until quite recently, grindery catalogues described stains, burnishing inks, waxes, varnishes and polishes, with instructions for their making-up in the workshop. Leno (1895) describes over fifty home-made preparations for improving the appearance of boots and shoes. The recipes include materials (often measured in 'penny-worths') such as: logwood chips, lamp-black, sweet oils, Bismarck brown, Burgundy pitch, burnt ivory, linseed oil, candied sugar, or juice of goat's thorn shrub. Diderot (c. 1760) gives some idea of the labour involved at that time:

'The bootmaker must choose for this operation a paved, tiled or cobbled place, where one is not afraid of fire, or place it under some large chimney; he attaches in the place that he judges most convenient, a chain which hangs down to 10 in. from the arch or thereabouts.

'He has besides him a saucepan in an oven, or on a small stove full of embers, which contains the material for blacking. This is made from one pound of yellow wax, two pounds of colophony which is pine resin, and lamp-black as wished; he lets all these materials melt together.

'He takes the boots that he has decided to wax (or black) but since one puts on the forefoot a different blacking from that put on the boot leg, he first attaches several pieces of leather to separate the forefoot from the boot leg, so that the blacking on the leg does not reach it.... He then takes the *waxing rod* which is iron with a wooden handle on the end, he puts it into a round ring which is on the end of the chain, then he drives it into the heel of the boot far enough to hold it well.

'After having thus prepared everything, he sits opposite the chain, supporting the boot tree horizontally with both hands, he lights some straw which he then holds under the boot leg to singe it i.e. to burn off the rest of the leather fluff which the rasp has failed to remove. He then takes the "*Gipon*" (this is what they call a collection of cloth rags) and he soaks it in the boiling blacking wax, he then smears it all over the boot leg; then constantly turning to and fro the boot tree in his hands over the straw fire which he keeps going all the time, having previously made a stock of straw by his side which is necessary to him for this operation. The heat of the fire penetrates the blacking wax, and he has great need to water at times the boot leg, for fear it will be burnt. It is usually necessary to take two hours to black one pair of boots. The bootleg being blacked, he lets it cool down.'

(c) Note on Waxes

(1) Beeswax (Cobbler's wax; Shoemaker's wax)
Beeswax, either pure or combined with other ingredients, was one of the traditional materials used by shoemakers. An important use was in the waxing of sewing threads; this consolidates the fibres, and helps to fill the awl holes made previously to take the threads (see *Sewing and Stitching*). Leno (1895) gives a recipe for a shoemaker's wax for similar purposes: 'equal quantities of pitch and resin with 10% of tallow'.

Holme (1688) recommends keeping balls of wax in water during hot weather to make them 'so indifferent hard that they may be wrought with'. Hasluck gives the same advice in his textbook of 1898.

Beeswax was also an ingredient of boot polish, made with the addition of turpentine, and with soap added to emulsify the mixture in water. Today synthetic waxes are compounded to give the required shine, water resistance and flexibility.

(2) Heel Ball
A typical recipe for this material is: Melt 8 oz of beeswax and 1 oz of tallow, add 1 oz of gum-arabic, and then add lamp-black unless a white heel ball is required. A 'better recipe' is described as containing 2 lb of beeswax, 3 oz suet, 4 oz ivory black, 2 oz best gum-arabic and 2 oz of rock candy.

Heel Ball was used to obtain a high gloss on sole edges and heels. These were first smoothed and shaped, and the Heel Ball was then spread with a heated Edge Iron or Glazer.

One of the best known makers of Heel Ball was Messrs Francis Ullathorne of London, who also supplied this material for rubbing monumental brasses.

Fit-Fang
Scots term for *Footstrap*.

Fitters Plough (Strip Awl) *Fig. 2:53, No. 6104 (p. 79)*
A blade like a nail claw, sharpened in the cleft and set in a wooden handle. It is said to have been used for trimming the edge of leather uppers. (See also *Closer's Welt Plough, Edge Shave*.)

Fitting Board
Listed by Devlin (1839) under 'Kit of the woman's man, price 4d'. Not identified but possibly a board on which to cut leather (see *Cutting Board*).

Fittings
A name given to pieces of leather (or other material) fixed to a last to alter its shape (see *Last*).

Flesh Side

The inner surface of a piece of leather, originally next to the animal's body. The outer surface is called the grain side (see *Grain*).

Foot: see *Cobbler's Foot*.

Foot Appliances

A name given to a large group of appliances made to fit inside a shoe to give added comfort. They include a variety of metal supports for the arch of the foot; grips to prevent the heel rising out of the shoe; heel cushions or pads to relieve 'foot jar' etc.

Foot Measurer: see *Measuring Tools*.

Foot Strap: see *Stirrup*.

Forepart *Fig. 2:3 (p. 28)*

The front of the shoe (or its sole or insole).

Forepart Fudge Wheel Iron

A name given by Barnsley (1890) to a tool like a plain Double Edge Iron, but with one of its guards detachable. Probably used to finish the edge of the welt after using the *Fudge Wheel*. Why one shoulder is detachable is not clear.

Forme

A name given to a type of paper pattern used in the process of pattern cutting.

French Chalk

A talc powder used in many trades as a dry lubricant, or to prevent adhesion. In the boot and shoe trade it is sprinkled between layers of leather (or lining) in the sole to prevent squeaking; sprinkled over the last to facilitate its removal; or dusted over the foot (or mould) when taking an impression of the foot, e.g. when measuring for a surgical boot.

French chalk is also sprinkled on leather to keep it clean: e.g. on the surface of the insole which is in contact with the last during the making process. The powder is dispensed from a dredger, usually of boxwood and made like a sugar sifter.

Fudge Wheel (Welting Wheel. The Boot Rand Wheel and Wheel Jigger, illustrated by Richard Timmins *c.* 1800, may be Fudges. The origin of the term 'fudge' is obscure; it may have been applied to this tool because it can be used to 'fake up' the welt to appear stitched.) *Fig. 2:102*
(See also *Bunking Wheel*; *Stitch Prick*; *Rand Tools* and *Seat Wheel*.)

A serrated wheel in the shape of a cylinder or a trun-

cated cone, set to revolve on a steel shank which is sometimes 'bent', and provided with a wooden handle, usually turned. The size overall is $5\frac{1}{2}$–6 in. (13.9–15.2 cm) and the wheels are cut with from eight to eighteen teeth per inch (2.5 cm). The width of the wheel varies, the narrowest has the most teeth and is used for the narrowest welts. The cone-shaped wheel allows it to be run closer to the upper.

One purpose of this tool is to imitate a hand-stitched welt; another is to tighten the stitches on the welt (instead of using a *Stitch Prick*) and to give them a regular and neat appearance. The earlier wheels had V-shaped teeth (instead of a more rounded shape) and this was done to imitate the impression made when using a Stitch Prick.

Hasluck (1898, p. 59) suggests that, 'As the stitch is wanted to show up boldly on the welt, the fudge wheel should be run round it before stitching is commenced. This wheel makes an impression on the leather resembling stitching and the real stitching will appear regular if the awl is put through exactly in the wheel marks.' Fudge Wheels are used hot, but not hot enough to damage the welt and stitches. A shoemaker (Mr W. B. Glasow, 1974) wrote: '. . . some Masters would not allow a Fudge to be used for their work, as when applied too hot it was said to overheat the upper in the region of the welt. They insisted on the use of a Prick Stitch instead.'

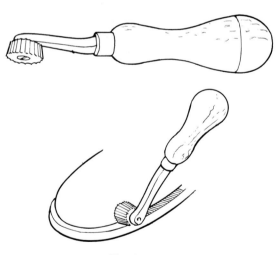

Fig. 2:102

Variants include:

(*a*) *Fudge with Changeable Wheels* *Fig. 2:103*
This model has the same appearance as the normal tool, but has a holding device at the head which per-

mits a change of wheel. A set of wheels of differing teeth are kept in the handle, which is hollowed out for this purpose.

Fig. 2:103

(*b*) *Welting Wheel*
Listed by Richter (*c.* 1910) and Barnsley (1927) this appears to be an ordinary Fudge Wheel. It is not certain whether its purpose differs from that of the Fudge.

(*c*) *Rand Wheel*
There is no mention of a Fudge in Devlin's list of the 'Kit of the boot-man' (1839, p. 113), but in the text (pp. 90–1) he writes of the 'Rand Wheel' being applied to a stitched rand, which, it may be inferred, is a sort of welt. He writes of the stitches 'being cleaned off from the wax, first with the rand-bone. ...The divisions were next made more perfect by the single *rand pricker* then in use (the forerunner of our present rand-wheel)', from which it may perhaps be presumed that the Rand Wheel was a forerunner of our modern Fudge Wheel. There may, however, be some connection here with the *Seat Wheel*, because rands were also sewn into the seat (see *Rand Tools*).

(*d*) Richard Timmins illustrates the following wheels (*c.* 1800, pp. 25–6):

(i) *Boot Rand Wheel Figs 2:10, No. 2965; 2:11, No. 2278 (pp. 36–7)*
A fudge-like wheel on a short straight shank, with a shallow lip (guard) to bear, presumably, on the edge of the rand or welt.

(ii) *Wheel Jigger Figs 2:10, No. 2967; 2:11, No. 2279 (pp. 36–7)*
As (i) above, but the wheel is mounted on a bent shank.

(iii) *French Rand Wheel Fig. 2:10, Nos 3080–4 (p. 36)*
Similar to (i) above, but the wheels appear to have cross-hatched indentations; one of the five examples illustrated has no lip, and another is mounted on what appears to be an all-wood handle which is almost certainly a *Seat Wheel* and contains a pocket for an extra wheel.

Furniture, Workshop: see *Bench and Seat*; and list under *Equipment*.

Garnet
One of the abrasive substances spread on a backing of paper or cloth. It is used as an abrasive for leather (see *Abrasives*).

Gauge: see *Measuring Tools*.

Gemming
A trade name for the process of making a canvas reinforcement to strengthen a thin cheap insole.

Glass Plate
A piece of plate glass used by closers and others on which to place leather when paring down the edges.

Glazer and Sleeking Iron (Burnishing Iron; Glazing Iron; Heel Slicker; Slick or Slicker; Scots: Bruiser. The term 'glassing' or 'glazing' is also applied to polishing operations in the leather-finishing process performed on Glassing or Glazing machines; one of them, a hand-operated roller, is known as a Hand Jigger.)
(See also *Bones and Sticks*; *Rubbing Down and Sleeking Tools* (list of); *Sleeker* under LEATHER MANUFACTURE, II. Currier's Tools; *Edge Tools*.)

A group of iron tools, used hot after applying wax, inks, Heel Ball or special polishes, for giving a lustre to the surface of the leather, especially to the soles and heels. Though some of the tools illustrated below appear very different from each other, many of them are interchangeable.

1. GLAZING IRON (Dummy Glazer; USA: Heel Slicker)
A beak-headed iron tool, mounted on a wooden handle, usually of the square 'kit' type, *c.* 6 in. (15.2 cm) long overall. Variants include:

(*a*) *Plain type Fig. 2:104*
With single beak.

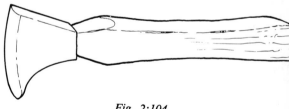

Fig. 2:104

(*b*) *Stepped or Cut-Down type Fig. 2:50, No. 6026 (p. 76)*
The 'step' fits over the welt or sole-edge.

(*c*) *French type Fig. 2:50, No. 6030 (p. 76)*
Barnsley (1927) illustrates this pattern with a short beak, but Marcel Joseph (*c.* 1920) illustrates eight

variants, most of which have a more pronounced beak than the English version. All are stepped, as (*b*) above.

(*d*) *Long Beak type Fig. 2:50, No. 6032 (p. 76)*

(*e*) *Combination type Fig. 2:105*
A stepped type Glazing Iron with the addition of a side-piece which can be used as an *Edge Iron.*

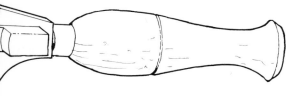

Fig. 2:105

(*f*) *Corrugated type Fig. 2:106*
American tool makers (e.g. Ross Moyer, USA, 1884) illustrate Glazing Irons ('Heel Slickers') with corrugations on the face. Enquiries in America and in this country have failed to explain the purpose of these corrugations; but it is thought that the grooves may have been intended to collect and hold the melted Heel Ball. A different explanation is offered by a Norwich shoemaker, Mr R. C. Pond (1976):

'The corrugated Glazing Heel Iron, I believe, but I am not certain, was used to finish tall heels on riding boots (Cowboy Type). The lifts were left proud at intervals and grooves made for the corrugated glazing iron. This was before spur boxes were introduced.

'An old boot with spur attached hung in my Father's workshop and his Father had it before him. We all admired the workmanship and the fancy coloured hand stitched pattern on the leg. It was a straight, fitting either foot. I remember my Father saying that the idea of the heel grooves was to stop the spur from slipping.'

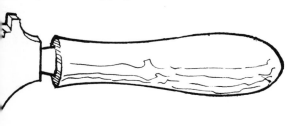

Fig. 2:106

(*g*) *Upper Glazer Fig. 2:107*
Carrot-shaped, and used presumably for glazing uppers.

Fig. 2:107

2. BOTTOM GLAZERS (Waist Burnisher; Sleeker) *Fig. 2:108*
Two-handed tools, with iron bodies of various shapes, and turned wooden handles, *c.* 14–16 in. (35.5–40.6 cm) long overall. They are intended for similar work to the Glazing Irons, but the use of two hands enables greater pressure to be exerted. They are used mainly for glazing soles and heels.

Fig. 2:108

Variants include:

(*a*) *Straight-Bodied Glazer Fig. 2:109a*
Half-round or oval in cross-section and of uniform width. They are often made from an old half-round file, with the teeth beaten smooth, and with a tang added at the other end in order to provide for two handles.

(*b*) *Fusiform Glazer Fig. 2:109b*
Similar to (*a*) above, but with a cigar-shaped body.

(*c*) *Egg-shaped Glazer Fig. 2:51, No. 6154 (p. 77)*
This has handles attached to the ends of an egg-shaped body, for dealing with curved surfaces.

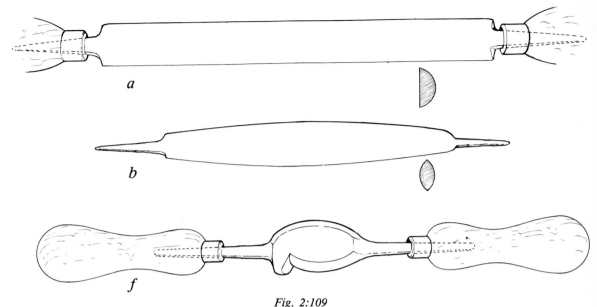

a

b

f

Fig. 2:109

(*d*) *Fish-Tail Glazer* Fig. 2:51, No. 6156 (p. 77)
A shallow V-shaped body, presumably so shaped to enable the same tool to deal with straight or curved work including the odd corner.

(*e*) *Bosher* (The origin of this name is not known.) Wedge-shaped in cross-section and probably used mainly as a burnisher for clogs (see *Bosher* in the CLOG MAKER section).

(*f*) *Dummy or Heel Glazer* (Heel Dummy) *Figs 2:109f; 2:110*
A solid body, roughly oval or occasionally round, with flat sides, and with a step or shoulder on one side. Made in three sizes for men, and in four for women.

This curiously shaped tool is designed to glaze the concave sides of a heel: the belly of the tool fits the curve. The shoulder can be used to set the edge of the top-piece as an alternative to the use of a Top Piece Iron (see under *Edge Iron*).

(*g*) *Wurtemberg Heel Glazer* (Curved Dummy)
A name given to a two-handed glazer with a sharply curved body, for glazing a Wurtemberg heel (see *Heel*).

3. FIDDLER (Strip Burnisher; Tiddler; Tiddling Iron; Tickler; Waist Burnisher) *Fig. 2:111*
A metal blade mounted in a handle, *c*. 8 in. (20.3 cm) overall. The blade is a very flat half-round in cross-section and curves slightly towards the tip. It is used, after warming, for applying a wax, e.g. Heel Ball, for glazing the heel-breast, waist and seat corners, and for general touching up.

Some makers use a blunt knife or strip of metal for the same purpose (see *Knife, Dull*).

Fig. 2:111

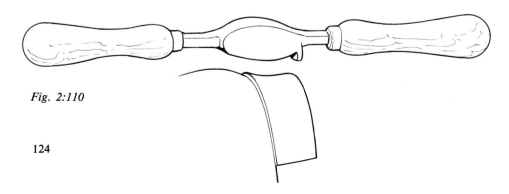

Fig. 2:110

Fig. 2:112

4.   S L E E K I N G   I R O N (Slick Iron; Sleeker; Slicker; Treeing Iron)   *Fig. 2:112*
A name given to two-handed glazing tools of various shapes, including the one illustrated. Other types have a heavier block-like body with concave surfaces.

These irons are used hot on the uppers of the finished boot, for smoothing and removing wrinkles and, after the application of a dressing, for polishing. This can be done on a 'Treeing Machine' which holds the shoes on their trees, extended horizontally for the operator to work on conveniently. Gresham (1920, Vol. III, p. 267) writes:

'A steel sleeker is the best tool for the purpose of sleeking, and much superior to either bone or wood. It is light to handle, and with it the operator can reach the edges of the upper without risk of damaging the welts and stitches.'

5.   C O Z E R
The term appears in a list of tools required for a repairer in Gresham (1920, Vol. IV, p. 22) where it is called a 'double-handled cozer'. 'Cozier' is an obsolete word for cobbler, from 'coser' (French *coudre*) to sew. The tool is most probably a Sleeking Iron.

Grader: see *Measuring Tools.*

Graft
A term used by shoe repairers for a new piece which is grafted to a sole. The edge of the graft is cut at an angle so that the new piece overlaps the old. (The same term is applied to the replacement of the rotted foot of a door post.)

Grain
The outer surface of a piece of leather originally bearing the hair, fur or wool. Each animal has a characteristic grain pattern. Soles usually have the grain side downwards resting on the ground; insoles usually have the grain side upwards so that the foot rests on it. Uppers normally have the grain side outwards except for suedes (see *Flesh Side*).

Grindery (An alternative term is 'Finding', used mainly in the USA and meaning 'supply' or 'provisions'.)

Grindery is a name commonly given to the materials, tools and appliances used by shoemakers (and often by other workers in leather) and extended to the shop or warehouse where these goods can be bought. The term may relate to the knife-grinding services at these establishments.

Pocock Brothers Ltd (incorporating Ullathorne & Co.), Leather and Grindery Merchants of London, in their catalogue of *c.* 1930 list their goods under the following headings: Sole leather; Dressed leather; Mercery (Buttons, Buckles, Laces, etc.); Shoe polishes, cleaners, etc.; Grindery (Nails, Rivets, Toe & Heel Plates, etc.); Thread (Hemp, Linen, Wax, etc.); Tools; Lasts, Jacks, Trees, and Stretchers; Finishing Requisites (Inks, Stains, Abrasives, Heel Ball & Waxes, etc.).

Hammer Rasp: see *Rivet Driver.*

Hammer, Shoemaker's *Figs 2:40–2:43*. Earlier examples: *Figs 2:7; 2:29 (pp. 33, 55, 66–9)*
For other hammering tools used by shoemakers see: *Closer's Hammer; Lasting Pincers; Nail Gun; Rasp; Rivet Driver; Welt Beater* under *Beater.*

1.   D E S C R I P T I O N
Ordinary Shoe Hammers have a mushroom-shaped face, and a flat cross pane. The handle is short — about 8 in. (20.3 cm) long. Some of these hammers are found with the face spread out beyond their original size by years of hammering. As one shoe repairer (William Martin, 1946) put it, 'my grandfather's hammer is my great favourite; its face has gone half-as-big again.'

2.   P U R P O S E
Shoemaker's Hammers are used for driving large nails, and for hammering damped sole and heel leather to consolidate it. Smaller nails were usually driven with a *Rasp* — a singular instance of one tool serving two quite different purposes (see *Rivet Driver*).

The method and purpose of hammering leather is described under *Lap Stone.*

The Shoemaker's Hammer is also used for the process known as paning or peening. This is done to the sole edge (both forepart and waist) and to leather heels, especially after repair. After damping, the leather is 'peened' with the pane end of the hammer

125

in a series of light blows to form a serrated surface, which is subsequently smoothed out with a rasp. The object is to case-harden the edges and the heel, and in the case of a repaired sole, the paning strokes are said to weld the new and old leather together. This process is also performed by the Cramping Hammer (see (i) below).

There must have been some doubts about the advisability of paning, as exemplified by the following paragraph from Devlin (1839, p. 40):

'The *edge* may then immediately be *pared*, without what is called *paning* – an old and injurious habit – and which means taking the pane, or upper part of the hammer, and striking with it along the forepart, so that the leather be marked with countless indentations – these indentations, in place of doing any service, only forcing the edge stitches from their natural places, together with portions of the welt and sole, which, in the wear, may start out and look very ugly. The best workmen, at present, never pane, except occasionally in the heel, or on being compelled by the narrowness of sole, and when it is necessary to make up the edge with a portion of the welt.'

Devlin's dislike of paning may perhaps be compared to the scorn expressed by craftsmen for the 'bodgers' who fill up the gaps in a badly fitting dovetail joint by hammering over the ends of the pins, or who hammer over a hairline crack in an iron casting.

3.   HISTORICAL NOTE
Shoemaker's Hammers are included in the following paintings and engravings:

c. 1650 (Holland)	D. Tenier's painting of a shoemaker (Antwerp) does not show any hammer of the later shoe types, but there is a large claw-hammer on the bench; and lying on a beating-block, there is a heavier looking Beating Hammer (see (d) below).
c. 1650 (Holland)	G. Terborch, in his painting of a shoemaker (Amsterdam), includes a hammer of the type now known as the 'common shoemaker's pattern' (see (a) below).
c. 1760 (France)	Though it may be unsafe to draw any final conclusions from the encyclopaedias of this time, Diderot's illustration of a Shoemaker's Hammer is unlike any of the English or French Hammers described below; it has a flat top, vertical face, and a long pane which does not

turn up at its end. Garsault's Hammer (1767) is nearer to the French shape.

c. 1800 (England) Fig. 2:7	Shoe Hammers illustrated by Smith's 'Key' (1816) have the usual round face but the pane is slightly flared, and down-curved like an adze. A similar hammer illustrated by Richard Timmins (c. 1800–50) is called a 'Best Bright Super London Shoe Hammer' though it is quite unlike the London Pattern as it is known today (see (b) below). But like the example in Smith's Key, and apparently unlike the later patterns, there is a decorative chamfer cut on the top of the head immediately over the eye.

4.   VARIANTS AND SPECIAL TYPES OF SHOEMAKER'S HAMMERS INCLUDE THE FOLLOWING: *Figs 2:40–2:43.* For earlier examples see *Figs 2:7; 2:29. (pp. 33, 55, 66–9)*
(*Note*: The hammers most frequently encountered in the workshops are described under paragraphs (a) and (b).)

(*a*)   *The Common Shoe Hammer   Fig. 2:40, No. 3004 (p. 66)*
This has a large, round face, with a neck which is hexagonal or round in cross-section, straight flat cheeks, and a straight or slightly down-turned flat pane.
Sizes: 00, 0, 1–6. No. 0 size has a $3\frac{1}{2}$ in. (8.8 cm) head with $1\frac{3}{8}$ in. (3.5 cm) diameter face. No. 4 size has a 5 in. (12.7 cm) head with $1\frac{3}{4}$ in. (4.4 cm) diameter face.

(*b*)   *The London Pattern Shoe Hammer   Fig. 2:40, No. 3002 (p. 66)*
The same face and neck as (a) above, but the rather ungainly, down-turned, straight pane is slightly flared, and it usually has a chamfered neck. (But see also Historical Note above under c. 1800.)
Sizes: 000, 00, 0. 1–6. No. 0 size has a $2\frac{7}{8}$ in. (7.3 cm) head with $1\frac{1}{2}$ in. (3.8 cm) diameter face. No. 4 size has a $4\frac{3}{4}$ in. (12 cm) head with $1\frac{3}{4}$ in. (4.4 cm) diameter face.

(*c*)   *American Pattern Hammer* ('Boston' Hammer)
Listed by Wynn, Timmins & Co. (1892) as a 'Boston Hammer', this appears to be the same as the English Common Pattern (see (a) above), except that it is finished bright.
    Some other American Shoemaker's Hammers are described under (j) below.

(*d*)   *Beating Hammer   Fig. 2:42, No. 3028 (p. 68)*
A heavy maul-like head, with one face round, and

the other almost rectangular. Used for beating soles to consolidate the leather (see under '2. Purpose' above). A similar hammer, shown lying on a beating-block, appears in the painting of a shoemaker by G. Terborch (Amsterdam, c. 1650).

A London shoemaker of Polish origin (1975) gave the name Crispin to a Double-Faced Hammer, and said that the two faces symbolised the heads of St Crispin and his brother Crispianus (see (*j*) *Crispin Hammer* below).

(*e*) *Boston Hammer*: see (*c*) above.

(*f*) *Clogger's Hammers*
(See also the CLOG MAKER section.)

(1) Clogger's Tacking Hammer. *Fig. 2:41, No. 3022 (p. 67)*. A light head with round face and a long pane ending with a claw. Used for tacking the upper to the wooden sole.

(2) Clogger's Ironing Hammer. *Fig. 2:41, No. 3020 (p. 67)*. Heavier than (1), with a round face and wedge-shaped pane. Used for nailing the irons to the sole.

(*ff*) *Closer's Hammer*: see separate entry.

(*g*) *Common Hammer*: see (*a*) above.

(*h*) *Cordwainer's Hammer Fig. 2:42, No. 3032 (p. 68)*
Illustrated by Barnsley (1927), this has a heavy head, a round knurled face and a down-turned pane. According to Mr George Barnsley it was used mainly in Canada and the USA. (See also (*j*) *Crispin Hammer* below.)

(*i*) *Cramping Hammer* (Cramp Hammer; Heeling Hammer; Waist Hammer) *Fig. 2:40, No. 3012 (p. 66)*
A round face, sometimes slightly convex, with a T-shaped pane at the end of a long narrow down-curving neck. Barnsley (1890) lists six sizes: The length of head in Size No. 1 is about 5 in. (12.7 cm) from the face to the pane end.

The original purpose of this hammer is uncertain, and perhaps not entirely clarified by Devlin's comment under a paragraph headed 'Kit of the woman's man' (1839, p. 115): 'Besides these there are many other pieces of kit now falling into disuse in consequence of the work going out of fashion, such, for instance, as the long-necked cramp-hammer, once necessary to the cramping in the sole at the heel of the high-heeled woman's shoe, the purpose of which is scarcely known to the majority of the present race of workmen.' (But see also *French and German Hammers* below.)

Today, the Cramping Hammer is used for paning

the sole edge, heel breast, and waists. In this work it has an advantage over the ordinary Shoemaker's Hammer, for its long neck prevents the handle from coming in contact with the heel. (See also *French Hammer* below.) Hasluck (1898, p. 22) describes the operation:

'Then hammer each side of the waist with the peen end of the waist or cramp hammer; this will knock the edge of the waist over, to cover the stitch, and also make it lie closer to the upper. This process will leave marks, but a second row of taps, made with the peen of the hammer held so that these lines shall cross the others, will make the edge more even, and also very firm at the side of the stitches. The waist can now be hammered along each side with the face of the hammer, and with the knife nicely trim each side to make it round and even.'

(See Devlin's objection to this process under 'Purpose' of main entry above.)

Another use of the tool was noted at Messrs John Lobb (1977), where makers were taking advantage of its long neck to drive nails into the heel from the inside of the shoe.

(*j*) *Crispin Hammer* (USA: Knights of Labor Hammer) *Fig. 2:41, No. 3016 (p. 67)*
This hammer is listed by Barnsley in the catalogues of 1890 and 1927. It has a heavy head with square cheeks, a knurled face, and a curiously shaped pane which ends in a flat, almost rectangular face.

An American version of what appears to be the same hammer is illustrated in the catalogue of Ross Moyer (1884, p. 173). It is named 'Knights of Labor Hammer' after the Association of Trade Unions of that name founded in Philadelphia in 1869. The hammer is inscribed 'Patented Mch 21 1871. July 2 1872'. On the same page there is a hammer named Crispin which is similar to that which Barnsley (1927) calls a *Cordwainer's Hammer* (see above). It is inscribed with the same patent number as the Knights of Labor Hammer. On the other hand, the same Hammer illustrated in the catalogue of the United Shoe Machinery Corporation (USA 1929) is called a *Lasting Hammer* and the caption reads, 'These hammers were originally designed for use by operators during the lasting operation, but have since been found very useful for general work throughout the shoe repairing shops. Furnished with either rough or smooth face.'

The purpose of these romantically named hammers is not clear, but Mr George Barnsley wrote (1975) that they were used mainly in the USA and Canada, and were probably used for 'driving in heavy shoe-nails – rarely called for today'.

(*k*) *Double-Faced Shoe Hammer* (Double-Faced Riveter's Hammer) *Fig. 2:27 (p. 53)*
Made in heavy sizes, this has round faces of unequal size, the larger one flat, the other often slightly domed. Used for general purposes, including the beating of sole leather and, judging by its occasional alternative name, for driving rivets. (See also *Beating Hammer* and *Crispin Hammer* above.)

(*l*) *Flounder Hammer*
A tool used in the process of blocking, but whether it is in fact a hammer is not certain. (See *Blocking Tools.*)

(*m*) *French and German Hammers*
These imported hammers are often encountered in the workshops. They are preferred by some makers, perhaps because of their long heads which enabled the user to drive nails into the heel from inside the shoe. They may be distinguished as follows:

(1) *'French' Pattern Figs 2:43, No. 3036; 2:8, No. D88 (pp. 69, 34)*
This has the typical 'continental' hump-backed head which curves gracefully down from the eye to the face on one side, and from the eye to a flat, slightly flared, pane on the other. In most cases, this pane is turned upwards at its extremity. The face, instead of being vertical as in the case of the English shoe hammer, is often tilted downwards by a few degrees. This may be helpful to the user when working seated; for with the arm held close to one's side, the tilt on the head avoids having to bend the wrist downwards to bring the face horizontal as it strikes the work. A variant has its head secured by straps, known as *languets*.

A retired London maker (W. B. Glasow, 1978) wrote that, like the Cramping Hammer, the French Hammer 'would also be used for peening, especially where the sole fits under the "breast" of a ladies' wood-heel shoe. I also used a peen for beating the bevelled waist of a shoe to get the bevel close to the upper while the sole is still damp (after Stitching).' (See also *Cramping Hammer* above.)

(2) *'German' Pattern Fig. 2:43, No. 3038 (p. 69)*
Like the French pattern, this has a long head, down-turned on both sides of the eye. But the plane is straight and not turned up at its extremity.

Note: The above descriptions of the French and German shoemaker's hammers are taken from examples seen in English workshops, and from engravings in the catalogues of English tool makers. But continental tool-maker's catalogues sometimes tell a different story. For example, the catalogue of Stahlschmidt Tool Co. (1911, p. 178), while showing typical German and French patterns (as we have described them), then proceeds to label a typical French Hammer as 'German Pattern'. This is not an isolated example, for the German tool makers, Ludvig Schmidt, illustrated only one type of Shoe Hammer in their catalogue (c. 1890) and this is the French pattern with a strapped head. And some confusion between the French and German types has been noted in other European catalogues.

(*n*) *Knights of Labor Hammer*: see (*j*) above.

(*o*) *Pegging Hammer*
A heavy, double-faced head shaped like a small-sized sledge hammer. As illustrated by Ward and Payne (1911), it appears that one of the faces is flat and the other domed. Presumably used for pegging, but for what particular purpose is not clear.

(*p*) *Press Hammer Fig. 2:42, No. 3030 (p. 68)*
A light, long, straight head, with a round knurled face and a chisel-ended pane. Purpose unknown.

(*q*) *Riveting Hammer Fig. 2:41, No. 3014 (p. 67)*
Listed by Barnsley (1927), this has a round knurled face, a smooth neck, and a pane which tapers to a point. The pane is magnetised so that a rivet can be picked up by its head, tapped in position, and then struck with the face.

(*r*) *Sizing Hammer*
A name given to a Marking Hammer used for imprinting the shoe size on the sole of a boot or shoe. They are said to have been made in sets of five, with a different shoe size cut on each face.

(*s*) *Waist Hammer*
Under a list headed 'Kit of the boot-man', Devlin (1839) includes a 'smaller or waist hammer' which he prices at 1s 0d as compared with 1s 6d for a 'large hammer'. A London maker (Mr B. D. Chalwin, 1975) said he used a 'waist hammer' with a smaller-than-usual face for hammering the narrow waists of ladies' shoes. (See also *Cramping Hammer* above.)

(*t*) *Wood Heel Hammer Fig. 2:41, No. 3018 (p. 67)*
A long, narrow head, the underside straight from the hexagonal face to the square-ended pane. A long head is used to drive nails into the heel from the inside of the shoe.

Hand and Finger Protectors (Hand Leathers)

(*a*) *Hand Leather* (Shoemaker's Mitten)
Devlin (1839, p. 23) writes that the *'hand-leather* is

called in France the *gant royale*, in honour, I suppose, of Prince Crispin ...'

A piece of leather, often made from an old leather glove with the fingers removed, worn when sewing to protect the hand. When purpose-made, a piece of leather about 10 × 3 in. (25.4 × 7.6 cm) is laced together at its ends, and a hole made in the side for the thumb.

Devlin (1839, p. 33) describes its use as follows:

'In sewing, the hand-leather is generally brought into use; it forms a safeguard for the back or tender part of the left hand, being held on by a hole through which the left thumb is passed, and fastened by a few stitches on the inner or palm side of the hand. In all strong work it is of very great service, keeping the thread from chafing the skin, for the thread in being twisted round this on the one side, and round the neck of the awl on the other, is rendered harmless when applying the necessary force in getting the stitch firmly drawn in.'

Hand and Finger Leathers are mentioned in two sixteenth-century works: see *Saint Hugh's Bones.*

(b)   Thumb-Leather (Thumb Stall)

These are small pieces of leather made to encircle the thumb and used for the same purpose as the Hand Leather (above). The OED quotes from Nashe *Martin's Months Minde* (1589), 'Farewell old shoes, thombe stall, and clouting lether'.

A similar device, called a Thimble, is used by sail makers; but it is made in metal or horn. The edges are turned up to prevent the thread slipping off.

(c)   Fingerstall

This is made by clickers for their own use from a small piece of waste leather. It is worn on the index finger to prevent it becoming sore from being pressed continually on the back of the Clicker's Knife.

(d)   Knife Binding (Knife cover)   Fig. 2:113; 2:6, Diderot Fig. 6 (p. 31)

A common method of avoiding sore fingers, from the continuous use of shoe knives, is to bind the part of the blade on which the finger presses with a ribbon of leather. This binding is often seen on Shoe Knives at the foot of the blade; and on Clicker's Knives, around the blade almost as far as the point. Diderot (*c.* 1760 *Cordonnier*) illustrates a Shoe Knife bound in this way.

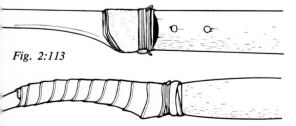

Fig. 2:113

Handles

Many of the handles fitted to shoemaking tools are different from those used in other trades. They are described and illustrated under the following entries: *Awls*; *Edge Irons*; *Knife.*

Heater (Finisher's Lamp; Lamp; Spirit Lamp)

Many of the tools used in the finishing process, including *Edge Irons*, *Glazers* and *Fudge Wheels*, are warmed before use. An open fire once served for this purpose, but this tended to produce a dirty iron with a burnt handle.

Heating methods to be found in the workshops include:

(a)   Candle   Fig. 2:114

In the older and smaller shops a candle end is often used, held by three nails driven into the bench.

Fig. 2:114

(b)   Spirit lamp   Fig. 2:115

Hasluck (1898, p. 137) recommends a 'sixpenny spirit-lamp' with stand.

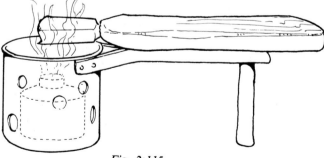

Fig. 2:115

(c)   Gas

Barnsley (1927) illustrates a 'Finishers Automatic Gas Lamp'. The hot plate or ring is pivoted so that when the tool is taken off the ring, a counterweight falls and turns off the gas.

Heel *Fig. 2:116*
The heel is attached to the rear end (or 'seat') of the sole to protect it from wear at the back, and also to give a fashionable and attractive look. An earlier purpose of the heel may have been to hold the foot more firmly in the stirrup when on horseback. The heel may consist of separate leather 'lifts' (known as

Fig. 2:116 Typical Heel Shapes
(*a*) Cuban heel. (*b*) Louis heel. (*c*) Military heel. (*d*) Square heel. (*e*) Wedge heel. (*f*) Wurtemburg heel.

a 'built or stacked heel') or of a block of wood or plastic covered with leather or other material. The bottom section of the heel, which rests on the ground, is called the 'top piece'.

There are many ways of attaching heels, from the all-but-disappearing stitch, to later methods of using nails, pegs, screws, or adhesives. When stitching, the awl, followed by the thread, is passed under the seat stitch (i.e. the stitch that holds the upper to the insole at the seat) and is then pushed forcibly up through the sole, and through the split lifts which form the substance of the heel. This is hard work for the maker; to ease the path of the awl the leather is first moistened and the awl is dipped in soap. (See *Awl, Heel*.)

The following are common heel shapes (*Fig. 2:116 opposite*):

(*a*) Cuban or Spanish heel
A fairly high but solid-looking heel, with a curved back and square breast.

(*b*) Louis heel
A high heel said to have been invented for Louis XIV of France (1643) to compensate for his shortness of stature; but according to Thornton (1970) it was in fact being worn before that time. However, it became fashionable throughout Europe and remains so to this day.

The term 'Louis' is applied today to several kinds of ladies' heel which have some or all of the following attributes: a gracefully curved 'hour-glass' waist, a flared top-piece, the heel breast covered by the rear part of the sole which is turned down over it. The *Oxford English Dictionary* (Supplement 1933) quotes from the *Daily Mail* of 1906: '. . . the Louis heel is regarded amongst women as a pedestal of superiority to be appropriated for personal adornment.'

Louis heels are usually made of wood, but covered with a thin coating of leather.

(*c*) Military heel
Similar to the Cuban but lower. It was probably developed for riding – as worn by cowboys in 'Western' films.

(*d*) Square heel
This is the ordinary heel with straight sides, as fitted to the majority of men's and children's shoes.

(*e*) Wedge heel
This appeared in Tudor times as a thickening of the sole at the heel-end. Today it is shaped like a wedge and fills up the whole space under the arch of the shoe.

(*f*) Wurtemberg heel (Pompadour heel)
This is shaped like a Louis heel, but it is usually built up of leather lifts instead of being made in wood.

Tools used when making up and fitting heels are described under the following entries: *Awl, Heel*; *Edge Irons* including Seat Iron; Top Piece Iron, Military Heel Iron; *Edge Plane*; *File, Shoemaker's* (Rand File; Back Rand File; Seat File); *Glazer and Sleeking Iron* (Dummy or Heel Glazer; Wurtemberg Heel Glazer); *Hammer, Shoemaker's* (see paning operation under 'Purpose'; Wood Heel Hammer); *Heel Making Machines*; *Heel Shave*; *Knife, Breasting*; *Knife, Buffing (and Scrapers)*; *Knife, Heel*; *Nail Gun*; *Seat Breaker*; *Seat Wheel*.

Heel Ball: see *Finishing Tools and Materials*.

Heel Making Machines
The following are typical examples of early machines operated by hand:

(*a*) Heel Cutter
A hand-operated machine for cutting heel lifts. Cutters of graduated sizes are hinged to a base, and the one selected is hinged over and forced down on the leather by blows from a wooden mallet.

A later version has a descending head, impelled by a flywheel, which drives a press knife through the leather.

(*b*) Heel Breaster
This resembles a small clog-sole maker's Stock Knife. Hinged to the bench at one end, the knife is forced downwards onto the breast of the heel to trim it.

(*c*) Heel Nailer
A head impelled by a flywheel which drives nails into the heel through the insole seat.

Heel Shave (Yankee Shave) *Figs 2:117; 2:27 (p. 53)*
An all-iron tool of spokeshave type measuring 8–9 in. (20.3–22.8 cm) overall, developed in America. The blade is curved (to produce a concave surface) and is made in different sweeps ranging from a shallow one for trimming the ordinary 'square' heel, to a sharply curved blade designed, for example, for the sides of a lady's Louis or Wurtemberg heel (see *Heel*). Barnsley list this tool with seven sweeps in their catalogue of 1890 and with twelve sweeps in their catalogue of 1927. Ross Moyer, the American toolmakers (1884), list fifteen different curvatures, of which two are listed as '1 pomp and 2 pomp'.

Metal spokeshaves designed for woodworking

have plane-type cutting irons, but the Heel Shave has a knife-shaped blade like that fitted to the ordinary wooden spokeshave, except that it is secured by set-screws instead of being tanged into the stock. The depth of cut is regulated by a swing-guard which is hinged at one end, but can be set by a screw at the other.

The purpose of this tool is to trim the sides of the heel. Some makers regard it as new fangled, if not debased, and declare that they do the job much better with a knife. But the intention was to make the work easier, particularly for the less skilled. Leno (1895, p. 208) writes that it requires some practice but 'when used by a trained hand there is little doubt [of its] superiority over the knife, rasp and etc.'

The trimming of the heel is done while the shoe is strapped on the knee. Some push the shave from them, others draw it towards them; the latter method has the advantage that the motion can be controlled by pressing the two thumbs on the heel.

The Heel Shave appears to have been developed in America in the second half of the nineteenth century. Whether it was at one time made of wood is not known. The saddler's and harness maker's spoke-shave, which is used to trim leather traces, is made in wood to this day.

Note: For another spokeshave-type of tool which some makers use on the heel see *Edge Plane*.

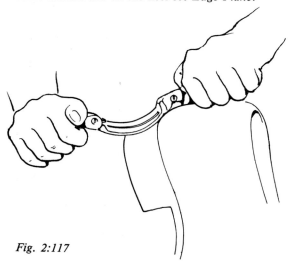

Fig. 2:117

Hessian Boot
Note: In the catalogue of Richard Timmins (*c.* 1800) the name Heisham or Heisian Sett is given to a tool probably used in making Hessian Boots (see *Seam Sett*).

A close-fitting top boot worn in the eighteenth century by troops in the German Grand Duchy of Hesse. They became fashionable in England during the reign of George III (1760–1820) and were still being worn in the mid-nineteenth century. Leno (1895, p. 10) describes them as 'perhaps the handsomest boot ever worn' — an opinion supported by Colonel Calverley of the Dragoon Guards, who sings in Gilbert and Sullivan's 'Patience' (1881):

When I first put this uniform on
I said as I looked in the glass
'It's one to a million that any civilian
My figure and form will surpass.
Gold lace has a charm for the fair
And I've plenty of that and to spare,
While a lover's professions
When uttered in Hessians
Are eloquent everywhere!'

A fact that I counted upon,
When I first put this uniform on!

When making the Hessian boot, the wrinkles on the instep, which in other top boots are smoothed out, were left as a form of decoration. The boots were worn with a tassle hanging from the front.

Holdfast   *Fig. 2:5 (p. 29)*
The ridge of leather left standing round the edge of the insole after feathering. (See also *Knife, Feathering*.)

Hollin or **Hollen Stick**: see *Bones and Sticks*.

Insole
The inside bottom part of a shoe on which the foot rests. It forms the foundation of the shoe to which the outside is attached. In a turnshoe (q.v.) the foot rests on the inner surface of the sole which also acts as an insole.

Knight (USA, 1877) mentions the use of cork for insoles and includes a verse from Athenaes (AD 200):
Suppose one's short, —
They put cork soles within the heels of her shoes.
(See also *Gemming*)

Iron: see *Edge Iron; Measuring Tools*.

Jack: see *Boot Jack*.

Jigger
A name given to devices and tools used in several different trades. It is applied to certain tools in the

shoe trade, mainly in its sense of moving a tool backwards and forwards.

The term will be found under the following entries: *Edge Iron*, Jigger Iron and Channel Jigger; *Fudge Wheel*, Wheel Jigger; *Jigger, Hand* in the section LEATHER MANUFACTURE, II. Currier's Tools.

Jockey: see *Boot Jockey.*

Joint Iron
Mentioned by Leno (1895, p. 84) when describing the making of heels. Possibly this tool is the same as one described by Hasluck (1898). (See Corner Beater under *Beater*.)

Key: see *Seam Sett.*

Kit
(See also *Saint Hugh's Bones*)
In the shoemaking trade the term 'kit' is often applied to the tools of the shoemaker. Tool makers, such as Barnsley (1890), appear to distinguish between 'Kit Tools' and 'Ordinary Shoe Tools'. The former include finishing tools, such as Edge Irons and Files; the latter include the more basic tools such as the knives, hammers, awls and pincers. But Devlin (1839, p. 17) writes that 'the tools of the shoemaker are in their collective form denominated his Kit'. He continues: 'Anciently, and in the old songs of the trade, they were called "St Hugh's bones", from a now almost forgotten, though somewhat pleasant tradition. In Stow, and in Randle Holme's *Academie*

of Armorie (1688), we find this term; as, also, in the still older romance of Crispin and Crispianus.' (See *St Hugh's Bones.*)
Note: The term 'Kit Stool' is sometimes given to the stool or bench on which a shoemaker or cobbler works. The tub used for steeping shoe leather is sometimes called a 'Water Kit'.

Knife

(*a*) *Historical Note* (See also *Knife, Paring*) Figs *2:1. 2:6 (pp. 18, 31) and 2:118*
Since the early use of metal some three to four thousand years ago, there have been two main kinds of knife used for cutting leather: a semi-circular knife (see *Knife, Half-Moon*) and the more conventional hand-knife, made like a modern table knife (see *Knife, Shoe*).

Egyptian paintings of c. 1450 BC and Greek carvings of c. 550 BC, both show shoemakers using knives of the 'half-moon' type. Why this particular design was preferred to the more conventional blade is something of a mystery; but there is evidence that by late medieval times the conventional blade became the more common tool, though the half-moon knife is still used to this day by saddlers and harness makers, who call it a Round Knife, and by makers of high boots.

Tenier's painting 'The Shoemaker' (c. 1650) shows a handled, conventional blade, rather like an English Clicking Knife, but larger; Diderot (c. 1760) illustrates both the half-moon and the conventional blades. In more recent times, the handled knife

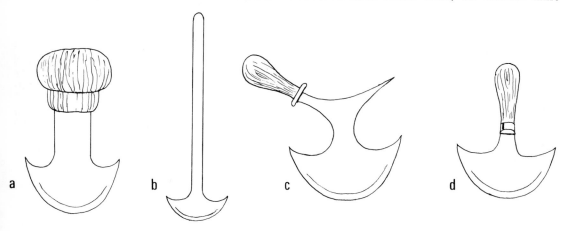

a   b   c   d

Fig. 2:118a Knives for cutting leather c. 1500 BC–AD 1950

Half-moon blades
(*a*) c. 1500 BC Egypt   } (After Petrie, 1917,
(*b*) c. AD 50 Europe   } Plate LXI)

(*c*) c. AD 1400 Europe (After Waterer, 1968, Plate 5)
(*d*) c. AD 1950 England (From author's collection)

(*continued overleaf*)

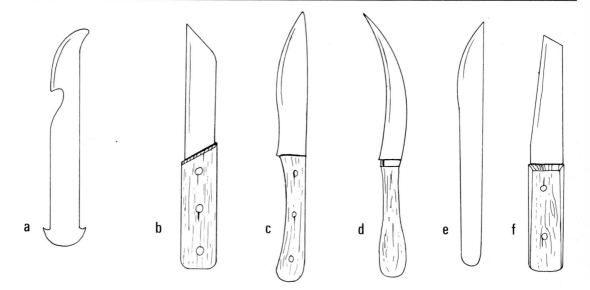

Fig. 2:118b Knives for cutting leather *c.* 1500 BC–AD 1950

Conventional blades

(*a*) *c.* 1500 BC Egypt. Foot of tool also cuts. (After Petrie, 1917, Plate LXIII)

(*b*) *c.* AD 50 Europe. (After Waterer, 1968, Plate 5)

(*c*) *c.* AD 1400 England. (After London Museum Med. Cat. 1940, Plate XIII)

(*d*) *c.* AD 1650 Belgium (From Northampton Museum Pictures, p. 59)

(*e*) *c.* AD 1950 continental Europe

(*f*) *c.* AD 1950 England

appears to be surviving only in England and America, while in continental Europe and elsewhere all-steel knives (known in England as Paring Knives or Tranchets) have become the shoemaker's general purpose knife. These all-steel knives are often curved longitudinally ('bowed') to facilitate paring and trimming operations. (See under *Knife, Shoe* and *Knife, Clicker's.*)

(b) Variants

Older shoemakers say that scissors should never be used in shoemaking, even when cutting thin upper leathers, cloth linings or paper patterns. They assert that the 'only true cut is made with a knife'. Perhaps this idea encouraged the tool makers to offer such a proliferation of types.

In the eighteenth century two, or at the most three, kinds of knife were sufficient; and this holds good today – at least among experienced makers. It is therefore surprising that in the late nineteenth century, few tools in the shoemaker's kit were made in so many different types and shapes as the knife. For instance, George Barnsley, the Sheffield tool makers, illustrated ninety-six different knives in their catalogue of 1890, and many of these knives were made in several different sizes and shapes. Fifty years later (in 1939) E. A. Berg, the Swedish tool makers, offered over sixty different knives listed under the names of the countries from which they sought orders. (Buyers liked the pattern they have grown accustomed to: today they have to put up with what the tool maker chooses to make.)

(c) *Classification of Shoemaking Knives*
When describing the many kinds of knife offered by the tool makers, the following general classification has been adopted:

Type	For examples, see:
1. *General Purpose Shoe Knives.* A blade of conventional shape, handled or all-steel, *c.* 8–9 in. (20.3–22.8 cm) overall. Can be used for nearly all shoe operations.	*Knife, Shoe* *Knife, Tranchet*
2. *Cutting out, or Clicker's Knives.* A narrow, pointed knife specially designed for cutting out the uppers, and also textile linings. Handled or all-steel.	*Knife, Clicker's* (See also *Knife, Half-Moon*)
3. *Paring Knives.* A knife with a broad cutting edge, specially designed for paring down leather to reduce its thickness ('skiving'). Often made to be pushed. Handled or all-steel.	*Knife, Paring*
4. *All steel 'Continental' Knives.* These knives are included under 1, 2 and 3 above.	
5. *Leather Cutter's Knives.* These are strong, handled, knives, often sickle-shaped, and are used for cutting thicker leather such as the soles.	*Knife, Butt*
6. *Special Purpose Knives*	*Knife, Breasting* *Knife, Lace Cutting* *Knife, Buffing* *Knife, Shanking Out* *Knife, Drag* *Knife, Welt* *Knife, Feathering* (See also: *Chanelling* *Knife, Hacking* *Tools*; *Peg Tools*) *Knife, Heel*
7. *Blunt Knives*, without a cutting edge.	*Bottom Filling Tool* *Knife, Lining*

Knife, Bit
The term 'bit' is sometimes used for welt and, by extension, for the knives used for cutting out or trimming the welt (see *Knife, Welt*).

Knife, Bottom Filling
This is not a knife, but a tool used for spreading a filling compound. (See *Bottom Filling Tool*; *Knife, Hot.*)

Knife, Breasting (Breast Knife)
(See also *Knife, Heel.*)
Patterns include:

(a) *Fig. 2:38, No. 2426 (p. 64).* A crescent-shaped pointed blade, used mainly for ladies' heels.

(b) *Fig. 2:38, No. 2428 (p. 64).* A straight blade with the sharpened edge sloping to a point at about 45° and used for men's shoes.

(c) A worn Shoe Knife is sometimes converted for use as a Breasting Knife (see illustration under *Knife, Shoe*).

The purpose of this knife is to cut the front of the heel (the breast) to the required shape, and to give it a fine surface, so that the layers of leather ('lifts') present an even, solid face.

Heel-breasting is one of the finishing processes designed to enhance the appearance of a shoe. Several writers stress the importance of this operation: thus Gresham (1920, Vol. III, 235): 'Breasting by hand was severe work, and only the best craftsmen could make a really good job of it. At the present day, heel-breasting is done by machine . . .'; or Hasluck (1898, p.129): 'Breasting the heels . . . adds much beauty to a boot, and is one of the many points that makes shoemaking an art.'

Knife, Buffing (and Scrapers) (Buff Knife; Buffer Knife; Buff Scraper; Scraper. Devlin (1839, p. 40) writes of a 'scraping or edge-knife'.)
(See *Edge-Scraper Plane*; and also *Sharpening Steel* for method of sharpening scrapers.)

The Buffing Knife is a scraper. One of its main purposes is to smooth the sole edges after rasping, but it is also used for scraping and smoothing other surfaces on the sole or heel. Another use is the scraping ('buffing') of the clicker's Block or Board in order to remove the effects of the knife cuts (see *Cutting Board*).

The name Buffing Knife is given to several tools, including:

(*a*) *Handled Buffer Knife Fig. 2:16, No. 209 (p. 42)*
This is a strong, factory-made, handled knife, *c.* 9 in. (22.8 cm) long overall, tapering outward from the butt to a broad point. An ordinary kitchen knife is often used for the same purpose.

(*b*) *Scraper Blade Fig. 2:33 (p. 59)*
A steel scraper of varying shapes. Like the wood-working Cabinet Scraper, the cutting edge is formed by 'turning' the ground edge with a hard steel rod to form a burr.

(*c*) *Home-made Scrapers*
These include pieces of freshly broken glass, pieces of saw or hacksaw blade, or, according to Hasluck (1898, p. 28), a piece of 'old stay busk'.

Knife, Butt (Bottomer's Knife; Counter Knife; Hide Knife; Ranging Knife; Rough-stuff Knife; Leather-cutter's Knife. A hooked knife of similar appearance is called a Lino Knife and is used to cut Lino.) *Fig. 2:14 (p. 40)*
A strong, handled knife, *c.* 8–10½ in. (20.3–26.6 cm) long overall. The blade is either sickle-shaped, tapering to a point, or is straight like an ordinary Shoe Knife but with a slightly concave edge. The wooden handle is sometimes hooked at the base ('caulked') to give the hand something to pull against, and is often turned with a series of shallow grooves ('reeded') to improve the grip. Cutters say that a knife 'worn thin at the throat' is an advantage, for it tends to make the blade more flexible.

The neb (or nib) on the back of some Butt Knives is a mystery. Like the nib on the back of Hand Saws, it may represent a vestigial survival of some decorative feature. Some leather-cutters use it for marking out, though others prefer to use a flat carpenter's pencil for this purpose. According to Mr George Barnsley, Director of the old-established Sheffield tool makers (1976): 'The cutter assessed what was to be removed, and the shape to be cut out, and used the neb with slight pressure to mark out. Turning the knife over, he then cut out the leather itself following the lines he had made.'

The Butt Knife is designed for cutting heavier leather, e.g. for soles, insoles, heel-pieces and welts. In use it is pulled towards the user with the point held downwards. The hide, which is stiff and not always very flat, is held down on the bench with heavy weights; and a back stop is fixed to the surface of the bench against which the hide bears while being cut. The edge being cut is held to overhang the bench sufficiently for the knife to penetrate without cutting the bench surface. (The weights used at the London leather merchants, Messrs R. Pangbourne & Co. (1977), were two conical 14 lb weights of the kind used by coal and grain merchants.)

The process of cutting is described by Gresham (1920, Vol. IV, p. 14): 'The cutting up of the butt is work of considerable skill. The necessary conditions are "a sharp knife and a clear conscience" as the trade proverb has it. ... The leather cutter's knife is kept sharpened on a half-round emery bat, or else on a piece of Indian pond bluestone'. (See also *Knife, Press*.)

Knife, Channelling: see *Channel Tools*.

Knife, Clicker's (Upper-Cutter's Knife. See *Clicker* for possible etymology.)
Though the traditional Half-Moon Knife is still used occasionally for cutting ('clicking-out') heavy skins such as those used for the legs of riding boots, the usual knife used by clickers is an ordinary knife with a sharply pointed blade. The fine point is needed when cutting out a narrow recess or corner in the leather.

The chief purpose of the Clicking Knife is to cut out leather uppers and linings. This is done with the help of a pattern on a special block (see *Cutting Board*). Gresham (1920, III, p. 64) recommends that: 'One quick cut should pass right through the leather and round the line of the pattern. As nearly as possible the action of the knife should resemble the quick motions of a draughtsman's pencil dextrously handled. You should always feel, as it were, the cutting edge of the knife, and direct it rather with the brain than with the fingers.'

A clicker could do all his cutting with an ordinary pointed knife, but will do much better with two: one with a hollow edge, the other with a straight edge. (Both these types are made in the two variants described below.) The hollow edge is used to cut upper leathers of normal thickness and is held so that the edge can be pulled directly into the cut at near right angles to the surface of the leather. If this method was used when cutting thin leather (let alone paper patterns or cloth linings) the material could drag or ruck. For this one needs a blade with a flat edge which can be used with a slicing action.

There are two types of Clicker's Knives in use today:

(a) Handled Clicker's Knife   Fig. 2:36 (p. 62)
A slender, pointed blade mounted in a wooden handle *c.* 8−9 in. (20.3−22.8 cm) overall. The blade has a curved back and, for the reasons given above, has either a concave or straight cutting edge.

When cutting, the clicker presses his outstretched forefinger on the back of the blade near the point. To avoid sore fingers, the blade is often bound with a ribbon of leather (see *Hand and Finger Protectors*).

(b) 'Extension' Clicker blade (American Handle Knife; Replaceable Blade Knife) *Fig. 2:37 (p. 63)*
Though the knife (*a*) above has survived in England, many workers today prefer to use a replaceable all-steel blade mounted in a special holder often called an 'American Handle'. Clickers often make their own blades for this type of knife from old hacksaw blades.

Some reasons why this knife has become popular are described in Gresham (1920, III, p. 67):

'For some time after the "cheese" knife [see *Knife, Half-Moon*] with its half-circle of steel, set in a handle, fell into disuse, clickers mostly employed a simple knife with a long flat blade; but when new it was often too long for quick manipulation, and its slenderness and flexibility was a drawback. When worn, the knife showed faults quite opposite. As it came close to the socket the blade was too stiff for good cutting, and so a large part of the blade had to be sacrificed. The two-fold defect suggested the remedy to an ingenious inventor. He devised the now famous "extension" or adjustable-bladed knives. The cutter can adjust the blade of the knife to the length which suits him, and always bring it to that level as it is worn down. Practically flat, and of equal thickness from end to end and at back and front, the blades are of the same flexibility throughout, being made of finely tempered steel.'

Knife, Cloth

Illustrated by Barnsley (1890) this appears to be a Clicking Knife with a straight-edged blade. It was used, presumably, for cutting linings, and also cloth such as satin used for making ladies' shoes. A straight-edged knife is used because the Clicking Knife with a curved blade would tend to ruck up the material.

Knife Cover: see *Hand and Finger Protectors*.

Knife, Dole

A broad knife used for thinning down leather. See *Knife, Paring* in this section, and under *Knife, Doling* in the GLOVE MAKER section.

The term is sometimes applied to other knife-like tools, such as a blade for applying Heel Ball. (See Fiddler, under *Glazer & Sleeking Iron*.)

Knife, Drag   *Figs 2:22 (p. 48); 2:119*
(See also *Edge Planes*)
A shallow concave blade on a shank offset from its wooden handle, designed to make a paring-cut on the pull stroke. The outer side of the blade is thickened (or curved on itself) to avoid damage to the upper when being used on the edge of the sole. The tool is *c.* 6 in. (15.2 cm) overall, and the blade is made in widths varying from 1−1½ in. (2.5−3.8 cm).

Its main use is for paring the edge of the sole, where it can be drawn round the forepart at a single cut. Elderly shoemakers declare that a good workman can do just as well with an ordinary shoe knife: it is true that Drag Knives are not commonly found in the shoemaker's kit.

Fig. 2:119

Knife, Dull

A name given to a blunt knife which, after warming, is used for applying a wax finish, such as Heel Ball. (See also Fiddler under *Glazer and Sleeking Iron*.)

Knife, Extension

A term applied to a blade which is used in conjunction with a special handle or holder. (See Extension Clicker Blade under *Knife, Clicker's*.)

Knife, Feathering (Feather Plough; Insole Knife)
Figs 2:53, No. 6112 (p. 79); 2:120
A 'push knife' mounted in a wooden handle, *c.* 6−7 in. (15.2−17.7 cm) overall. The tip is a bevel-sharpened blade, bordered by a fence ('safe edge') set at right angles to it, which acts as a guide.

The purpose of the tool is to cut 'feathers' round the edge of the insole. These are grooves made during the 'making' process when the upper and welt are being stitched to the insole (see the first paragraph under 'Process' in the introduction to this section). Vertical cuts are first made with an ordinary knife round the edge of the insole; one at about $\frac{1}{8}$ in. (0.4 cm) from the edge, and another at about $\frac{3}{8}$ in. (1 cm) from the edge. (This distance is dependent on the size and type of shoe.) The edge or the upper will eventually lie in the outside feather; and stitches will be sunk along the inside feather. After the Feathering Knife has cut away the unwanted leather from both inside and outside feathers, the space between, known as the 'holdfast', is left standing.

There are two types illustrated: one with a blade and fence; the other with a 'stepped' blade, forming two sharpened edges at different levels, intended presumably to trim both the feather and the top of the holdfast at the same time.

Note: No mention of the Feathering Knife has been found in trade catalogues before *c.* 1900.

Fig. 2:120

Knife Guard (USA: Gage)   *Fig 2:16*
A metal cap which can be slipped on the end of a knife which enables it to be used close to the upper (or to some other part of the shoe) without damaging it. A small length of cutting edge is left uncovered just below the tip of the blade.

A variant illustrated by Knight (USA, 1877, p. 2161) is described as a 'gage or guard having a turned up lip, and adjustable by means of a slot and thumbscrew to determine the depth of the cut'.

Knife, Hacking (Chopper; Chopping Knife)   *Figs 2:121; 2:54 (p. 80)*
A rough knife, often smith-made from an old file, with 'scale' handles made of wood or leather. The back is thickened to withstand hammering. Like the Glazier's Hacking Knife (which it closely resembles) it is made with either a straight blade, or with the blade set at an angle to the handle.

Fig. 2:121

Used in repair work, e.g. for removing worn lifts from the heel. 'Hacking' is really a misnomer, for worn leather, particularly that of the sole, must be removed gently to avoid damage to the upper.

Knife, Half-Moon (Cheese Knife; Cutting out Knife; Half-Circle Knife; Round Knife)   *Figs 2:23; 2:118 (pp. 49, 133)*
(See also Round Knife under *Knife* in the HARNESS MAKER AND SADDLER section; under *Knife, Moon* in the section LEATHER MANUFACTURE, II. Currier's Tools; and under Parchment Knife in the entry *Parchment and Vellum Maker* in the MISCELLANEOUS TRADES section.)

This ancestral knife was at one time used by most workers in leather. Its general development is illustrated under the entry *Knife*.

During the last century these knives varied in shape from true segments of a circle to something merely rounded, or crescent-shaped. The size varies from 5 in. (12.7 cm) to 8 in. (20.3 cm) across the top which may be straight or slightly concave.

Very few, if any, of these knives are still in use for boot and shoemaking (see *Knife, Clicker's*); those that are, are used for the comparatively heavy skins and long cuts of riding boots. Why this form of knife has survived at all is difficult to explain. John Waterer writes about it in the *Oxford Companion to the Decorative Arts* (1975) as follows:

'Why this particular form was evolved is something of a mystery. It cannot be said to fulfil any one specific purpose with distinction, although in skilled hands by gradually moving from one end of its curved cutting edge to the other (e.g. when cutting a long strap from heavy hide) a consistently sharp edge can be brought into play, whilst its broad flat surface held vertically serves as a useful directional guide. This knife is used without a straight edge of wood or metal such as is sometimes employed along with a small knife, but it follows a guiding line marked on the surface of the leather with a blunt awl. Some workers also use it as a skiving knife, holding the blade more or less horizontally. It is certainly not a tool for the amateur.'

On the other hand, Mr J. H. Thornton, in a letter to the author (1979), wrote that when helping the BBC to make a film on medieval shoemaking, the shoemaker he found to do the job learned to use an old Moon Knife, and cut leather very successfully with it in front of the camera.

Knife, Hawk's Bill
A name sometimes given to a shoemaker's knife which has a down-curving point.

Knife, Heel (Heel Paring Knife) *Figs 2:16, No. 208; 2:39, No. 2210 (pp. 42, 65)*
A handled knife with a convex ('bellied') cutting edge, *c.* 7 in. (17.7 cm) overall. It is intended for trimming leather or wooden heels, mainly those fitted to ladies' shoes.

Note: Other knives used for trimming heels are described under *Knife, Breasting.* The name Heel Knife is sometimes given to other knives, for example *Knife, Welt.*

French Heel Knives of c. 1767
Very different types of Knife for shaping wooden heels are included in an illustration in Garsault's *Cordonnier*, Plate II (1767). One of these is unusually long, *c.* 17–18 in. (42.1–45.7 cm) overall. Garsault explains that this is 'so that it can be held against the workman's forearm to steady the hand'. The blade is gently bowed in the lateral plane, as if to give a hollowing out; another has a blade with a double curve, mounted in a long horn-shaped handle, and looking rather like a bowl-maker's Hook Knife. It may have been used to hollow out the seat of the heel to make a bed for the upper and insole.

Knife, Hot
A name given to a knife (often an old table knife) that is heated before use. Its purpose is to cut the tarred felt that is inserted to fill the space between sole and insole; the blade is heated to prevent the tar (or pitch) from sticking to it. (See also *Bottom Filling Tool.*)

Knife, Lace Cutting *Fig. 2:38, No. 2420/22 (p. 64)*
A strong handled knife of the shoe type, with a broad pointed blade. Used for cutting out leather boot and shoe laces. (See also *Lace Making Tools.*)

Knife, Lining (Wrinkled Knife) *Fig. 2:39, No. 2550 (p. 65)*
This tool is used for removing wrinkles from the linings of pumps and similar footwear. As Leno writes (1895, p. 52): 'Nothing produces more discomfort than a ruffled lining.' (See also Lining Pliers under *Pincer, Plier or Nipper.*)

As illustrated by Barnsley (1927), this is a narrow, tapering, flexible blade with a rounded tip. Mounted in a wooden handle, it measures *c.* 10 in. (25.4 cm) overall. The edges are left blunt like a paper knife. Owing to its length and flexibility, it could be slid down inside the shoe between upper and last, to remove wrinkles.

The name Wrinkled Knife is applied by Devlin (1839, p. 114) to what is probably a similar tool.

Under 'Kit of the woman's man' he writes: '... a wrinkled knife (1s 6d), the name coming from the use it is put to in dispersing and making smooth the wrinkles on the inside of pump boots.'

Knife, Linoleum (Lino Knife)
This has a hooked 'hawk's bill' blade with a sharpened point, and is similar to some lighter versions of the leather cutter's *Butt Knife.* Knives of this shape are apt to be called 'Lino Knives' even when used by leather workers.

Knife, Lip (Safety Knife)
A short handled knife of the shoe type, with its square tip turned over to form a protective lip or knob. This acts as a guard to prevent cutting the upper by mistake when trimming the sole edge. (See also *Knife Guard.*)

Knife, McKay Stitcher
A short handled knife, with tip of the blade tapering to a point. Used for cutting off thread ends inside the shoe when sewn with a McKay or Blake type sewing machine.

Knife, Paring (Skiving Knife; Doling Knife: *doler* is a French verb meaning 'to smooth'.)
(See also *Knife, Doling* in the GLOVEMAKER section and *Knife, Paring* in the BOOKBINDER section.)
The terms 'paring', 'doling', or 'skiving' are applied to various thinning-down and trimming operations. Skiving (making a feathered edge) can be done with ordinary shoe knives, especially if shortened and cross-ground – see (*b*) below; but reducing thickness away from the edges demands a more specialised knife, as described in (*a*) below.

(*a*) *Paring Knife* (French Knife) *Figs 2:39, Nos 2500/20 (p. 65); 2:122(a)*
This has a broad blade *c.* 2½ in. (6.4 cm) wide, bevel-sharpened across the end like a chisel, either straight across or at an angle. The handle is a flat oval in cross-section to enable the knife to be held horizontally – or nearly so. It is thus suitable for taking a thin shaving off the surface of the leather by pushing; and it can also be used for paring edges. This method of reducing thickness required so much skill that many makers preferred to buy their skins ready pared down by the currier (see LEATHER MANUFACTURE, II. Currier's Tools)

Barnsley (1927) illustrates two Paring Knives of the 'push' type, which may have been used instead of the 'French' pattern above. One has an asymmetrical blade described as a 'chop' pattern; the other has a triangular-shaped blade rather like a painter's Chisel Knife. This blade bears a close resemblance to one found at a Roman site in London of *c*. AD 1000 – a site where leather working is thought to have been done'(Rupert Cook, 1977).

(*b*)   *Use of Shoe Knives for paring Figs 2:17; (p. 43); 2:122(b)*

The all-steel 'continental' shoe knife is frequently used for edge paring (see under *Knife, Shoe*).

Ordinary handled Shoe Knives are often used for the same purpose, but with an edge ground at about 45° across the width of the blade, and used by pushing.

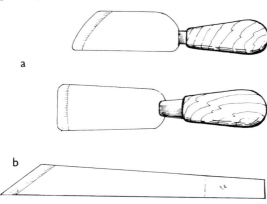

Fig. 2:122

(*c*)   *Splitting Machine*

The paring operations described in (*a*) above can be done by a hand-operated Splitting Machine: this is described in the HARNESS MAKER AND SADDLER section.

Knife, Peg: see under *Peg-Fitting Tools.*

Knife, Press (Cutting Die). In the glove trade this tool is called a Webb *Fig. 2:123*

Early in the nineteenth century a shaped die was developed that cut out the sole and uppers rather like a kitchen pastry cutter. This tool eliminated the use of hand knives in the factory. It consists of a strip of steel forged to the outline of the piece of leather to be cut, its lower edge bevelled and sharpened on the outside. More recently, these knives are made from ready-sharpened steel strip which can be bent cold to the desired shape. They are sharpened along both edges, thus avoiding the need for two Press Knives, one for the left sole and one for the right.

The leather to be cut is laid on a hardwood or composition base, the Press Knife is placed in position, and the ram of a power or hand operated press is forced down upon it.

Fig. 2:123

Knife, Punch *Fig. 2:123*

A *Press Knife* as above, but designed for hand use. A heavy mallet, often of rawhide mounted on an iron head, can be used for driving it.

Knife, Rubber

Special knives are made for cutting rubber in the making up of rubber soles, overshoes or rubber boots. They are mostly all-steel, similar to the ordinary shoemaker's knives, but the blades are hardened and tempered to resist the effect of abrasive substances often present in rubber compounds. Berg (*c*. 1939) illustrates seven differing rubber trimming knives, which are similar to ordinary Shoe Knives; and nine differing rubber cutting knives of the clicking type.

Knife, Seat

A name sometimes given to the *Welt Knife* because this knife can also be used for trimming off the burr left on the edge of the seat after rasping the heel.

Knife, Shanking-Out

Illustrated by Plucknett (1931, p. 249) this has a folded, U-shaped blade like a Saddler's *Race Knife*. It is shown mounted on the butt of a wooden handle which carries a circular welt trimming knife on the other end (see under *Knife, Welt*). It was used for bevelling the waist, though many makers prefer to use a worn-down Shoe Knife for this purpose.

Knife, Shoe

This is a general purpose knife used by shoemakers for most cutting work, including some of the special operations, such as edge paring; and even when the knife is well worn down and pointed it can be used as a *Clicking Knife* for cutting out.

All these knives are sometimes found with a strip of thin leather tied round the base of the blade to prevent sore fingers (see *Hand and Finger Protectors*).

Four types of ordinary shoe knives are to be seen in the workshops:

(a) Conventional Shoe Knife with · a wooden handle Figs 2:13; 2:16; 2:35 (pp. 39, 42, 61)
An ordinary knife blade riveted into a wooden handle, usually oblong in cross-section, and measuring 8–9 in. (20.3–22.8 cm) overall. There are a great many variants: the blade edge can be straight, swept back, slightly concave ('hollow back') or convex ('bellied'); the point of the knife is supplied 'to taste' in shapes known as clip, bevel, broad, spear or sheep's foot.

(b) Earlier examples of the conventional Shoe Knife Fig. 2:8 (p. 34)
Earlier versions of the common Shoe Knife, as illustrated by Richard Timmins (*c.* 1800), have a relatively heavy, straight blade, with a 'broad' point and a round handle. It is interesting to observe that E. A. Berg (1939) illustrates a knife of this shape and calls it an American Shoemaker's Knife.

(c) Conventional Shoe Knife with worn-down blades Fig. 2:124
After much wear and re-sharpening, the blade edge becomes more and more hollow; and when this hollow almost meets the back of the blade, the thin end of the blade is removed and the knife sharpened 'on the cross', i.e. at an angle across the width of the knife, and used as illustrated below or for similar work.

(d) All-steel 'continental' type knife (often known as 'German' or 'Swedish' knives but now made in this country). *Fig. 2:17 (p. 43)*
(See also *Knife, Paring*; *Knife, Tranchet*.)
These all-steel blades have no separate handle, but the steel shank is sometimes bandaged in thin leather for comfort. The blades vary in length from 6–9 in. (15.2–22.8 cm). Some are the same width throughout their length; but most others, including some listed by Berg (1939) as 'English and American types', are wider at the point and taper slightly towards the butt. Most of these blades are sharpened 'on the cross' and are then often listed as Paring Knives; but many others, including those listed by Berg as 'South American, mid-European and Oriental', have points ground in the varied shapes of the clicker's cutting-out knife (See *Knife, Clicker's*).

Many of these knives have curved blades which, in the language of the trade catalogues, mean that they are gently bowed in the plane of their length – not to be confused with the curve of a Butt Knife that is sickle-shaped. The object of the curve (which is reversed for left-hand users) is to keep the hand away from the work, and to avoid injury to the upper when paring the sole edge, especially in shoes with a very narrow welt.

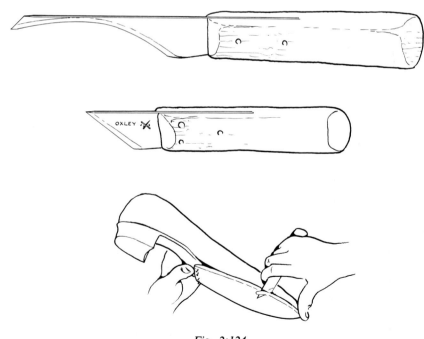

Fig. 2:124

Knife, Stafford   *Fig. 2:15 (p. 41)*

Illustrated by Barnsley (1890) these knives are long and slender with wooden handles, *c.* 8–9 in. (20.3–22.8 cm) overall. The blades are narrow, pointed or rounded, some with a straight edge, others with a slightly concave edge like a Clicker's Knife. Mr George Barnsley wrote (1974) that they are used for 'cutting out patterns and upper leather'. A retired London maker (W. B. Glasow, 1975), to whom the illustrations were shown, wrote, 'It looks like a Skiving Knife, i.e. for reducing and levelling the thickness or substance of a sole or innersole, or for preparing stiffeners. At least that is what I should use such a knife for.' *Wright's English Dialect Dictionary*, under 'Stafford', quotes from S. O. Addy's *Glossary of words used in the neighbourhood of Sheffield (1888)*: 'A Knife the head or point of which is not quite round, but slightly flattened.'

It remains uncertain why this group of knives were given the name Stafford. A likely explanation is given by Mr W. G. Ibberson OBE, Chairman of George Ibberson, the Sheffield Cutlers. He wrote (1977):

'The Stafford Knife was probably made in Sheffield for the Stafford boot and shoe trade during the last century or earlier. It could have been that for some reason, maybe no more than a whim, the Stafford men wanted a knife with a blade different to others and the cutlers called it the Stafford Knife. There is a parallel to this in the "Ettrick" knife, so called because it was first made specially for the farmers and shepherds of Ettrick vale. It became popular in northern districts and was everywhere known by the name "Ettrick". The blades were curved a little differently to other patterns and the haft was shorter than the standard knives.'

Knife, Tranchet   (From the French *tranchet*, meaning a shoemaker's knife, or a cutter)   *Fig. 2:18 (p. 44)*

The Tranchet is an all-steel shoemaker's knife. It differs from the all-steel 'continental' type shoe knife in being parallel from the spear-shaped point to the butt, instead of tapering downwards from point to butt (see *Knife, Shoe*). Some are illustrated as slightly hollowed across the width of the blade. It is a general purpose knife and is in common use today.

Knife, Welt   (Bit Knife; Welt Cutter; Welt Plough; Seat Knife: Shooting-out Knife; Welt Trimming Knife; Welt Trimming Plough. Other alternative names are mentioned under the variants below.)
(See also *Welt Tools*)

Nomenclature. The alternative names given to this tool are rather confusing. The term 'bit' is an alter-native name for the welt itself; the term 'plough' is already applied to several tools that cut when pushed along the surface of the work, including the *Closer's Welt Plough* which, it may be added, has nothing in common with the Welt Knife, except that it is pushed; the term 'Shooting-out' comes from a Norwich maker (see quotation below) and implies the forward thrust of the Welt Knife in use.

The Welt Knife is a cutting tool designed for levelling and trimming the surface of the welt after it is sewn in. Except for the circular type (see (*c*) below), it is worked by pushing. The head of the tool contains a fence or guide which prevents damage to the upper against which the tool bears while being run along the surface of the welt.

Judging from the tool maker's catalogues, it appears to have been developed in the late nineteenth century; before that time the welt was trimmed with the point of an ordinary shoe knife, and some makers still prefer this method.

A Norwich maker (Mr R. C. Pond, 1973) wrote to the author as follows about welt trimming:

'The term "Shoot" implies the forward thrust of the knife and the flick of the wrist when "Shooting Out". The reason for "Shooting Out" is that when the sole edge is rasped a burr is formed on the welt edge, since this welt leather is more resistant to the rasp than the sole leather because the welting is grease tanned. The welt is boned before "Shooting Out" to flatten the stitches, so that the shooting-knife blade which runs over the welt surface does not cut any stitches.'

Variants include:

(*a*)   *Welt Knife with 'finger' guide* (Though called a 'Yankee Welt knife' by Pocock (*c.* 1930) this is probably a mistake).   *Fig. 2:53, No. 6108 (p. 79)*
This is the commonest type of knife used for trimming the welt; it measures *c.* 5–6 in. (12.7–15.2 cm) overall. The curved shank has a cutting edge ground across the end, leaving a 'finger-guide' at the side. When pushed along the welt, the 'finger' is kept in contact with the upper and so acts as both guide and fence.

A variant illustrated by Knight (USA, 1877, Vol. III, p. 2760), called a Welt Trimmer, has a hook-shaped shank so that in use it is dragged rather than pushed. The shank is float-cut to serve (presumably) as a *Rand File* for trimming the seat. It may be added that the Welt Knife is sometimes called a Seat Knife owing to its occasional use for removing the burr left on the edge of the seat after rasping.

(*b*) *Welt Knife with 'safety fence'* (Safety Welt Knife) *Fig. 2:53, No. 6110 (p. 79)*
A similar tool to (*a*) above, instead of the finger-guide, the edge of the shank is turned through a right angle to form a fence which rests against the upper.

(*c*) *Welt Trimming Knife with a circular cutting head* (Circular Welt Cutter; American Welt Plough; Boston Welt Trimmer) *Fig. 2:28 (p. 54)*
According to Leno (1895, pp. 207–8) this tool is an American invention, and he writes that 'when used by a trained hand, there is little doubt of its superiority over the knife, rasp, etc.'

The circular cutting head is either mounted in a wooden handle, or is cast in one piece with the handle. These iron handles are hollowed for lightness, and given a V-shaped butt for 'setting the welt'. More rarely, a drag knife is fitted to the butt of the wooden handle for trimming the waist (see *Knife, Shanking-Out*).

This tool is not pushed, but is held at right angles to the side of the shoe like a knife. It is provided with two fences: a rebate across the circular head which bears on the sole edge and prevents damage to the upper; and a plate screwed to the head which acts like the sole of a plane and controls the depth of cut.

(*d*) *Welt-Making Cutters*
These are sometimes called Welt Knives but serve the quite different purpose of cutting out the strips of leather for making the welt itself. They are described under *Welt Tools*.

Lace-Making Tools

The following are tools used for cutting out, forming, and tagging leather laces for boots, shoes or gaiters. The methods described are sometimes used for cutting strips of leather for other purposes such as for welts or edge-binding strips. (See also *Welt Strip Cutter* in the CLOG MAKER section; *Welt Tools* in this section; and under *Whip Maker* in the MISCELLANEOUS section.)

(*a*) *Knife Fig. 2:38, Nos 2420 and 2422 (p. 64)*
Barnsley (1927) illustrates a 'lace cutting knife' which has a strong blade with a broad point. A knife of this kind could be used in various ways, including the common method of pulling a piece of leather with the left hand against the edge of a knife stuck in the bench, while using the right thumb as a guide. The 'spiral' method is described by Leno (1895, p. 157):

'Modern shoemakers as a rule purchase their laces, a practice that assuredly does not recommend itself on the ground of economy, inasmuch as a mere youth can be taught the art of cutting them, and the material used may be picked from the waste basket. ... Select from the discarded small pieces a bit of soft calf or mellow kip. ... Through the centre of this drive an awl or tack, and with a sharp knife cut the leather to the form of a circle. This done, cut a nick in its edge of the width of the lace, and taking the edge of the leather as your guide, cut at an equal distance from the edge till the released slip is sufficient to furnish a hold. At the bottom of this cut fix the cutting part of a sharp thin-pointed knife, which should be made to slightly penetrate the board in order to the keeping of it firm. Draw the awl or tack, and then holding the knife steady with the left hand and using a finger thereof to regulate the width of the cut, pull the released end till the whole of the piece of leather has been converted into a lace.'

(*b*) *'Lace and Welt' Cutter Fig. 2:38, No. 2424 (p. 64)*
This is a name given to a small, cast-iron, purpose-made cutting device which incorporates both a cutting blade and an adjustable fence, and appears to have been operated on the pull stroke. (See also *Welt Tools*.)

Home-made devices in wood made on the lines of a harness-maker's Plough Gauge may be seen occasionally in the workshops of shoemakers and repairers.

(*c*) *Tag Metaller*
The following tools are used to fix a metal tag on the end of a leather or textile lace. These tags are small pieces of sheet metal formed into a tube that can be compressed to grip the ends of the lace. Perforations in the metal, with burred edges on the inside, secure adhesion. Two varieties have been noted:

(1) *Pliers Fig. 2:125* Made in the form of pliers, with stepped jaws designed to squeeze the tag.

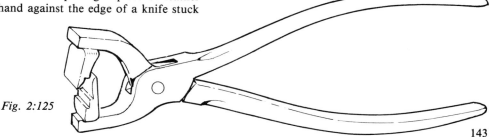

Fig. 2:125

(2) *Lace-Tag Fitter* (Lace-Tipping Tool) *Fig. 2:126* A device with a sliding jaw operated by a rocking lever. The jaws are designed to squeeze two sizes of tag.

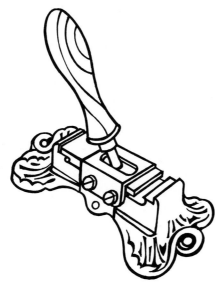

Fig. 2:126

(d) *Lace Drawer* *Fig. 2:11, No. 917 (p. 37)*
Illustrated by Richard Timmins (*c.* 1900) this is a flat iron bar measuring *c.* $2 \times \frac{1}{2}$ in. (5 × 1.2 cm) and tanged for a wooden handle. Three countersunk holes in the head are probably used, like the harness-maker's rein-rounder, for rounding a leather lace.

Lamp: see *Heater.*

Langstick
Scots term for a stick or bone used for rubbing down leather (see *Bones and Sticks*).

Lap Stone or Lap Iron (Yorkshire clogger: 'Knee Last') *Figs 2:127; 2:43 (p. 69)*
A stone or iron plate, *c.* 5–7 in. (12.7–17.7 cm) wide. Some of the stone examples are large beach or river pebbles, flattened on one face; the example illustrated below is a piece of siltstone and was found in the United States among the tools of a shoe-maker's kit. Lap Irons were often made from an old flat iron, sometimes with the handle removed; when factory made, they were rounded iron castings with a flat face, often provided with a central lug underneath which rested between the knees to prevent it from slipping off.

The Lap Stone or Lap Iron is laid on the knees and used as an anvil when hammering dampened sole and heel-lift leather. (See *Hammer, Shoe*; and also *Roller* under Tanner's Tools in the LEATHER MANUFACTURE section).

The process is described by Hasluck (1898, p. 72) as follows:

'Sit upon a low stool, and place the lap-iron face upwards on the thighs, just above the knees; hold the leather grain side downwards, and, commencing from the centre, hammer it all over. Let each stroke be even, straight, and firm: strike with the face of the hammer, and do not bruise the leather.'

The purpose of the hammering is to compact the fibrous tissues of the leather in order to increase its resistance to wear and damp.

It used to be said that you could tell when you were near the town of Northampton by the sound of the lap stones. But perhaps it should be added that there is also a saying in the trade that 'Good leather needs little hammering. Bad leather won't stand it.'

Since the early years of the century, hand-hammering was gradually superseded by mechanical rolling. Small, hand-operated rolling machines, often with a concave and convex roller running together, began to appear in the workshops. But, even today, shoemakers will say that the old-fashioned soaking and knee-hammering is the best.

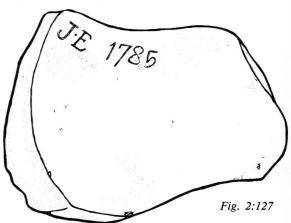

Fig. 2:127

Last (The term comes from an Old English word for footstep. A Scots term for last is 'deevil' or 'divel'. Trade names such as Broken Last, Easy-Exit Last or Wedge-Hinge Last relate to lasts specially designed to facilitate their removal from the shoe.) *Fig. 2:128*
(See also *Cobbler's Foot, Measuring Tools* and *Last Maker* in the section MISCELLANEOUS TRADES.)

A last is a model of a foot and serves as a mould on which to make a shoe. But the last is not always an identical model of the foot, for it is often modified to meet the demand of some prevailing fashion, like the shape of the toe.

In addition to its use as a mould on which to make a shoe, the last in some methods of construction is also a process-tool, for it is an essential part of a particular operation, e.g. an anvil for turning over nail points.

The part of the last that forms the instep is usually made to be detachable, so that it can be removed easily from the shoe. In the bespoke trade, lasts are made in wood for each customer after careful measurement of both his feet. Lasts for factory-made riveted shoes and for repair work are usually made in cast-iron so that the points of the rivets can be clenched.

A customer's wooden last can be altered to accommodate minor changes in the foot by attaching pieces of leather at strategic places. These are called Fittings; pieces of leather tacked to the edge of a last to increase width are called Runners.

Last Hook (Last Crook; USA: Shoe-key) *Fig. 2:128*
A metal hook, usually provided with a cross or ring-shaped handle, *c.* 8 in. (20.3 cm) long for shoes and *c.* 18 in. (45.7 cm) long for top boots.

Last hooks are used for pulling out the last from a finished or partly finished shoe. The hook is inserted in the hole which is drilled laterally through the back of the last.

When a last is hard to extract ('stuck fast') the cross handle is held on the ground with the two feet, the hook inserted, and the shoe pulled off the last from above.

Lasting Nail (Lasting Tack) *Fig. 2:129*
This traditional Nail was made in iron and well finished. It had a 'double' square head, a needle-sharp point, and was made in sizes $1\frac{3}{8}$–2 in. (3.5–5 cm).

They were used for fastening down the upper temporarily whilst it was stretched over the last. The large head prevented the leather slipping off and facilitated the nail's removal after stitching.

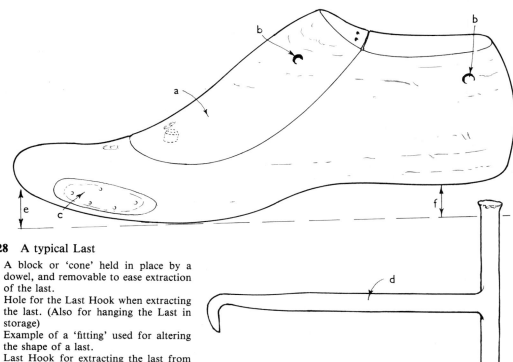

Fig. 2:128   A typical Last

   (*a*)   A block or 'cone' held in place by a dowel, and removable to ease extraction of the last.
   (*b*)   Hole for the Last Hook when extracting the last. (Also for hanging the Last in storage)
   (*c*)   Example of a 'fitting' used for altering the shape of a last.
   (*d*)   Last Hook for extracting the last from the shoe.
   (*e*)   Distance known as the 'toe spring'.
   (*f*)   Distance known as the 'pitch', i.e. the heel height.

Commenting on their extremely sharp points a shoe repairer related that in order to take a few from the box, one inserted a finger and a bunch of tacks would adhere painlessly to the finger by their points.

It was regarded more as a tool than as an ordinary nail, for it could be used again and again.

This nail is illustrated by Garsault (*c.* 1767) and described as a *Clou à monter*. Though still used for holding thick uppers, e.g. for shooting boots, these nails have been largely replaced by wire nails such as shoe rivets.

Fig. 2:129

Lasting Pincers and Dogs (Scots: Turkiss. Richard Timmins *c.* 1800 and George Barnsley *c.* 1890 call them Shoe Pincers. For other names of this tool see under the variants below.)   *Fig. 2:130*
(See also Lining Pliers under *Pincer, Plier or Nipper,* which are used in the lasting process.)
The Blocking Pincer, which is similar to the Lasting Pincer except that it has a straight nose, is described under *Blocking Tools.*

Lasting Pincers have serrated jaws designed for gripping leather: they are used for straining the leather uppers over the last. The jaws that grip the edge of the uppers are usually curved downwards in order to keep them in line with the direction in which the leather is being pulled.

One or both jaws are thickened at their base to form what is known as an 'anvil'. This anvil serves both as a fulcrum (the plier itself acting as the lever) and as a hammer for driving tacks. A tack can be held in the jaws of the Plier, pushed through the upper into the last, and then hammered in with the anvil.

Historical Note   Fig. 2:131
Two earlier examples of the Lasting Pincer are illustrated: one is from a picture by the Dutch artist David Teniers (1610–90) in the Northampton Museum. The heavy jaws are cut square across the front and act, presumably, as a fulcrum when stretching the upper over the last. The other is from an engraving in Diderot's Encyclopaedia under *Cordonnier* (*c.* 1750). Here also, the thickened jaws serve as a fulcrum and possibly as a hammer too.

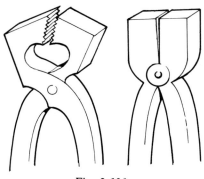

Fig. 2:131

1.   PLIER-TYPE LASTING PINCERS

(*a*) *'Common' or 'English' type* with square anvil.   *Figs 2:132, 2:26 (p. 52)*
Richard Timmins (*c.* 1800) and Barnsley (1890) illustrate the following sizes:

Size Mark:	00	0	1	2	3	4	5	6	7	8

Approx. length: $6\frac{1}{2}$ 7 $7\frac{1}{2}$ 8 9 $9\frac{1}{2}$ 10 (inches)
The sizes 6, 7 and 8 are described as 'larger sizes'.
The smaller sizes are used when lasting the toe, for it is difficult to take out the 'pipes' (wrinkles) with a larger tool.

Variants of the 'common' Pincers include the following: the nose may be broad or narrow, square or rounded. In some instances, there is a distinct 'hump' on the back of the upper jaw. (Examples with straight jaws are Blocking Pincers: see *Blocking Tools.*) A nail claw may be provided at the foot of the handle.

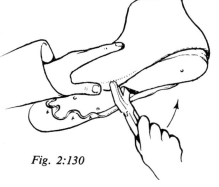

Fig. 2:130

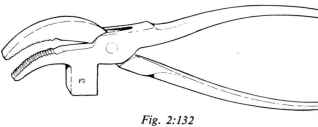

Fig. 2:132

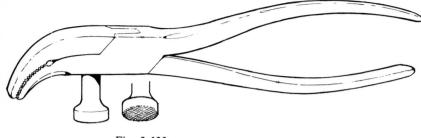

Fig. 2:133

(*b*) *'Whitcher' type* with round anvil   *Fig. 2:133*
This tool is similar to the 'common' Lasting Pincer described above, except that the 'anvil' or hammer is bell-shaped or cylindrical instead of square.

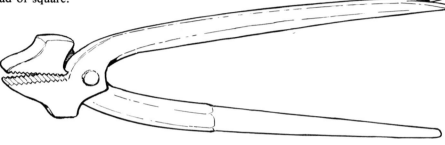

It is included in Barnsley's catalogues of 1892 and 1927, but the term 'Whitcher' is used only in the latter. The tool is not mentioned by Richard Timmins or Wynn, Timmins & Co. in their catalogues of *c.* 1800, 1892 and 1900.

It would appear that the term 'Whitcher' originates from the USA. D. A. Saguto (1982) writes:

'Over here, the term "Whitcher" is applied to the common pattern lasting pincer. I don't know what Mr Whitcher did to get his name stamped onto these pincers, but I've seen several pairs so marked. I have one pair made by J. Knell (who patented the round hammer lasting pincer in the 1880's), stamped "J. Knell" on the handle and "Whitcher" across one of the jaws. The name "Whitcher" seems to have become a standard term in shoemaker's jargon here for the lasting pincer with squared or round hammer.'

(*c*) *French or 'Continental' type* (also known as 'Swiss' or 'German' type)   *Figs 2:134; 2:26 (p. 52)*
These are distinguished by straight jaws with anvils formed on the outer surface of both. Some are provided with a transverse V-groove in each joint, possibly for gripping an awl stuck fast in the leather.

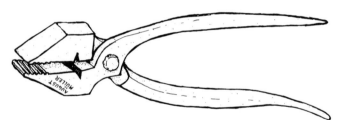

Fig. 2:134

(*d*) *Swedish type*   *Fig. 2:135*
These have short jaws which are often slightly curved. The handles are nearly parallel: this gives a better leverage than bowed handles because one can grasp them at a greater distance from the joint. Comparing the relative advantages of the English and other pincers, Plucknett (1916) comes down heavily in favour of the Swedish. When quoting figures to prove that the Swedish Pincer develops a stronger grip with less effort, he adds 'Why do not our English toolmakers study this and why do not those who have to use the tools demand the best design?' But he commends the English Pincer for its curved jaws which prevent a sharp bend in the leather when levered over the last.

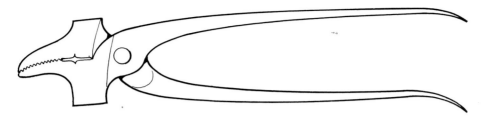

Fig. 2:135

(e) 'Boston' type

Illustrated by Wynn, Timmins & Co. (1892) and made in sizes 0–5, it appears to be like the English model but has rather shorter jaws; and the upper jaw has a smooth rounded contour without a 'hump'. This pattern is described in Richard Timmins' catalogue of *c.* 1800 as 'New Shape or Patent' but in later catalogues as 'Boston pattern'. Two of their catalogues (*c.* 1860 and 1892) list (but do not illustrate) an 'American Pattern or Medium Bend' model priced the same as the Boston pattern. (See also American Lasting Nippers below.)

(f) *Magazine Lasting Plier and Nailer*

An attempt to simplify the lasting operation is described by Swaysland (1905, p. 166) as follows:

'One of the most difficult operations in hand lasting is the apparently simple operation of feeding the tacks before knocking them in with the hammer head of the pincers. The laster usually used his mouth as a kind of reservoir for tacks; he feeds these through his lips, picking them out with the jaws of the pincers, and frequently incidentally pulling out his moustache as well. This crude method of tacking causes the mere tacking operation to consist of three movements: taking the tack from the mouth with the pincers, sticking it into the leather, and then driving it with the pincer head. The "Standard Rotary New Pincer" simplifies this operation. These pincers have a tack reservoir and a tack feeding arrangement under the control of the operator. . . . The operator, having seized the upper and pulled it over by a movement of the handle, feeds the tack, which is planted in the upper, he then simply drives the tack with the pincer head; this is an enormous saving of time.'

(But see also *Nailing Tools*.)

2. LEVER-GRIP TYPE LASTING TOOLS (Bull Dog; Shank Laster; Waist Drag)

These tools have the same purpose as the Lasting Pliers described above, but they are designed for dealing with stout, hard leathers which make hand-lasting difficult and arduous, particularly at the waist. A special feature of these tools is the 'lever-grip': a grip that becomes tighter the harder the leather is stretched. This comes about because pressure on the fulcrum, when using the tool as a lever, automatically closes the jaw – without the operator having to squeeze the handles any harder.

There are several variants, of which the following are examples:

(a) *Bull Dog Pincer* Figs 2:136; 2:28 (p. 54)

This tool, which measures *c.* $9\frac{1}{2}$ in. overall, has one of its handles mounted in a wooden handle, while the other, left short, is placed against the side of the last to act as a fulcrum.

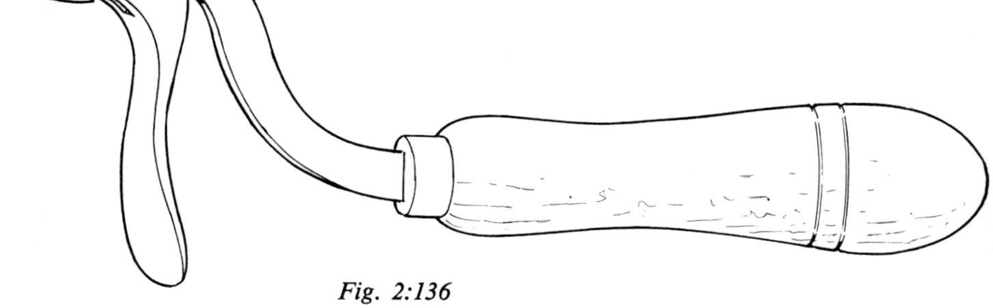

Fig. 2:136

(b) Waist Drag Fig. 2:137
A name given to a lasting tool exhibited in the Northampton Museum. It measures *c.* 11 in. (27.9 cm)
overall. The lower jaw is connected by a crank to the
wooden handle; the upper jaw has a short arm which
is pressed home by the back of the fulcrum when the
tool is levered over the last.

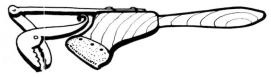

Fig. 2:137

3. TWIN-JAWED LASTING TOOLS (Boot Shank
Machine; Crab Laster; Crab Shank Laster; Double
Dog Laster; Lasting Dogs; Waist Dog; USA: Shank
Laster)
These twin-jawed lasters were seldom used on
normal boots and shoes, but they were useful for
lasting the stout leathers of sea boots, sewer boots,
fishing boots and certain military boots. They were
mainly used when lasting the waist (shank); and also
when the clicker did not leave sufficient margin on
the upper for an ordinary Lasting Pincer to grip on.
They differed from the lasting pliers described above
in being operated by the power of a screw and in
being able to draw both edges of the upper over the
last at the same time.
    There are several variants, of which the following
are examples:

(a) Caliper type Figs 2:138; 2:28 (p. 54)
This ingenious instrument consists of two jaws set on
each foot of a caliper. A screw, with a left and right
thread, engages with the inner part of each jaw,
leaving the legs of the caliper free. This is done so
that the jaws can be dropped over the edges of the
upper before beginning the lasting operation, by
merely drawing the legs together by hand. They are
kept apart by the flat piece of laminated spring steel
that is fixed across the joint of the caliper. A
remarkable feature of the tool is that when the legs
of the caliper are drawn together, the jaws open by
themselves, ready to grip the edge of the leather.
    The earliest mention we have seen of this tool is in
Barnsley's catalogue of 1890. Examples examined in
the workshops appear to have been of French make.

*(b) American twin-jawed Lasting Tools Fig.
2:139*
The *Journal of the Early American Industries
Association* (USA, 1970, Vol. XXIII, No. 2)

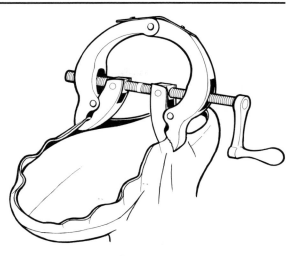

Fig. 2:138

describes the 'lazy-tong' examples illustrated here,
one operated by screw, the other apparently by an
adjustable, racked quadrant.
    A curious variant, called a 'Shank Laster', is
illustrated in Knight's *Dictionary of Mechanics*
(USA, 1979). It is a tong-like instrument in which
each jaw is provided with a device for gripping the
leather.

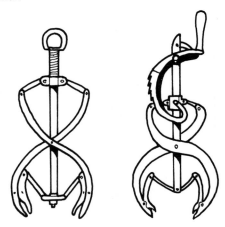

Fig. 2:139

4. AMERICAN   LASTING   NIPPERS   WITH
ADJUSTABLE FULCRUM
There are a number of mid nineteenth-century
American Lasting Nippers about which some par-
ticulars have been given us by Mr W. Downes (USA,
1979) and Mr A. L. Saguto (USA, 1980).

149

(*a*) *Fig. 2:140* In this example, the fulcrum is adjustable by sliding over a rack on one handle, thus making one tool serve for both small and large lasts.

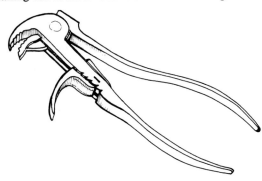

Fig. 2:140

(*b*) *Fig. 2:141* In this example, the Patent (L. B. Richardson, Athol, Mass. Oct. 11 1859) claims that a pivoting fulcrum permits the nipper jaws to end up pulling the leather flat along the sole of the last. It is probably intended only for boots.

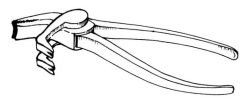

Fig. 2:141

(*c*) *Fig. 2:142* This example is named 'Hayden's Patent Shank Laster', is similar to (*b*) above but has a single hinged foot. It is pulled in the normal way, but the hinged foot-piece is braced against the waist opposite the pull. Once the pull has been taken, the hinged foot will collapse inwards, giving an extra bit of pull. The foot is set in whichever hole is required, depending on the width of the waist. This assures that the foot will collapse at the proper time.

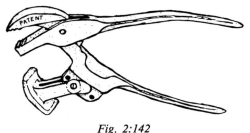

Fig. 2:142

(*d*) *Fig. 2:143* This example is advertised as 'Wilt's Patent Shank Laster with Magoun's improvements' and adds that Thos. P. I. Magoun is also the Inventor and Proprietor of a Folding Chair, a Folding Desk, and an Improved Piano Polish copyrighted 1870. This Laster has double cranked 'lazy-tong' handles, with a movable fulcrum to 'fit any size last'.

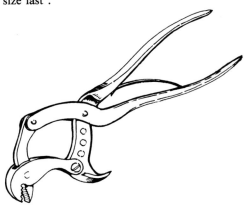

Fig. 2:143

Last Stand (Lasting Jack)
Special stands are made for holding the Last: this enables the shoemaker to work standing rather than sitting, with the Last held down on his knee with a *Footstrap*. Free-standing last vices, known as Last Jacks, were designed to hold Lasts of all sizes.

Lift: see *Shoehorn*; and see *Heel* for the 'lifts' of a built heel.

Lingel
Scots term for shoemaker's waxed thread.

Machines for Shoe-Making
By the middle of the nineteenth century many one-man workshops possessed a few hand- (or foot-) operated machines. These included an Eyeletting Machine, for fitting eyelets for the laces; a Leather-Rolling Machine, for consolidating sole leather without hammering; and the greatest labour-saver of all – a Sewing Machine. In the factories, the installation of both hand and power machines gradually replaced almost every hand process. Leno (1895, p. 159) describes the changes:

'The rapid march of invention is in no trade so forcibly illustrated as in that of the boot and shoemaker. It is considerably less than fifty years since it obtained a footing and, at the time of writing, it may be fairly said to have triumphed in every department of this important industry ... it has attacked clickers, closers, and makers, in the boot and shoe trade; in fact it would be hard to say whom it has failed to attack, and, what is more remarkable, whom it has not more or less discomforted. Soles and lifts, uppers and parts of uppers, are each cut to the desired shape at a simple stroke; stitches are set with the rapidity of lightning; and pegging, nailing, paring, and finishing are worked by magic or something closely akin to it, if magic answers in any sense to its stereotyped description.'

The following is a selection of the names of hand- (or foot-) operated machines being made in the period 1880–1910; many of them are of American origin:

Beeding	Lasting
Bevelling	Pegging
Blocking	Rand Cutting
Buffing (18 varieties)	Rolling (to replace the
Bunking	hammering of soles
Channelling	etc.)
Crimping	Seam Rubbing
Cutting Out	Sewing (Ross Moyer,
Edge Setting	USA, 1884, lists over
Edge Trimming	thirty different sewing
Embossing	machines)
Eyeletting	Skiving
Grooving	Sole Moulding
Heel Breasting	Sole Rounding
Heel Burnishing	Sole Scouring
Heel Moulding	Splitting
Heel Pressing	Toe-cap Punching
Heel Setting	Treeing
Hook Trimming	Vamp Folding and
	Polishing

Marking Out Tools

The tools used for marking out the leather before sewing and nailing are described under the following entries:

(*a*) Tools for marking out before sewing: see *Pricker Tools* (For similar tools used by harness makers and saddlers, see *Pricker* in that section.)

(*b*) Tools for marking out sole and heel for nails: see *Nail Marker*.

(*c*) Tools for marking out before inserting pegs: see *Peg Wheel*.

(*d*) Tools for marking leather to simulate stitching: see *Fudge Wheel*.

(*e*) Tools for separating and improving the appearance of stitches: see *Stitch Prick*.

Measuring Tools

These tools and appliances are used for measuring the customer's feet and the last that is made for him; for measuring the thickness of leather; and, when a shoe is to be repeated in different sizes, for the process known as grading.

Numerous contrivances have been developed which aim to reduce the labour (and the skill needed) in taking measurements of the foot. But from recent observation it appears that bespoke makers continue to use the old and simple methods: a *Size Stick* for the length of the foot; a *Tape* for the girth of the heel, instep and the ball of the foot; and the plan of the foot is recorded by the customer standing on a sheet of paper while the shoemaker marks an outline with a flat 'carpenter's' pencil.

When writing about the measuring of a customer's foot, many authors stress that a sympathetic understanding is as important as geometry. And, as Leno puts it (1895, p. 25), 'A want of proper understanding between measurer, last-fitter, and maker, is more often than not the cause of misfits. There is nothing in the shoemaking business that requires a fuller mastery of the entire trade than measurement.' It may be added that Leno begins his chapter on measurement by quoting from Sir John Vanbrugh's play 'The Relapse, or Virtue in Danger' (1697) as follows:

'Lord Toppington – Hark thee, Shoemaker! these shoes ain't ugly, but they don't fit me.
Shoemaker – My Lord, methinks they fit you very well.
Lord Toppington – They hurt me just below the instep.
Shoemaker – (feeling his foot). My Lord, they don't hurt you there.
Lord Toppington – I tell thee, they pinch me execrably.
Shoemaker – My Lord, if they pinch you, I'll be bound to be hanged, that's all.
Lord Toppington – Why, wilt thou undertake to persuade me I cannot feel?
Shoemaker –Your Lordship may please to feel when you think fit. I think I understand my trade.
Lord Toppington – Now by all that's great and powerful, thou art an incomprehensible coxcomb, but thou makest good shoes, and so I'll bear with thee.
Shoemaker – My Lord, I have worked for half the people of quality in town these twenty years, and

'twere very hard I should not know when a shoe hurts, and when it don't.'

The following measuring tools are described below:

(1) *Foot Measurers*
    (*a*)　Size Stick
    (*b*)　Tracing Block
    (*c*)　Mechanical Foot Measurers

(2) *Tapes and Rules*
    (*a*)　Tapes
    (*b*)　Rules

(3) *Pattern-Cutting and Grading Tools*
    (*a*)　A Cutting Surface
    (*b*)　Clicking Knife
    (*c*)　Rule and Tape Measure
    (*d*)　Dividers
    (*e*)　Fixed Allowance Dividers
    (*f*)　Grading Machine
    (*g*)　Pattern-Binding Machine

(4) *Substance Gauges*
    (*a*)　V-Slot Gauge
    (*b*)　Circular Gauge
    (*c*)　Rectangular Gauge
    (*d*)　Fitting-up Gauge
    (*e*)　Substance Gauge for uppers
    (*f*)　Stitch Gauge

(5) *Note on the term Iron*

1.　FOOT MEASURES

(*a*)　*Size Stick* (Randle Holme, 1688: 'Some term it a Gage or Shoe Measure') *Fig. 2:34 (p. 60)*
During the last 300 years or more, many Size Sticks have been made in the form of a Caliper Gauge. The common form is a flat strip of hardwood, graduated in shoe sizes, with a stop at one end against which the heel rests, and an adjustable stop at the other end which is moved along the stick until it touches the toe. The fixed stop is sometimes graduated to measure the height of the heel.

The Size Stick is usually made to fold, or, as was the case in the eighteenth century and before, to be telescopic. This was done to enable the user to carry the stick conveniently with his other kit or in the pocket of his apron. When extended, it is 15–16 in. (37.5–40 cm) long. But a somewhat larger and heavier version, called a Counter Size Stick, which is used on the counter to check the size of a customer's shoe, is about 20 in. (50 cm) long, and does not fold.

Size Sticks are used by shoemakers and retailers for measuring a customer's foot so that he can choose a last of the correct size.

Historical Note *Fig. 2:144*
The stops are known as 'feet' because in former times they were often carved to represent a boot: the sole and heel forming the fixed stop, the shoe upper the sliding stop. Randle Holme writes (1688, p. 522) '. . . the shoemaker's measure, by which he taketh the length or size of all feet whether children, men or women; the said measure being made that it runs one piece into another, that the feet at each end coming together make one perfect shoe.'

Since, the mid-nineteenth century, folding 'feet' have been made from slender pieces of brass or hardwood, so that they lie flat when the stick is folded. Wooden feet are often hinged to the stick by an ingenious version of what the rule makers called a 'ruled joint', in which the two metal discs or tongues fit into saw kerfs cut in the 'heel' of each foot; and these heels are so designed that they will open to 90° and no more.

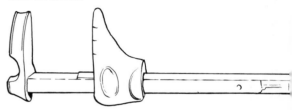

Fig. 2:144　A seventeenth-century Size Stick

The Scale *Fig. 2:145*
The scale of English shoe sizes has altered considerably over the centuries, and today differs slightly from those used in continental Europe and in America.

The English shoe-size scale is in fact two scales, one scale following on from the other, and both marked out with the same intervals between graduations. The zero point is 4 in. (10 cm) along the stick from the fixed heel-stop, and the scale advances by thirds of an inch up to size 13 (children). Thus size 1 is $4\frac{1}{3}$ in. (10.3 cm) long and size 13 is $8\frac{1}{3}$ in. (20.8 cm) long. The adult scale begins again at size 1 ($8\frac{2}{3}$ in.; 21.6 cm) and continues normally to size 14 (13 in.; 33 cm).

The American Size Stick is similar to the British except that the markings begin lower down the stick: the child's size 0 is at $3\frac{11}{12}$ in. (9.8 cm). The French markings begin at zero centimetres and run in consecutive numbers to the end in steps of two-thirds of a centimetre known as 'Paris Points'.

J. H. Thornton points out in his article on 'The English Shoe-size Scale' (1951), 'It is a typically English scale comparable with the other fantastic

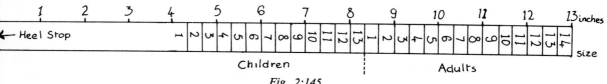

Fig. 2:145

weights and measures which occupy a few pages of our pocket diaries and hours of a schoolchild's working life.' In his detailed study Thornton describes his search for the origin of the scale and writes:

'With the advent of the mass-production of ready-made shoes in the 19th century, it became necessary ... to standardize the shoe-size scale and so there gradually emerged the scale of today. All the available evidence tends to show, however, that in its present form it is a 19th century product based on earlier scales which, so far, have only been traced back to the 17th century. Unless fresh evidence is forthcoming we must regretfully discard the popular idea that we are using a scale and a size-interval that date back to mediaeval times.'

Mr Thornton later told the author that 'the markings on English size sticks and tapes often go far beyond even the largest foot, e.g. up to size 42. A manufacturer of these tapes, when asked why, replied it was probably because he had never been told where to stop!'

(b) Tracing Block Fig. 2:146

A wood block or a metal device in which a pencil is held diagonally with a screw. It is used for tracing round the foot so that the pencil line is exactly the same as the foot contour, and not slightly outstanding because of the thickness of the pencil. The point of the pencil comes out exactly at the bottom angle, immediately below the vertical edge which is pressed against the foot as it is moved round it.

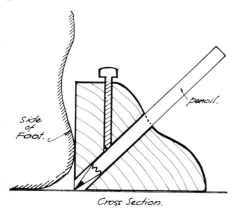

Side of Foot.

pencil.

Cross Section.

The Tracing Block

Fig. 2:146

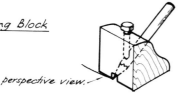

perspective view.

(c) Mechanical Foot Measurers
Among those in use are the following:

Drawing Frame

A wooden plate with one part hinging upwards at right angles to it. A sheet of paper is pinned to it. When the foot is placed upon it, a plan of the sole is drawn on the horizontal part of the paper, and an elevation of the foot is drawn on the upright section.

Ellis' Pedistat and Scott's Pedameter

These are trade names for foot-measuring devices made in the form of a low platform. The foot is placed on the platform on which are mounted (with screw adjustments) a number of moving parts which move along scales. When these parts make contact with certain points of the foot and heel, the scales give the dimensions required.

2. TAPES AND RULES

(a) Tapes
Described by Hasluck (1898) as a 'Shoemaker's penny tape measure', current examples are 24 in. (60.9 cm) long, with brass ends, and graduated in inches and eighths on one side and with shoe sizes on the other. Instead of using a tape, some makers use a strip of paper which they wrap round the part of the foot to be measured, and then nip a tear on the edge to mark the length.

(b) Rules (Devlin, 1839: 'Bit of Rule')
Both steel and wood Rules are used for general purposes in shoemaking. They are graduated like the Tapes. Barnsley (1890) lists a boxwood rule 20 in. (50.8 cm) long which he calls a 'Clicking Stick'.

The term 'Bit of Rule' appears in Devlin's list of Closer's Tools (1839). According to June Swann of the Northampton Museum, this is a familiar term in that area and not only among shoemakers. The term may derive from the common use of a piece of carpenter's folding rule which, after being accidentally broken off, fits conveniently in the apron pocket.

3. PATTERN-CUTTING AND GRADING TOOLS
Today, when fashion is of major importance, some large firms have separate designers and pattern-

153

cutters, traditionally one person would carry out both functions (and even some clicking as well).

Swaysland writes (1905, p. 39):

'The ideal pattern-cutter is a scientific artist ... it [is] indispensable that he be accustomed to great precision in measurement; that he makes provision for the alteration in shape and dimensions of the materials ... and certainly not least that he produces footwear that are artistic in shape. The art of the pattern-cutter is seen at its highest in the designing of sole shapes ... The curves are so delicate and so complicated ... the actual shaping depends largely on the individual skill of the workman.'

The chapters on pattern-cutting and grading by such authorities as Swaysland (1905), Plucknett (1916), Gresham (1920), and Thornton (1953), may bewilder the reader by their complexity and will readily convince him of the truth of Swaysland's words quoted above.

The tools used include:

(a)   A Cutting Surface
This may be wood, glass, zinc or plastic.

(b)   A Clicking Knife
This must have a blade suitable for cutting paper, i.e. it must be straight and not curved.

(c)   A Rule and *Tape Measure*

(d)   Dividers
A pair of Dividers of about 4 in. (10.1 cm) size for marking out 'allowances' that have to be added to 'net' patterns for such things as folding edges, underlay for stitching etc.

(e)   Pattern-Cutter's Fixed Allowance Dividers
Fig. 2:147
These were introduced to avoid having to alter the Dividers continually. They were made up in sets of

two-pronged forks. (Some shoemakers used the two-pronged *Stitch Prick* or *Brad Marker* if not in possession of the tool made specially for the job.)

A purpose-made set of dividers is illustrated here, made by Edward Duckenfield of Northampton during the period 1898–1910. It is named a Clicker's Grader in Richter's catalogue (*c.* 1910), but this may have arisen because clickers in small factories might also have been pattern-cutters.

(f)   Grading Machine
Today, hand grading is rarely done. Instead the work is performed by grading machines which are designed on the principle of the pantograph which, based on the geometry of the parallelogram, will copy a shape to any required scale. The early grading machines were hand-operated and cut out paper patterns in the required sizes. Now the machines are power driven and will cut out board.

(g)   Pattern-Binding Machine
Used for fixing a brass (or other metal) edge binding to a cardboard pattern to prevent knife damage. A flat metal strip is passed through rollers to give it a U-section and is then squeezed on the pattern edge by a hand-operated machine. Where necessary corners are mitred and adjoining ends soldered.

4.   SUBSTANCE GAUGES (Bottom Stock Gauge; Edge Gauge; Leather Gauge; Rough Stuff Gauge)
Metal gauges used for testing the thickness ('substance') of bottom stock, e.g. the leather used for making soles. They can also be used for checking the face-width of *Edge Irons* that are used for setting-up and burnishing the edge of the sole.

These gauges are graduated in what are termed 'Irons' (1 iron $= \frac{1}{48}$ in.; 12 irons $= \frac{1}{4}$ in.). They are shaped like engineer's wire gauges. Variants include:

(a)   V-slot Gauge   Fig. 2:148
This is graduated on both sides of a V-shaped slot, one side in irons and the other in millimetres.

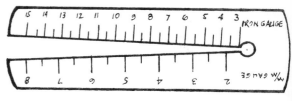

Fig. 2:148

(b)   Circular Gauge (Circular Edge Gauge)   *Fig. 2:149*
This is graduated in irons but with openings (known as 'gates') cut on the circumference of a circular

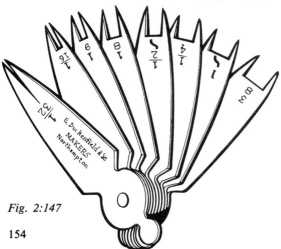

Fig. 2:147

154

plate. The thickness of the leather is measured by finding the gate into which its edge will fit.

Fig. 2:149

(*c*) *Rectangular Gauge   Fig. 2:150*
These are graduated as (*b*) above, but the gates are cut on both edges of a rectangular plate.

Fig. 2:150

(*d*) *Fitting-up Gauge*
In a letter to the author, Mr J. H. Thornton (1975) writes as follows:

'There is also a rather misleading "fitting up" gauge which at first sight appears to be an ordinary notched gauge but in fact has the gaps or notches stamped *smaller* than the actual gap they indicate; I seem to remember the difference is about 1 iron up to about 14 and 2 irons up to 24. The reason for this is that when the "fitter up" is assembling the bottoming components he takes into account the fact that during the shoemaking operations some compression will take place so that, for example, putting together an 8-iron sole, a 3-iron middle and a 5-iron welt produces in theory a 16-iron edge, but in fact this will be 14-iron. The fitting-up gauge would measure 16 but read 14.'

(*e*) *Substance Gauge for Uppers*
This is similar to an engineer's Dial Gauge but is fixed to the end of a U-shaped casting so that the thickness of leather can be measured at some distance from the edge.

(*f*) *Stitch Gauge*
A wood or metal fork-like tool with two prongs exactly 1 in. (2.5 cm) apart. It was used as a guide when counting the number of stitches per inch.

5. NOTE ON THE TERM 'IRON'
As explained in the following letter from Mr J. H. Thornton (1977), the term 'iron' derives from the connection between the thickness of sole leather and the face width of the *Edge Iron* used to set and burnish its edge.

'In June 1951, there appeared in the Journal of the British Boot and Shoe Institution a long article by me on *The English Shoe-Size Scale* in which I traced the origins and development of our curious system of measurement. As a result the following letter appeared in August of the same year:

"Sir, With reference to your *Journal* just issued for June 1951, I was rather interested by the remark on page 514 about the Iron being $\frac{1}{48}$th part of an inch, which implies that this came about by chance or caprice. I can very well remember, while attending the Technical School at Northampton, the grand old man of technical education, Mr Swaysland, talking about the way retailers ordered the substance of their shoes by $\frac{1}{4}$ edge, light $\frac{1}{4}$ and stout $\frac{1}{4}$. He stated that there could be no such thing as a light $\frac{1}{4}$ or a stout $\frac{1}{4}$. It was either a $\frac{1}{4}$ or something else. Now the Iron system just fits into these edges, a light $\frac{1}{4}$ being an 11 Iron, a $\frac{1}{4}$ being a 12 Iron, a stout $\frac{1}{4}$ being a 13 Iron and a light $\frac{5}{16}$ths being a 14 Iron, etc., so that the Iron system marries perfectly into the old system which most boot retailers used when ordering their boots and shoes. The old bespoke bootmaker always used to cut his own finishing Irons for his edges and presumably the term 'Iron' has logically derived from this. In my opinion the adoption of $\frac{1}{48}''$ as the standard of measurement was a decision of genius in view of the manner in which it fitted into both the old method of edge measurement and the official British standard of weights and measures.
Yours faithfully,
Fred B. Collinson
Collinson's Cut Soles Ltd., Field Lane,
Litherland, Liverpool, 21."

'Swaysland died in 1918 and it is not clear from Collinson's letter whether he actually used the name "iron" in his lectures; Collinson himself, however, uses it quite freely, and when I came into the trade in 1933 it was in general use, both for edge measurement and for sole substance measurement.
'All this suggests to me that the term "iron" began to be used as a measurement *c*. 1920 or during the

early twenties, first to measure Edge Irons and then, by working backwards as it were, to measure the thickness of the leather.'

Mock-Stitch Wheel

A name given to the wheel of cylindrical shape mounted on a wooden handle like a Fudge or Bunking Wheel. The circumference of the wheel is cut to imprint an appearance of stitching on the welt or on top of the sole. (See also *Bunking Tools*.)

Richter (*c.* 1910) advertised a Mock-Stitch Wheel as follows: 'A perfect imitation of stitch. Will raise an oval stitch and prick it up at the same time. Made in any width and number of stitch for men's and ladies' goods.'

Nails

(See also *Lasting Nail*.)

Nails are used in the boot and shoe trade for the attachment of soles and heels, and also as an armour to resist wear. Their use has a long history (see *Cobbler's Foot*).

As a means of attachment, nails and rivets are usually regarded as inferior to stitching: but as Plucknett points out (1916, p. 257), '... it is the cheapest style of manufacture ... and being easy to repair it is a popular attachment for low-priced goods where flexibility is of minor importance.'

The points of nails used for attachment must be sufficiently malleable to turn without breaking (clench) when they impinge on an iron last. This also enables the nail to hold two or more parts firmly together: hence the name 'rivet' given to certain slender nails used for this purpose.

The following are common examples of nails used:

Boot and Shoe Nails Fig. 2:151

(*a*) *Rivet* ($\frac{3}{8}$–1 in.; 1–2.5 cm). A slender nail made in steel or brass. Used for attaching soles and heels in 'riveted' work, as a substitute for sewing.

(*b*) *Tack* ($\frac{1}{4}$–$\frac{3}{4}$ in.; 0.6–1.9 cm). Usually a 'cut' nail used for tacking on heels and soles to hold them in place before fixing.

(*c*) *Tingle* ($\frac{1}{4}$–$\frac{1}{2}$ in.; 0.6–1.2 cm). A smaller version of the Tack; made in various patterns. (The term is related to the medieval German *Zingel* – a little tack or hook.)

(*d*) *Brad* ($\frac{3}{8}$–1 in.; 1–2.5 cm). Its rectangular head is suitable for the outside tread of a heel.

(*e*) *Cut Bill* ($\frac{3}{8}$–1 in.; 1–2.5 cm). Made in steel, with a rectangular cross-section. Used on heels and toes to resist wear. Some are serrated to give a more secure hold. (Some makers wet them before use, believing that the rust will make them grip better.)

(*f*) *Cutlan Stud* ($\frac{3}{8}$–$\frac{5}{8}$ in.; 1–1.6 cm). These are cut bills with a head extending on two sides.

(*g*) *Heel Stub* ($\frac{1}{2}$–$\frac{3}{4}$ in.; 1.2–1.9 cm). A nail used as an alternative to the rectangular headed nails (*e*) and (*f*).

(*h*) *Tip Nail* ($\frac{3}{4}$–1 in.; 1.9–2.5 cm). Made of malleable iron with round or square heads. Used for attaching iron tips to heel and toes.

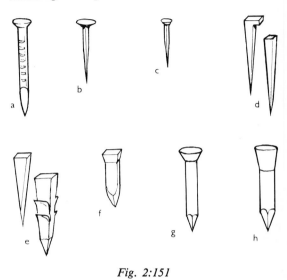

Fig. 2:151

Boot and Shoe Hobs Fig. 2:152

Examples of Hobs driven into the surface of sole and heel to resist wear:

(*a*) Welsh Square		(*d*) Ridge
(*b*) 'Patent'		(*e*) Mearn
(*c*) Clinker		(*f*) Victoria

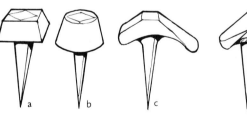

Fig. 2:152

Nailing Tools

Until about twenty years ago, nails and rivets, though considered inferior to stitching, were widely used as means of attaching soles in lower-priced boots and shoes. Today, the common alternative to stitching is the moulded-on or stuck-on sole.

Nailing tools are described under the following entries: *Hammer*; *Lasting Nail*; *Lasting Pincer*; *Nail Gun*; *Nail Holder*; *Nail Marker*; *Pig's Foot* (and Nail Claw); *Rasp*; *Rivet Driver*.

Among the workshop 'aids' to nail-driving, mention must be made of the human mouth. Anyone who watches a shoemaker or repairer at work will recognise this description of *c.* 1850, quoted by Thomas Wright (1922):

'I have often watched the riveters at work, with their mouths full of rivets, but I used to be afraid to speak to them lest in replying to a question, they might swallow, and so waste, I knew not what weight of marketable metal.'

A more technical account of this process appears in *The Amateur Mechanic* (Waverley, 1910, Vol. II, p. 242):

'Whatever may be the opinions from a health point of view, it is certain that the quickest riveting speed is obtained by holding the rivets in the mouth. Place a small quantity in the bottom of the mouth under the tongue. A little practice enables the worker to single out the rivets with his tongue, bringing them forward, one at a time, between the teeth, the rivet point projecting first between the lips; at the same moment, the left hand is brought upwards to the mouth, taking hold of the rivet in the middle with the finger and thumb, and it is then an easy matter to bring the rivet straight down to the riveting line point first. Hold the rivet at a slight angle. Whilst the rivet is held in position with the finger and thumb, tap the rivet head with the driving file to fasten, then drive flush with one or two taps.'

It may be added that a skilled operator can remove rivets from his mouth with the Lasting Pincers – and the right way round.

Nail Claw: see *Pig's Foot*.

Nail Gun (Heel Nailer; Heel Fixer; Nail Driver; Ramhead Hammer; Tubular Hammer) *Fig. 2:153*
A plunger operated inside a tube, *c.* 12 in. (30.5 cm) overall, with a short feed tube on one side for inserting nails.

The end of the tube is placed on the spot where a nail is required; the plunger is raised, a nail is dropped into the feed tube, and the plunger forced down upon it.

This tool is mainly used for driving nails from inside a boot or shoe, where it is difficult to use a hammer.

A variant is made with a magnetic plunger. This holds the nail, and a feed tube is not needed.

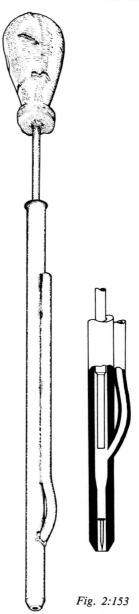

Fig. 2:153

157

Nail Holder and Nail Chest (Nail Box; Nail Dish; Nail Cup; Revolving Nail Holder)

(*a*) *Nail Cup Fig. 2:154*
One of the most popular Nail Holders was a revolving 'nail cup', described in the catalogue of one of the grindery merchants as 'the Repairer's Friend'. Made usually in cast-iron, it contained 6—8 compartments and was designed to revolve on a low stand so that any compartment could be turned towards the user.

Fig. 2:154

(*b*) *Nail Chest Fig. 2:155*
Some makers and repairers also used a small wooden chest, often suspended on the wall, which contained a nest of small drawers, of the type illustrated.

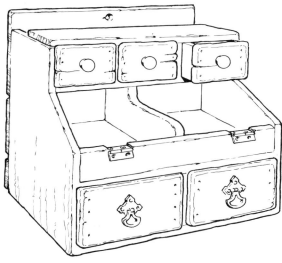

Fig. 2:155

Nail Marker (Brad Marker; Brad Pricker; Nail Punch; Two-Pronged Awl)
There are two types:

(*a*) *Brad Marker: mainly for heels Fig. 2:156*
A tool rather like a screwdriver in appearance, but with a forked blade. At the Hertford Museum there is a set of Brad Markers with the forked end in 5 sizes. One of the examples illustrated here has a wooden cross-handle and may have started life as a screwdriver.

The tool is used for marking the edge of the heel top-piece for receiving brads (or other nails), and for ensuring that they are evenly spaced. The tool is 'stepped' round the heel, one prong at a time, giving a succession of evenly spaced indentations.

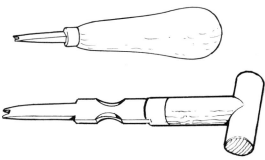

Fig. 2:156

(*b*) *Nail-Marking Punch: mainly for soles*
When marking out soles for nailing, a stout Punch with serrated teeth is used; or, alternatively, a wheel marker, such as a *Peg Wheel*.

Note: Tools for marking stitches etc. are listed under *Marking Tools*.

Naumkeag Buffer (Naumkeag Wheel)
A term included here because it is a name given to an abrasive 'head' used mostly for scouring the waist of a shoe. It is a conical or mushroom-shaped wheel, covered with an abrasive, which is attached to a Finishing Machine. The name was in use in 1890 and may come from the inventor or maker of the machine.

Needle
Unlike the harness makers, shoemakers use a bristle instead of a needle for guiding the thread through awl-made holes in the leather. But needles with eyed points are used in Sewing Machines (see *Awl*; *Bristle*; *Sewing*).

Nipper: see *Pincer, Plier or Nipper*.

Paring Horn
A flat, thin piece of horn, roughly rectangular in shape. This is held against the upper to protect it

when trimming the welt with a knife. Devlin (1839, p. 53) describes a slightly different method:

'In taking off, should the sole in the first instance be carefully prepared, there is little trouble with the knife, at least round the edge, perhaps none. But if not so prepared, the piece of kit called the paring horn, or, as is often used, the sharpened shaft of a large pewter spoon, is run along between the upper and the sole, accompanied by the knife which cuts as it goes; the piece of horn or pewter held in the left hand and the knife in the right.'

Paste Horn   *Fig. 2:157*

A small cup for holding paste. Traditionally made by sawing off a section from the base of a cow-horn, they often appear bent over to one side.

The paste, which is used for sticking down linings, was, until recent times, made from flour.

Fig. 2:157

Patie Bowie (Peter Bowie)

Scots term for a length of bone or wood used for rubbing down. See Petty Boy under *Bones and Sticks* for origin of the term.

Peg

Boot and shoe pegs are small wooden pins of round or diamond-shaped cross-section, about $\frac{1}{2}$ in. (1.2 cm) long and an $\frac{1}{8}$ in. (0.3 cm) thick.

Pegs were used in the seventeenth century for building up heel lifts, but it was not until the early eighteenth century that pegs became a common alternative to both sewing and rivets for joining upper to sole and sole to inner sole. Pegs are driven by a smart blow from a hammer into holes previously bored by an awl.

Pegs have the helpful property of swelling when wet, and so help to make the boot watertight. Metal rivets were not so successful for, when the leather soles became soft with continuous wetting, they tended to slip on the metal fastenings and let the water in. Pegged boots continued to be made for seamen and farmers until the moulded rubber 'Well-

ington' provided a cheap and more effective alternative.

A London shoemaker told us that before rubber or plastic soles became common, he made 'hundreds of pairs' of pegged shoes for yachtsmen: nailed soles would have scratched the deck.

Tools used in pegging are described in the following entries.

Peg-Fitting Tools

'Peg-Tool' is the name usually given to a special rasp, float or cutter designed to break or cut off the tips of pegs when they protrude inside a boot or shoe, and to smooth up afterwards. They are made in two sizes, about 10–12 in. (25.4–30.5 cm) long for normal work, and about 12–18 in. (30.5–45.7 cm) long for reaching down the leg of a riding or sea boot.

The rasp or cutting head is forged on the ends of a shank which is usually bent to a shallow S-shape to facilitate working inside the shoe. Some have a wooden handle with a single rasp or cutting head; others have a working head at each end, but facing opposite ways. These working heads are made for cutting, breaking, scraping, or rasping; sometimes heads that perform two or more functions are mounted on the same shank.

Peg Tools are sometimes home-made from old woodworking or farrier's rasps, beaten smooth in the centre for holding and bent into a shallow S-shape.

It should be noted that in more recent times, cutting off pegs inside a shoe has been done with side-cutting nippers with long handles (see under *Pincers*); but a rasp is still needed for smoothing up afterwards.

The following variants are listed under their own special names – which are sometimes alternatives to the general term 'Peg Tool'.

(*a*)   *Peg Awl*: see *Awl, Peg.*

(*b*)   *Peg Breaker* (Peg Float)   *Figs 2:19, No. 9; 2:20, No. 4 (pp. 45, 46)*
These are float-cut, i.e. with coarse horizontal serrations, usually made with half the teeth slanted in one direction, and half in the other, so operating on both the pull and push stroke.

The end of the peg is caught in one of the teeth and then broken off; after which the tool can be used to smooth up.

(*c*)   *Peg Cutter   Fig. 2:19, Nos 7 and 8 (p. 45)*
Peg Cutters are made with chisel-like blades, set to cut when lying flat, and provided with a short fence to prevent the tool from slipping off the peg. Some

have opposing blades, set in a forked stock, to cut when either pushed or pulled. (See also Cutting Pincers under *Pincer, Plier or Nipper*.)

(*d*)   *Peg Knife* (Balloon Knife; Hoop Knife; USA: Yankee Cutter).
These have blades set at right angles to the stem. They can be used when held almost vertically for cutting off peg tips at the heel end; or for scraping down inside a boot or shoe afterwards. There are several variants, including:

> 1.   *The Balloon Knife   Figs 2:19, Nos 10 and 11; 2:20, No. 21 (pp. 45, 46)*
> Ring-shaped, rather like a cooper's Round Shave, with a single or double edge.
>
> 2.   *The Hook Knife   Fig. 2:20, Nos 20 and 20$\frac{1}{2}$ (p. 46)*
> A hook-shaped blade like that used by a spoon or bowl maker. A similar tool is used for trimming ladies' wooden heels.
>
> 3.   *Combination Tools   Figs 2:19; 2:20 (pp. 45, 46)*
> These include those with a blade at one end, and a rasp or float at the other.

(*e*)   *Peg Rasp* (Insole Rasp)   *Fig. 2:19; 2:20*
A Peg Tool with a rasp-cut head sometimes combined with a Peg Cutter at the other end. Used for cleaning up and smoothing the inside of a boot or shoe.

(*f*)   *Peg Rifler*
The same as the Peg Rasp, but usually shorter, i.e. about 10 in. (25.4 cm) overall. The working surfaces are either rasp or file cut.

(*g*)   *American Peg Tools*
The following do not appear in English tool catalogues:

1.   Ross Moyer (USA, 1884, p. 191) illustrates a Peg Float consisting of a small circular float-cut plate pivoted at its centre on the end of a long handle. A similar instrument, which they call a Heel Break, has the circular float-cut plate fixed at right angles to the end of a flat metal shank. There are three small holes in the shank whose purpose is not explained. In the Leather Findings catalogue of Henry Arthur (1874) the shank is made of wood.

2.   Knight (1877 under 'Float') illustrates a short float-cut head on the top of a stout stem which is fitted to the bench. A shoe can be held sole-uppermost, with the head inside the shoe, and then pushed back and forth to smooth the inner sole.

Note: Wynn, Timmins & Co. (1892) illustrates a handled, float-cut Peg Breaker of the ordinary

English type (*a*) above, but calls it an 'American Shoe Peg Breaker'.

Peg-Making Tool   *Fig. 2:158*
In the mid-nineteenth century many ingenious machines were developed, some hand-operated, for making and fitting pegs. The peg-making tool described below was found by D. A. Saguto in 1982 in Pennsylvania, USA. It was probably intended to be used by the shoemaker himself.

Mr Saguto, who also provided the drawing, wrote: 'I have tried this, and it works quite well. I can make about 20 pegs in 5 mins. This is about half the amount needed to peg together one shoe heel.'

The tool consists of an oak clamp *c.* $9\frac{3}{8} \times 1\frac{1}{8}$ in. (23.8 × 2.8 cm) for holding a strip of peg timber, and a knife for pointing and splitting the pegs. The back of the blade shows hammer marks where it was beaten to split off the strips for pegs. The jaws of the clamp have been formed by sawing the block in two for about two-thirds of its length, and then shaving the upper half to a thin bevelled edge.

The illustration shows the peg-cutting knife held in the workman's right hand; it is pulled towards him in the direction of the arrow. The strip of peg timber is shown in the jaws of the clamp at (*a*), the open end of which he holds fast in his left hand. The end (*b*) of the clamp is braced against his chest during the cutting. When one side of the peg strip has been bevelled, it is turned over in the clamp and the other side is bevelled to form a bilateral point along one edge of the strip. (*c*) shows the pegs split away from the pointed strip and ready for use.

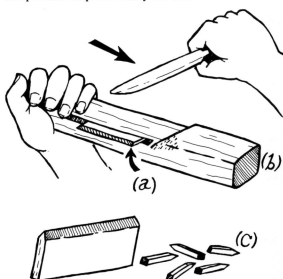

Fig. 2:158

Peg Wheel *Figs 2:22, Nos 30–33 (p. 48); 2:159*
A star-shaped wheel, mounted on a handled stem, *c.* 6½ in. (16.4 cm) overall, and used for marking positions for pegs. All have a fence which bears on the edge of the sole or heel. Some have a moveable wheel to mark out a line of pegs at different distances from the edge. Wheels are provided with teeth varying from 4–7 teeth per inch.

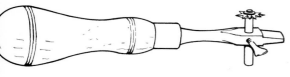

Fig. 2:159

Pig's Foot and Nail Lifters (Nail Claw; Sprig Lifter; Tack Lifter) *Figs 2:54, Nos 6170, 6164; 2:55, Nos 6180/82/84 (pp. 80, 81)*
(See also *Sole Prizer*; and *Pig's Foot* in the CLOG-MAKER section.)
Similar in appearance to a woodworker's Tack Lifter, but more heavily made. It is fitted with a wooden handle, often hooped for driving, or in iron throughout.
A variant, known as a Sprig Lifter, has a narrower claw; this is designed to catch and hold the head of very small nails.
The Pig's Foot is used by shoemakers for 'stripping', i.e. the removal of nails and the lifting off of soles.

Pincer, Plier or Nipper (Pincher; Shoe Pincer; Shoe Nipper) *Fig 2:160*
(See also *Punches*.)
Nomenclature in this group of tools is confused. Makers' catalogues and text books call them Pincers, Pliers, Nippers – or even Tongs.
The following tools belonging to the Pincer and Plier family are used by shoemakers:

(*a*) *Shoe Pincers* (Shoe Nippers; Tower Shoe Pincer) *Fig. 2:44, No. 4210 (p. 70)*
These are made like carpenter's pincers and are used for extracting nails and ripping off old soles and heel lifts. 'Tower Shoe Nippers' is a name sometimes given to a strong Shoe Pincer which is 'left in the black', i.e. not polished.

(*b*) *Shoe Pincer with hammer* *Fig. 2:160, No. 3*
Similar to (*a*) above, but with a hammer head ('anvil') added to one jaw. This can be used for driving nails, or for giving an added leverage when wrenching off old soles etc.

(*c*) *Cutting Pincers* (Manchester Nipper) *Fig. 2:44, Nos 4200, 4220 (p. 70)*
There are two types: one a 'carpenter's' pincer with a flat-topped head adapted for cutting off protruding nails; the other, a long-handled side cutting plier, sometimes known as a Manchester Nipper, used for cutting off nails or pegs inside the shoe.

(*d*) *Lasting Pincers*: see *Lasting Pincers and Dogs.*

(*e*) *Lining Pliers* (Lining Pincers) *Figs 2:160(1) (overleaf); 2:44, No. 4180 (p. 70)*
(See also *Knife, Lining*.)
A plier with reverse-taper ('beaver-tail') jaws used for pulling the shoe lining over the last. The thinness of the jaws enables the shoemaker to reach the lining if it is hidden behind the upper; and their width ensures a strong pull with less risk of tearing the material.

(*f*) *Pincers for special purposes*
Blocking Pincers: see *Blocking Tools*
Button-Hole Punch Plier etc.: see *Button Tools*
Eyelet Plier etc.: see *Eyelet Tools*
Punch-Hole Pliers etc.: see *Punches*
Stretching Plier: see *Stretchers*
Tag-Metalling Plier: see *Lace Tools*

(*g*) *Identification of leather-working Pincers* *Fig. 2:160 (overleaf)*
The illustrations are intended for the identification of some of the pincers to be seen in the workshops.

Plane, Clicker's Block (Block Plane; Cutting-Block Surfacing Plane) *Fig. 2:161 (p. 163)*
(See also *Cutting Board*.)
An American metal Plane about 16 in. (40.6 cm) long designed to pare up the face of a clicker's cutting block after wear.
Mr W. Downes (USA, 1978), who has made a special study of this unusual plane, has sent us the following account of it:

'The American inventor of this plane, George E. Franklin of Natick, Mass., stated the need in 1873 as follows:

'"In using dies for punching or cutting shoe soles and uppers, and other stock, it is customary to use blocks of wood with the end of the grain uppermost, the top surface being faced off for smoothness. As such a block becomes too much worn for practical use, it is cut down with an adze to a plane below the lowest depression worn by the dies, and is then surfaced off with a smoothing plane. This method of

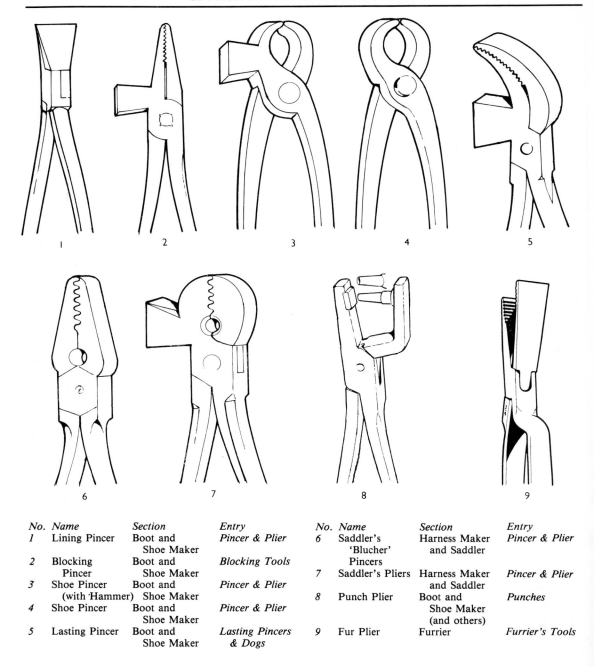

No.	Name	Section	Entry	No.	Name	Section	Entry
1	Lining Pincer	Boot and Shoe Maker	*Pincer & Plier*	6	Saddler's 'Blucher' Pincers	Harness Maker and Saddler	*Pincer & Plier*
2	Blocking Pincer	Boot and Shoe Maker	*Blocking Tools*	7	Saddler's Pliers	Harness Maker and Saddler	*Pincer & Plier*
3	Shoe Pincer (with Hammer)	Boot and Shoe Maker	*Pincer & Plier*	8	Punch Plier	Boot and Shoe Maker (and others)	*Punches*
4	Shoe Pincer	Boot and Shoe Maker	*Pincer & Plier*	9	Fur Plier	Furrier	*Furrier's Tools*
5	Lasting Pincer	Boot and Shoe Maker	*Lasting Pincers & Dogs*				

Fig. 2:160 Typical Pincers and Pliers used in leather working.

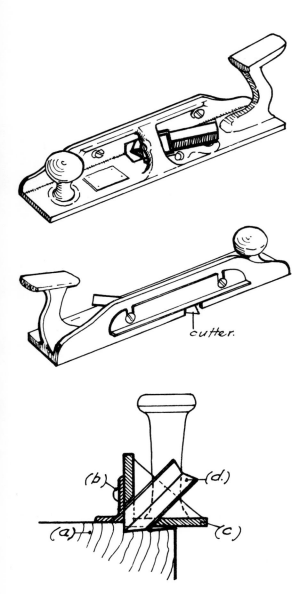

Fig. 2:161 Clicker's Plane

(*a*) The cutting block
(*b*) Depth stop rests on surface to be planed
(*c*) Plane bed rides on the cut wood
(*d*) V-Cutter, United Shoe Machine Co. version

surfacing a block is very slow and laborious, and does not result in procuring a uniform surface. My invention has reference to a method of surfacing such a block by means of a plane alone . . ."

'The Franklin plane is a combination of a regular rabbet plane and a side rabbet plane. It cuts a series of narrow rabbets across the end grain of the cutting block until the whole surface is restored to smoothness. The plane is unique in that two cutters are involved, one cutting vertical to the bed of the plane, the other, flush with the bed. The two cutters are adjacent, and are held at right angle to each other, with the cutting edges projecting through the side of the iron bed. A depth stop, on the same side, rests on the surface to be planed. The cutting starts at one edge of the block surface, and narrow cuts are made, up to $\frac{3}{8}''$ wide, with each pass of the plane. The cutters are held in a pivoted mount; they can be swung out from the side of the plane to cut a wider rabbet. During the planing operation, the depth stop rides on the uncut wood, while the plane bed rides on the cut wood. The advantage appears to be that all the wood surface, to the depth damaged by the punch cuts, can be removed with one series of passes across the surface. The fact that the rabbet cuts are narrow, limits the force required to a reasonable amount. The jack plane length of the bed helps keep the surface level; and the consequent mass of the plane makes possible enough momentum to cut across the block without stopping.

'The plane is not easy to use successfully. The horizontal cutter is cutting across the end grain of a hard wood like a chisel, and without the help of the mallet that one would use with a chisel. This may be the reason for a change in design that was made in a United Shoe Machine Company version of the plane. In this plane the cutting edges are not at right angles, but form a vee. The cutter is made in one piece and cuts like a corner chisel in which the edges are at less than 90 degrees to each other. One edge is still vertical, but the other is no longer flat with the bed of the plane. Consequently, the surface that is left after planing has a ridge left on it for each pass of the plane. To obtain a final smooth surface would require following up with a regular smoothing plane or a block plane.

'The advantage of this plane over the other would seem to be that the end grain is no longer cut at right angles to the grain, but at a skewed angle. This should make pushing the plane easier, but at the price of finishing with a smoothing plane.'

Pricker

A name sometimes given to an awl (see *Awl, Dart*).

Pricker Tools

Note: For tools serving the same purpose for harness makers and saddlers, see *Pricker* in that section. (See also *Marking Tools* in this section.)

These are toothed instruments designed for making a series of holes in the surface of the leather to guide the awl before sewing. (There is some evidence that the tools were also occasionally used on thin leathers as a substitute for the awl.)

The teeth of these tools are usually round in cross-section, but occasionally they are slightly flattened to produce a very short slit at right angles to the edge being sewn. The teeth of the saddler's pricking tools are similar, except that the flattened teeth are set at 45° to the edge of the work.

There are two kinds:

(a) *Stabbing Pricker* (Prick Iron) *Fig. 2:22, Nos 28, 38 (p. 48)*

A steel punch, straight or curved, provided with teeth which in Barnsley's catalogue of 1892 are 12–24 per inch on the straight, and 14–22 per inch on the 'circular' tool. Their purpose is thus described by Devlin (1839, p. 58), who also includes a warning:

'The generality of closers have latterly a habit of marking these rows, and indeed all other sorts of stabbing, with a toothed instrument, called a *pricker*, the pricker being struck down upon the leather in the required direction, and thus marking the holes for the entrance of the awl. This, however, though it may facilitate the learner, is not altogether a praiseworthy improvement, the sharp edges of the teeth of this tool often times fracturing the leather in a way which the awl never does. Boots through this custom are seen to fly open along the stabbing rows...'

Devlin then describes various precautions to avoid '... causing great injury to the leather ... which may occasion the whole stabbing row to break asunder in the lasting of the boot, or in its wearing – a misfortune of no uncommon occurrence.'

(b) *Pricking Wheel* (Closer's Wheel; Stabbing Wheel; Wheel Pricker). *Figs 2:10, Nos 3077/78; 2:22, No. 26 (pp. 36, 48)*

A rowel mounted in a forked carrier, with teeth varying in number from 12–24 per inch. Those illustrated by Richard Timmins (*c.* 1800) are provided with a fence short enough to bear on the edge of thin leather without coming into contact with the bench. Used as in (a) above, they should not be confused with the lighter Tracing Wheels used by dressmakers and milliners.

(c) *Clamming Marker*

A name given in the catalogue of Henry Arthur ('Leather and Findings', USA, 1874) to a Pricking Punch with a wooden handle. Used, presumably, for marking stitches on leather which is being held in a *Clamp*.

Prick Stitch: see *Stitch Prick*.

Puff Stick (Loop Stick; Toe Poker)   *Fig. 2:56, No. 6138 (p. 82)*

An S-shaped stick about 9 in. (22.8 cm) long.

A toe puff is a stiffening for the toe-end of a shoe to give protection to the toes. Leno (1895, p. 144) writes that its introduction 'has been a perfect blessing to thousands, more especially to those who have riding or cocked-up toes'. The alternative name Loop Stick is probably borrowed from the harness trade, where a piece of wood of this name is used as a foundation and guide when making loops for straps.

It is used for pushing the toe-cap from inside if it appears irregular after coming off the last, or if the toe-cap of one shoe appears different from that of the other.

The stick is also used to push the toe-cap forward from the inside: this has the effect of lowering a thick, high toe-cap, to give it a more elegant appearance.

A variant is made of iron with a small shield-shaped piece forged on the end.

Pumice Stone

This is used in the leather trades (a) by shoemakers for smoothing down bristles (see *Sewing*) and (b) by curriers, for rubbing off any remaining hairs from the hide (see LEATHER MANUFACTURE).

Pump

This is a slipper or turnshoe of light weight, usually kept on the foot by its close fit and having no fastenings. (See Pump Iron under *Edge Iron (g–h)*.)

Punches for hole-punching

Note: Punches made for other purposes will be found under *Punches* in the HARNESS MAKER AND SADDLER section, and under *Button Tools*, *Nail Master*, and *Pricker Tools* in this section.

These Punches are used mainly for making round lace-holes which are later usually fitted with metal eyelets (see *Eyelet Tools*). The diameter of the holes punched varies from *c.* $\frac{1}{32}$ to $\frac{3}{16}$ in. (0.1–0.4 cm); they are given numbers 00 to 10 in the makers' lists.

Randle Holme (1688) sang the praises of the 'Genteel Punch ... being an emblem of safety, for by the help thereof both Sandals and Shoes are made secure on the feet, by which means we may Go, Run, or Leap without Jeapardy'.

The main types of round Punch used by shoemakers are:

(*a*) *Hand Punch* (Shoe Punch) *Fig. 2:25 (p. 51)*
Similar to the punches used by saddlers, but with a round cutting edge rather than a choice of round, oval or flat. There are four types:

(1) A metal shank designed to be struck with a hammer. It consists of a short, tapering tube with its lower edge sharpened to the size of the hole required. The tube is tapered so that the small pieces of leather punched out can escape without jamming the tool. The tapered tube rises upward for about 1 in. (2.5 cm), exposes a side outlet, and is then merged with the shank. Fifteenth-century examples may be seen in the Museum of London.

(2) The same as above, but with the nose screwed to take different sized bits.

(3) A punch mounted in a wooden handle, presumably intended to penetrate thin leather by hand pressure. That illustrated by Wynn, Timmins & Co. (1892) is named 'Improved Boston Shoe Punch'.

(4) The Wad Punch. *Fig. 2:47, No. 4356 (p. 73)*
This tool is intended for producing small washer-shaped pieces of leather rather than for making holes. (The term 'Wad' relates to their use in muzzle-loading guns.) In shoemaking the Punch was used for making studs for football boots.

(*b*) *Plier Punches* (Spring Plier; Toe-cap Plier. The cutter, when detachable, is called a Bit, Tube, or Nipple.) *Figs 2:162; 2:25; 2:45 (pp. 51, 71)*
A plier in which one jaw holds the bit, while the other jaw carries a brass anvil (or pad) on which the sharp edge of the steel bit can impinge after penetration without damage to its cutting edge. The handles are sprung to hold the jaw open until squeezed; some handles have a magazine fitted to the inner side which holds several bits of different sizes.

A plier with longer jaws, for reaching a more distant point in the leather, is known as a Toe-Cap Punch Plier.

(*c*) *Revolving Plier Punch* (Star Punch) *Fig. 2:45, Nos 4310 and 4312 (p. 71)*
In this plier a turret of 4–6 different sized bits is mounted on one of the jaws; a spring latch mechanism enables any one of these bits to be set to face the 'anvil' jaw, ready for action. Today, these pliers are usually pressed from steel sheet for the sake of lightness; earlier models were solid forgings, with square or hexagonal turrets.

(*d*) *Pricking Plier Punch* (Pricking Tool)
A name given to a punch made like (*a*) above, but the bit is solid, and is intended to punch holes round the edge of the heel top-piece to take the nails.

(*e*) *Fancy Punch Plier* (Brogueing Punch; Perforating Plier) *Fig. 2:46, No. 4320 (p. 72)*
Made like the ordinary Plier Punch, but there is an adjustable guide fitted to the 'anvil' jaw.

The bits are made in several patterns (mostly round) for perforating holes in toe-caps, and in parts of the Oxford and Brogue style of shoe, on which this type of decoration is made. Leno (1895, p. 77) disapproves: 'This punching of a toe-cap is, however, an abominable practice, only equalled in folly by the flowered toe-cap once so common in boots worn by women. It destroys the integrity of the leather, and so renders it incapable of fulfilling its purpose.'

(*f*) *Machine Punches* *Fig. 2:49 (p. 75)*
There are many hand- or foot-operated punching machines, most of which are provided with Eyelet Closing Bits as well.

Pykin Awl
Scots term for (probably) a *Peg Awl*.

Race for cutting channels or grooves: see *Channel Tools*.

Rag Stone
Devlin (1839, p. 113) includes 'rag stones for pointing awls' in his list of 'The boot-closer's kit'. The term 'rag' was applied to coarse stone used for sharpening tools.

Fig. 2:162

Rand Tools (In some early nineteenth-century catalogues, including that of Richard Timmins, the term 'rand' is spelt 'Rhan'; Randle Holme (1688) spells the word 'Rann'.)

The word for welt in both German and Dutch is *rand*; and since the seventeenth century the words 'rand' and 'welt' in this country have become confused, if not interchangeable. For example, Randle Holme (1688), when defining a rand, gives a fair description of a welt. One of the shoemakers quoted below calls a rand a 'storm welt'.

In many trades the term 'rand' implies a strip of material, edge, or a border. In shoemaking, the term is applied to a strip of leather roughly triangular in cross-section, or folded to form a U in cross-section, sewn into the upper/bottom seam (or elsewhere) for the purpose of (*a*) added resistance to damp and/or (*b*) to add strength to the joint – particularly in securing the heel.

J. H. Thornton wrote to the author (1978) that a turnshoe sometimes had an extra wide rand included in the seam so that this becomes a welt to which a first sole, and later, a repair one, can be stitched. It was an intermediate stage between a turnshoe and a welted shoe, appearing c. 1500.

Few, if any, of the Rand Tools listed below are still in use, but some of them are known to older retired shoemakers. The following remarks are quoted from conversations with some of them, mostly in the London area.

(*a*) 'The Boot Rand Iron is for ironing up the edges of two welts, i.e. the rand and welt proper. This extra rand is called the "Rand Cork", known in the trade as a French Cork ... it provides space to waterproof the bottom of the shoe by inserting a layer of cork in the "well" caused by sewing in the two welts.'

(*b*) 'A rand is sewn around the heel (usually a Riding Boot). This is a very strong method of securing the heel because when the sole is attached the heel is then sewn-down by looping each stitch with its neighbour ... there is a tendency to wrench off the heel when using the Boot-Jack especially if the heel is only nailed on. ... This method of attaching the heel is known as a "German Seat": alternatively when a welt is continued around the heel it is then called a "Russian Seat".'

(*c*) 'When making riding boots I put in a rand made of folded upper-leather. This was when the welt was taken all round the boot. It was called a "randed welt". I don't know whether the rand improved the boot, but customers asked for it.'

(*d*) 'The rand is a storm welt sewn in between the upper and welt. We used a Rand File or Seat Breaker to level it off round the seat.'

Rasp (Shoe Rasp)   *Fig. 2:12 (p. 38)*
(See also *Abrasives*; *Files*; *Peg Tools*; *Rivet Driver*.)
A short Rasp *c.* 8 in. (20.3 cm) long. Like the farrier's rasp (which it resembles except in being shorter and lighter) there is no handle, and the two halves of the rasp are made to cut in opposite directions.

There are a great many variations in the shape and cut of teeth, including:

Tools with the term rand as part of their name will be found under the following entries:

Name	Purpose	See under:
Rand File (Seat File) Back Rand File	A File or Float used for trimming the seat of the heel.	*File, Shoemaker's*
Rand Fitter	Included in Devlin's 'Kit of the boot-man'. Purpose unknown.	
Rand Iron	One of the family of Edge Irons for setting and burnishing the sole edge.	*Edge Iron* (Boot Rand Iron)
Rand Key Rand Bone	Probably a stitch or scratch bone, used mainly for rubbing down stitches on the rand (later, welt).	*Bones and Sticks* (Bone Tools)
Rand Pricker	A tool for separating the stitches on the rand (later, welt).	*Stitch Prick*
Rander	A name given to a machine for trimming heels.	
Rand Wheel	Probably the ancestor of both Fudge and Seat Wheel.	*Fudge*; *Seat Wheel*

(1)   One side flat, the other half round;

(2)   Both sides half round, resulting in an oval cross-section (a pattern known as 'French' or 'Boston');

(3)   One side rasp-cut, the other file cut.

The Rasp is used for smoothing and finishing soles, sole-edges and heels. Hasluck (1893, p. 124) gives detailed instructions on how to use a Rasp, and stresses the importance of using the fingers as a guard to prevent injury to the upper. The half-round side of the rasp is used to give the edge of the heel its slightly hollowed contour; the flat side is used for smoothing the forepart edges, after which any 'nap' or 'burr' appearing on the extreme edge is smoothed off with the file-cut side of the rasp. This file-cut side is also used for bevelling and polishing the heads of any rivets driven into the sole and top piece.

Shoemaker's Rasps are also used for driving small nails — a remarkable instance of the same tool serving two purposes with complete success. (See also *Rivet Driver* below.)

Rivet Driver (Driver; Froggatt's Rivet Driver; Hammer File; Hammer Rasp; Knocker)   *Figs 2:54, No. 6146 (p. 80); 2:163*
(See also *Nailing Tools*; *Rasp*.)
The name Rivet Driver is given to a shoe file or rasp that has been altered in shape to make it more convenient to use as a hammer. It is *c.* 8 in. (20.3 cm) long, usually file-cut on one side, and one end is left uncut to serve as a handle.

The shoemaker's File or Rasp is one of the few tools in any trade that is made to perform two quite different functions. Besides being used for smoothing down it also serves as a hammer for driving small nails or rivets. Shoemakers say that the rough surface of the tool makes it possible to strike a nail at an angle without slipping off the head, and this roughness also prevents the nail from 'flying out' when struck, as it tends to do when using a smooth-faced hammer.

A variant made with a nail-claw at the butt of the handle is listed by some tool makers as 'Froggatt's Rivet Driver'.

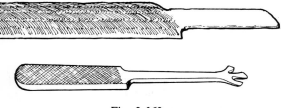

Fig. 2:163

Roset End (Rosit End)
A Scots term for end of a thread (used in sewing leather) which is stiffened with resin.

Rubbing Down and Sleeking Tools: see *Bones and Sticks*; *Edge Irons*; *Glazer and Sleeking Iron* (includes Cozer; Bosher; Dummy; Fiddler); *Knife, Buffing* (and Scrapers); *Paring Horn*; *Seam Sett*.

Saint Crispin
The patron saint of the shoemakers, whose festival is celebrated on 25 October.

Many of the legends and stories concerning shoemakers relate to St Crispin who supported himself by shoemaking while preaching the gospel. He was martyred in AD 288 at Soissons in France. (See under *Folklore* in the introduction to this section and also *Saint Hugh's Bones* below.)

Saint Hugh's Bones
(See also *Kit*; *Bones and Sticks*; and the note on St Crispin in the introduction.)
A shoemaker's kit of tools is sometimes known as 'St Hugh's Bones'. The name originated in the story of St Hugh, or Sir Hugh, as he was sometimes called. According to one version of the legend, St Hugh was a Prince of Britain, son of Arviragus, the King of Powisland. He fell in love with Winifred, daughter of the King of Flintshire. She became a Christian, and St Hugh adopted her faith. They were both put to death for their beliefs about AD 300.

St Hugh had learnt the trade of a shoemaker to support himself after losing his wealth in a shipwreck. He preached the gospel by day and made shoes at night. Thomas Deloney (1597) relates that when St Hugh was in prison, awaiting death, his fellow journeymen shoemakers 'never left him, but yielded him great relief, so that he wanted nothing that was necessary to him; in requital of which kindness he called them "Gentlemen of the Gentle Craft"'.

After his death, his brother shoemakers took his bones from the gibbet and made them into tools, and from that time shoemaker's tools were called 'St Hugh's Bones'. In France, by some intermingling of two legends, a shoemaker's kit is sometimes called a 'Saint-Crepin'.

Thomas Deloney also composed a list in verse of the tools that were to be known in future as St Hugh's Bones: The following version comes from his book *The Gentle Craft* printed in London by Robert Bird in 1637:

'My freinds, I pray you list to me,
And marke what S. Hughes bones shall be.

First a Drawer[1] and a Dresser[2]
two Wedges,[3] a more and a lesser:
A pretty blocke three inches high,
in fashion sqared like a Die,
Which shall be called by proper name,
A Heele blocke[4], the very same.
A Hand-leather[5] and a Thumb-leather[6] like wise
to pull out shoo-threed we must despise;[7]
The Needle and the Thimble,
shall not be left alone
The Pincers and the pricking Awle
and the rubbing stone.[10]
The Awle steele and Tackes,
the Sow-haires[8] beside,
The Stirrop[9] holding fast,
while we sowe the cow-hide.
The whetstone,[10] the stopping sticke,[11]
and the Paring knife[12]
All this doth belong,
to a Journeymans life
Our Apron is the Shrine,
to wrap these bones in:
Thus shrowd we Saint Hugh,
in gentle lambes skinne . . .
Content, content, and then after many merry
    songs they departed
And never after did they travell without these
    tooles on their backes:
which ever since were called Saint Hughes
    bones.'

Tools mentioned in the above extract.
A correct interpretation of sixteenth-century tool
names may be impossible; the following are some
suggestions:

1. *Drawer*   } Meaning uncertain.
2. *Dresser* }

June Swann (Northampton Museum, 1978) thinks
they may be knives (Drawer = Butt Knife; Dresser =
Clicker's Knife), for knives are the shoemaker's first
essential, and only a Paring Knife is included, at the
end of the poem.

    Dresser is a fairly common term in various trades:
for instance, a plumber's Dressing Stick is a hardwood stick used for shaping sheet lead; and the tanner's two-handled Fleshing or Unhairing Knives are
sometimes called Dressing Knives.

3. *Wedges*
See p. 179 under *Stretcher*.

4. *Heele Blocke*
The OED describes this as 'a block used in fastening
a blank heel or a "lift" to a shoe' and quotes Thomas
Dekker's *The Shoemaker's Holiday or the Gentle*

Craft (1600), 'Hoe, Boy, bring him a heel-blocke,
heers a new journeyman.' But Mr J. H. Thornton
(1978) thinks that it may be a block of wood from
which the heel was cut. Another possibility is that it
might be the block which appears in paintings of that
time on which a shoemaker places his stirrup-foot.
(See 9 below, and *Bench and Seat*.)

5. *Hand Leather*
Worn to protect the hand when tightening a thread.
(See *Hand and Finger Protectors*.)

6. *Thumb Leather*
Worn, presumably, for the same reason as 5 above.

7. 'Despise'. Probably a misprint for devise.

8. *Sow-haires*
Probably pig bristle, which is fitted to the end of the
sewing thread to serve as a needle. (See *Sewing and
Stitching*.)

9. *Stirrop*
A strap looped over the shoe to hold it on the knee,
and held tight under one foot. (See *Stirrup*.)

10. *Rubbing Stone* and *Whetstone*
Presumably a stone for sharpening awls and knives.

11. *Stopping Sticke* (Dekker: 'a good stopper')
Mr J. H. Thornton (1979) points out that since this
term appears next to whetstone in Deloney's poem, it
is probably a stropping stick on which knives are
stropped after stone sharpening. (See *Sharpening
Bat*.)

12. *Paring Knife*
This could be an ordinary shoemaker's knife, or
what is known today as a Paring or Skiving Knife,
which is used for paring down edges when making a
seam. (See under *Knives*.)

Sandstick   *Fig. 2:164 (opposite)*
Two wooden boards *c.* 14 in. (35.5 cm) long designed
to hold an abrasive sheet (such as glass paper), and
used for the final smoothing of heels and soles. One
of the boards has a flat outside surface and the other
is rounded.

    The edges of the sheet are folded and held between
the boards, which are then tied together at their ends
to hold the sheet securely.

Scissors and Shears   *Fig. 2:56 (p. 82)*
(See also *Shears* in the GLOVE MAKER section.)
An older generation of clickers and closers used only
a knife even when cutting the most delicate leathers
or textile linings. But scissors and shears have come
increasingly into use. Most of them are similar to the

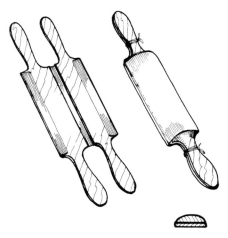

Fig. 2:164

stout scissors or heavy shears used by tailors. Some have serrated-edged blades.

Scissors are included among the tools illustrated by Garsault (1767), but not by Diderot. They are included by Devlin (1839) in his 'Kit of the woman's man'. Hommel (1937) illustrates a smith-made pair of scissors, $9\frac{3}{4}$ in. (24.7 cm) long, used by itinerant shoemakers in China.

Cutting by knife would be difficult without a bench, and it is probable that the English shoe repairers who took to the road in the eighteenth and nineteenth centuries, started using scissors for cutting out patches and similar work.

Scraper: see *Knife, Buffing*

Seam Sett (Seam Setter; Sett: in the USA this tool is sometimes called a Key.)
These are burnishing tools. Like the *Edge Irons*, the steel head is tanged into a wooden handle, usually of the 'square' type, with an overall length of *c.* 5–6 in. (12.7–15.2 cm). The head is usually square or beaver-tail shaped, and the working face is cut with one or two simple concave depressions, or left flat with a short guard. Some are made in hardwood throughout.

Used mainly by closers, they are designed to smooth down and flatten a seam, and, to quote Devlin (1839, p. 61), 'in order that the stitches may appear clean and pretty looking'. Devlin mentions the use of Seam Setts no less than five times in the course of his book. In one (p. 70), when dealing with the closing of a top-boot, he writes about the construction of the tool itself:

'The *seam-set* should have no sharpnesses, or jags, or notches, and be flat-cut, or deeper, just as the delicacy or greater strength of the article may render necessary; each separate stitch shewing itself in its clear perfect form, without any sign of force upon it, the sides of the setter catching closely in at the roots, and leaving a glistening impression along each side of the leather: the crease in the middle of the setter, also, leaving the like appearance in the centre of the seam.'

Variants

(1)   The following are mentioned by Devlin (1839):

(*a*)   *Hessian Sett* (Richard Timmins *c.* 1800 calls it a Heisian Setter or a Heisham Sett) *Figs 2:10, No. 2962; 2:11, No. 913 (pp. 36, 37)*
A square-shaped head with a raised fillet across the centre of the working face (see *Hessian Boot*).

(*b*)   *Stabbing Sett   Fig. 2:11, No. 907 (p. 37)*

(*c*)   *Welt Sett   Fig. 2:21, No. 18 (p. 47)*
(The term 'welt' in this context relates to a welted seam in which a strip of leather is sewn in: for explanation see under *Closer's Welt Plough*.)

Devlin (1839, p. 28) writes as follows about the use of these tools:

'After the lining, the upper has to be set; a matter soon effected; the flat-seam-set, or, if stabbed, the stabbing-side-set, being heated at a candle (though this is not necessary, and might from the danger of the practice be well dispensed with) and a little dissolved gum being rubbed on the seam, the set is immediately to be somewhat forcibly and briskly pressed along the line of stitching, which thus takes an almost instant polish, and being also hardened, the upper becomes ready for shop; that is, to be sent to the maker, or shoe-man.'

(2)   George Barnsley's catalogue of 1890 illustrates the following Setts (whether they were all used on seams is not certain):

(*a*)   *Single Top Sett   Fig. 2:21, No. 15 (p. 47)*
The head has a groove at one edge of the convex face, next to the guard.

(*b*)   *Binding Sett   Fig. 2:21, No. 16 (p. 47)*
The head is cut with a single groove and guard; it may have been used for setting the bound top edge of an upper.

(*c*)   *Double Top Sett   Fig. 2:21, No. 17 (p. 47)*
As (*a*) above, but with two grooves.

(*d*)   *Seam Sett   Fig. 2:21, No. 19 (p. 47)*
A head cut with two parallel grooves.

Note: *Fig 2:10, Nos 2920/24 (p. 36)*
Richard Timmins (*c.* 1800) gives the caption 'Seam Sett' to a set of four heads that look more like *Edge Irons* of the Forepart type.

(3) The Ross Moyer Manufacturing Co.'s catalogue (USA, 1884) illustrates a wooden 'Seam Rubber' (p. 173) which resembles the Seam Presser used by sail makers; also a number of hand- and foot-operated machines in which the boot is held in a jack, while a roller or burnishing iron is drawn along the seam, to rub it down.

Seat

The seat is the rear end of the sole or insole on which the heel of the foot rests. The terms French, German, or Russian seat, signify different methods of attaching the heel to the seat.

Seat Tools are used in the following order:

(The heel is sometimes 'peened' beforehand with a hammer; this drives the leather at the seat over the stitches that join the heel, sole and upper together.)

1. The horizontal edge of the seat is trimmed with knives (see *Knife, Shoe* and *Knife, Welt*).

2. The vertical edge of the seat is trimmed and smoothed with the *Seat Breaker*.

3. The vertical edge of the seat is set and imprinted with a decorative pattern (see *Seat Wheel*).

Seat Breaker (Breaker; Boot Breaker; Seat File; USA 1890: Rahn Break)　*Figs 2:165; also 2:10, Nos 2927 and 2930: 2:11, Nos 916 and 922 (pp. 36, 37)*

A wide, flat head with a serrated (or occasionally plain) face, tanged into a wooden handle. Length: 5–7 in. (12.7–17.7 cm) overall. On one side of the head there is a guard which is designed to run in the joint between the seat and the upper. This guard is removable (held by a set screw) so that the teeth can be re-cut when worn; the guard is also held in position by lugs. The face is often cut at a slight angle, sloping towards the fence, so that when holding the tool at an upward slant, the face makes a vertical contact with the edge of the heel.

With the guard bearing on the seat junction, the tool is run round the heel in sweeping strokes, to smooth and/or harden the surface just below the seat, and so prepare for the decorative imprint of the *Seat Wheel*.

Historical Note:
There is no mention of the tool in Diderot (1760), or Garsault (*c.* 1769); but Devlin (1839, p. 90), when describing the older stitch-rand method of attaching a heel (which he claims is vastly better at resisting the strain of the Boot Jack), writes as follows:

'But the stitched-rand, beside the stitching, has still an additional labour. The rand is to be *broke* – that is, with the tool called *the breaker*, having a toothed face, the doubled heads of the stitches are to be severely pressed, torn and spread about, so that the whole face of the rand shows nothing but hemp; though this breaking is not to be till after the heel is built and sewed down – the heel in the stitched-rand boot not being sewed down from the seat-stitch, but from above the rand, close underneath at the root of the sole piece. The heel built, sewed, and the rand broke, the rand is then, in the course of general *taking-off*, to be made – that is, coloured and set-up with a thick gum dissolved in ink; and when the boot-man is about to perform his final operations, the *rand-wheel* is run around, and the rand finished.'

Commenting on the above, A. L. Saguto (USA, 1980) writes, 'I suppose that Devlin's words, "pressed, torn and spread about", were a slight exaggeration of roughing up the rand stitches. In this manner, the neatness of these stitches would matter little, since they are covered with "thick gum", the impressions of the rand-wheel giving the ultimate finished look.'

Contemporary illustrations include Richard Timmins (*c.* 1800), who shows the modern tool, with the caption 'Boot Breaker'; and Charles Tomlinson (*c.* 1860) who calls it a 'Breaker' and illustrates a tool with the toothed face on the side of the head, instead of on the top.

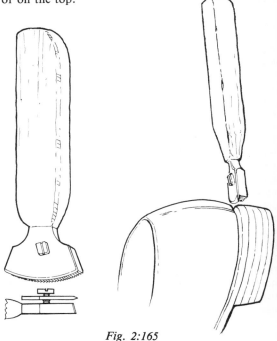

Fig. 2:165

Seat Wheel (Slide Box Wheel. Richard Timmins *c.* 1800: Rand Wheel; French Rand Wheel. Ross Moyer, USA, 1884: Box Wheel; French Key Wheel). *Figs 2:166; 2:167. Also 2:10, Nos 2965, 3080, 3081–4; 2:11, No. 2278 (pp. 36, 37)* (*Note:* There is some confusion both in nomenclature and function between the Seat and Fudge Wheels; these are discussed under the entries *Fudge Wheel* and *Rand Tools*.)

Similar to a Forepart *Edge Iron*, except that the head is fitted with a milled wheel which is let into the face of the iron. The tool is set in a wooden handle of the shoemaker's 'square' type, $5\frac{1}{2}$–7in. (13.9–17.7 cm) overall. There is a single guard which runs in the seat junction next to the upper. Broader wheels are used for long boots, and these are sometimes referred to as 'French'. A plate and set-screw on one side of the head enables the edge of the wheel to protrude by varying amounts, and also allows the wheel to be changed.

A version illustrated by Richard Timmins (*c.* 1800, p. 25) has a wider, cross-hatched wheel; and one has a 'square' wooden handle containing a pocket for a spare wheel. They are listed as 'French Rand Wheels' and are almost certainly a form of Seat Wheel, but probably intended only for heavy boots.

The Seat Wheel, after heating, is run round the seat of the heel in order to set the edge of the seat, and at the same time to produce a decorative marking on the seat edge. Today these markings are a plain series of short lines; in the nineteenth century there were other devices, including a series of chevrons, keys, wavy lines, hearts and trefoils.

Leno (1895, p. 136) devotes a long paragraph to the care of the Seat Wheel. Some extracts are given below; they exemplify the attention paid by shoemakers to the performance of their tools:

'Great care is necessary in the selection of this piece of kit, for if the bearings and slide at the back and the screw affixing the slide are not fitted in the most accurate manner, and made of the very best material, it will cause endless trouble and disappointment. The best workmen, when in possession of a good seat wheel, always take the greatest care of it, and guard it with great jealousy. When making a choice of this article, take it to pieces by unscrewing the back and examine its bearings, and, above all, take care that the roller fits the slot quite close when cold. When heated a wheel so fitted will be found to run quite free, if properly made. ... In no case should the wheel be thinner than the slot in which it acts, or it will never set distinctly, and can never be depended upon to run true. ... The position or inclination of the face of the wheel to the guard must

be adapted for the description of work for which it is intended; for instance, a spring heel is made square; but a Wurtemburg is set quite under, so that in cutting the face of the wheel, these differences must be provided for. ... In fixing the wheel, it should be so placed that the bottom of the milling is level with the face, if thus accurately fixed, it will set up a seat as smoothly as though the quarter crease wheel and face were formed of one solid piece.'

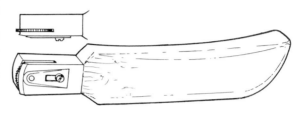

Fig. 2:166

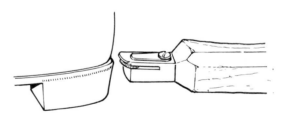

Fig. 2:167

Setting Board
A tool included in Devlin's 'The boot-closer's kit' (1839, p.112), described as 'generally lignum vitae or some other hard wood'. Probably used as a hard surface on which to lay the uppers when setting the seams (see *Seam Sett*).

Sewing and Stitching
Nomenclature In the handworking trade the terms 'sewing' and 'stitching' are often applied as follows:

			Common name of Awl used*
Sewing:	(1)	The joining together of insole, upper and welt	*Sewing Awl*
	(2)	The closing of the component parts of the upper	*Closing* and *Stabbing Awl*
Stitching:		The joining of sole to welt	*Stitching Awl*

*see under *Awl*

For convenience, the term 'sewing' will be used for most of the joining operations mentioned below.

Sewing Machines for use on leather were developed during the middle years of the nineteenth century. Before this, the art of hand-sewing – one of the oldest surviving crafts practised by man – had reached a peak of efficiency and good looks immediately apparent in the hand-sewn footwear of that time. The art is practised with equal perfection by some of the bespoke makers today and, it may be added, by some of the growing number of harness makers and saddlers.

The component parts of factory-made shoes are now often joined together with adhesives, but simulated stitches are sometimes added for the sake of appearance.

Nineteenth-century textbooks devote many pages to the art of hand-sewing, the preparation of threads, the attachment of the bristles, and to the form of the stitches. Some typical hand-sewn stitches are illustrated in the HARNESS MAKER AND SADDLER section under *Stitching Tools*.

(a) The sewing operation Fig. 2:168

Hand-sewing is done while the boot or shoe is held between the knees by means of a *Stirrup*. A leather *Hand Protector* is normally worn on the left hand to protect it from being abrased by the thread.

A bristle (which serves the shoemaker as a needle – see below) is attached to each end of a length of thread. One end of the thread is held in each hand, and one of the hands also holds an *Awl*. The position of the stitches having been marked with a *Pricker Tool*, the awl is pushed into the leather until its point protrudes about $\frac{1}{8}-\frac{1}{4}$ in. (0.4–0.8 cm) on the other side. As the awl is withdrawn it is followed by the bristle, and when this is pushed right through, the second bristle (attached to the opposite end of the thread) is entered from the other side and pulled through. The two bristle-ends of the thread are now pulled in opposite directions until the stitch is tight.

Leather has a special property that makes sewing,

if done properly, particularly effective: the stitch hole, if of the correct size, will grip a waxed thread so tightly that the joint will hold firm and remain water-resistant, even after the exposed loops of the stitches have become worn through.

Sewing inside a shoe is known as 'blind stabbing' and is thus vividly described by Devlin (1839, p.21):

'certainly the most beautiful process in the whole trade; regular, easy, and rapid, and to the eye of the spectator a matter even of marvellous description. Quickly goes in the awl, and as quickly is out again, but not before the hair from the fingers of the left hand has found the passage, without being at all directed by the sight, but literally in the dark; and hence the term *blind stabbing*, the right-hand hair immediately following in the opposite course, the closed thumb and fore-finger of either hand nipping at the moment the hairs from these different directions, and drawing the same as instantly out, at once completing the stitch.'

The term 'stitching aloft' is applied to stitches joining a sole to the welt when the stitches are left showing on the surface of the sole, instead of being sunk in a channel. If the stitches wear through, the joint is held together by the tightness of the threads in the substance of the leather.

Fig. 2:168

(*b*) *Bristle and Thread Fig. 2:169*
A characteristic feature of hand-sewing in the shoe trade is the use of a hog's bristle instead of a needle. It is not clear when this came about, but it was the recognised method by *c.* 1700. It is an ingenious idea, for, as the shoemakers say, a bristle can 'turn a corner'; thus it can lead a thread through a hole which, if made by the Sewing Awl, for example, often follows a slightly curved path. Today, hogs' bristles have been mostly replaced by nylon bristles.

Joining a bristle to the end of the thread, known as 'bristling', needs considerable skill. The aim is to ensure a smooth continuity between bristle and thread. One of the best methods of bristling is called 'rolling'. The 'split-hair' end of the bristle is the one which is attached to the thread. This end is waxed, together with the tapering strand at the end of the thread which is twisted round the lower part of the bristle.

Until the 1900s shoemakers made their own threads from flax or hemp, twisting them by rolling on a leather apron, after applying wax. (John Waterer (1968) writes that this operation is depicted on a Roman tombstone of the second century AD, and was ancient even then.) Wax prevents the thread from unravelling, protects the thread against rot, and helps it to grip firmly in the leather.

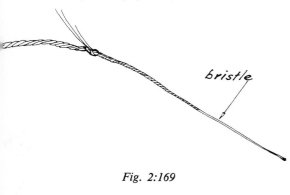

bristle

Fig. 2:169

(*c*) *Tools used in sewing* are described under the following entries: *Awl*; *Bunking Tools*; *Fudge Wheel*; *Hand and Finger Protectors*; *Needle*; *Pricker Tools*; *Rand Tools*; *Sewing Block*; *Stitch Cutter*; *Stitch Gauge* under *Measuring Tools*; *Stitch Prick* (*Stitch Separator*); *Stitch Tightener*.

Sewing Block (Closing Block; Hand Stabbing Block; Knee Block; Seam Block) *Fig. 2:170*
Devlin (1839, p. 20) writes of the shoemaker's boy being taught to close children's shoes either in the Clamp or on the Block – 'that somewhat half round

clump of wood, which he lays along his left thigh, held down by the stirrup'.

According to a London closer (Mr W. Graysmark, 1976) the Sewing Block was 8–10 in. (20.3–25.4 cm) long and made from a piece of 2 × 2 in. (5 × 5 cm) hardwood, rounded on top. The block is held on the knee by a Stirrup (strap) which is split at the top so that it holds the two pieces of leather in position while exposing the join for sewing a flat seam.

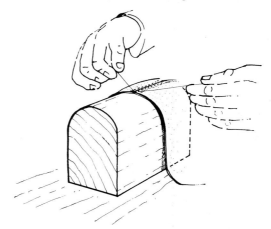

Fig. 2:170

Shank
A name given to a strip of wood, fibre-board, metal or plastic, placed centrally in the waist of a shoe, held between the sole and insole. Its purpose is to resist excessive bending at the waist, and in some types it acts as a filler in this area. When high heels were introduced at the end of the sixteenth century, leather shanks were used.

The term 'shank' is also an alternative name for the waist – the narrow part of the sole or insole under the arch of the foot. Tools relating to this part of a shoe include Shank Laster (see under *Lasting Pincers and Dogs*); Shank Iron (see under *Edge Iron*).

Sharpening Bat (Bat; Buff or Buffing Strap or Strop; Stopping or Stropping Stick; Rap Stick; Rifle. Scots: Whittie. *Note*: the term 'Rifle' comes from the Old French *riffle*, and is a dialect word for the whetstone used by mowers for sharpening their scythes.) *Fig. 2:171*
A wooden stick, flat or four-sided, with a handle formed at one end. Length *c.* 13–16 in. (33–40.6 cm) overall.

The four-sided version usually has three sides

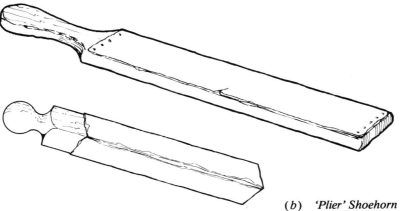

Fig. 2:171

covered with emery cloth (or other abrasive), graded from coarse to fine; and the fourth side is covered with leather to act as a strop for a final sharpening. It is usually home-made.

When necessary, shoe knives are first ground on a stone; they are then dipped in water and held flat on the Bat for final sharpening and stropping.

Sharpening Steel (Buffer Steel)   *Fig. 2:18 (p. 44)*
Two types of Sharpening Steel may be found in a shoemaker's kit. One is like a Butcher's Steel, and is used for the sharpening of knives; the other resembles a currier's or joiner's 'turning' steel, and is used for turning the edge of a scraper.

Shave: see *Edge Plane*; *Edge Shave*; *Heel Shave*.

Shears: see *Scissors and Shears*.

Shoehorn (Puller-on; Shoe Iron; Shoe Lift. The term Shoe Lift, when applied to a Shoehorn, should not be confused with the 'lifts' that make up a built heel.)
These homely implements, used for easing the foot into a boot or shoe, are also found in the workshops where they serve for the insertion or removal of the last.

(*a*)   *The Ordinary Shoehorn   Fig. 2:8, No. 3073 (p. 34)*
Shoehorns vary from the plain iron of the workshop to the polished horn or decorated metal specimens to be found in the home. The usual shape is a tapered, gutter-shaped blade, with the narrow end serving as a handle. In the workshop version, the handle is sometimes bent backwards at right angles to the blade.

(*b*)   *'Plier' Shoehorn   Figs 2:172; 2:6, No. 3 (p. 31)*
An implement illustrated by Diderot (*c*. 1760) who calls it a 'chausse-pié anglois' (English shoehorn). It is a plier-like tool with thin flat jaws. One handle is shaped like the conventional shoehorn of today, and was probably used as such.

The jaws of the tool were probably not used for pulling a shoe on to a human foot, but for pulling a turnshoe on to the last.

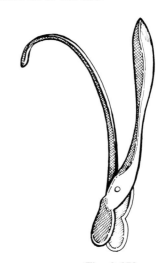

Fig. 2:172

(*c*)   *'Skin' Shoehorn*
As illustrated by Garsault (1767) this is not a horn but a strip of cowhide (or other suitable skin) with the hair left on, and used for the same purpose. Garsault called it a '*chausse-pied*' (shoe-horn) and writes that they were used by 'those men who only consider themselves properly dressed in shoes that are so tight that they can only be got on by force.' June Swann,

of the Northampton Shoe Museum, adds the comment that

'...the shoe-lift of cattle hide with hair on seems to have been a simple and cheap method for shoemakers. It appears in an engraving by Jacob van de Heyden, 1636, putting on a woman's shoe. Back in 1906 a strip of leather was still used by shoemakers when re-lasting a shoe. The sutor's testament carol (late fifteenth century) bequeaths his "chaspy and his shoying horne", which suggests there is a difference. I know of no surviving examples.'

Sutor   = Souter, Scots dialect for shoemaker.
chaspy = *chausse-pied*, French for shoehorn.

Hair on one side of the skin gives an advantage provided that the hair side of the skin is placed next to the heel of the foot, with the hair pointing downward. This would give the foot a slippery surface on which to slide into the shoe, while the flesh side of the skin remains rough and stays in contact with the inside surface of the shoe.

This quality of fur being smooth in one direction only ('don't stroke a cat the wrong way') is made use of by skiers who, before the days of ski-lifts, fastened skins to the underside of their skis when going uphill. With the hair pointing backwards, the skier can still slide his skis uphill over the snow, while the downward pointing hair prevents the skis from slipping backwards.

Size Stick: see *Measuring Tools.*

Skive: see *Fig. 1:25* in the BOOKBINDER section *(p. 11).*
Shoemakers use this term, which is adopted from the old Norse word *skifa*, for the operation of cutting leather to reduce its thickness, e.g. at the edges for making a scarfed (overlapped) joint.
Other relevant entries include: *Closer; Feather; Knife, Feathering; Knife; Paring; Splitting Machine.*

Slicker: see *Glazer and Sleeking Iron.*

Slide Box Wheel: see *Seat Wheel.*

Snob (Scots: Snab)
A slang term of obscure origin for shoemaker or cobbler. (See introduction to this section.)

Sole
Part of the shoe that is in contact with the ground. If the shoe has a separate heel, the bottom section next to the ground is called the 'top piece'. (See the entry *Bottom.*)

Sole-Forming Block
A tool illustrated in Garsault's *Cordonnier* (1767), plate II, no. 4. There is an example of this tool in the Boot Shop of the Colonial Williamsburg Foundation in Virginia, USA.

This tool is a block of hardwood with a hollowed-out depression sunk in its surface. Garsault explains that it was over this hollow 'that the Cordwainer places the sole to dish it in the middle, which he does with blows of his hammer-handle, so that the sole bends upwards all around in the shape of a Gondola'.

Mr D. A. Saguto (USA, 1980), an authority on eighteenth-century shoemaking, writes that since the 'straight lasted shoe' was the vogue in Garsault's time, and for some time after, the curvature of last bottoms tended to be more pronounced; consequently it was necessary to impart a degree of curvature to the out-sole before stitching.

Sole Plane: see *Edge Plane.*

Sole Prizer (Lifting Awl; Sole Lifter)   *Figs 2:173; 2:55, Nos 6172–8 (p. 81)*
(See also *Pig's Foot.*)
A tool made like a small, strong screwdriver, awl or cold chisel. The wooden handles are sometimes hooped to withstand driving with a hammer. Another type has a blade which is a flat oval in cross-section.

Sole Prizers are used for 'stripping', i.e. for removing worn soles, especially from riveted or screwed shoes. After inserting the tool at a weak point and levering the sole away, the released sole is grasped with pincers to complete its removal.

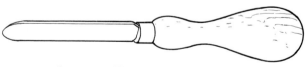

Fig. 2:173

Souter
Scots term for shoemaker or cobbler.

Split Lift
A name given to strips of leather, wedge-shaped in cross-section, which are used for building up the heel. These strips are notched at the centre of their thin edge, bent into the shape of the heel, and then hammered flat on the Lap Iron. Today Split Lifts are usually cut by a Press Knife into the required horseshoe shape.

Splitting Machine

It is almost impossible to split leather evenly with a hand knife, and because of its interlocking fibrous structure, leather cannot be torn apart – even when started with a knife cut. Consequently, before the invention of the Splitting Machine in the early nineteenth century, the only method of reducing the substance of a hide or skin was by shaving off the flesh side with some form of Paring or Currier's Knife. This method wasted all the material that was cut away, whereas the Splitting Machine literally cut the leather into two (or more) complete layers, of which even the layer nearest the flesh of the animal had some use.

Note: The name 'Splitting Machine' is also given to a hand-operated machine described in the HARNESS MAKER AND SADDLER section which is used for thinning down a piece of leather.

Spring Key

Illustrated by Ross Moyer (USA, 1884, p. 187), this appears to be a tool for setting an edge or seam (see *Seam Sett*).

Spur Box

This is a metal socket, about $1\frac{3}{4}$ in. (4.6 cm) long and of square cross-section, with a squared recess at one end containing a simple spring-catch mechanism. The box is buried in the back of the heel.

The dress spur has no straps, but instead is provided with an extension between the arms which is held in the spring catch within the Spur Box, thus holding the spur securely to the back of the heel, just high enough to prevent the rowel from striking the ground.

The spur block, commonly fitted to Field boots, is a small piece of leather which protrudes at the back of the heel on which the arms of a strap-on spur rest.

Stamp (Ring Punch) *Fig. 2:10, No. 2968 (p. 36)*
(See also *Punches*)
Two kinds of stamps are used by shoemakers:

(a) Figure Stamp
A metal punch with size numbers cut on the end. They were used at one time for marking shoe sizes on the sole.

(b) Ring Stamp
A metal punch, usually circular, made in sizes from *c.* $\frac{3}{16} - \frac{3}{8}$ in. (0.6–1 cm) diameter. A design of consecutive circles (or occasionally some other device) was cut on the end. They were used for decorating the holes left in the insole after lasting: these are nail holes, made when positioning the inner and outer soles on the last. These holes are first filled with wax;

the Ring Stamp is then warmed and punched over the hole to seal it.

The punch is illustrated by Diderot (*c.* 1760) and captioned *Etoile*, presumably because of the star-shaped impression it makes in the leather.

Steel, Shoemakers: see *Sharpening Steel*.

Stick: see *Bones and Sticks*.

Stirrup (Footstrap; Kneestrap; Strap. Scots: Fit-Fang, Cashel, or Whang; whang is a Scots term for a thong or a narrow strip of leather. A 'Stirrop' is included in Deloney's list of tools in *The Gentle Craft*, *c.* 1597.) *Figs 2:6; 2:61*

A strap (or occasionally a cord) used to hold a boot or shoe firmly on the knee when lasting and sewing. The strap is looped over the work and passes underneath one foot. A buckle is sometimes provided to adjust the length of the strap. (See also *Bench and Seat*.)

Footstraps are shown in pictures of shoemakers by D. Teniers and G. Terborch (both *c.* 1650), and by Diderot (*c.* 1760). In these pictures the foot round which the strap is looped is propped up on a block about $2\frac{1}{2}$ in. (6.4 cm) high; this is done to raise the knee to a convenient height for working. Today, in this country at least, the block is not needed, for most makers sit on a lower stool.

The following are eighteenth-century variants:

(a) The Cabriolet Fig. 2:174/5
The term 'cabriolet' is used by Garsault (1767, *Cordonnier*, plate II, fig. 30), for a shoe last with a spike protruding from its sole, which, he explains, serves as a device to be held on the knee by a stirrup-strap.

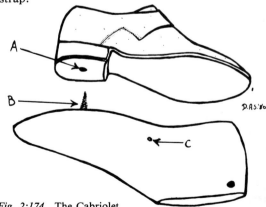

Fig. 2:174 The Cabriolet
  A   Hole in base of heel
  B   Threaded spike
  C   Stirrup stop pin

Mr D. A. Saguto (USA, 1980), a writer on eighteenth-century shoemaking, describes its use as follows:

'The *Cabriolet* is a device made from a shoe last. It is held on the knee up-side-down by the stirrup-strap, with the spike up. This spike is pressed or screwed into the main nail hole in the centre of the wooden heel of the shoe being sewn. The device serves to hold the finished, unlasted shoe in an upright position to enable the seam that Garsault calls *la boite* (the box) to be sewn. This is a strange little seam that reinforces the heel covering, by sewing it to the base of the quarters with a stabbing seam.'

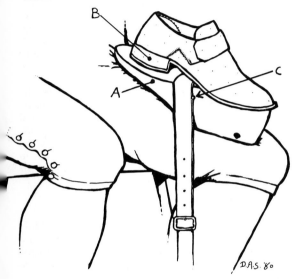

Fig. 2:175 The Cabriolet with a shoe mounted upon it

  A   The Cabriolet
  B   Shoe-heel screwed onto the spike
  C   Stirrup stop pin

(b)   *Stick and stirrup   Fig. 2:176*
Described by Mr Saguto, this is an eighteenth-century method of holding the strap tight over the work. The lower end of the strap is looped under a stick on which the feet rest.

Stitch Cutter
Made like a narrow V-shaped chisel, this tool is intended for cutting through old stitches when making a repair.

Stitching: see *Sewing and Stitching*.

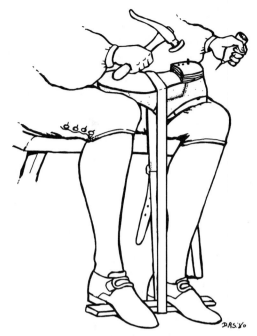

Fig. 2:176   Stick and stirrup

Stitch Prick (Prick Stitch; Stitch Pricker; Stitch Marker; Stitch Separator; USA: Stitch Divider. Devlin, 1839: Rand Pricker.)
Note: The name 'Stitch Prick' (and the operation described as 'pricking up the stitches') sometimes leads to confusion with one of the *Pricker Tools* described previously which are used as a guide for sewing. And the identification of the Stitch Prick may be confused by its similarity to a Channel Opener – or even a Screwdriver.

The Stitch Prick is a handled tool *c.* 6 in. (15.2 cm) long overall. One type looks like a small screwdriver and indeed screwdrivers are sometimes used for the same purpose. But the factory-made blades are flatter, and are curved to enable the user to work closer to the upper when pricking out stitches on the welt. Some of the blades were 'double' – see variants below.

The purpose of the Stitch Prick is to make an indentation on the welt between each stitch in order to tighten the stitches, and to improve their appearance: the operation makes the stitches look bolder and more prominent. The *Fudge Wheel* serves a similar purpose, and was developed to reduce the labour of separating the stitches one by one. But in the opinion of a retired London shoemaker (Mr W. B. Glasow,

177

1977) the Fudge was 'less successful in tightening the stitches, and moreover some Masters would not allow a Fudge to be used on their work, for when applied too hot it was said to overheat the upper in the region of the welt'.

Plucknett writes (1916, p. 252):

'The tool is easy to use, though it requires care to ensure regularity in the depth of the impressions. These, like the marks of the fudge-wheel, should always be at right angles to that particular part of the feather, but this requires practice, especially at the toe. If through any cause the stitches are unequal in length, the irregularity can be modified considerably by pressing the tool so that it pushes the long stitch into a shorter space. Stitches that are out of line can often be trued up with the prick stitch.'

Hasluck (1898, pp. 95 and 135) gives a slightly different view of the Stitch Prick's function. He explains that the stitching on the welt may be 'pricked up' or 'fudged', or left plain (in which case the welt is said to be 'blind') or the stitches may be sunk in a channel made in the welt, and subsequently fudged to imitate stitching. When comparing the Stitch Prick with the Fudge, he says that the Stitch Prick 'throws up each separate stitch, and forms them into a row like little beads' instead of making a series of raised ridges as the Fudge would have done.

Variants include:

(*a*) *The Single Stitch Prick* described above *Figs 2:177; 2:53, No. 6102 (p. 79)*

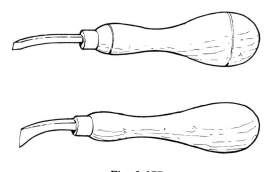

Fig. 2:177

(*b*) *The Double Stitch Prick* *Fig. 2:53, No. 6100 (p. 79)*
The head of the blade is grooved and consequently may be confused with a Brad Marker (see *Nail Marker*), or even with a *Crease* (see the HARNESS section). The groove encompasses each stitch, making an indentation on each side of it, and thus

speeding up the job of 'pricking up' the stitch. Each tool was made to accommodate a definite size of stitch, so that a set of these tools was necessary; the 'single'-bladed tool could be used for any size of stitch.

(*c*) *Rand Pricker   Fig. 2:11, No. 920 (p. 37)*
Illustrated by Richard Timmins (*c*. 1800) this appears to be the same tool as the double Stitch Prick described above, but the blade is bent. Judging by a long description of the operation by Devlin (1839, pp. 89, 91) the Rand is 'sewn in before the welt is sewed: it being a strip of upper leather, with the grain taken off, extending from one corner of the heel to the other, and about an inch in width'. Devlin continues that, after sewing, 'the divisions between the stitches were made more perfect by the single *rand-pricker* then in use (the forerunner of our present rand wheel)'. (See *Rand Tools*; *Seat Wheel*; *Fudge Wheel*.)

(*d*) *Home-Made Examples Fig. 2:82*
Many of these tools are obviously home-made, sometimes, as mentioned above, from old screwdrivers. But Hasluck illustrates one (1898, p. 73) which appears to be made from the blade of an old table fork, like that illustrated under *Channel Tools*.

(*e*) *Machines*
Today, the work of the Stitch Prick is done by a Stitch Separating Machine in which the indenting tool, like the hand-worked Stitch Prick, finds its way between the stitches. The Welt Wheeling Machine operates a wheel with the same spacing of teeth as the stitch length; this presses on the welt, but does not always coincide with the stitches it is supposed to separate; in this it resembles the Wheel used by hand-workers (see *Fudge Wheel*).

(*f*) *Bunking Iron*
A near-relation of the *Stitch Prick* family (see *Bunking Tools*).

Stitch Tightener
A name given to a piece of bent stick used by some shoemakers for tightening stitches. The end of the thread is taken a couple of turns round the stick and then pulled.

Straights
A name given to boots made with no difference in shape between the left and right foot. Elderly people sometimes say that in their younger days, if one boot was injured (e.g a tear to the upper) only one new shoe had to be bought, and that was a great saving. But J. H. Thornton (1978) thinks that this was not

the reason for the introduction of 'straights', but a possible bonus afterwards. He writes:

'The facts as I see them (and based on the examination of thousands of excavated shoes) are that until about 1600 shoes were made left and right (very markedly so in the 14th and 15th centuries); then, with the introduction of high heels, they became straight. The coincidence of the two events may be because lasts for high-heeled shoes are much more difficult to make as a mirror-image pair, left and right. So, they became straight and remained so until the invention of the irregular-shape copying lathe in 1819 with its ability to turn a matched pair with no more difficulty than a straight last. However, it was many years before "straights" disappeared and they still survive for some types of footwear.'

Stretcher
(See also *Boot Tree*.)

The need to stretch a boot or shoe to make it more comfortable must have presented a problem from the earliest days of shoemaking. In his *Academy of Armoury* (1688) Randle Holme remarks: 'SHOE-MAKERS love to put ladies in their stocks; but these WEDGES like Merciful Justices, upon Complaint soon do ease and deliver them.' 'These wedges', judging by the rudimentary illustrations, are the ex-

pansible lasts described below under (*a*). They were illustrated by Diderot (1760), see *Fig. 2:6a. (p. 32).*

There are three kinds of stretchers:

(*a*) *Expansible Last or Tree* (Shoe Expander or Distender)

A wooden last which, being made in two sections, can be expanded inside the boot or shoe by forcing the sections apart with a wooden wedge.

Knight (USA, 1877) describes several variants under the following entries:

'Boot Stretcher: A two-part last containing both screw and levers for expansion, with "changeable knobs" that can be located to stretch a particular part.

Boot Tree: A last (or tree) mounted on a trestle. A wedge is forced between the two halves of the last by means of a foot-operated lever.

Shoe Stretcher: In this simple device, the upper part of the last (the Cone) is elevated by a metal screw.'

(*b*) *Screw-operated distenders Fig. 2:178*

In this metal device a toe-piece and a heel-plate are driven apart by means of a screw. In a more elaborate version, sometimes known as a 'Boss Stretcher', the toe-piece is replaced by two arms which are forced outwards inside the shoe when the screw is turned.

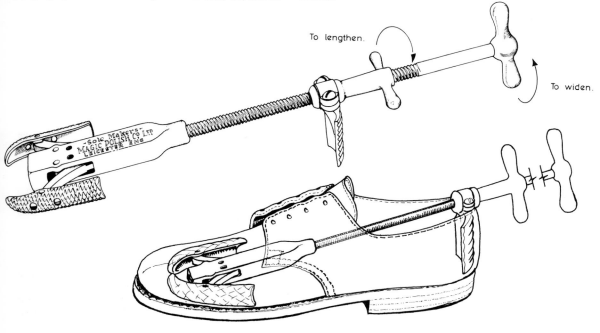

To lengthen.

To widen.

Fig. 2:178

(c) Stretching Pliers (Bunion Stretcher) *Fig. 2:56, No. 6214 (p. 82)*
A strong plier, *c.* 10 in. (25.4 cm) long, in which one jaw ends in a ring and the other in a ball. The purpose of this tool is to relieve the pressure over a tender spot. In operation, the dampened leather is forced against the ring by the ball, thus elevating a small area of the upper.

Striper

A name given by Ross Moyer (USA, 1884, p. 189) to a tool resembling an Edge Iron. The caption reads, 'For Finishing the Stripe on the bottom of Boots and Shoes. Made in 5 sizes No. 1–5.'

Its purpose is uncertain, but this tool may be intended for finishing what in this country are known as 'strip waists'. They are thus described by Swaysland (1905, p. 198):

'The strip is put on after the bottom is made out. A narrow strip is marked off with the knife at the side of the waist from the front to the heel, to about the joint of the forepart. The strip thus marked is inked with a brush and allowed to dry. When dry, it is burnished with a strip burnisher, or as it is sometimes called, a tiddler, and then a little white fake is rubbed up on it.'

Tab

The front part of the upper which rests on the instep, and which carries the facings and lace-eyelets. The term 'closed tab' implies that the tabs are sewn across the bottom, as in the case of an Oxford shoe where they are stitched *under* the vamp edge. The term 'open tab' relates to tabs that rest *above* the vamp, but are not stitched to it along their front edges, so that they may be opened all the way down: an example is the Derby or Blucher boot, in which a broad and folded tongue is stitched to the tabs and front of the upper, so making the boot weather-tight (see illustration in the introduction to this section).

Tack Lifter: see *Pig's Foot.*

Tag Tool: see *Lace-Making Tools.*

Tapes: see *Measuring Tools.*

Thread: see *Sewing and Stitching.*

Thread Holder *Fig. 2:6a, No. 35/36 (p. 32)*

The ball of thread for sewing is normally held in a round wooden or tin box with a small hole in the centre of the lid through which the thread can be drawn out.

The thread holder illustrated by Diderot (1760), described as a *Caillebotin*, appears to be made like a miniature beehive from twisted straw or rush.

Toe Beater: see *Beater.*

Toe Poker: see *Puff Stick.*

Tongue

An extension from the top of the vamp, which rests on the instep. Its purpose is to cover the instep of the foot where it is exposed by the gap between the tabs, and to cushion it from the pressure of the lacing. A bellows tongue is folded upwards each side and stitched to the underside of the tabs to seal off the opening against the entry of water.

Toothing Scraper (Solutioning Scraper)

A strip of steel, with fine pointed teeth along one edge, mounted in a double handle like a spokeshave. It is used for roughing a surface to provide a key for an adhesive solution when sticking soles or patches.

Top

Shoemaker's term for that part of the sole and heel that actually touches the ground. For an explanation of the terms 'top' and 'bottom' (see *Bottom*).

Top-Piece

The bottom section of a heel which actually rests on the ground. (See diagram of Boot in the introduction.)

Tree: see *Boot Tree.*

Turnshoe Tools *Fig. 2:180*

A turnshoe is a shoe which is made inside-out (normally with the flesh-side outwards) by sewing the lasting-margin of the upper to the edge of a single sole which also acts as an insole. The shoe is then turned the right way out, so that the grain side of the leather is on the outside of the shoe, and the upper-to-sole seam is now inside. It is thought that the turnshoe method of construction was introduced to this country by the Saxons.

The following are tools used in the process of turning the shoe:

(a) Turnstick Fig. 2:179
A hardwood stick, about 9–12 in. (22.8–30.5 cm) long, with a shallow S-bend in its length. One end is pushed into the shoe, the other rests against the stomach; the stick is held in this position to keep the toe in shape when turning the shoe.

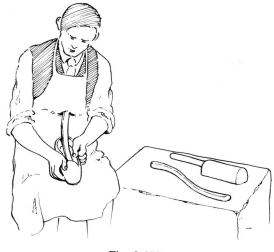

Fig. 2:179

(b)   Turning Iron
Illustrated by Ross Moyer (USA, 1884, p. 166) this is a metal version of the Turnstick. One end is fixed to the bench, the other is bent over towards the worker. It is used when standing at the bench.

(c)   Turnshoe Mallet (Guts Mallet)   *Fig. 2:179*
(See also *Beater*.)
A wooden mallet *c*. 10 in. (25.4 cm) long overall. The head is a rough half-cylinder in cross-section, rather like a plumber's Dresser.

This tool is exhibited in the Street Shoe Museum and is labelled 'Guts round-backed Mallet'. It is said to have been used for beating or shaping a turnshoe round the toe and heel, and for flattening the bottom. The derivation of the term 'guts', which appears to be peculiar to Somerset, is not known.

Upper
The parts of a boot or shoe which cover the top of the foot, and which are situated above the sole. (See diagram in the introduction.)

Vamp
The front section of a shoe upper which covers the toes and part of the instep. If the shoe has a separate toe cap, then the vamp is the name given to the remainder of the front section. (See diagram in the introduction.)

Veldtschoen (Veldshoe)
A Cape-Dutch name for a light shoe originally made of cured but untanned hide. In this country the term

is applied to a large number of different shoes in most of which the upper, instead of being lasted-in, is 'flanged' outward all round the shoe. A rand is often added to the outer surface of the flange before stitching through to the sole.

The name is also used, but rather inadequately so, for the Welted Veldtschoen. In this the lining is lasted inwards and sewn with a welt to the insole, and the outside upper is flanged outwards and stitched down to the welt and sole. The result is a water-resistant shoe suitable for field sports.

Waist (Sometimes called Shank, it is often incorrectly called the instep which is the name for the top of the foot or shoe.)
The Waist is the narrow part of a shoe sole or insole under the arch of the foot. (See diagram of a boot in the introduction.)

Waist Strap
Listed by Devlin (1839, p. 113) as part of the 'Kit of the boot-man'. Its purpose is unknown. It is probably not a Foot Strap, for he already lists a 'stirrup' under 'Boot-closer's kit'.

Wax: see *Finishing Tools and Materials*.

Wellington Boot
A name given to a calf-length boot. The story goes that these boots were introduced by the Duke of Wellington in the early years of the nineteenth century: it is said that the Duke disliked long boots, and ordered that his boots should be made to come up only as far as the calf.

Rubber Wellingtons were introduced in the 1860s, and today the 'Wellie' is worn occasionally by almost everyone as a dependable waterproof boot. They have become the working boot of the farm worker, and of those employed on muddy building and civil engineering sites.

Welt (The terms Welt and Rand are applied loosely both to the welt proper and sometimes to leather strips used for other purposes: for example, the so-called welted seam, see *Closer's Welt Plough*; and to the clog welting-strip, see *Welting Strip Cutter* in the CLOG MAKER section.)   *Figs 2:5 (p. 29); 2:180*
The welt is a strong strip of good quality leather sewn round the lasting margin of the upper, and joining it to the insole. The sole is then stitched to the welt by a second seam.

The welt appears to have been developed from the *Rand*, and as mentioned above, the two names are sometimes interchanged. The welted method of shoe construction was introduced in this country *c*. 1500,

181

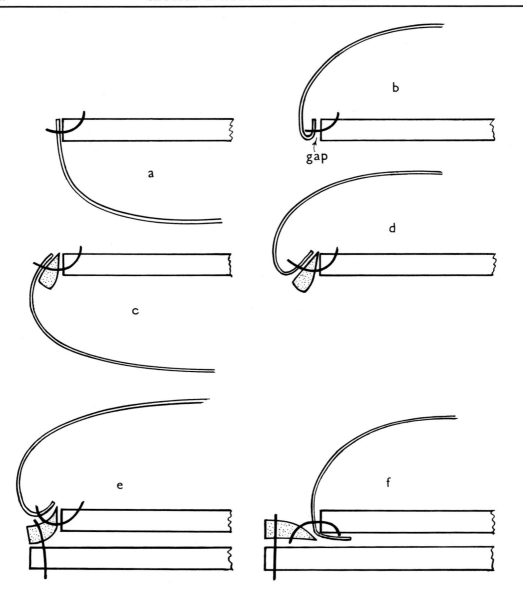

Fig. 2:180 Evolution of Welt. (From information kindly provided by J. H. Thornton, Northampton College of Technology, 1974.) See also *Turnshoe Tools*, and introduction *Fig. 2:5*

(*a*) Turnshoe of the Saxon and early medieval period – before turning.

(*b*) The same – after turning.

(*c*) Turnshoe of the mid-fourteenth century with a rand inserted to fill the gap between upper and sole – before turning.

(*d*) The same –. after turning.

(*e*) Turnshoe of *c.* 1500 with the rand extended to form a welt to which an outside sole is sewn.

(*f*) Shoe after *c.* 1500 with insole, welt and sole sewn together in the same relative positions as today, no turning being necessary. By the seventeenth century the inseam (i.e. stitches joining welt/upper/insole) had moved from the edge of the insole to the outer surface in which a sewing channel had been formed – see diagram of a hand welted shoe: *Fig. 2:5 (p. 29)* and is still used today both in hand and machine working. A big advantage of the welt method of construction is that it makes for easier replacement of the sole when repairs are necessary.

The term 'storm welt' refers to a wedge-shaped strip of leather which is sewn into the joint ('feather') between upper and welt proper. This is done as an added protection against damp.

Welt Beater: see *Beater*.

Welt Jigger: see Rand Wheel under *Fudge Wheel*.

Welt Tools
(See also *Lace-Making Tools*.)

1. TOOLS FOR MAKING WELTS

(*a*) *Shoe Knife*
A starting knife cut is made in a leather sheet the width of the welt from the edge, and long enough to provide a grip for the finger and thumb. A Shoe Knife is stuck into the cutting board by its point; then, taking hold of the end of the strip, the leather is pulled against the edge of the knife, while using the thumb as a guide.

(*b*) *Welt Cutter Fig. 2:38, No. 2424 (p. 64)*
A short knife blade and adjustable fence mounted on a casting in which is incorporated a ring-handle. The tool is placed over the edge of a leather sheet and drawn along to cut out the welt strip.

(*c*) *Welt-Cutting Machine*
Illustrated by Ross Moyer (USA, 1884, Fig. 12), this appears to be made like a domestic mangle. The upper roller contains about twenty circular knives spaced at the width of a welt away from each other. The hide is drawn against the knives by the lower roller.

(*d*) *Welt Mill* (Welt Gauge; Welt Runner; Welt Skiver) *Figs 2:181; 2:22, No. 37 (p. 48)*
This device consists of a small block of hardwood *c.* $3\frac{3}{4}$ in. (9.5 cm) long. One end is slightly hollowed to take a *Stirrup* (strap) for holding the Welt Mill on the knee; on the other end is a sloping metal plate, grooved at the centre to guide the welt, and bordered by racks to hold the knife.

The purpose of the tool is to level or reduce the thickness of the welt. The welt is laid in the groove, and a knife is placed across a pair of the notches selected to hold it at the required level. The welt is then pulled against the knife edge to shave it. (A basket maker's Shave is occasionally used as an alternative to the Welt Mill. This has a blade fitted across a wooden stock *c.* $4\frac{1}{2}$ in. (11.4 cm) long. The thickness of the cut can be altered by means of a set screw.)

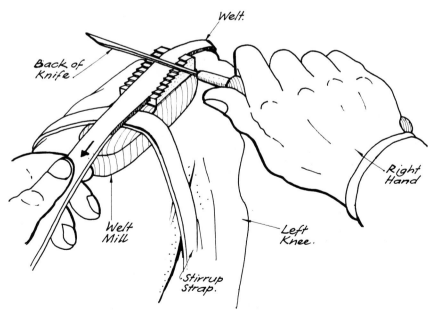

Fig. 2:181 Welt Mill in use

(*e*)　*Clog Welts*

The narrow 'welt strips' used for clogs can be made on a special cutting device (see *Welting Strip Cutter* in the CLOG MAKER section).

(*f*)　*Welt Marker*　*Fig. 2:11, No. 925 (p. 37)*

Richard Timmins (*c.* 1800) illustrates a 'Women's Welt Marker'. This is a tanged metal bar *c.* 4 in. (10.1 cm) long overall. There are six teeth cut along one edge at $\frac{3}{8}$ in. (1 cm) intervals. The tool was probably used for marking out welt strips.

2.　TOOLS FOR TRIMMING WELTS

(*a*)　*Welt-Trimming Knives*: see *Knife, Welt*.

(*b*)　*Welt Plough*

A tool with a V-shaped blade used for trimming the so-called welted seam (see *Closer's Welt Plough*).

(*c*)　*Welt Sett*

This is used to smooth and flatten a welted seam (see *Seam Sett*).

(*d*)　*Welt Fitter*

A tool listed by Devlin (1839, p. 113) under 'Kit of the boot-man'. Its appearance and purpose are unknown (see *Fitter's Plough*).

(*e*)　*Welt Iron* (Welt Rubber)

An Edge Iron for use on the welt (see *Edge Iron*).

Whang

Scots term for *Stirrup* (Footstrap).

Wheel Tools

Tools that contain wheels for marking and imprinting and pricking will be found under the following entries:

Boot Rand Wheel: see *Fudge Wheel*
Bottom Wheel: see *Crow Wheel*
Bunking Wheel: see *Bunking Tools*
Chopping-up Wheel: see *Bunking Tools*
Closer's Wheel: see *Pricker Tools*
Crow Wheel, Fancy Wheel: see *Crow Wheel*
Fudge Wheel, Janking Wheel: see *Bunking Tools*
Jim Crow Wheel: see *Crow Wheel*
Mock Stitch Wheel, Peg Wheel,
　Pricking Wheel: see *Pricker Tools*
Rand Wheel: see *Fudge Wheel* and *Seat Wheel*
Seat Wheel, Slide Box Wheel: see *Seat Wheel*
Stabbing Wheel: see *Pricker Tools*
Waist Wheel: see *Crow Wheel*
Welting Wheel: see *Fudge Wheel*
Wheel Jigger: see *Fudge Wheel*

Whittie

Scots term for a sharpening stick. (See *Sharpening Bat*.)

Wooden Burnishing and Smoothing Tools: see *Bones and Sticks*; *Edge Iron*; *Seam Sett*.

Yerkin

A Scots term for a side seam of a shoe. According to the Oxford English Dictionary the verb 'yerk' or 'yark' was originally applied to bootmaking, e.g. to draw stitches tight.

Yickie-Yeckie

Scottish for piece of bone or wood used for rubbing down (see *Bones and Sticks*).

3

Clog Maker

A stout leather shoe with a wooden sole, often iron-shod, was the traditional clog worn until recent times in the North of England. It kept the feet warm and dry at a comparatively low cost. They are still sometimes worn by those working in rough or wet conditions, for instance, by miners, foundrymen and tanners.

Wooden-soled sandles or shoes have been worn in Britain since Roman times, by both rich and poor. But from the eighteenth until the early twentieth century clogs were the ordinary footwear of many poorer people. In the textile mills of northern England clogs were as much a part of the mills as the looms themselves; and their clattering sound on the streets each morning and evening is something elderly people still remember. That clogs and poverty were equated in people's minds is exemplified by several common sayings, such as, 'clogs to clogs in three generations'; or the Yorkshire adage about girls who aimed for a husband above their station: 'she wouldn't have clogs and boots never came'.

Information on the clog-making trade and methods will be found in the books listed in the Bibliography under Jack Hill (1979), J. Geraint Jenkins (1965) and Evelyn Vigeon (1977).

The term clog is applied to other wooden or part-wooden footwear, including the following:

Fig. 3:2

(a) The Sabot Figs 3:2; 3:11
This is a single piece of wood roughly cut into shoe form. They were worn in many parts of continental Europe, especially where leather was expensive and wood cheap. The special tools used for making them are found occasionally in English workshops (see *Sabot-Making Tools* below).

(b) The Patten Fig. 3:3
This is not a shoe, but an overshoe, and was worn in England by all classes of people (see *Patten* below). Earlier leather shoe construction was not water-proof, hence the need for this extra protection in bad weather.

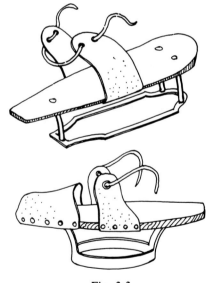

Fig. 3:3

Process
The sole blocks were made in the woods by outdoor workers, and later finished in the clog-maker's shop. (See *Clog Sole Maker's Tools* p. 188.)

185

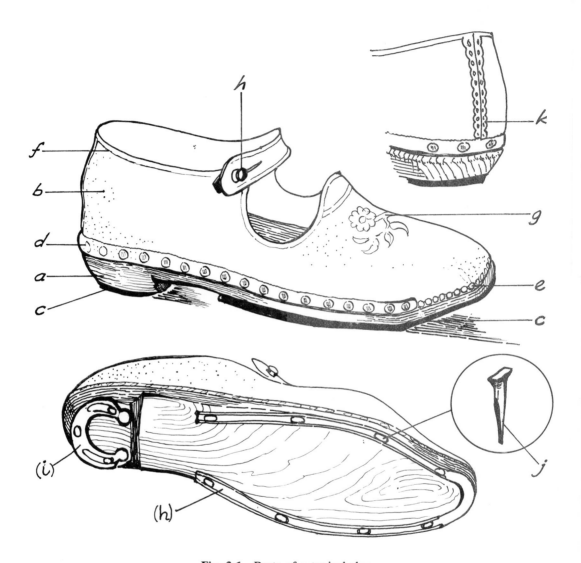

Fig. 3:1 Parts of a typical clog

(*a*) Wooden sole
(*b*) Leather upper
(*c*) Clog-Irons: see (*h*) and (*i*) below
(*d*) Welt and welt nails which fasten the upper to the sole. (The rebate round the edge of the sole, in which the upper is nailed, is called the 'grip'.)
(*e*) Brass nails round the toe

(*f*) A scored line cut along edge to simulate binding (see *Binding Cutter*)
(*g*) Decoration sometimes cut on the vamp (see *Crimper*)
(*h*) Clog-Iron of the type known as a 'duckbill neb'
(*i*) Heel Iron
(*j*) 'Tip' nail for attaching irons to sole
(*k*) Example of a decorative seam

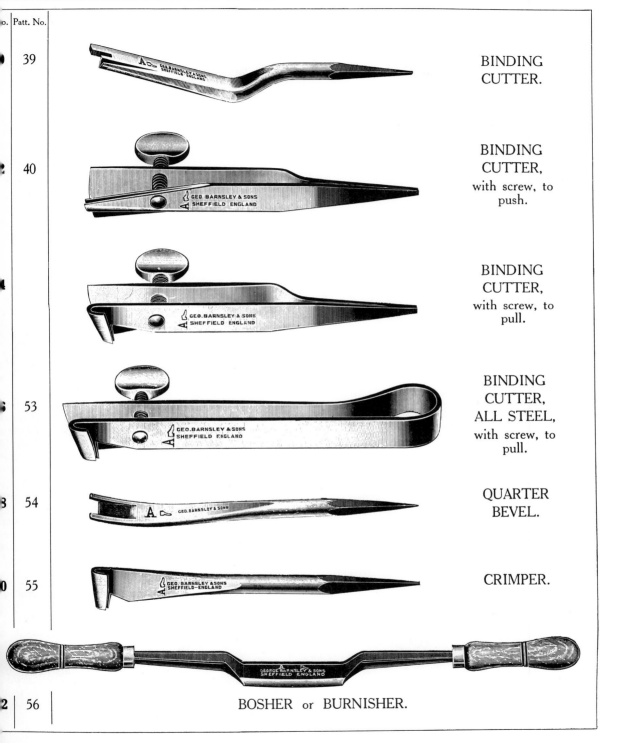

o.	Patt. No.		
	39		BINDING CUTTER.
2	40		BINDING CUTTER, with screw, to push.
4			BINDING CUTTER, with screw, to pull.
6	53		BINDING CUTTER, ALL STEEL, with screw, to pull.
8	54		QUARTER BEVEL.
0	55		CRIMPER.
2	56		BOSHER or BURNISHER.

Fig. 3:4   Clogger's Tools. (George Barnsley & Son's catalogue, Sheffield 1927)   187

The leather uppers were made with shoemaker's tools, and also with a few tools specially developed for clog making which are described below.

The Tools

Binding Cutter (Binding Knife; Drag)

A cutting tool *c.* 5–7 in. (12.7–17.7 cm) overall, with a V-shaped chisel or race type cutter, and a fixed or adjustable fence. In spite of its name, it is not used for cutting the strips of leather that are sometimes sewn along the exposed edges of boots and shoes, but is used to imitate such bindings by means of a scored line cut at a short distance from the edge of the leather.

Among the many variants, the following are typical:

(*a*) *Fixed-fence type* with V-chisel cutter *Fig. 3:4, No. 6550*

A crank-shaped shank with a forked head. One prong is the cutter, the other a fence fixed at about $\frac{1}{8}$ in. (0.4 cm) from the cutter. Operated on the push stroke.

(*b*) *Compass type* with V-chisel cutter *Fig. 3:4, No. 6552*

One leg carries the V-cutter, the other leg is a sprung fence, adjustable by means of a thumb-screw. Its rear end is welded to the stem of the tool, which is tapered to serve as a tang on which a wooden handle can be driven. Operated on the push stroke.

(*c*) *Compass type* as above, but made from a solid forging. *Fig. 2:22, No. 40 (p. 48)*

(*d*) *Compass Race types* *Figs 2:23 (p. 49); 3:4, Nos 6554/56*

These are of compass design, but instead of the V-shaped cutter, one leg is folded over at its foot to form a drag-knife (like a harness-maker's *Race Knife*) designed to cut a groove when pulled. A variant is made from a single strip of steel which is bent over like a sugar tong.

Bosher (Burnisher) *Fig. 3:4, No. 6562*

A two-handed tool belonging to the family of shoemaker's *Glazer and Sleeking Irons*. It is used, after heating, for applying waxes to soles and heels and for smoothing surfaces and ironing out wrinkles. It is made in several different shapes, but that used in the clog trade usually has a straight wedge-shaped body.

Clog-Iron Making Tools

Clog-iron making was a separate trade, which, like nail or chain making, was carried out by specialist smiths. Until recently several clog-iron makers still worked in Yorkshire and Lancashire.

Their forges were equipped with hearth, bellows and a foot-operated tilt-hammer, called an 'Oliver', and an anvil (block) set in an earth-filled box. Tools included: a *Fulling Iron* used with the Oliver to form the grooves in the clog-iron in which the nail holes were later punched; a *Hollowing Tool* for shaping the front iron; and a *Heel Turning Tool* for shaping the semi-circular heel iron. The nails used have T-shaped heads designed to lie in the groove of the clog-iron. The heel iron has its ends hammered into circular flanges ('neps'), and three nails secure it to the heel of the clog. The front iron runs the whole length of the sole from waist to toe and is flattened at the toe, which, as with all clogs, is turned upwards clear of the ground. Eight nails (but sometimes less) secure the front iron to the sole (see *Nails; Steady*).

Clog Sole Maker's Tools

Wooden clog soles were made in two stages: the sole blocks were first cut and roughly shaped by outdoor workers in the woods; then, after seasoning, the sole-blocks were trimmed and shaped into clog soles in the clog maker's workshop.

The Sole-Block Maker

Itinerant sole-block makers lived in temporary huts in the woods for several weeks in early summer. The timber was sawn into short lengths, cleft, roughly shaped into sole-blocks with a Stock Knife and then stacked for seasoning. The stock knife is described under *Clogger's Paring Knife* below. The wood used was alder, sycamore, or beech. Alder is particularly suitable since it cuts well and is light in weight; beech is heavier but more durable. Much of the alder was cut from the alder groves of South Wales and the border counties where the soil and climate are favourable to its growth. J. G. Jenkins (1965, p. 19) points out that the sole-block makers found it easier to take a few simple tools to the forests rather than take timber, often from inaccessible coppices, to a permanent village workshop.

The Clog Sole Maker *Fig. 3:5*

The block was finally shaped to form the sole in the clog maker's workshop with the tools described below. Mr C. Powell, a Manchester clog maker (1979), described to the author how he was supplied with clog soles:

'In the early 1920s clog sole makers used to tour the North West industrial and coal mining areas, working for two or three days at one clog shop, then moving on to the next, completing the circuit every three or four months.

'I remember one Mike Sweeney, a tall Irishman, who used to make clog soles for my father. He would call, always unexpectedly, work for two or three days, make three or four dozen pairs of clog soles, then move on to the next clog shop. He was a first-class craftsman but some of the men were not up to his standards – often making clog soles with a slight cast in them.'

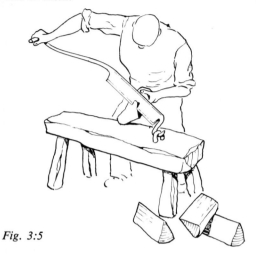

Fig. 3:5

Tools include the following:

Stool (Chopping Block; Chopping Horse) *Fig. 3:6*
A sturdy four-legged stool with an eye-bolt screwed to the top to take the hook on the end of the knife.

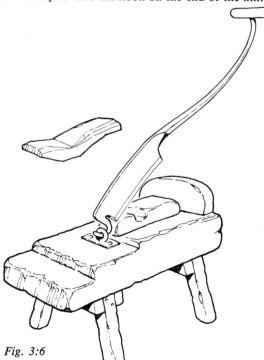

Fig. 3:6

Clog Sole Knives Fig. 3:7
An iron bar about 4 ft (1.21 m) long, onto which a blade is forged or bolted. One end of the bar has a T-shaped handle, the other a hook which engages with the eye-bolt on the stool. In operation, one hand holds the rough sole-blank, while the other, by levering the knife up and down, pares away the unwanted wood.

Clog Knives are made with three different blades, as follows:

(*a*) *Clogger's Paring Knife* (Stock Knife)
A straight blade about 13 in. (33 cm) long and $3\frac{1}{2}$–4 in. (8.8–10.1 cm) wide. Used for paring off waste and trimming flat surfaces.

(*b*) *Clogger's Hollowing Knife*
A curved blade 4–6 in. (10.1–15.2 cm) long and 4 in. (10.1 cm) wide. Used for hollowing the upper side and edges of the sole.

(*c*) *Clogger's Gripper*
A narrow V-shaped tool, which is fitted in place of a blade. Used for cutting the channel round the edge of the sole into which the leather uppers are nailed.

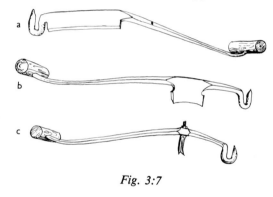

Fig. 3:7

Crimper
(According to the *Dictionary of Occupational Terms* (1927) the term 'Crimper' is also applied to the worker who cuts ornamental patterns on the uppers of clogs.)
A cutting tool about 6–7 in. (15.2–17.7 cm) long, designed to cut decorative patterns on the surface of the leather. There are two types:

(*a*) *The Drag Crimper Fig. 3:4, No. 6560*
A type of Race Knife, cutting on the pull stroke, used mainly for tracing the design.

(*b*) *V-Chisel Cutter*
A V-shaped knife, cutting on the push stroke, for deeper cuts.

189

Miss Evelyn Vigeon writes as follows about this decorative work (*Journal of the Costume Society*, 1977):

'Most cloggers also made the highly decorative crimp clogs which went by a variety of names which indicate their purpose such as Dandy clogs, Dancing clogs, Sunday or "neet" clogs, and "coortin" or "walking out" clogs. Another version, at least in the Manchester area, was the miners' "top" clogs to distinguish them from those worn down the pit. ...The clogger would either draw up his own design, often at the suggestion of the customer, or use a purchased iron pattern. Hearts, butterflies, and flowers were very common, but the design could reflect the customer's hobby such as pigeon fancier.'

Hammer, Clogger's

The following hammers are used by cloggers:

(*a*) *Clogger's Tacking Hammer Fig. 2:41, No. 3022 (p. 67)*
A light claw hammer with a round face, long chamfered neck, and a long tapering claw. Used for driving nails which secure the welting and the lower edge of the upper to the recess, known as the 'Grip', which is cut along the sole edge.

(*b*) *Clogger's Ironing Hammer Fig. 2:41, No. 3020 (p. 67)*
A hammer with a round face and cross pane, used for driving nails when fixing sole and heel irons. The narrow, rounded, pane can be used for bedding the nail heads into the fulling groove in the iron.

(*c*) *Knocking-off Hammer*
A name given to a relatively heavy hammer used for driving a *Pig's Foot* when removing the upper for re-clogging.

Knocker-up (Boot or Clog Breaker; Breaker) *Fig. 3:8*

A name given to a hand-operated machine designed to separate the upper from the sole when one of them is in need of repair; or for removing a worn clog-iron.

The machine, which is about 23 in. (58.4 cm) high, is made like a miniature Mortising Machine. A chisel is forced vertically downwards by means of an iron lever. The lever operates a toothed quadrant that engages with a rack on the back of the chisel housing. By lowering the lever, the chisel is forced down on the work. (See also *Pig's Foot*.)

Last, Clogger's *Fig. 3:9*

Wearers of clogs do not demand a close fit; consequently lasts of standardised sizes and shapes are

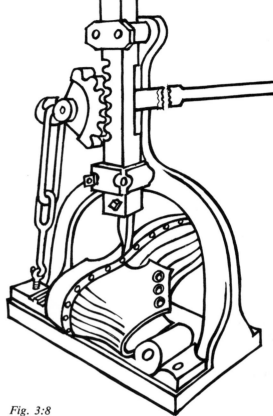

Fig. 3:8

used by cloggers on which to mould the upper. Unlike shoemaking, the upper is taken off the last before assembly so that it can be nailed to the sole.

Clog-maker's lasts differ from shoemaker's in having a greater upturn in the toe, known as 'toe spring'. This helps the wearer of an unbending sole to walk by rocking the clog from heel to toe. The lasts are not made left and right as in shoemaking — though the fastenings provide for this on the finished clogs.

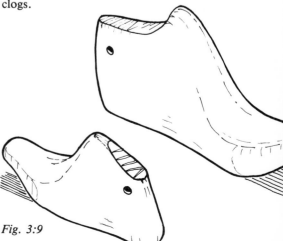

Fig. 3:9

Nails

These include:

(i)   Tip nails, with oblong heads, designed to sink into the groove of the clog irons. Sizes $\frac{3}{4}$–1 in. (1.9–2.5 cm).

(ii)   Welting nails for fastening the upper to the sole. These are 'cut tacks' and made in sizes $\frac{5}{8}$–1 in. (1.6–2.5 cm).

(iii)   Brass clog nails used for both fastening and decoration round the toe of the clog. Sizes $\frac{3}{8}$–$\frac{5}{8}$ in. (1–1.6 cm).

Note: Power-driven staples are beginning to replace nails for fastening the uppers to the soles (1975).

Nail Pricker

An awl with a chisel point (like a bradawl) mounted in a shoemaker's awl-handle. Used for making a small hole through the welting and upper into the grip on the sole edge. The hole is made at a downward angle so that the nail will follow the hole without the risk of splitting the sole.

Nail Table   *Fig. 3:10*

A round table, about 34 in. (86.3 cm) in diameter, round which a group of cloggers worked. The surface is divided into compartments to hold a supply of nails and irons within reach of each worker. The example illustrated was used in the basement of William Bradwell, Clog Maker of Besses O'th Barn, near Manchester (*c*. 1850–1953). Mr Bradwell said, 'We looked white and pale in those years sitting all day in the dark but for a glimmer from a pavement light.'

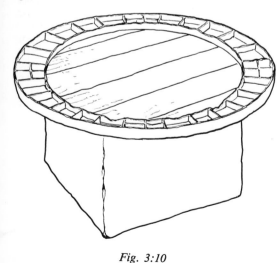

Fig. 3:10

Pattens   *Fig. 3:3*

According to the Oxford English Dictionary, the origin of the term 'patten' is uncertain. It was applied at different periods to various kinds of footgear; but since the seventeenth century, 'patten' is the name given to a wooden sole held on the foot by a leather loop over the instep, and mounted on an iron ring (or two wooden cross pieces) by which the wearer is raised an inch or two from the ground.

Randle Holme (1688) defines the patten as follows:

'What the Paten is, your Gentlewoman will tell you; it is a thing of Wood like a Shooe sole, with Straps over it, to tye over the shoe, having an Iron at the bottom, to raise the wearer thereof from the Dirt; by means whereof clean shoes may be preserved though they go in foul Streets.'

Pattens appear to have been worn mainly by women. Thus, Wright's Dialect Dictionary, quoting from a glossary of Derbyshire words (1894): 'Pattens are . . . another article of foot gear for women, and intended to enable them to go about in wet weather with dry feet, and to "slosh", "slush" and "swill" indoors and out . . . In these all women in my young days patted about their household work.'

Pattens were noisy in wear. A church near Swinton (Lancashire) is said to have displayed a notice, 'Ladies are requested to take off their pattens before entering.' In her *Life of Charlotte Brontë* (1857), Mrs Gaskell relates that Miss Branwell (who came to look after the Brontë children after their mother died in 1821) 'dreaded the cold damp arising from the flag floors in the passages and parlours of Haworth Parsonage . . . I have heard that Miss Branwell always went about the house in pattens, clicking up and down the stairs, from her dread of catching cold'.

The making of the soles was similar work to that of the clog sole maker. The forging of the irons became a specialised trade on the same lines as that of the clog-iron makers; a grooved stake or steady was fitted to the anvil to hold these irons while working on them.

Pig's Foot   *Fig. 2:55, Nos 6180/82/84 (p. 81)*

This tool is similar to a woodworker's Tack Lifter or Nail Claw, but it is more heavily made, and it has a flat, instead of a curved, claw. It is made in iron throughout, or with a wooden handle which is often hooped to withstand blows from a hammer: the tool is hammered when it is driven like a cold chisel for removing old clog irons, or when removing a worn sole.

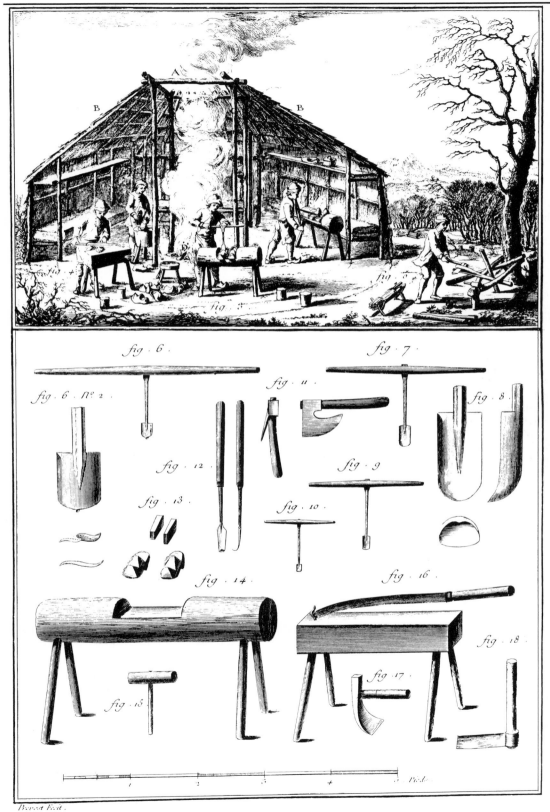

Fig. 3:11 Sabot making. From Diderot's Encyclopaedia (*Economie Rustique*), France *c.* 1760

A Manchester clog maker (Mr C. Powell, 1978) describes how he removes an old sole without injury to the upper:

'Place the clog between both knees when sitting on the clogging stool. Position the blade of the Pig's Foot below the welting and grip of the clog sole; then strike the Pig's Foot with the hammer, repeating this operation all round the clog sole at $\frac{1}{2}$ in. intervals. Finally, insert a strong awl and open the split in the grip by a downward levering motion. This allows the nails to be extracted more easily from the clog sole.'

Quarter Bevel   *Fig. 3:4, No. 6558*
A light cutting tool with a forked blade similar to the saddler's *Edge Shave*. The two prongs act as a fence and the sharpened web between them does the cutting. It is used for bevelling the top edge of the upper, or for paring off surplus leather from the lower edge of the upper after it has been attached to the sole. Some cloggers prefer to use a shoe knife for this purpose.

Sabot-Making Tools   *Figs 3:2; 3:11*
Unlike the English clog, which is a wooden sole surmounted by a leather upper, the European sabot is made entirely of wood. Some of the special tools used for making sabots are occasionally found in English workshops; they are still used in the USA by amateur sabot makers.

Typical sabot tools include the following: (*Note*: The numbers printed in brackets after some of the tools relate to the number of the tool engraved in Diderot's plate, see *Fig. 3:11*.)

(*a*)   *Chopping Block* – on which a sabot blank can be roughly chopped to shape.

(*b*)   *Clave* – on which the rough sabot can be wedged while working upon it. (14)

(*c*)   *Shaving Horse or Stool* – on which the shaped blank is trimmed with a Bench Knife. (16)

(*d*)   *Axe and Adze* – of the cooper's type used for trimming. (11 & 17)

(*e*)   *Augers* – for excavating the inside of the sabot. The process is known as 'lowering the bottom'. (6–9)

(*f*)   *Chisels and Gouges* – for trimming the inside of the sabot.

(*g*)   *Hook and Spoon Knives* – for the final trimming inside the sabot. (12)

(*h*)   *Race Compass* – for inscribing decorative patterns, usually flowers and leaves, which are sometimes cut on the front of the sabot. (See *Race Tools* in the HARNESS MAKER section.)

Size Stick   *Fig. 2:34, No. 11 (p.60)*
This is a less elaborate version of the shoemaker's Size Stick. It consists of a square boxwood stick *c.* 16 in. (40.6 cm) long, with a short stop at one end. It is graduated with the usual two scales. According to a Manchester clog maker (Mr Powell, 1978) the 'old sizes for clogs were two sizes larger than the shoe size, that is to say a customer who wore a size 8 shoe would require a size 10 clog – now they are the same'. (See *Size Stick* in the BOOT AND SHOE MAKER section.)

Steady (Stithy)
This is the clogger's version of the *Cobbler's Foot* and is normally held in the same way, between the legs.

It is chiefly used to support a clog sole when nailing on the irons.

It measures *c.* 24 in. (60.9 cm) high and is often home-made. See also *Clog-Iron Making Tools* and *Hammer, Clogger's*.

Variants include:

(*a*)   *Single Post Steady   Fig. 3:12*
This is used when nailing on irons before attaching the upper. The wear near the foot of the post was caused when the steady was held horizontally across the knees and the lower end used to hold a clog while riveting clasps etc. (The example illustrated was in the workshop of H. Brierley, Clog Makers, Rochdale, Lancashire, 1960.)

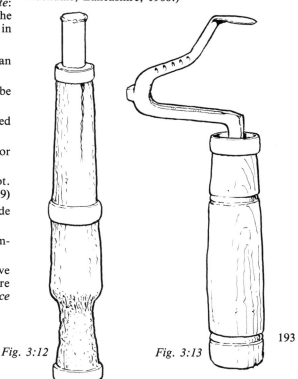

Fig. 3:12   *Fig. 3:13*

193

(b)   Single Arm Steady *Fig. 3:13*

This Steady is used for nailing on irons after the upper is attached. The clog is supported on the bent arm with the sole upwards. (This Steady comes from workshop of William Bradnell, Clog Makers, Besses O'th Barn, Lancashire, 1953.)

(c)   Combined Headed Steady *Fig. 3:14*

The two types illustrated are in the West Yorkshire Folk Museum in Halifax (1977).

The vertical post is used as in (*a*) above, and the curved arm is used as in (*b*). The short side-arm has a slight depression on its surface on which the sole-iron can be rested when being hammered to fit the sole.

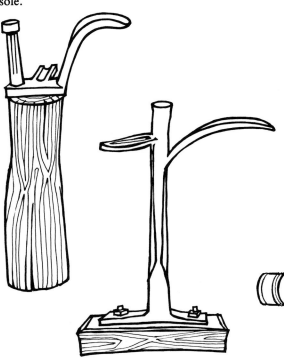

Fig. 3:14

Welting Strip Cutter *Fig. 3:15*

(See also *Lace-Making Tools* in the BOOT AND SHOE MAKER section.)

The term welt is applied by cloggers to the thin strip of leather which lies under the row of nails that secure the upper to the grip along the edge of the sole. This strip should not be confused with the much thicker shoemaker's welts to which the sole of a boot or shoe is stitched.

Methods of cutting the welting strips include:

(a)   Hand cutting.

This method is described by Mr C. Powell (Swinton, 1977) as follows:

'The way we cut strips of welting is with a very sharp pointed knife stuck vertically into a piece of board. You place the piece of welting you are going to cut on the board. Make a cut into the leather the width of the welt from the edge (between $\frac{1}{4}$ and $\frac{3}{8}$ in.), long enough to give a good grip for the finger and thumb. Take the strip of welting in the left hand — place the right thumb nail on the edge of the welting as a guide, and draw the welting into the knife blade.'

(b)   Adjustable Hand Cutter

A tool used for cutting these strips is illustrated. It is inscribed 'Bacon's Patent Cutter No. 151906'. The knife stuck into a board (as above) is replaced by a short blade held in place by a wooden hand screw. The piece of leather to be cut is laid on the board and guided by contact with the vertical peg which acts (instead of a thumbnail) as an adjustable fence. The leather is then pulled towards the knife.

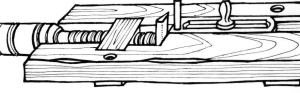

Fig. 3:15

—4—

Decoration of Leather

The inherent qualities of leather make it suitable for a wide range of decorative treatments. Most methods of doing this rely on the early and remarkable discovery that vegetable tanned leather, after being damped in water, can be moulded or pressed into shapes which, after drying out, retain their shape indefinitely.

Fig. 4:1 Diagrammatic illustration of leather decoration, with sectional views of each treatment described in the following pages.

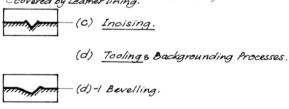

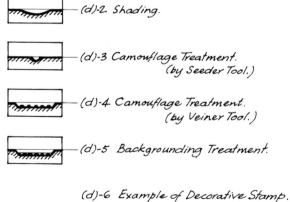

(a.) *Modelling* (Recessed Surface.)

(b) *Embossing* (Raised Surface.)
 └ Leather filling at back (shavings & glue.)
 └ covered by Leather lining.

(c) *Incising.*

(d) *Tooling & Backgrounding Processes.*

(d)-1 Bevelling.

(d)-2 Shading.

(d)-3 Camouflage Treatment.
 (by Seeder Tool.)

(d)-4 Camouflage Treatment.
 (by Veiner Tool.)

(d)-5 Backgrounding Treatment.

(d)-6 Example of Decorative Stamp.

Fig. 4:1

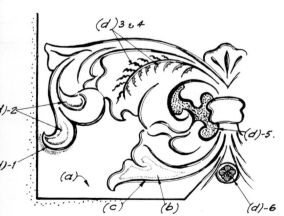

Historical Note

In the eighth century AD the Spanish town of Córdoba became famous for its leather, first white or dyed red, and later gilded. (Hence the English term 'cordwainer', the earlier name for a shoemaker.) Decorative techniques requiring the use of tools, such as incising and modelling, were developed during the Middle Ages. By the end of the sixteenth century Holland was a centre for making fine leather embossed in relief, coloured, and used for wall coverings, table covers, as well as for smaller objects. The decoration of leather was practised to a lesser extent in other parts of Europe, including England, especially for bookbinding, covering caskets, and the sheaths of knives and daggers. The Spaniards are said to have introduced the art of leather decoration to South America. In the nineteenth century, the Mexican saddlers who excelled in the art, taught the trade to the saddlers of the border states: hence the so-called Western saddle with its elaborate decorations.

The art of decorating leather declined in England during the Industrial Revolution, but a revival occurred from about 1900, partly as a result of the interest in handicrafts inspired by William Morris and his followers. At the present time there is a flourishing revival both here and in the United States of America.

Tools for decorating leather

The tools described below are grouped under the decorating process in which they are mainly employed. But it should be emphasised that workers in this field might not make any such sharp distinctions between one process and another: they might use a tool for a purpose other than that for which it was intended; and some use tools from other trades altogether, for example, the Saddler's Crease.

Leathers intended for decoration are best vegetable-tanned so that they will absorb the moisture that is applied to make the decorative process effective. Metal tools are plated to prevent the stains that would result from contact with the dampened leather.

The tools used for ornamentation of book covers are described in the BOOKBINDER section under *Finishing Tools* and *Gilder's Tools*. Similar tools are used for decorating leather table tops by table liners and gilders.

Backgrounding Tools (Some of these tools are often referred to simply as Punches or Stamps.)   *Fig. 4:2*

This group of tools are intended for general backgrounding, tooling and 'camouflage' treatments. Most of them are made from round metal bars 4–5 in. (10.1–12.7 cm) long and of $\frac{1}{8}-\frac{1}{4}$ in. (0.4–0.7 cm) diameter, plated to prevent staining, and with the handle sometimes milled to give a good grip.

Examples include:

(*a*) *Beveller*

The working head has a curved face to avoid too sharp an impression at its edges. Bevellers are used to 'put-down' (depress) the areas around the lines of a design, to set the design in relief. The Beveller is held upright with the front face inserted into the cut; the tool is then struck sharply with a small Mallet and then moved along the cut, and struck with the Mallet as it goes. The effect is to compress the leather by small successive hits as the bevelling proceeds.

(*b*) *Shader*

The Shader is similar to the Beveller except for its pear-shaped head. It is held in the same way as the Beveller, and can be pushed along while striking with a mallet to cover a given area. The process depresses areas inside the design to give contour relief and shading.

(*c*) *Seeder*

(*d*) *Veiner*

These stamps are used for seeding, i.e. for 'powdering' surfaces; and in the case of the Veiner, for impressing vein-like marks. They are used for emphasising the contours of a design.

(*e*) *Backgrounding Tools*

The heads of these tools are necessarily small, from $c.\frac{1}{16}-\frac{1}{4}$ in. (0.2–0.7 cm); they are round, rectangular, oval or pear-shaped. The pear-shaped tool is especially useful for the areas between two converging lines. The small heads of these punches have their faces cut to impress a background made up of chequers, stars or dots. This treatment helps the main design to stand out in greater relief.

(*f*) *Decorative Stamps*

The example illustrated is one among hundreds of devices used for the decoration of leather. These include every imaginable form of star, trefoil, dot, flower or leaf; patterns of basket-weave or coiled rope; and heraldic devices such as the fleur-de-lys, Tudor roses or wheat ears.

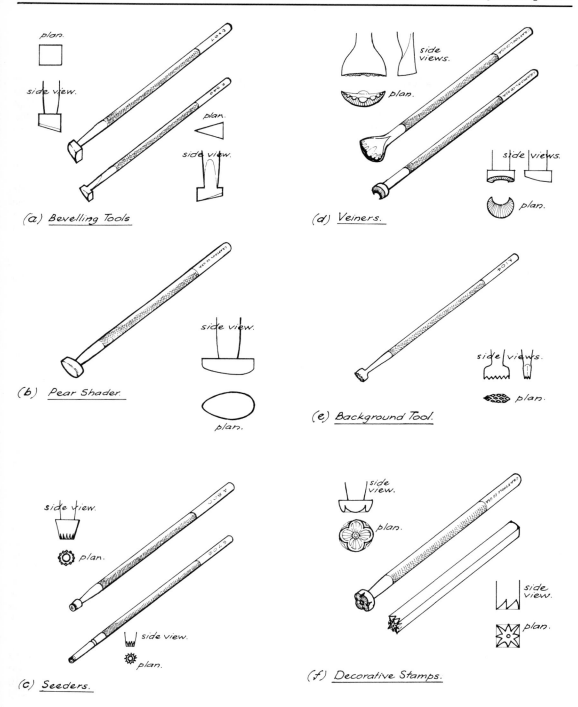

plan.

side view.

(a) *Bevelling Tools*

side views.

plan.

side views.

plan.

(d) *Veiners.*

side view.

plan.

(b) *Pear Shader.*

side views.

plan.

(e) *Background Tool.*

side view.

plan.

side view.

plan.

(c) *Seeders.*

side view.

plan.

side view.

plan.

(f) *Decorative Stamps.*

Fig. 4:2 Backgrounding Tools.

Embossing Tools *Fig. 4:3*

Embossing tools are about 6 in. (15.2 cm) long, handled like the *Modelling Tools*, with a blade ending in a solid, polished 'ball' of varying sizes. The purpose of embossing is to cause parts of the design to stand out in relief from the surface of the leather. The leather is dampened and the design is transferred from the paper design to the grain side by tracing. The outline of the area to be embossed is worked with a Modelling Tool so that an impression of this outline becomes visible on the reverse (or flesh) side. With this side uppermost the embossing tool is then applied with a circular motion to areas inside the outline, to raise it gently and gradually so that it stands out on the grain side of the leather to the required height.

If the raised parts stand out more than $\frac{1}{16}$ in. (0.2 cm) they need to be 'filled' at the back. There are several types of filling which include leather parings mixed with paste, or wax. When the filling is half set, any details that need to be added to the embossed areas are made with a Modelling Tool and the work can then be left to dry out. Finally, a piece of lining leather is stuck to the back to cover the filling.

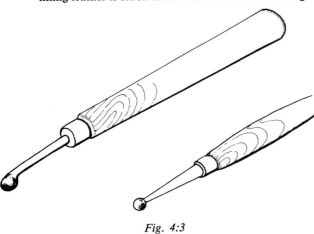

Fig. 4:3

Incising Tools *Fig. 4:4*

In this process the design is cut on the surface to a limited depth, the cut 'opened' with an *Opener* (see below) and subsequently 'gone over' with *Modelling* and *Background Tools*.

Incised work is often called 'carved work', but the term is misleading since nothing is taken away from the surface of the leather. The leather needs to be at least 1.5 mm thick, and well dampened before work begins. The work is done on a firm smooth surface, such as a slab of marble.

The tools used include:

(a) *Incising Knife*

About $5\frac{1}{2}$ in. (13.9 cm) long overall, with a slender pencil-like handle and a narrow, skew-sharpened steel blade. The knife is held upright at right angles to the surface of the leather and drawn towards the user, guided with a finger of the left hand held against the flat of the blade. The depth of cut varies according to the design.

(b) *Swivel Knife*

This knife, which has largely displaced the Incising Knife, is of American origin of *c*. 1900. The main body of the knife is known as the 'barrel'; this holds the blade which is secured by a small set-screw. The blade's cutting edge is normally straight, but angled blades are used for fine work. The barrel is free to swivel at the joint just below the yoke – a distinctive feature which gives this knife its name. The first finger is held over the yoke, while the barrel can be 'swivelled' by the other fingers, except for the little finger which rests on the flat of the blade to steady it.

The cuts are made at right angles to the surface of the leather using only a corner of the blade. The knife is inclined forward and pulled towards the user. To change direction, the barrel of the knife is turned while the yoke is held still. This enables the user to follow any curve exactly: it is this ability of the knife to follow curves so easily that makes the tool unique.

(c) *The Opener*

This tool resembles a *Modelling Tool* but has a blunter point. The point is placed in the incised cut, and the outer edge of the incision is pressed downwards. The tool is pushed forwards to the end of the cut, and the area uncovered by the Opener is then gone over with modelling tools.

Modelling Tools *Fig. 4:5*

The purpose of the modelling process is to impress a design in low relief on the grain side of the leather. This pressure is applied with modelling tools.

Modelling Tools are about $5-6\frac{1}{2}$ in. (12.7–16.5 cm) long, and usually mounted in a wooden handle. The tools are often double-ended: the second blade may be a variation from the basic shape, or it may be a tapering point to be used as a Tracer (see below).

The leather, usually calfskin, is dampened slightly on the grain side to plump up the fibres and produce the plastic condition suitable for receiving the impressions of the tool. The paper on which the design is drawn is laid on the grain side of the leather and fixed into position so that the main lines of the design

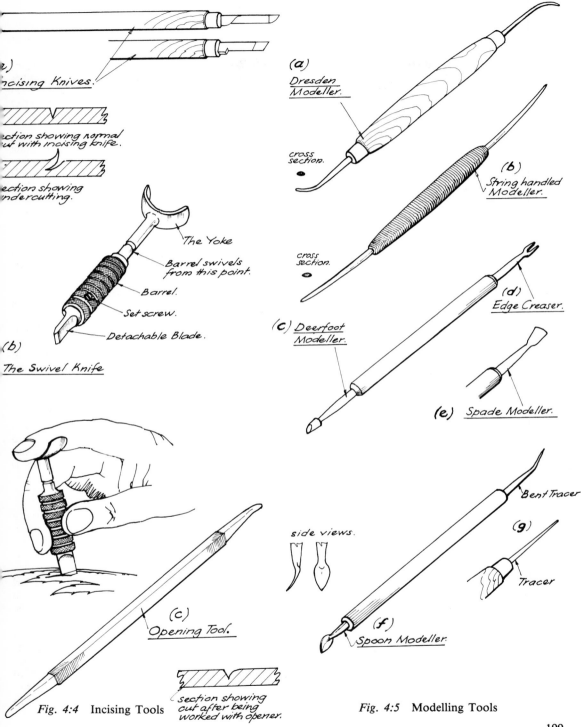

(a) Dresden Modeller.

cross section.

(b) String handled Modeller.

cross section.

(c) Deerfoot Modeller.

(d) Edge Creaser.

(e) Spade Modeller.

Bent Tracer

(g) Tracer

side views.

(f) Spoon Modeller.

Incising Knives.

section showing normal cut with incising knife.

section showing undercutting.

The Yoke

Barrel swivels from this point.

Barrel.

Set screw.

Detachable Blade.

(b) The Swivel Knife

(c) Opening Tool.

Fig. 4:4   Incising Tools

section showing cut after being worked with opener.

Fig. 4:5   Modelling Tools

can be transferred to the leather with a *Tracer* tool. Holding the appropriate Modelling Tool as one would a pencil, the area surrounding the outline is depressed to leave the design in low relief.

Modelling tools include:

(*a*)   *Dresden Tool*
The name may relate to its delicate blade which makes it specially suitable for impressing small lines of detail and for flattening small background areas where other modellers might not be suitable.

(*b*)   *Modeller*
The example illustrated is all-metal with its handle wound with string for holding.

(*c*)   *Deer Foot Modeller*

(*d*)   *Edge Creaser*
Used for marking edges.

(*e*)   *Spade Modeller*

(*f*)   *Spoon Modeller*

(*g*)   *Tracer*
Used for transferring the main lines of a design from paper to the leather.

Polishing and Burnishing Agates (Agates; Burnishers)   *Fig. 4:6*
Agate heads of varying shapes are set on handles of wood or, occasionally, bone or ivory. The agate heads illustrated are known as 'dog tooth', 'flat' or 'point'. The dog tooth example is *c.* 14 in. (35.5 cm) long and intended for use with pressure from the shoulder.

These tools are used for burnishing and polishing leather surfaces. Larger examples, used for burnishing leather book covers and gold leaf, are illustrated under *Polishing and Burnishing Tools* in the BOOKBINDER section.

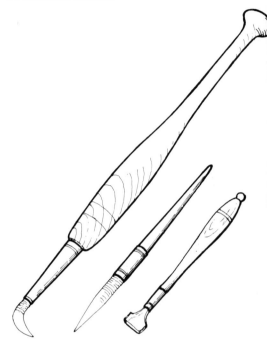

Fig. 4:6

—5—

Driving-Belt Maker

Historical Note   Figs 5:1; 5:2

The spinning wheel was probably the first machine in which motive power was transmitted by a flexible belt from one wheel to another. It reached Europe from the Far East in the fourteenth century. Joseph Needham FRS (1965, Vol. 4, p. 103) writes of 'strong indications which point to Chinese textile technology as the focus of origin of all such belt-drive machinery'.

After the introduction of steam engines in the eighteenth century, some kind of belt drive was the most usual method of transmitting power in the factories. Anyone whose working life started in the factories of the 1920s will remember the forest of driving belts running from line-shafting at ceiling level down to each machine on the shop floor. This system began to decline in the 1930s, owing to the growing use of electric motors: motorised drive became part of each machine.

Leather belting must have the strength to transmit the power required of it. It must be flexible enough to bend round small pulleys and then straighten out as it moves; it must have a surface which does not slip over the pulleys round which it travels; it must not stretch unduly; it must have a long life.

Process

The belts are usually made from oxhide butts, vegetable-tanned, and cured with cod oil and tallow. The butts are first cut into strips of the required width, then tapered at the ends, and the cut ends roughened. The strips are then cemented together, and the joints stitched, sewn or riveted (see *Belt-Fastening Tools*). The edges of the belt are consolidated by rounding and burnishing (see *Belt Edge Rounding Tools*).

Initially the belts were made with harness-maker's tools. Gradually a few specialised hand tools were developed, and also machines for strip cutting, skiv-ing (i.e. tapering the cut ends), presses and clamps for use when cementing joints, machines for sewing with copper wire, and riveting machines.

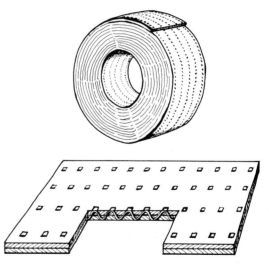

Fig. 5:1   A roll of double lace-sewn belting with a diagram to show the lacing.

The workshop (often known as the 'strap shop') contained a long bench on which complete lengths of belting could be laid out flat. Part of its width was often covered with a steel plate − a typical one measured 40 ft (12.19 m) long × 12 in. (30.5 cm) wide. This was used as a bed on which the belt was flattened and the cemented joints compressed with a heavy roller. A slot was often formed along the front of the bench in which a belt could be placed on its side with its edges exposed for rounding and burnishing.

Fig. 5:2 From a photograph taken in *c*. 1900 of belt makers working in the strap shop of Messrs Webb & Sons, Tanners, of Stowmarket, Suffolk.

by Ross Moyer (USA, 1884) has its blade hollowed out longitudinally, perhaps for the thread to lie in. Its purpose is uncertain, but it seems probable that it was used for lacing.

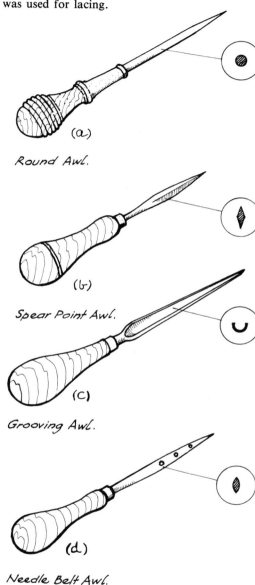

Round Awl.

Spear Point Awl.

Grooving Awl.

Needle Belt Awl.

Fig. 5:3

Awls for beltmaking　*Fig. 5:3*
Awls used by Driving-Belt makers include the following:

(*a*)　*Round Belt Awl*
A stout pointed awl of round cross-section, *c*. 8 in. (20.3 cm) overall, probably used for opening holes in leather and textile belts to take joint fasteners.

(*b*)　*Spear Point Awl*
About 7 in. (17.7 cm) overall, these have a diamond-shaped cross-section, similar to the *Harness Awl* (see HARNESS MAKER AND SADDLER section). It is used for sewing and lacing the belts, e.g. at the joints.

(*c*)　*Grooving Awl*
A tapering hollow blade of half-cone shape, rather like a woodworker's Taper Bit, *c*. 9 in. (22.8 cm) overall. The edges are ground square. Its use is not clear, but Isaac Jackson's catalogue (*c*. 1909) states that it 'can also be used as a Reamer or Borer. Invaluable for Leather Belts'.

(*d*)　*Needle Belt Awl*
This is the name given by Isaac Jackson (*c*. 1909) to an awl of oval cross-section, with three holes of descending diameter cut in the blade. That illustrated

Belt Edge Rounding Tools
The tools used for rounding and burnishing the edges of a driving belt included the following:

202

(*a*) *Edge Rounding Tool* (Cornering Tool) *Fig. 5:4*
A tool of spokeshave type with a V-shaped sole, and similar to the metal spokeshave known as a Chamfering Shave. The cutting iron is slotted for adjustment by set-screw. (An ordinary woodworker's spokeshave was also used for rounding belt edges.)

Fig. 5:4

(*b*) *Edge Burnishing Tool* *Fig. 5:5*
The examples illustrated are factory made in metal. Both provide a smooth, semi-circular concave surface for burnishing the edge of the belt. Not all belt makers would have this special tool; as N. W. Portway (Combs Tannery, Stowmarket, 1980) relates: 'I have seen a number of tools used for doing this job which are literally the first bit of wood which comes to hand with a groove rounded out somewhere near the middle. The tool was used to glaze or burnish the edges of belting, usually after a very light application of glue to the edge.'

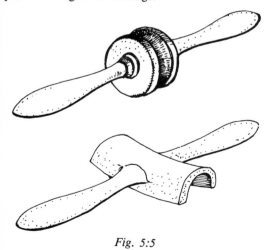

Fig. 5:5

Belt-Fastening Tools
Belts could not be made longer than one skin without joins. These joints were sewn or riveted as well as cemented when the size and strength of the belt required it. Rawhide laces, twisted thread, cord or wire were used for sewing according to the purpose and strength required of the belt. The stitching was sometimes countersunk on the running side of the belt, and any rivets used had to be flush fitting on the running side.

Leather belts usually left the manufacturer as a single coil which needed to be cut exactly to the required length and have the two ends fastened together before use. Fasteners were also used when a belt had to be shortened after stretching in service.

A typical belt-joining kit would include a sharp knife (or a Belt-Plane, see under *Plane, Belt Makers*) for trimming the ends to be joined; a set square (it is essential to make the cut ends a perfect right angle otherwise the belt will run off its pulleys); the special tools for the type of fasteners being used; and possibly a Belt Clamp for drawing together and holding the ends to be joined.

There were many devices for joining the end of the belt to save the task of lacing, or as an addition to lacing, including rivets and 'patent' screwed fasteners which required a special key to screw them on or off. For lighter work there were a number of patent clasps or grips that could be hammered into the ends of the belt.

Belt-Punching Tools
The following are typical examples of tools made for punching holes in the ends of a belt to take laces or fasteners:

(*a*) *Gee Screw Cramp* *Fig. 5:6*
The end of the screw is hollowed to punch $\frac{3}{16}$ in. (0.6 cm) or $\frac{1}{4}$ in. (0.7 cm) holes.

Belt Punch with Hollow Steel Screw

Fig. 5:6

(*b*) *Belt Plier Slot Punch Fig. 5:7*
Designed to cut a slot-shaped hole to take 'Greens
patent fasteners'.

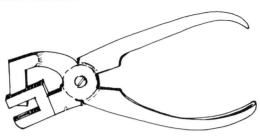

Fig. 5:7

(*c*) *Round-belt Plier Punch Fig. 5:8*
A plier adapted for cutting a round belt to length and
also for punching a hole through the belt for the
fastener.

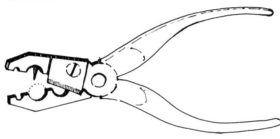

Fig. 5:8

(*d*) *Belt Punch with adjustable Gauge Fig. 5:9*
An ordinary hollow punch mounted in a plier with
parallel jaws, but fitted with an adjustable fence on
the lower 'anvil' jaw. This can be set so that when the
end of the strap is brought to bear on the fence, a
row of holes can be punched at the required distance
from the end of the belt.

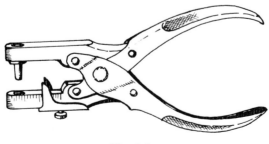

Fig. 5:9

(*e*) *Band Punch*: see Band Punch under *Punch* in
the HARNESS MAKER AND SADDLER section.

Belt Clamp *Fig. 5:10*
A rectangular frame used for drawing the ends of the
belt together for fastening while upon the pulleys.
The long sides of the frame are threaded for this pulling operation, which is done by turning nuts, or by
a bevel-gear assembly, or, in the case of a lighter version of the clamp, by means of a lever.

Fig. 5:10

Needle *Fig. 5:11*
Needles are employed for reinforcing joints with
thread, and a harness-maker's collar needle is often
used for this purpose. This has a curved point, with
a diamond-shaped cross-section at the bend. Made in
sizes from 3–8 in. (7.6–20.3 cm) long.

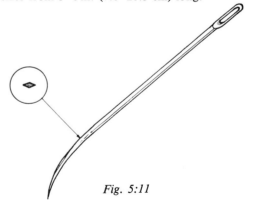

Fig. 5:11

Plane, Belt Maker's *Fig. 5:12*
A metal plane with a flat sole $5\frac{3}{4}$ in. (14.8 cm) long,
with a cutter $2\frac{3}{8}$ in. (6 cm) wide, bedded at about 25°,
and with an adjusting screw of the traditional
Stanley type. The throat is adjustable by moving a
plate at the toe. A wooden cross-handle is supported
by the side plates.

This plane was introduced in 1870 by the American Stanley Rule and Level Company. The present Stanley Works inform us (1978) that the plane underwent several design changes between 1870 and 1943, when it was discontinued. It was one of the original Bailey adjustable planes and incorporated many of the Bailey patents.

In 1902 it was listed as a 'Stanley No. 11 Adjustable Belt Maker's Plane'. Its purpose was thus described: for 'chamfering down the laps of a Belt, before fastening them together. It is equally well adapted to use in repairing Belts in all large manufacturing establishments.'

Rounding Plate
This tool is described and illustrated under Rein Rounding Plate in the entry *Rounding Tools* in the HARNESS MAKER AND SADDLER section. It can be used for making round leather banding which is used for driving light machines. To obtain adequate length, this type of belting is cut spirally from the hide.

Sewing Clamp (Clamp; Stitching Horse)
For holding the driving belt while sewing, belt makers use the same type of clamp as other workers in leather. (See *Clamp* and *Stitching Horse* in the HARNESS MAKER AND SADDLER section.)

Fig. 5:12

6

Furrier

The term 'fur' is given to the hairy coat of such animals as the beaver, bear, mink and rabbit. The skins of these animals, when dried, are called peltry; when the skin has been preserved by a mild form of tanning, it is usually given the name fur. 'Fur' is also applied to the hair cut from the skin for making felt hats.

Apart from the manufacture of such articles as fur rugs, the main work of the fur trade today is to convert animal pelts into clothing. In general the work is divided between the factory where the pelts are preserved, cleaned and dressed, and the furrier's workshop where the furs are cut, made up into garments, and prepared for sale.

Skin clothing with the fur outwards is represented in cave drawings in northern Spain and elsewhere; these belong to the Neolithic period of some 12,000 years ago. But it is known that long before that time man made use of animal skins for protection from cold, and from the abrasions of daily life.

Evidence of early methods of preserving skins from putrefaction are given in the LEATHER MANUFACTURE section. Modern methods of tanning fur are indicated under the paragraph 'Process' below.

Though fur clothing is known to have been used in classical times in Greece and Rome, the gradual development of woven cloths made the use of animal skins less necessary, except in the snowbound countries of the extreme north. But coarse sheepskins continued to be worn during the Middle Ages by working people (as they are today by shepherds in central Europe); and, more for decoration than necessity, the better-off continued to wear fur until the present time.

It was not until the early part of the nineteenth century that fur garments became widely used, at least by the better-off: S. P. Denning's portrait, painted in 1823, shows Princess (later Queen) Victoria at the age of four wearing a black sealskin coat (Dulwich Gallery). The great popularity of sealskins for all kinds of clothing began with the invention in *c.* 1800 of a method for removing the stiff top hair from sealskins without damaging the silky plush-like 'under wool' – a process said to have been known to the Chinese in antiquity. There followed a boom. 'Unexpectedly this novelty turned into the greatest money spinner the Fur Industry ever hit upon', writes Francis Weiss (1977).

Gradually, the fur trade began to employ skins other than seals, and then began the slaughter by trappers of thousands of other fur-bearing animals which continues to this day. The first coats of Astrakhan mink and other costly skins first appeared about 1885, and culminated in the legendary creations exhibited in the Paris World Fair of 1900. Weiss relates that 'a close fitting "Princess-dress" of 164 superb small wild Canadian mink skins required 200 hours of the cutters and 1000 hours of hand-sewing time'.

The making of leather and the preparation of fur are separate trades, but their method of preserving the skin is essentially the same. An important difference between the two is the furrier's concern to prevent the fur being damaged by the tanning process.

(1) Fur dressing (see *Fur-Dressing Tools* p. 207).
After removing the flesh and a gentle washing in a hot liquor of soap and soda, fur-bearing skins are given one of the milder tannages such as oil-dressing (with animal or vegetable oils or even butter), or the skins are treated with a solution of alum and salt, sometimes with the addition of barley meal.

After the process is completed, any surplus grease is removed by 'tumbling' in sawdust (see *Drum* below) and the skins are then dried on frames. The finishing process includes the 'bringing up of the hair' by beating and other methods (see *Canes* p. 207).

(2) Making up (see *Furrier's Tools* below).
The cutting out and making up of furs by the furrier

demands the specialised skills and tools of the tailor and dressmaker; in addition, a number of special tools have been developed for this trade. These are described below.

Fur-Dressing Tools
Hand tools and equipment used for preserving and dressing furs include the following:

(a) Bat
A flat, bat-shaped piece of wood made in different sizes according to the size of the skin for which it is to be used. It serves as a cutting board when placed inside the cased (i.e. closed) skin which can then be opened by a cut down the belly.

(b) Scraping Knife (Beaming Knife)
A two-handed, blunt-edged knife, used for removing fat from certain skins that can be worked on a beam without injury. This tool looks like the tanner's *Unhairing Knife* (see the section LEATHER MANUFACTURE, I. Tanner's Tools).

(c) Fur-Fleshing Knife (Fleshing Knife) *Fig. 6:1*
After the removal of fat with the Scraping Knife (above) it is still necessary to remove the thin membrane on the flesh side (the areolar tissue) so that the preserving oils to be applied will be absorbed. This work cannot be done on a tanner's beam because the fur would prevent the skin from lying flat. So the skin is shaved by pulling it across the knife, instead of pushing the knife across the skin.

The knife is about 2 ft. (60.9 cm) long and 4 in. (10.1 cm) wide, sharpened on one edge and mounted vertically on a 4 ft. (1.21 m) stool, on which the worker sits. The lower end of the blade is inserted in the stool near the seated worker; the top end is secured to an upright support fitted at the far end of the stool. The worker takes the skin in both hands, and with the knife between them, he works the skin to and fro against the edge of the knife. Great care has to be taken to avoid making too deep a cut.

Fig. 6:1

(d) Kicker (Trampling Machine)
Formerly skins were trodden under foot in a vat in order to work in the oil and chemicals needed to preserve them. Hand- (and later, power-) operated machines were developed which consisted of two upright wooden legs which move alternately back and forth in a vat in the same manner as a pair of human legs.

(e) Drum
After the preserving process, surplus grease and loose hairs are removed by 'tumbling' the skins inside a revolving wooden drum into which sawdust is added to absorb grease.

(f) Cage
After the above process, the skins are revolved inside a drum made of wire mesh. This shakes the sawdust out of the fur.

(g) Canes
These are used for beating furs to remove dust and broken hairs and 'to fetch the hair up' — a process that improves its appearance. The skins are laid on low upholstered benches, and are beaten by hand with canes about 30 in. (76.2 cm) long. Traditionally, the canes used are from the East India palm, Rattan.

(h) Roping
A rope is tied between two points, or sometimes wound on a pole, and the dampened fur is drawn back and forth over it. The purpose of this process is to break up and disentangle the hair, and it also helps to stretch the skin.

(i) Stretcher
Various appliances are made for stretching small skins. One is a bench-mounted triangular frame or 'tongue' which is placed inside the closed skin and then made to expand when the worker leans his back against an arm, forcing the two sides of the frame apart.

Furrier's Tools
Hand tools used by furriers include the following:

(a) Nailing Board
A wooden board measuring *c.* 5 × 4 ft (1.52 × 1.21 m) on which skins are stretched and subsequently dried. The skin is first wetted and then stretched by hand from the centre in the direction that will correspond to the contours of the garment to be made. Next, with the help of the Fur Pliers (below) the skin is stretched and then nailed to the board. Subsequently, the board is leant against the wall for the skins to dry.

An 'office' stapler is sometimes used instead of nails or 'pins': a staple can hold a skin securely at a sharp bend with less risk of the holes being enlarged by dragging. (See also *Toggle* in the section LEATHER MANUFACTURE, II. Currier's Tools.)

(*b*)　*Fur Plier* (Furrier's Pincer)　*Fig. 6:2*
A steel plier about 9 in. (22.8 cm) long overall, with one handle straight and the other bent. It is used for holding in place and nailing down the skin after stretching. The jaws are slightly splayed, with square ends, and are serrated inside to grip the edge of the skin; they are hatched on the outer surface for nail driving. (When the skin is stretched by hand, without using pliers, the pins or nails are driven by a short length of flat steel, used like a shoemaker's *Rivet Driver*.)

The straight handle of the plier enables it to be used close to the board on which skin is being stretched; the bent handle, held uppermost, leaves space for the fingers. One of the handles is often clawed for extracting nails.

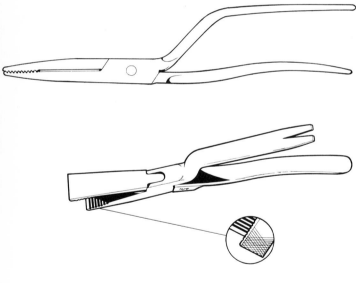

Fig. 6:2

(*c*)　*Rubber*　*Fig. 6:3*
A wedge-shaped wooden handle measuring about $4\frac{1}{2} \times 4$ in. (11.4 × 10.1 cm) with a blunt metal blade inserted into the lower edge.

Like the currier's Sleaker, it is pushed along the flesh side of the skin as part of the stretching process; it is also used for smoothing down seams.

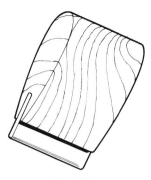

Fig. 6:3

(*d*)　*Furrier's Knife* (Trimming Knife)
When cutting fur, the knife is not forced downwards onto the material, for to do this might injure the hair. Instead, the knife is applied lightly, mainly on the flesh side, and usually while the skin is held clear of the bench so that the point of the blade just penetrates the skin without cutting the hair. There are two types of knife:

(1)　The standard type　*Fig. 6:4*
This is about 5 in. (12.7 cm) long, without a separate handle. The whole knife fits into the palm of the hand, with the forefinger held on a thickened portion of the back of the knife.

To make the knife more comfortable to hold, it is often provided with brass mounts, one brazed on the tail of the knife, the other on the back. According to a furrier at Messrs Martin Rice Ltd (London, 1978), the brass mount on the tail can also be used for marking, i.e. when it is desired to cut the skin down the middle. The tail of the knife is pressed on the fur side and this shows through on the flesh side: a line can then be drawn between the two marks as a guide for cutting.

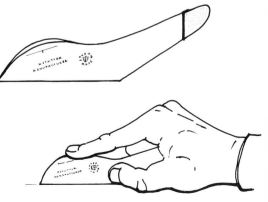

Fig. 6:4

(2) A modern type *Fig. 6:5*
This consists of a split brass or aluminium stock shaped to the traditional contours of (*d*(1)) above. A replaceable steel blade (e.g. a broken-off razor blade) is held between the two halves of the stock.

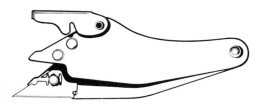

Fig. 6:5

(e) Needle
Round needles of size 9 or 10 are used for the hand-sewing of fine furs, but a three-sided 'glover's needle' is used for heavier work.

(f) Shoulder Press
These are boards shaped like small gravestones, about 7 in. (17.7 cm) wide, with a rounded top, and mounted on a heavy wooden base. They are used by furriers for placing under a garment to enable the shoulder to be set with a pressing iron.

(g) Comb
A steel comb mounted on the end of a short wooden handle. The fur is combed to disentangle matted hair and to remove loose hairs.

(h) Marking Hammer (Needle-Stamp; Pricking Hammer) *Fig. 6:6*
A pattern of spikes mounted on a small plate is inserted into the head of a special hammer. The spikes are arranged in the form of letters or other insignia, and the tool is used to identify the skin.

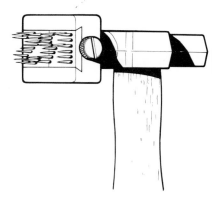

Fig. 6:6

7

Glove Maker

Historical Note

One of the oldest surviving examples of a glove came from an Egyptian tomb of *c.* 1300 BC. It was provided for use in the next life. Like other early gloves it was made with tagged laces for holding the glove firmly on the hand; it was not until recent centuries that gloves were made to 'fit like a glove'. The embroidered lines ('pointing') on the back of modern gloves are thought to be a vestigial survival from the days when gloves were secured with laces. 'Point' is an archaic word for a tagged lace.

Like early foot coverings, gloves were probably first made as much for protection against abrasions as for warmth. Protective gloves are still made for those in certain occupations.

Leather gloves have been made on a large scale in Britain during recent centuries. Though based in central workshops, much of the work was put out to village workers in their cottage homes. Describing the miles of delicate seams joined with thirty-two stitches to the inch, Waterer writes (1968), 'one pities the women and girls who scraped a meagre living from such exacting work'. The industry was mainly confined to areas in or near Worcester, Ludlow, Yeovil and Woodstock.

No one who looks at the history of the glove can fail to notice the curious fact that it had many symbolic uses. For instance, for centuries the casting down of a glove served as a challenge to combat; and a glove was also used as a sign or token for the transfer of property.

Process   Fig. 7:1

(1)   Preparation of the skins

The skins of many different animals have been used for making gloves, but those chiefly used in England since *c.* AD 1500 are from sheep and goats. Leather used for making gloves must be tough and strong yet supple and comfortable to wear. The dressing of skins for this purpose occupied a surprisingly long time. Formerly done by the glovers themselves, but later by the curriers, this work includes the paring down of the skin to a fine uniform thickness, and the softening of the skin by kneading and staking. Some account of this process is given under the entries *Knife, Moon* and *Staking and Perching* in the section LEATHER MANUFACTURE, II. Currier's Tools. Mechanical aids were late in coming: for instance, this softening process was still being done by trampling under foot when Mrs Henry Wood described it in her nineteenth-century novel, *Mrs Halliburton's Troubles*:

'When the skins came in from the leather-dressers, they were first washed in a tub of cold water. The next day warm water, mixed with yolks of eggs, was poured upon them, and a couple of men, barelegged to the knee, got into the tub and danced upon them, skins, eggs and water, for two hours. Then they were spread in a field to dry, till they were as hard as a lantern horn; then they were "staked", as it is called, a long process, to smooth and soften them.'

(2)   Cutting

In the glove trade, the cutter's work includes the preliminary stretching and manipulation of the skin, as well as the cutting of the skin into separate parts required for making a glove.

The skins are first 'cooled', i.e. slightly damped by being laid between layers of damp sawdust, and then pulled to their maximum length. The cutter does this by holding one end of the skin on the bench with his left hand, and then pulling the other end of the skin with his right hand resting on the right thigh. When the skin is pulled tight in the direction of neck to butt, it is measured and cut into the most economical widths. Mr Troughton (1974) wrote that, 'To an onlooker, all this pulling and stretching of the leather may seem superfluous, but the práctice goes back to an age when perfection was more important than speed.'

It may be of interest to compare this statement with two earlier opinions. In his book on the glove trade, Ellis writes (1921, p. 63):

'Intuition, born of experience, and skill in manipulating the skins are the cutter's real equipment. The first step is to pull and stretch the skin to ascertain its "spread". A cutter will spend some time in this way on a single skin, pulling it lengthways and sideways, and so working out every inch of material to advantage.'

A century and a half before, in Diderot's Encyclopaedia (*c.* 1760, *Gantier*, p. 474) the writer asserts: 'If the worker is clumsy and his cutting is badly understood, he loses all, and the workers then say that the shears have dined before the master.'

Having completed the stretching work, the cutter now turns to the cutting proper. This begins with a process known as 'tranking', i.e. the cutting of the widths into the pieces required. (The term 'trank' comes from the French *tranche*, a cutting, and is applied by glovers both to the piece of skin from which the glove itself is cut, and to the glove-piece itself.)

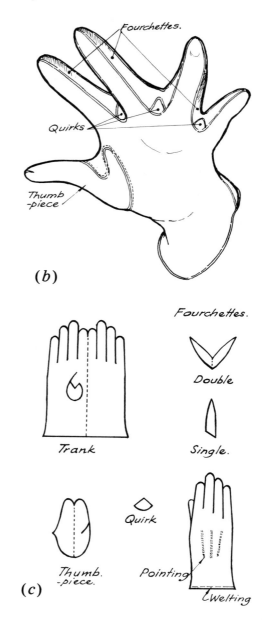

(*b*)

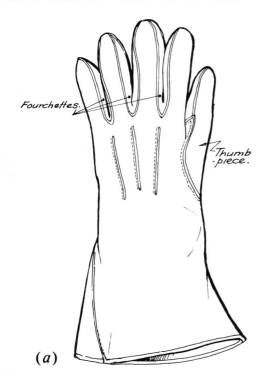

(*a*)

Fig. 7:1   (*a*)   Back view of a typical glove, with plain pointing.
        (*b*)   Foreshortened view of the palm to show Fourchettes and quirks.
        (*c*)   Parts of a typical glove before and after assembly.

Each of these pieces was then pulled into shape and, using cardboard patterns, trimmed nearer to their final size with shears and scissors. This cutting operation was later done 'in one go' with a punch shaped to the finished part required (see *Knife, Web*).

An additional part of the cutter's work was to match up the cut-out pieces to make matching pairs: since different parts of the skin vary, this needed considerable judgement, especially since economy in the use of valuable glove leather was important.

Tools used by the cutter are described under the following entries: *Gauge, Glover's*; *Knife, Doling*; *Knife, Spud*; *Shears*; *Size Stick*.

(3)   Making and finishing
Making up includes the hand- or machine-sewing of the glove sections to form the complete glove. It is followed by lining (if provided), binding of the edge (known as welting), and, when needed, the attachment of buttons. For tools used see under *Sewing Tools, Lining Hand*.

'Pointing' is the term used for the three rows of stitching worked on the back of the glove, often forming three raised ridges in the leather (see historical note above). Pointing is sometimes replaced or augmented by embroidery, or decorative perforations (see *Preen*).

'Laying-out' is the term used by glovers for the pressing and ironing needed to improve the appearance of the finished glove (see *Laying-Out Tools*).

Dolly: see *Laying-Out Tools*; *Hedger's Glove Dolly*.

Donkey: see *Sewing Tools*.

Gauge, Glover's
Gauges were used by cutters to guide them when stretching a trank to meet the requirements of a particular size of glove. They were also used by foremen to check the stretching operation and to ascertain what size of glove could be made from the trank. (Trank is the name given to a piece of skin from which the glove is to be cut out.)

Two types of gauge are described below:

(*a*)   *Crossed Stick* (Crucifix)
A pair of sticks fixed together at the centre, and made in different sizes. It was used for marking the centre line down the trank, and acted as a guide when stretching the trank to suit different sizes of gloves.

(*b*)   *Glove Maker's Rack* (Also known by its French name: *Ridelle*.)
It has not been possible to examine an example of

this instrument. It is thus described by a retired glover, Mr J. E. Troughton (1978):

'It was used by the cutters of those firms who prided themselves on their French connection. It consisted of a stamp having five blades; about six inches long. One, at the end, was fixed, the others movable and operated by a threaded rod made in such a way that the distance between the blades stayed in the same ratio for different sized tranks. The stamp was used with a pad impregnated with printer's ink. A scale in French inches ran across the centre of the blades thus signifying by the printed marks the amount of stretch in each quarter of the trank. The important purpose was to ensure that the *seams* of the gloves should remain *straight* on the wearer's hands and not twisted around the back of the hand.'

A simpler version of the gauge had fixed blades and required a separate instrument for each group of tranks.

Glove Stick: see *Laying-Out Tools*.

Glove Stretcher   *Fig. 7:2*
A wooden tong-like tool *c.* 12 in. (30.5 cm) overall, with long, tapering jaws. It is often provided with an in-built spring between the handles which keeps the jaws closed until the handles are pressed together. After inserting the jaws into a finger of the glove, the handles are pressed: this opens the jaws and stretches the finger.

This tool is used for inspecting a particular finger during manufacture; and, until recent times, they were needed at home to open and smooth out the fingers of gloves after cleaning.

Fig. 7:2

Glove Tree
A wooden 'hand' on a stand, *c.* 9 in. (22.8 cm) high overall. It is usually made in sections like a Boot Tree, to make it easier to take out of the glove.

Trees were used in laundries, glove workshops and at home for drying gloves. They were also used for display. A tree on a longer stand, *c.* 18 in. (45.7 cm) high, was 'used when whitening military and coachmen's gloves.

Hand: see *Laying-Out Tools*.

Hedger's Glove Dolly

A club-like length of wood, about 3 ft. (91.4 cm) long on which to support the stiff leather of a hedger's glove while sewing. Hedger's gloves are made of a thick leather with no fingers. (This tool was seen in the private collection of Mr J. Hawkins at Pitstone, Hertfordshire, 1977.)

Knife, Doling or Paring (*Doler* is a French verb meaning 'to smooth'.)

The modern Doling Knife looks like a broad version of the woodworker's Paring Chisel. Used in several different trades, including shoemaking and book-binding, it is described under *Knife, Paring* in the BOOT AND SHOE MAKER section. Earlier Doling Knives may have been much broader: that illustrated by Diderot (*Gantier, c.* 1760) looks more like a cheese board.

The Doling Knife is used for removing unwanted thickness. It was probably used only for smaller pieces of leather; a circular Moon Knife appears to have been used for larger skins (see *Knife, Moon* below).

In operation the leather is laid on a slab of marble or slate, and the knife is made to cut by pushing. If the piece of skin is large enough, one end is held by pressure of the worker's stomach against the edge of the bench; the other end is held in his left hand. Ellis (1921, p. 55) writes that doling 'calls for extreme dexterity, for the slightest slip on the part of the operator would gash the skin and often the operator's own wrist'.

When Diderot describes gloves which 'one can easily put into the shell of a nut', one may suppose that he had in mind the effect of this operation.

Note: Shakespeare's 'glover's paring knife'
In Shakespeare's 'Merry Wives of Windsor' (Act I, Scene IV, line 21) Mistress Quickly, speaking about Master Slender, asks: 'Does he not wear a great round beard, like a glover's paring-knife?'

Ellis (1921, p. 55) writes that Mistress Quickly was speaking of the 'round or moon-shaped Glover's Knife, familiar to many readers as one of the symbols of the glover's art'. (See *Knife, Moon* below.) In the present writer's opinion, this specialised knife, used by glovers and others for reducing the thickness of a skin, does not look much like a man's beard. A more likely explanation is provided by the late Mr John Waterer, the well-known authority on the leather trades. In a letter to the author (1975) he pointed out that the glovers in Shakespeare's time, like most other leather workers, used the ancestral semi-circular *Round Knife* for cutting out, and that this knife does look rather like a 'great round beard'.

It may be added that in those times the term 'paring' meant simply 'to cut' and particularly to cut to shape. (See Round Knife under *Knife, Saddler's*, in the HARNESS MAKER AND SADDLER section.)

Knife, Moon (Glovers often call this tool a Circular or Paring Knife.)

This knife is described under *Knife, Moon* in the section LEATHER MANUFACTURE, II. Currier's Tools. It was used for paring down a skin to a uniform thickness – an operation known as 'grounding'. Until recent years, paring with this knife was performed by the glovers themselves, but today this operation is more often done in the currier's shop.

Knife, Spud (The Oxford English Dictionary states that 'spud' is a word of obscure origin for – among other implements – 'a short and poor knife or dagger'.) *Fig. 7:3*

A knife-shaped implement *c.* 8 in. (20.3 cm) overall, with a blunt edge and a rounded back. It is not used for cutting, but for smoothing out the frilly undulating edge of a trank. These undulations were caused by previous stretching and have to be smoothed out before the gloves are cut out.

The process may be described as follows: the trank is laid on the bench with its 'frilly' edge overhanging the edge near the worker. The left hand holds down the trank on the bench while the right hand clasps the knife by its handle. A gap is left between the blade and the thumb into which the 'frilly' edge of the trank is introduced so that it can be pressed between the thumb and the blunt front edge of the knife.

From now on, the edge of the trank is smoothed out by a rhythmic sequence of first pressing and then releasing; the operation is repeated across whole width of trank with the left hand keeping in step.

To gain extra pressure, the back edge of the knife bears against the bench and gives out what Mr J. E. Troughton (1979) describes as 'a rat-tat-tat like the rhythm and beat of a side-drummer – quite nostalgic to me'.

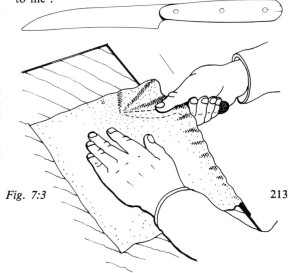

Fig. 7:3   213

Knife, Web (Punching Knife. Note: In the boot and shoe industry these tools are called *Press Knives*.) *Fig. 7:4* and see *Fig. 7:1c* for shapes of other Web Knives.

A punch formed by a strip of steel sharpened along one edge, and shaped to the outline of the desired part to be cut out. The most common Webs are: the Trank Web (the back and front of the glove punched out in one piece); the Thumb-Hole Web (a punch now made integral with the Trank Web); and the Fourchette Web, a punch for cutting out the gusset sewn in between the fingers. Early examples of these punches were mounted on wooden bases.

Before the introduction of modern machine presses, the Web Knives were forced down upon the leather in a hand press operated by a long lever, or by a central screw with a cross handle weighted at the extremities of the cross-bar and known as a Fly or Swing Press.

The Web Knife was developed in France c. 1819. Mr J. E. Troughton (1978) informed us:

'Although the webs or punches were invented in 1819, rural glovers were reluctant to invest the necessary capital to acquire the fine punches as produced by competent engineers. Because of the initial cost they tolerated substitutes made by local handymen, the village blacksmith for example. In some of the specimens I have seen these could have shaped little more than the finger-tips; the operation was completed by using scissors, or by chisel and block.'

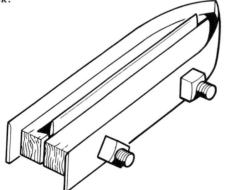

Fig. 7:4 A home-made Web Knife for cutting Fourchettes. (*Fig. 7:1(c)* illustrates the shapes of other web knives used by glove makers.)

Laying-Out Tools
The following tools are used in the laying-out process – the pressing and smoothing operation for improving the appearance of the finished glove.

(*a*) *Dolly Stick* (Laying-Out Stick; Rolling Stick; Stretching or Turning Stick) *Fig. 7:5*
A fusiform-shaped stick c. 12–16 in. (30.5–40.6 cm) long. It looks like a chair-stretcher, and in fact a discarded chair-stretcher of the Windsor type was often used as a Dolly Stick. The gloves were rolled up in a damp cloth for a short time, and then laid flat on the bench and smoothed with the Dolly which was operated like a rolling pin. The tapered ends of the Dolly were used for stretching the glove fingers and for turning them inside out. Mr J. E. Troughton (1978) writes as follows:

'The earliest recollection I have of this tool in use is that of a neighbour sewing in linings as an out-worker in her cottage adjacent to my mother's. The glove having been turned inside out, the stick was pushed up each finger in turn to steady the glove while the fabric lining was stitched to the seams of each finger. The stick was then used to facilitate the turning of the lined glove to its finished state. It was a shockingly paid job by standards of 60 years ago, let alone by wages of today.

'I think the real purpose of the stick's bulbous centre was to roll down the seams. Of course every worker in the factory had at least one of these sticks so the purposes to which they were put were many and varied – a cutter might use one to improve the appearance of a rough-looking bit of leather; the slitter (in the early days when the Web Knife cut only one half of the glove) used one to roll down the centre fold of the trank.'

Fig. 7:5

(*b*) *Glove Stick* (Widener) *Fig. 7:6*
Similar to the Dolly Stick, but with the centre left square and used mainly for stretching fingers.

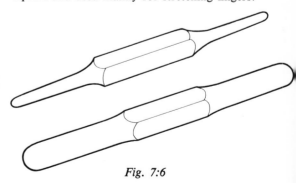

Fig. 7:6

(*c*) *French Dolly and Glove Sticks* *Fig. 7:7*
Those illustrated below are copied from Diderot's
Encyclopaedia (*c.* 1760) under *Gantier*. The stick
with tapered ends is named *Renformoir* (stretcher);
the other, shaped with deep corrugations rather like
a chessman, is called a *Demoiselle*; and is described
as 'pieces of turned wood which serve to open the
fingers of new gloves'. The purpose of the corrugations is not clear.

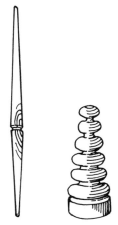

Fig. 7:7

(*d*) *Hand, Glover's* *Fig. 7:8*
A solid iron 'hand' of flattened shape over which the
gloves are drawn to smooth out creases and wrinkles
– a substitute for the more laborious use of a Glove
Stick. They have four fingers, leaving the thumb to
be finished separately with a Glove Stick or with
separate thumb-pegs fitted on the bench nearby.
(The drawing was made in the glove factory of Dent-
Fownes Ltd. of Warminster.)

Earlier metal Hands were solid and had to be
heated in an oven or on a stove; the workers would
lay out as many pairs as they could before the iron
got cold and had to be reheated. Later, a hollow
hand was heated by steam. Those illustrated below
are heated by an in-built electric element with
thermostatic control.

Fig. 7:8

Lining Hand (Former)
A rudimentary 'hand' mounted on a stand. It was
made in wood but later in metal, in which case the
fingers are spring tipped to compress or lengthen
according to the length of the glove fingers.

It is used for fitting glove linings. Formerly, the
glove was turned inside out, the lining sewed along
the seams, and the glove turned back again – a slow
operation. Today, the lining is pulled over the metal
hand, the fingers are tipped with adhesive, and the
glove is then pulled over the lining.

Measuring Wheel *Fig. 7:9*
A small metal wheel of $\frac{5}{8}$ in. (1.6 cm) diameter, with
its circumference ground to a fine edge, mounted on
the end of a metal handle, *c.* $4\frac{1}{2}$ in. (11.4 cm) long
overall. Each revolution covers a distance of 2 in.
(5 cm).

Like the wheelwright's Traveller, this tool is used
to measure the length of a curved or irregular
contour. And, like the Traveller, there is a 'nick' on
the circumference to act as a starting point.

Fig. 7:9

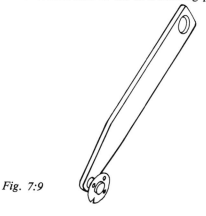

Needle: see *Sewing Tools.*

Perch: see under *Staking and Perching Tools* in the
section LEATHER MANUFACTURE, II. Currier's Tools.

Preen
A punch used with a mallet for punching holes as
part of the decorative pointing on the back of gloves.

Sewing Tools
These include:

(*a*) *Needle, Glover's* (sometimes called a 'square'
needle) *Fig. 7:10*
Needles used for the hand-sewing of leather gloves
are eyed, round in cross-section at the butt, but

215

three-sided towards the point. They are made in eight sizes from *c.* $1\frac{1}{2}$–2 in. (3.8–5 cm) length overall.

There is some difference of opinion concerning the purpose of the three-sided cross-section, but most users say that it eases penetration. Simple experiments indicate that when sewing in soft leather, a slight twist or wriggle of a three-sided needle tends to loosen it and so reduce friction; the same action applied to a round needle seems less effective.

In a letter to the author, Mr A. W. Landman of the British Leather Manufacturers Association (1979) wrote:

'The shape of the needle influences the pressure required to penetrate the leather. The fibre density of leather is such that it is preferable to cut the fibres, whereas in textile sewing, the weave is so loose that the fibres can be pushed aside. The latter is in fact highly desirable as the cloth can be seriously weakened if the fibres are cut. For leather however, there is no tendency to fray and the weakness is solely dependent on the proportion of holes to uncut leather.

'A triangular section is preferred because it cuts into the fibres whereas a round needle has to push its way through the dense structure. Modern needles for sewing leather are either wedge-shaped (again with a cutting edge) or have a triangular point which cuts the initial hole to be followed by the round shank which then widens the hole to accommodate the thread.

'I had thought this was a recent development but obviously the old glovers have learnt by experience something which we are only now learning to explain.'

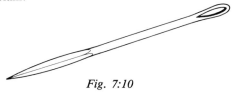

Fig. 7:10

(*b*) *Donkey* (Donkey Frame; Glover's Donkey; Glover's Jockey) *Fig. 7:11*
A metal or wooden vice with serrated jaws, mounted on a post of convenient height for a seated worker. The jaws are opened and closed by means of a foot pedal connected to one of the jaws by a metal rod.

The purpose of the Donkey is the same as that of the harness-maker's Clamp – to hold the edges of the leather together when sewing. The serrations on the jaws act as a guide for the needle, to ensure regular spacing. According to Leyland and Troughton (1974), in most districts the Donkey was not con-

sidered necessary and the stitching was done entirely freehand. Today, the Sewing Machine has replaced hand-sewing.

Fig. 7:11

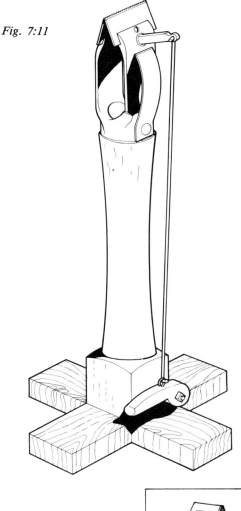

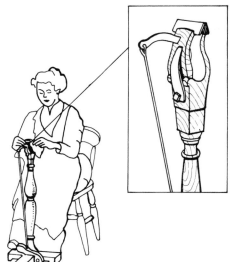

216

(c) *Sewing Machines*

Since the mid-nineteenth century, when Sewing Machines were first used, hand-sewing has gradually declined. Sewing Machines were developed to handle all the stitching operations on a glove, including the decorative pointing.

Most of the principal types of stitches or seams have names derived from the French, as follows:

Prix-seam (Prick Seam; PXM). The two edges of the leather are placed back to back and sewn through parallel to the edge, leaving both raw edges exposed. A strong sewing for men's gloves, or for ladies' gloves of the heavier type.

Piqué (PK). One of the edges of the leather is lapped over the other leaving only one edge showing. Suitable for ordinary weight gloves for ladies.

Brosser or Roundseam. The leather is placed back to back and the thread is stitched through and over the edges. Used for thin, lightweight gloves.

Inseam. The gloves are stitched on the 'wrong' side and then turned.

Shears

Shears used by glovers were of two types:

(*a*) The so-called Spring-Bow or Sheep-shear type, measuring about 14 in. (35.5 cm) overall. Many glovers prefer this type because the spring 'opens to cut again'.

or

(*b*) Tailor's Shears of the heavy, hand-forged type.

Shears are used for cutting the skins, and, before the invention of the *Web Knife*, for cutting out the more intricate shape of the glove itself. Knives such as those used by shoe clickers cannot easily be used in the glove trade, for the skins used for gloves are soft, and might stretch out of shape under the knife. But hand knives are used for cutting the heavier leathers used for hedger's mittens, motor-cycle gauntlets and industrial gloves.

Size Stamp

A metal punch, mounted in a wooden handle *c.* 5–6 in. (12.7–15.2 cm) overall, with the head cut to imprint glove sizes numbered 00 to 11 or 12. The figures are marked in printer's ink just inside the back of the glove.

Some glove makers used stencil plates instead of stamps, and in recent years woven size tabs have come into use.

Size Stick   *Fig. 7:12*

There are two types:

(*a*) *Tapered Size Stick   7:12*

A graduated wooden stick of square cross-section, *c.* 12 in. (30.5 cm) or 16 in. (40.6 cm) long, tapering from $\frac{3}{4}$ in. (1.9 cm) at the thick end down to $\frac{1}{4}$ in. (0.6 cm) at the other. The narrow end is often covered by a small brass cap which can be used for marking the skin by making a small indentation.

All four sides are graduated so that when dropped back on the bench after use, the graduations will be visible however it may be lying. The reason for the taper is not clear but it has been suggested that the narrow end is useful for measuring inside a finger.

Most of these sticks are graduated in inches, though some may be found graduated in 'pouces', the French 'inch', which is equal to 27.07 mm. (The English inch is 25.4 mm.) Glove sizing was established in France in the early eighteenth century, and is based on a measurement round the width of the hand: a person whose hand measures 8 inches (20.3 cm) around the hand would take a glove sized 8.

Fig. 7:12

(*b*) *French Size Stick*

A flat stick, *c.* 13 in. (33 cm) long, about 1 in. (2.5 cm) wide, and $\frac{1}{4}$ in. (0.6 cm) thick, with parallel sides, graduated on both sides into 12 French 'inches'.

Staking and Perching Tools

These tools are used for stretching and softening a skin. The process was at one time part of the glover's work, but in more recent times the operation was left to the currier. A description of the tools and the process will be found under the above entry in the section LEATHER MANUFACTURE, II. Currier's Tools.

— 8 —

Handbag and Purse Maker

Many handbags and purses are the modern descendants of the wallets, holsters, and riding accoutrements that were at one time an important sideline of the harness trade, and were made with the tools of that trade. Today, these everyday articles are mostly made by specialist bag and purse makers. The best of them reveal the same excellence of workmanship and design as do their forbears. The tools described below are those that have been developed to meet particular needs of the modern lady's handbag trade.

Bag Framer's Tools *Fig. 8:1*
The making of the framed handbag and purse has been developed since *c.* 1880 and is now a specialised industry producing lady's bags in a great variety of materials and design.

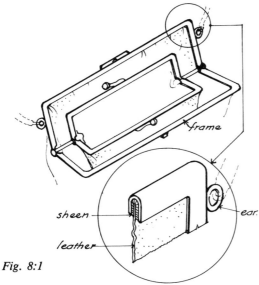

Fig. 8:1

218

The purpose of the frame is to protect and stiffen the edges of the leather, and to provide an attachment for handles and for fastening devices. Framing tools are used for fitting the frames to the leather. These include:

(*a*) *Bag-Frame Pliers*
These special pliers have a 'hawks-bill' or hook-pattern upper jaw, i.e. the upper jaw is turned down at right angles to close with its tip end meeting the horizontal lower jaw. Three types are used in the framing process, all of similar general shape, but each with an upper jaw shaped for a particular purpose.

(1) Bag-Frame Opening Plier *Fig. 8:2*
A wedge-shaped upper jaw which opens out the U-section of the frame to receive the edge of the leather.

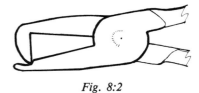

Fig. 8:2

(2) Bag-Frame Lifting Pliers (Corner Plier; Puller Plier) *Fig. 8:3*
A thin upper jaw for pushing the leather into the U-section of the frame, particularly at the corners. The leather edge is doubled over the tip of the upper jaw and then forced into the frame, with the horizontal lower jaw bearing against the outer edge of the frame.

Fig. 8:3

(3) Bag-Frame Closing Plier (Frame Squeezer Pliers) *Fig. 8:4*

These are used for squeezing together the U-section of the frame so that it grips the edge of the leather. There are two types:

A hawk's-bill type plier like those described above, but with a rather thick upper jaw; and a plier of more conventional type, designed for heavier work, with a toggle action and with wide, flat jaws. (A piece of leather is folded over the work when using Closing Pliers to avoid damaging the frame.)

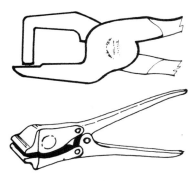

Fig. 8:4

(b) *Bag-Frame Pushers* (Tucking Tools) *Fig. 8:5*
Small trowel-like tools with square or heart-shaped blades. They are used for tucking the leather into the frame as an addition to, or substitute for, the Bag-Frame Lifting Pliers (above). The edge of the leather is doubled over the blade of the tool and pushed inside the U-section of the frame.

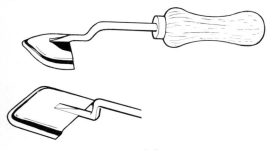

Fig. 8:5

(c) *Framing Stand* (Riveting Standard; Standard)
A flat metal block about 10 × 8 in. (25.4 × 20.3 cm) mounted on a stem which rises from a heavy base-plate. It is used as an anvil for riveting the frame and attachments.

(d) *D-ring Pliers* *Fig. 8:6*
D-rings are stout wire rings made in the form of a D and used for connecting handles to bags and luggage cases. A plier is needed to open the ring to enable it to be hooked into a bag-frame, or into a luggage handle plate, and another plier is needed for closing the D-ring to secure it. This can be done with two separate pliers, but the example illustrated combines both functions. It has cross-over jaws with lips for opening the D-ring, and 'nicks' in the jaws to hold the D-ring when closing it together.

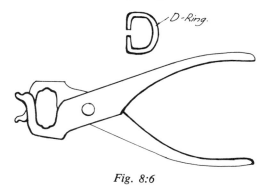

Fig. 8:6

Gauge Knife *Fig. 8:7* (a) *below*; (b) *overleaf*
This small steel tool, *c.* 5 in. (12.7 cm) long overall, has an eighteenth-century look about it, yet does not appear in early tool catalogues. It is used today in the handbag and 'fancy' leather goods trade for trimming margins after the edge of the leather has been turned.

The tool consists of a stem rising from a small circular base in which there are two slots. One slot holds a removable cutting blade, the top of which is supported at the head of the stem; the other slot holds a 'sprung' fence which is riveted to the stem; both are adjustable by means of a thumb-screw in the base.

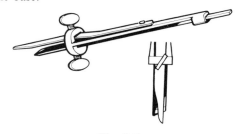

Fig. 8:7a

The tool is used as follows: the leather is cut to the approximate size required and the edges pared. The pared edge, known as the 'turnover', is folded over the edge of a zinc pattern, known as a 'Tin'. This is usually done with a bone *Folder* (see BOOKBINDER section). The unwanted edge of the turnover is then trimmed off with a Gauge Knife, using the Tin as a backing for the leather being cut, and also as a guide for the fence which bears against the edge of the Tin.

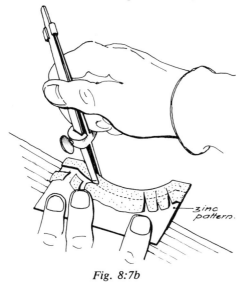

Fig. 8:7b

Purse Crease

A name given to a harness-maker's Crease used on purses, bags, holsters etc. (See *Crease* in the HARNESS MAKER AND SADDLER section.) They are made to imprint single, double or treble lines; as in harness work, this is done to consolidate and decorate the edges of the leather.

Thonging Tools

Note: For thong cutting see *Lace-Making Tools* in the BOOT AND SHOE MAKER section.

Thongs are narrow strips of leather used for binding, for example, in harness collar making, as a substitute for thread. But the tools described below have been developed in recent times for the purpose of binding the edges of bags and pouches, mainly for decorative purposes.

(*a*) *Thonging Chisel Fig. 8:8*
All-iron punches with one, two or three prongs, each bevel-sharpened for producing slits in the leather to take thongs.

Fig. 8:8

(*b*) *Thonging Needle Fig. 8:9*
A flat piece of steel with one end split and provided with a 'pock mark' to catch the end of the thong.

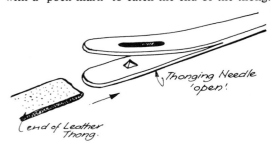

Fig. 8:9

9

Harness Maker and Saddler

Whittaw was an early name for men who tanned skins with alum, producing a white leather. It later became a dialect term for harness maker or saddler: as late as 1859, George Eliot in *Adam Bede* (chapter 6) wrote, '. . . the great barn doors are thrown wide open, and men are busy there mending the harness, under the superintendence of Mr. Goby the "Whittaw", otherwise saddler.'

Knacker is a dialect term of obscure origin for a harness maker or saddler. According to the Oxford English Dictionary there is no apparent connection with its other sense – a buyer of worn-out horses for slaughter.

There is evidence that horses were first tamed about 4,000 years ago by the peoples of central Asia. We know little about the first steps, though we can probably agree with Professor Gordon Childe's suggestion (1942, p. 90) that once man learnt to harness animal power, 'it was natural to transfer the pack from man's (or generally woman's) shoulders to the shoulders of some dumb beast'.

The practice of slavery may have delayed the exploitation of animal power, but those who trained the first horses not only acquired a superiority in warfare, but set mankind on the path of material progress. Steam and oil power are only a hundred or more years old, and before their coming, and apart from wind and water power in the factories, the horse alone met every need of travel, transport and fieldwork.

The traction harness of antiquity consisted of breast and girth bands. If the breast band slid upwards, it exerted a choking pressure on the windpipe, and it was eventually replaced by the breast strap, which is still used for light loads today. A great step forward was made in the fifth century AD when the Chinese invented a traction harness which enabled the horse to throw all its weight against a padded collar: it eventually facilitated long-distance transport and travel, and made horses available for heavy ploughing. (The early development of the collar is described in a remarkable study of equine harness by Joseph Needham and Lu Gwei-Djen, 1960.)

E. M. Jope (1954) gives the following useful summary of the development of horse-riding:

'The effective use of the horse as a riding-animal was largely developed by the nomadic peoples of the steppe-lands of Asia during the last millennium BC. The practice was diffusing into eastern Europe from about 800 BC, adding a considerable element of the offensive arms of warlike peoples. Horse-riding seems, however, to have been a rapid development in Greece, being recorded on vases from the late eighth century. By classical times cavalry had superseded chariotry as an instrument of war.

'The earlier steppe nomads must, like the earlier Greeks, have ridden bareback. Horse-riding was not fully effective until some form of firm saddle and stirrup gave the horseman a secure seat, especially important to the warrior. Both these improvements arose on the steppes, whence they were transmitted eastward and westward, probably by the semi-nomadic horse-riding peoples. Other important items of riding-equipment, the shoeing of horses, the curb-bit, and spur, seem to have developed first in the west, the last two not reaching the Far East until modern times. Thus the full development of horse-riding equipment resulted from an interaction of west and east, just as did that of horse-traction.'

Like the collar harness, the modern type of saddle stemmed from a better understanding of the horse's anatomy. The need to avoid pressure on the horse's windpipe encouraged the development of the collar; the need to avoid pressure on the horse's spine led to the invention of the saddle-tree which, being shaped like an inverted V, rested on each side of the spine instead of on the spine itself. The same idea was later applied to the 'cart' saddle which supports the shafts of a cart or cab.

Folklore

It is pointed out in the introduction to the BOOT AND SHOE MAKER section that there was a considerable amount of folklore surrounding that trade. What is perhaps rather surprising is the apparent lack of legend and folklore surrounding the trade of the harness maker and saddler. Why this should be is not clear.

We suggest in the introduction mentioned above that the shoemakers needed legends (and patron saints) as some compensation for their humble position in society. The making of saddles and harness, often for noble owners, may have been considered a higher form of trade than the 'gentle art' of sewing up boots and shoes for the common people.

Though the harness trade itself seems without folklore, there is of course plenty surrounding the horse itself, from classical mythology through to the present day. And everyone knows that it is lucky to find an old horseshoe, and to nail it to the house door, with the ends uppermost, as a protection against evil. (It is said that Nelson had one nailed to the mast of the *Victory*.) On the other hand, though it is commonly supposed that horse brasses were intended to keep out the 'evil eye', there seems no evidence to support this idea.

The trade since c. 1800

Besides making harness, saddles and collars, the saddler was often called upon to make or repair anything made in leather, even boots and shoes if the village was temporarily without a cobbler. Among the commonest of non-saddlery products were the beautiful purses, wallets and riding accoutrements that many saddlers made as a sideline, and which are now collector's pieces; also the making of pump leathers, safety belts (see *Industrial Leather* in the MISCELLANEOUS section), leather trunks and uniform cases, horse boots, and even, as recorded by a saddler for L. J. Mayes (High Wycombe Museum, 1958), an artificial arm:

'A man was sent to me from the old workhouse at Amersham, with a tip from the Master to say he could get a job if he'd an arm to wear. So they sent me the bit of hook iron and I had to get on with the rest which was merely to get a block of wood to put the hook iron in, and then put the leather round the wood, and then extend the leather just sufficiently up the stump of his arm so that he could buckle it on.'

Some of these men also kept a stock of bits, bridles, leather soaps, mane combs and other stable requisites, for the convenience of the local people.

Ewart Evans in his *The Farm and the Village* (1969) quotes from an account given by Leonard Aldous, a harness maker born in 1900 at Debenham in Suffolk:

'We used to go round the farms to collect the harnesswork and bring back sets of harness for repair. But in my early days it was quite common for some of the old horsemen to walk anything up to two or three miles, and sometimes more, to bring harness down to the shop. They came down in their own time, after they'd left work, and they'd have a small job done; and then they'd take it back ready for work the next morning. The main reason was that these horsemen were so jealous, in a way, and particular about their horses, that they wouldn't put another piece of harness on belonging to another horse. Each horse had his own harness; and if it couldn't be spared to be sent down to the shop for repair, the horseman brought it himself, got it seen to and took it back ready for work the next day.'

The hand tools described below were used by individual harness makers and saddlers who were one of the key tradesmen in the self-supporting communities of almost every town and larger village.

But in a few towns, notably in Walsall, factories were established which turned out harness, saddles and saddle-trees on a big scale, not only for the great number of horses working on the roads and farms, but also for the army. For example, Walsall alone supplied 25,000 sets of harness to the British Army during the first twenty months of the Crimean War. And this was repeated on an even larger scale during the Boer War and the First World War. In 1917 the army had half-a-million horses and mules, and they all needed either draught harness, riding harness or pack saddles.

Factory production requires a division of labour, not only the broad divisions between making bridles, saddles, or collars, but the work itself was subdivided between cutting out, stuffing, stitching etc. In addition it was necessary to separate new work from repairs; and black harness (for farm and draught horses) from brown harness (riding saddles and bridles): this division was necessary, as Edward Lawrence wrote (1975): 'The unbelievable amount of grime from the black harness work made light-coloured stitching on new bridles etc. impossible for days until one's hands were clean again.'

Factory-made saddles and harness were mostly of high quality: the combination of skilled handwork, simple machines, and some division of labour, could reduce costs without reducing quality. This applied particularly to town workshops, as described by Mrs K. S. Woods (1949):

Fig. 9:1 A saddler's shop. (Drawing by James Arnold)

'Some of the best harness-makers live in towns, just as some of the most beautiful and best-groomed horses are to be seen in the towns. Many an otherwise dreary street leading from a railway station is cheered by the railway company's beautiful, well-groomed horses, with their oiled harness and brightly shining brasses. The vanmen share with the saddlers the pride in their work.'

Decline of the trade after c. 1900

Anyone whose boyhood began before the First World War will remember the disappearance of the horse from roads, fields, and from the cab-filled streets of the city; and with them, the gradual melting away of the horse keepers, grooms, van drivers, horse dealers, harness makers, saddlers, farriers, grain and hay merchants, and other people whose livelihood depended on the horse. Within a space of about thirty years the horse's 4,000-year-old monopoly of transport came to an end, and the age of motor cars and farm tractors began.

The recent revival of interest in riding for pleasure has brought work to the saddlers, and also to the few remaining farriers. Many elderly tradesmen have suddenly found themselves in demand, partly to train a new generation of younger men and women. As a saddler expressed it (Norwood, 1977): 'A lot of people are under the impression that this is a dying trade, but the people in it are dying quicker than the trade.'

Harness and saddle making

Compared with the average cobbler's or shoemaking shop, the saddler's workshop is usually larger and lighter. There may even be found a chair for a customer. Some of the furniture used is listed below under the entry *Furniture*.

Only the best leathers can be used for harness. Most of it is made from cattle-hide butts, vegetable-tanned, and finished to a high standard. Strength and resistance to wear is needed for straps, such as girths and traces: the safety of the horse, and the safety of the rider or driver, depends upon them. The old advertiser's slogan 'There is no substitute for leather' certainly holds for the harness and saddle trade, for, with the possible exception of nylon web,

223

no other material yet invented will stand up so well to the continuous bending and stretching that riding and traction imposes.

After centuries of harness and saddle making, standard patterns and tables of strap dimensions are available. But the saddler has still to rely on his own judgement, careful measurement, and skilled cutting, to produce something that will not only fit both horse and rider, but also look sound and elegant. Andrew Lawson (1978) quotes Mr M. Martin, a London saddler, as follows:

'It takes me two and a half days to make a saddle. The old saddlers used to take a week. In most trades these days quality has deteriorated, but we have only slipped a little. For instance, they used to do twelve stitches to the inch, while we only do eight ... You've got to be a bit of an artist in this trade. You have to know exactly what you're doing before you do it. You have to recognise a line and a curve that's good. You can go some of the way with a ruler and pattern, but after that point you're on your own.

'I can tell a saddle I made from about twenty paces. Every saddler has his own style. But the people you teach take after you. I might have to go a little nearer to recognise a saddle by someone I taught.'

For a description of the saddle-making process the reader may refer to step-by-step accounts listed in the Bibliography under COSIRA (1973), and J. H. L. Shields (1975). There are descriptions of the harness-making process in the well-known manuals listed under W. N. Fitz-Gerald (1875) and Paul N. Hasluck (1904).

The number of hand tools available to harness makers and saddlers has increased enormously during the last 200 years, as exemplified by the following table:

Diderot's Encyclopaedia (Paris c. 1760) illustrates 29 tools
Blanchard's catalogue (Paris c. 1900) illustrates 150* tools
J. Dixon's catalogue (Walsall c. 1950) illustrates 114* tools
* excluding variants of the same tool.

Some of the special tools used in saddle-making, excluding general tools such as knives, awls etc., are listed below:

Operation	See Entry
Preparing the tree	*Saddle Bar Stretcher*
	Saddler's Hammer
	under *Hammers*

Operation	See Entry
Webbing the tree	*Web Stretching Tools*
Blocking the seat	Saddler's Pincers under *Pincers and Pliers*
Making and fitting the skirts and seaming in	Skirt Shave under *Edge Trimming Tools* *Seam Turner*
Setting the seat	Blucher Pliers under *Pincers and Pliers*
Making and Blocking Flaps	Edge Iron under *Edge Trimmng Tools* *Flap Block*
Fitting the panel	Panel Needle under *Needles*
Stuffing the seat etc.	*Carding Tools* Seat Awl under *Awl Stuffing Iron*

Note: Mr Edward Lawrence, whose letters to the author are frequently quoted below, is a saddler and harness maker working near Canterbury.

Fig. 9:2 Diagram of typical heavy draught shaft harness. (Drawing by James Arnold)

Number	Name of Part (Mainly from S. England)	Alternative Name & Notes
(1)	Headstrap	Headstall; Crown; Head piece
(2)	Cheekstrap	Cheek; Cheek piece
(3)	Brow Band	Forehead Band; Front
(4)	Noseband	Nose
(5)	Winker	Blinker
(6)	Bit	
(7)	Throatlash	Throat
(8)	Rein	Check Rein. In riding and carriage harness one rein is attached to the cheek ring of the bit, and another (if fitted) to the curb ring.
(9)	Forewale	Collar Roll. Straw-filled leather tube at front of collar.
(10)	Afterwale	Leather covering to the straw-filled 'body' which lies against the horse's neck.
(10a)	Body	
(11)	Hames	Heams; Hamewoods, Hame-sticks; Jambles; Sales; Seals.
(12)	Housen	Housing. (Smaller version: Cape)
(13)	Cart Saddle or Pad	Ridge Pad
(14)	Bridge	Ridger Housing

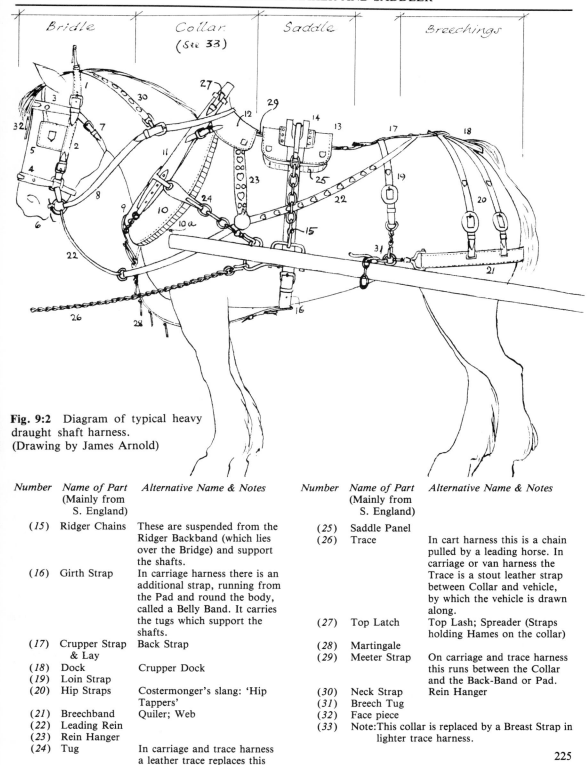

Bridle   *Collar.* (See **33**)   *Saddle*   *Breechings*

Fig. 9:2 Diagram of typical heavy
draught shaft harness.
(Drawing by James Arnold)

Number	Name of Part (Mainly from S. England)	Alternative Name & Notes
(15)	Ridger Chains	These are suspended from the Ridger Backband (which lies over the Bridge) and support the shafts.
(16)	Girth Strap	In carriage harness there is an additional strap, running from the Pad and round the body, called a Belly Band. It carries the tugs which support the shafts.
(17)	Crupper Strap & Lay	Back Strap
(18)	Dock	Crupper Dock
(19)	Loin Strap	
(20)	Hip Straps	Costermonger's slang: 'Hip Tappers'
(21)	Breechband	Quiler; Web
(22)	Leading Rein	
(23)	Rein Hanger	
(24)	Tug	In carriage and trace harness a leather trace replaces this chain: see No. 26.

Number	Name of Part (Mainly from S. England)	Alternative Name & Notes
(25)	Saddle Panel	
(26)	Trace	In cart harness this is a chain pulled by a leading horse. In carriage or van harness the Trace is a stout leather strap between Collar and vehicle, by which the vehicle is drawn along.
(27)	Top Latch	Top Lash; Spreader (Straps holding Hames on the collar)
(28)	Martingale	
(29)	Meeter Strap	On carriage and trace harness this runs between the Collar and the Back-Band or Pad.
(30)	Neck Strap	Rein Hanger
(31)	Breech Tug	
(32)	Face piece	
(33)		Note: This collar is replaced by a Breast Strap in lighter trace harness.

225

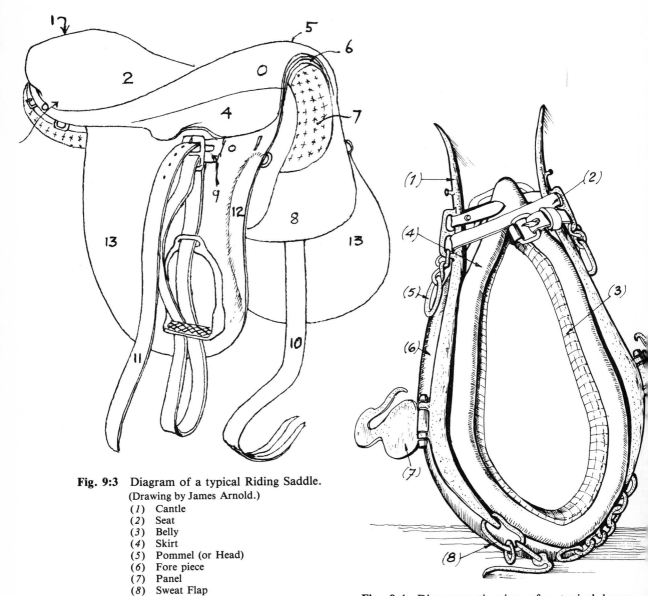

Fig. 9:3 Diagram of a typical Riding Saddle.
(Drawing by James Arnold.)
- (*1*) Cantle
- (*2*) Seat
- (*3*) Belly
- (*4*) Skirt
- (*5*) Pommel (or Head)
- (*6*) Fore piece
- (*7*) Panel
- (*8*) Sweat Flap
- (*9*) Stirrup Bar
- (*10*) Girth (or 3 separate straps)
- (*11*) Stirrup strap
- (*12*) Knee Roll
- (*13*) Flap

Fig. 9:4 Diagrammatic view of a typical heavy draught collar. (Drawing by Norman Purnell.)
- (*1*) Hame
- (*2*) Hame lash
- (*3*) Body
- (*4*) Forewale
- (*5*) Rein ring
- (*6*) Afterwale
- (*7*) Tug hook
- (*8*) Dog-shackle and chain

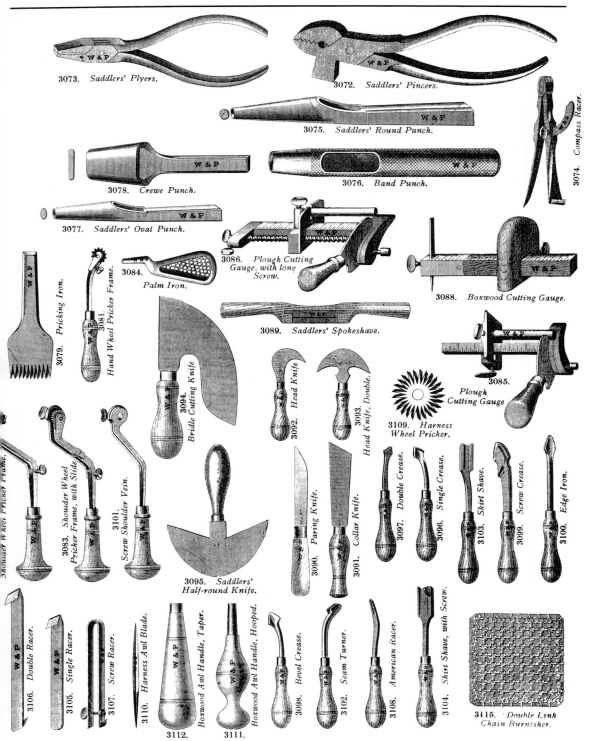

3073. Saddlers' Plyers.

3072. Saddlers' Pincers.

3074. Compass Racer.

3075. Saddlers' Round Punch.

3078. Crewe Punch.

3076. Band Punch.

3077. Saddlers' Oval Punch.

3086. Plough Cutting Gauge, with long Screw.

3088. Boxwood Cutting Gauge.

3079. Pricking Iron.

3081. Hand Wheel Pricker Frame.

3084. Palm Iron.

3089. Saddlers' Spokeshave.

3085. Plough Cutting Gauge

3094. Bridle Cutting Knife.

3092. Head Knife.

3093. Head Knife, Double.

3109. Harness Wheel Pricker.

Shouder Wheel Pricker Frame.

3083. Shouder Wheel Pricker Frame, with Slide.

3101. Screw Shoulder Vein.

3090. Paring Knife.

3091. Collar Knife.

3097. Double Crease.

3096. Single Crease.

3103. Skirt Shave.

3099. Screw Crease.

3100. Edge Iron.

3095. Saddlers' Half-round Knife.

3106. Double Racer.

3105. Single Racer.

3107. Screw Racer.

3110. Harness Awl Blade.

3112.

3111.

Boxwood Awl Handle, Taper.

Boxwood Awl Handle, Hooped.

3098. Bevel Crease.

3102. Seam Turner.

3108. American Racer.

3104. Skirt Shave, with Screw.

3115. Double Link Chain Burnisher.

Fig. 9:5 Harness and saddler's tools. (Ward & Payne's catalogue, page 155, Sheffield, *c.* 1900)

227

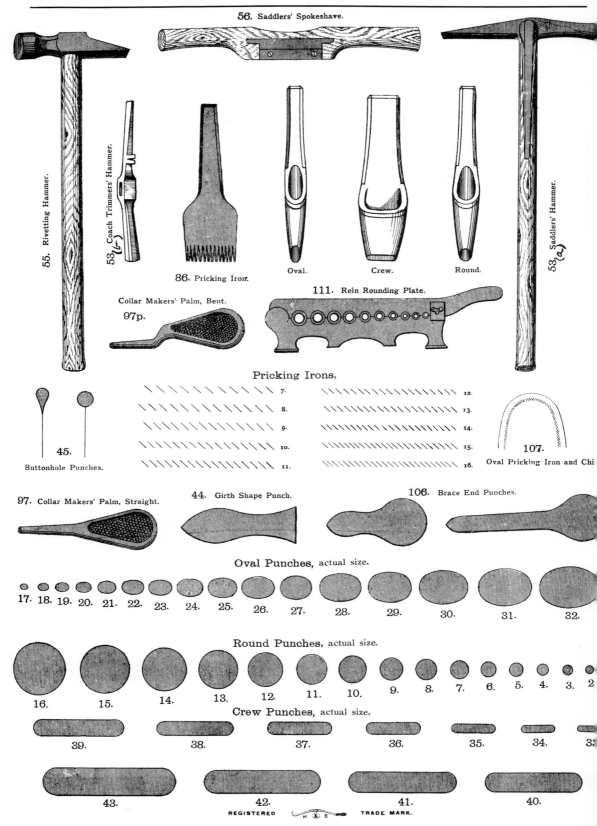

56. Saddlers' Spokeshave.

55. Rivetting Hammer.

53(b). Coach Trimmers' Hammer.

86. Pricking Iron.

Oval. Crew. Round.

53(a). Saddlers' Hammer.

Collar Makers' Palm, Bent.
97p.

111. Rein Rounding Plate.

Pricking Irons,

45.
Buttonhole Punches.

7.
8.
9.
10.
11.
12.
13.
14.
15.
16.

107.
Oval Pricking Iron and Chi

97. Collar Makers' Palm, Straight.

44. Girth Shape Punch.

106. Brace End Punches.

Oval Punches, actual size.

17. 18. 19. 20. 21. 22. 23. 24. 25. 26. 27. 28. 29. 30. 31. 32.

Round Punches, actual size.

16. 15. 14. 13. 12. 11. 10. 9. 8. 7. 6. 5. 4. 3. 2

Crew Punches, actual size.

39. 38. 37. 36. 35. 34. 3

43. 42. 41. 40.

REGISTERED   H & S   TRADE MARK.

228 **Fig. 9:6** Harness and saddler's tools. (Hampson & Scott's 'Equine Album', page 117, Walsall, *c.* 190

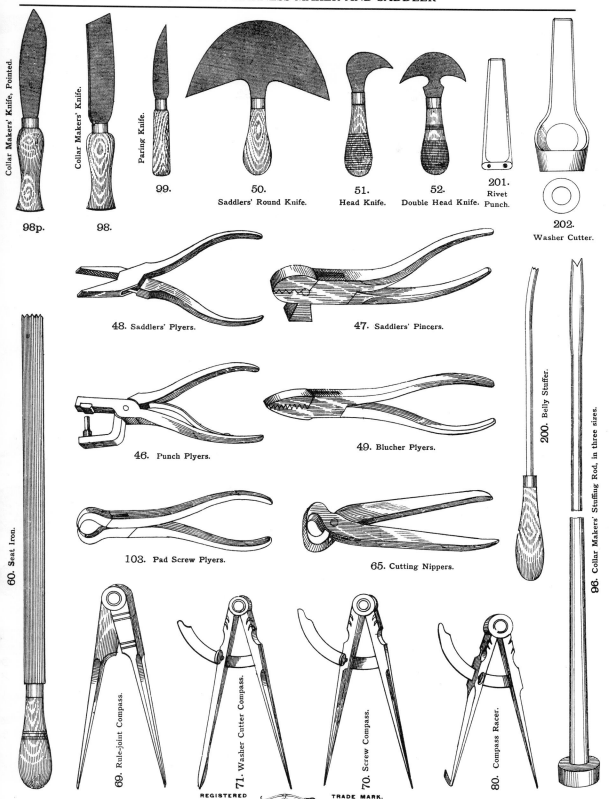

Collar Makers' Knife, Pointed.
Collar Makers' Knife.
Paring Knife.

98p.
98.
99.

50.
Saddlers' Round Knife.

51.
Head Knife.

52.
Double Head Knife.

201.
Rivet Punch.

202.
Washer Cutter.

48. Saddlers' Plyers.

47. Saddlers' Pincers.

46. Punch Plyers.

49. Blucher Plyers.

60. Seat Iron.

103. Pad Screw Plyers.

65. Cutting Nippers.

200. Belly Stuffer.

96. Collar Makers' Stuffing Rod, in three sizes.

69. Rule-joint Compass.

71. Washer Cutter Compass.

70. Screw Compass.

80. Compass Racer.

REGISTERED   H & S   TRADE MARK.

Fig. 9:7   Harness and saddler's tools. (Hampson & Scott's 'Equine Album', page 118, Walsall, *c.* 1900)

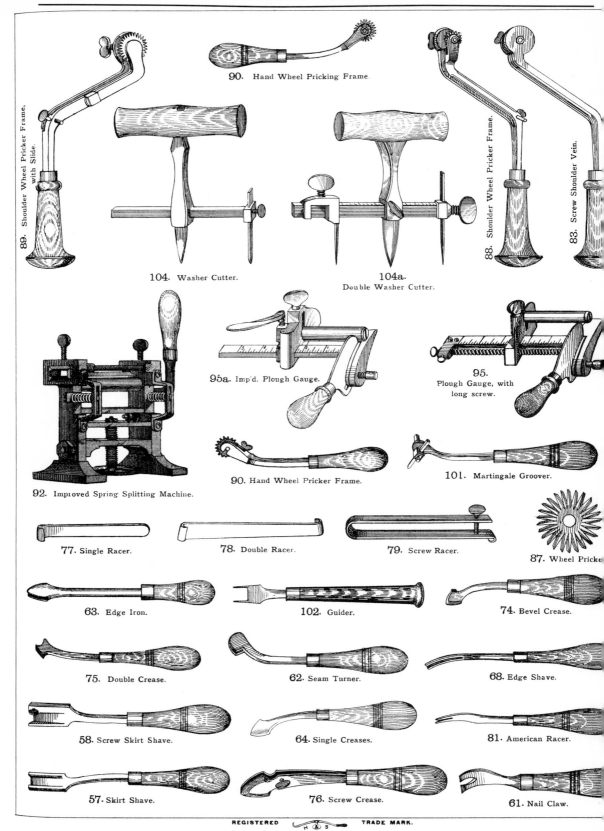

89. Shoulder Wheel Pricker Frame, with Slide.

90. Hand Wheel Pricking Frame.

88. Shoulder Wheel Pricker Frame.

83. Screw Shoulder Vein.

104. Washer Cutter.

104a. Double Washer Cutter.

92. Improved Spring Splitting Machine.

95a. Imp'd. Plough Gauge.

95. Plough Gauge, with long screw.

90. Hand Wheel Pricker Frame.

101. Martingale Groover.

77. Single Racer.

78. Double Racer.

79. Screw Racer.

87. Wheel Pricker

63. Edge Iron.

102. Guider.

74. Bevel Crease.

75. Double Crease.

62. Seam Turner.

68. Edge Shave.

58. Screw Skirt Shave.

64. Single Creases.

81. American Racer.

57. Skirt Shave.

76. Screw Crease.

61. Nail Claw.

REGISTERED   H & S   TRADE MARK.

Fig. 9:8 Harness and saddler's tools. (Hampson & Scott's 'Equine Album', page 119, Walsall, c. 19

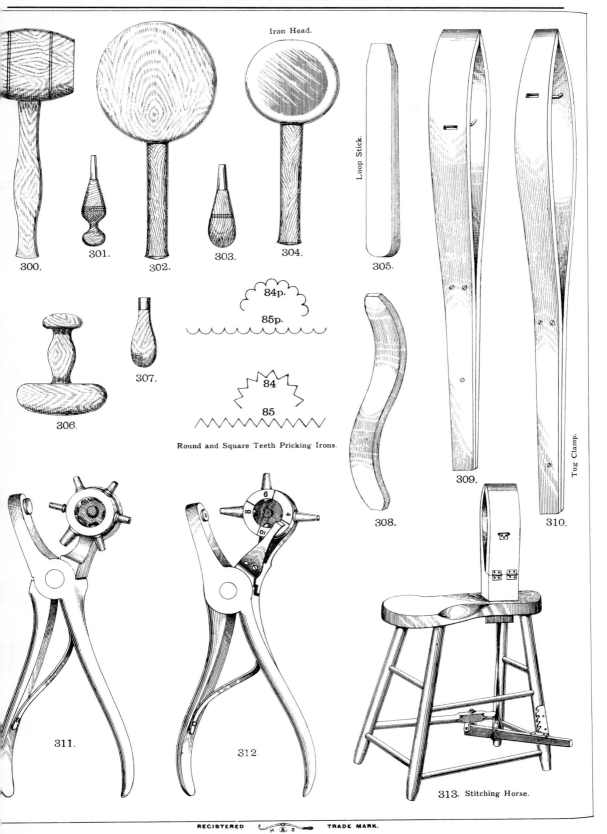

Iron Head.

Loop Stick.

300.   301.   302.   303.   304.   305.

306.   307.

84p.

85p.

84

85

Round and Square Teeth Pricking Irons.

308.

309.

Tug Clamp.

310.

311.   312.

313. Stitching Horse.

9:9   Harness and saddler's tools. (Hampson & Scott's 'Equine Album', page 120, Walsall, *c.* 1900)   231

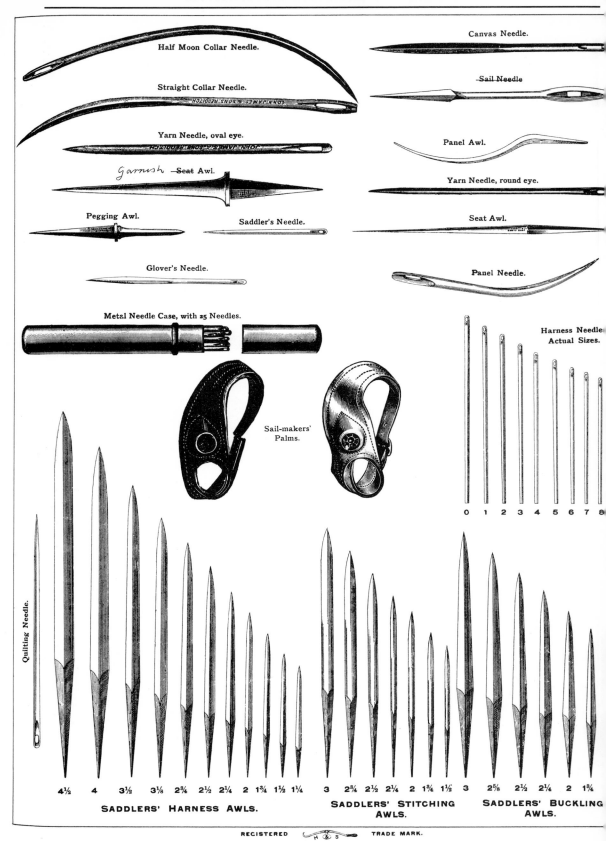

Fig. 9:10 Harness and saddler's tools. (Hampson & Scott's 'Equine Album', page 121, Walsall, *c*

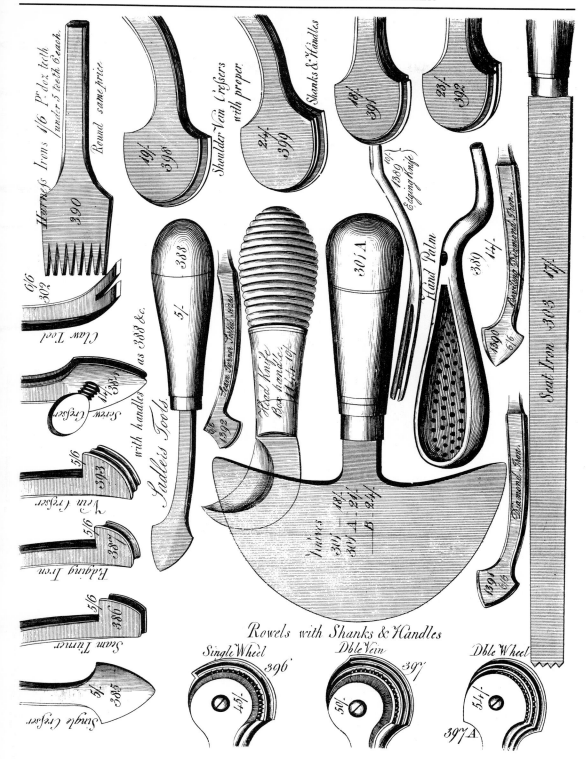

Fig. 9:11 Harness and saddler's tools. (Richard Timmins' catalogue, page 62, Birmingham, *c.* 1800)

French harness and saddler's tools *Figs 9:12–9:15*
The following four pages are from the catalogue of
G. Krempp, Paris, *c.* 1900. These illustrations appear to be identical to those illustrated by Simonin Blanchard in their catalogue of about the same date, and whose tools are well known in this country.

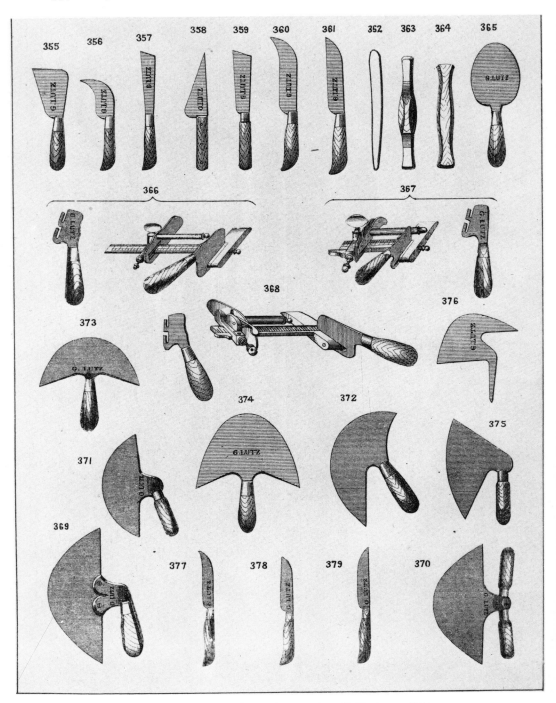

Fig. 9:12 G. Krempp's catalogue, plate II. Paris, *c.* 1900.

355–61 Knives, various	363–4 Crease or Edge Tools	365 Spatula	369–75 Round Knives
362 Polishing Bone	366–8 Plough Gauges		376–9 Hungarian Round and other knives

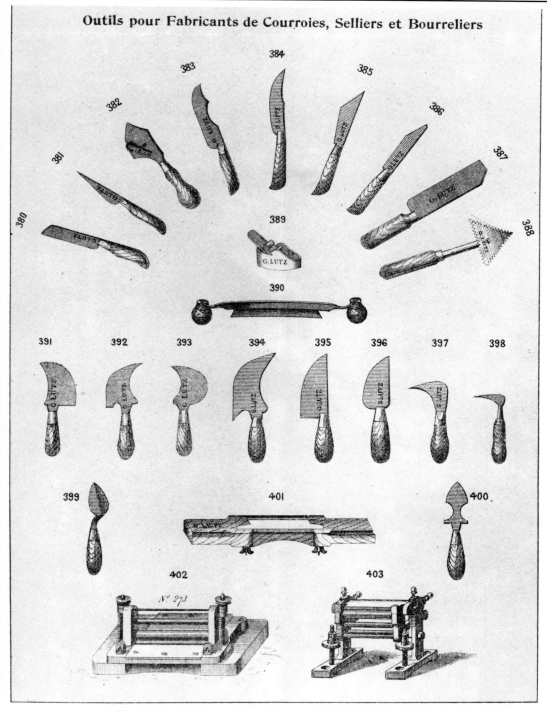

Outils pour Fabricants de Courroies, Selliers et Bourreliers

Fig. 9:13 G. Krempp's catalogue, plate III. Paris, *c.* 1900

380–7	Knives, various	390	Draw Knife	400	Knife scraper
388	Scraper	391–9	Knives, horn-shaped and others	401	Spokeshave
389	Plane for making joints			402–3	Splitting Machines

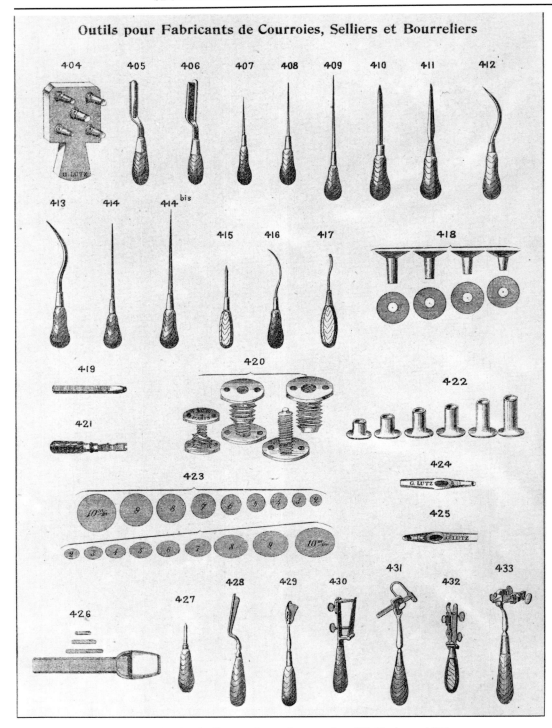

Fig. 9:14 G. Krempp's catalogue, plate IV. Paris, *c.* 1900

404	Plate for weaving rope reins (?)	420	Screw-Buttons for straps
405–6	Gouges	421	Key for Screw-Buttons
407–17	Awls, various	422	Eyelets
418	Copper Rivets	423–6	Round, oval and crew Punches
419	Rivet Punch	427	Square-point Awl
		428–33	Channellers, various types

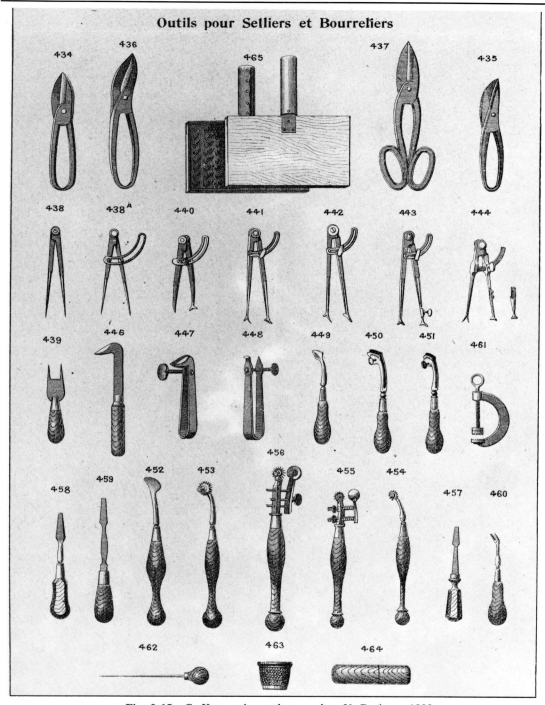

Outils pour Selliers et Bourreliers

Fig. 9:15   G. Krempp's catalogue, plate V. Paris, *c.* 1900

434–7	Hand Shears	449–51	Crease Tools	461	Cramp
438	Compass	452	Burnisher	462	Coach-maker's Awl
439	Fixed Compass (See *Guider*)	453–6	Pricker Wheels	463	Thimble
440–4	Race Compasses	457–9	Screw Drivers	464	Needle Case
446–8	Grooving and Race Tools	460	Nail Claw	465	Carding Tool

Awl *Figs 9:10; 9:16*
(See *Needle*; *Stitching Tools*. Also *Awl* in the BOOT
AND SHOE MAKER section)
The length of awl blades used for stitching vary from
$1\frac{1}{4}-4\frac{1}{2}$ in. (3.1–11.4 cm) and when mounted in a
handle measure 4–7 in. (10.1–17.7 cm) overall. The
handles are usually pear-shaped, but shoemaking-
type handles are sometimes seen.

Awls used by harness makers and saddlers include
the following:

(*a*) *Harness Awl* (Bridle Awl) *Fig. 9:10*
Hampson & Scott's catalogue of *c.* 1900 lists eleven
sizes of blade from $1\frac{1}{4}-4\frac{1}{2}$ in. (3.1–11.4 cm) long.
They are used for making holes in the leather to
prepare the way for the thread.

The blades are diamond-shaped in cross-section
and taper towards the point. This shape makes for
easier penetration, and if the awl 'sticks' a slight
twist will loosen it. A diamond-shaped hole also
enables the stitches to 'set better' and consequently
look better, for the thread will lie neatly in the corner
formed by the sharp edge of the awl. To secure
uniformity in the angle of the stitch the saddler is
helped by a *Pricker*.
Note: The advantage of using a needle of a diamond-
or triangular-shaped cross-section is also discussed
under *Sewing Tools* in the GLOVE MAKER section.

As in shoemaking, the size of hole made must be
such that the thread is tightly·gripped by the leather
which surrounds it, so that even when the thread is
worn through the joint will hold – at least for a time.

(*b*) *Stitching Awl* (Bayonet Pointed Awl) *Fig.
9:10*
A variant of the Harness Awl (above) in which only
the pointed end of the blade is diamond-shaped in
cross-section, leaving the lower part round. The
blade sizes ranged from $1\frac{1}{2}$ to 3 in. (3.8–7.6 cm).

(*c*) *Buckling Awl* (Belt Awl; Strap Awl; Young
Sword; Thomas Newton, 1865: Thong Awl) *Fig.
9:10*
Similar to the Harness Awl (above), but somewhat
stouter. The blades are listed in seven sizes from $1\frac{1}{2}-$
3 in. (3.8–7.6 cm) long.

These awls are intended for heavier work, such as
the attachment of buckles which necessitate penetration of two or more layers of leather; also work on
heavy leather, such as that used for the harness of
farm horses, or for carriage traces.

Randle Holme (1688) writes: '*Buckling Awl*, in the
blades these differ but little, but the hafts are much
contrary one to the other . . . thus a *strong haft*, such
as is fit to abide a blow on the head of it, when in

working with it, a necessity urgeth, and a force is
required.'

Under the alternative name of Belt Awl, this awl
was used for lacing driving belts on the farm and in
factories (see the section DRIVING-BELT MAKER).

(*d*) *Collar Awl* (Drawing Awl; Lacer; Lace Awl)
Fig. 9:16 and also *Fig. 9:10* for *Collar Needles*
A blade *c.* 5–11 in. (12.7–27.9 cm) long with a
large eye at the point. It is used for stitching or lacing
the afterwale to the body of a horse collar, or the
panel to a cart-saddle pad. The thread, or thong, is
carried by the eye at the point of the Awl. (An almost
exactly similar tool, known as a Lawyer's Bodkin, is
used for binding documents together with tape.)

Fig. 9:16

(*e*) *Panel Awl* *Fig. 9:10*
Illustrated by Hampson & Scott (*Equine Album, c.*
1900, p. 121), this appears to be a Harness Awl bent
to a shallow curve. Its purpose is presumably for
stitching the panel – the padding under the saddle –
but it should be noted that the name Panel Awl is
also sometimes given to a Seat Awl (see below).

(*f*) *Seat Awl* (Panel Awl; Quilting Awl; Regulating
Awl; USA: Pad Awl) *Fig. 9:10*. See also *Stuffing
Iron*
A slender pointed awl, round in cross-section, made
in eight blade lengths – from $3\frac{1}{2}$ to 7 in.
(8.8–17.7 cm). Its purpose is similar to that of the
upholsterer's Regulator – to adjust the position of
the stuffing – in this case in the panels and certain
other parts of a saddle. Edward Lawrence writes as
follows about this operation:

'. . . the longer, heavier version was used for
regulating the serge covered panels, which work, if
done properly, was perhaps the most strenuous task

in making a saddle, next to lacing in the panel. A seemingly vast amount of flock was systematically rammed into two or three stuffing holes in each side of the serge panel (after fixing-in) using a small stuffing iron and was then twisted or screwed into place with the seat (regulating) awl, a great deal of careful force being used in the final stages.'

(g) Garnish Awl Fig. 9:10
A plain round, tapering spike *c.* 3–4 in. (7.6–10.1 cm) long, and thicker at the base than other awls. The same type of awl is used by upholsterers and carriage trimmers for enlarging holes or for other purposes. An earlier use is thus described by Randle Holme (1688): 'A Pricking or Garnishing Awl, this is for to make holes to adorn and to Garnish Sadle Skirts with Silk, Silver, or Gold thread.'

(h) Straining Awl
A plain round, tapering awl used for stretching material over a saddle tree. Edward Lawrence writes:

'...at Champion and Wilton these were invariably made from old seat awls, which when the very fine tapering and highly polished points eventually broke, were reground to a bluntish point and used for such jobs as fixing-in panels. Three or four were sometimes needed when tacking and lacing-in, then removed afterwards. They could also be used for holding various work to the bench top.' (See also *Web Stretching Tools*.)

(i) Bent Awl (Backing Awl)
A name given by Hasluck (1904) to an ordinary shoemaker's *Sewing Awl* used for 'putting in wire in saddle flaps for fastening the panel; they have other uses also'. (See *Awl, Sewing* in the BOOT AND SHOE MAKER section.)

Bench (Cutting Bench; Punching Bench) *Figs 9:1; 9:17*
Among the several benches in the workshop, one is often reserved for punching (see *Punch*). The cutting bench is about 9 ft. (2.74 m) long to take the longest hides.
   A peculiarity of the trade is that the tool rack is often made from a strap nailed down at intervals to form loops in which the tools are held. (See also list under *Furniture*.)

Bevelling Machine
Illustrated in the catalogue of Joseph Dixon (*c.* 1950), this is one of the hand-operated machines that were developed towards the end of the last century.
   It consists of a roller pivoted between brackets mounted on a small cast-iron base about 5 in.

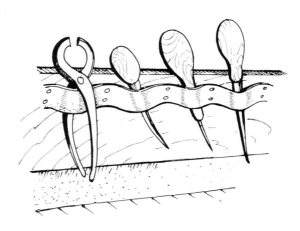

Fig. 9:17

(12.7 cm) wide; the blade, set at an adjustable angle, is fixed above it. The purpose of the tool is to bevel the edge of a strap: this is done by pulling the straps, guided by a fence, between the angled blade and the roller below.

Blinker Press: see *Winker Press*.

Blucher: see *Pincers and Pliers*.

Bones and Sticks (Rubber) For illustrations see *Bones and Sticks* in the BOOT AND SHOE MAKER section, *Fig. 9:35* under *Crease* in this section. See also *Smasher*.

(a) Bones Fig. 9:35
As in the shoemaking trade, pieces of bone, hardwood, horn, or occasionally ivory, are used for rubbing down and smoothing stitches and seams, and for blocking loops etc. Deer bone is preferred for heavier work such as rubbing down traces.
   Harness makers and saddlers also use a sharpened edge of a bone for marking out, and even as a substitute for a *Crease*. A semi-circular notch on the edge of a bone is used for burnishing strap edges, and when finishing round straps.

(b) Rubber (Trace Rubber)
A name given by Hasluck (1904, p. 28) to a piece of hard, close-grained wood or of thick glass about 6 in. (15.2 cm) square, with a V-shaped groove on one edge. He writes: '... it is used to smooth down two

edges whipped together, or for flattening and levelling any two substances, such as leather and linen pasted or stitched together; it is also used to rub stitching on the underside of traces or any double straps, and for rubbing or stretching damped leather.'

(c) Seat Roller (Rolling Pin)

A roller made in hardwood, about 2 ft. (61 cm) long and 1–2 in. in diameter. Among its uses is flattening and smoothing the seat of the saddle. Edward Lawrence writes that he himself used 'an old ebony or rosewood desk ruler for "rolling" the saddle-seat after initial blocking, and again after final fixing, to close the pores that were opened when wetting and straining the pigskin over the tree. The process also gave a fine polish and sheen to the finished work.'

Bouncer: see *Smasher*.

Carding Tools

An iron instrument with teeth like a comb employed by saddlers for cleaning and disentangling the fibres of the flock or wool used for stuffing parts of a saddle. A *Mane Drag* is sometimes used for the same purpose.

Channel Tools

The tools designed to cut channels in saddlery and harness are of three kinds:

(1) Those which make a closable cut, in which stitches can be sunk, and the cut subsequently closed: e.g. *Martingale Groover* and *Channeller*.

(2) Those which cut an open channel intended for decoration, or to facilitate a sharp fold in the leather: e.g. *Race Tools*.

(3) Those which imprint a shallow channel without cutting the leather: e.g. *Crease*.

Note: For similar tools used by boot and shoe makers see *Channel Tools* in that section.

Channelling or grooving tools are described under the following entries: *Channeller* (American Channeller); *Crease*; *Martingale Groover*; *Race Tools* (inc. *American Racer* and *Compass Racer*). Also: *Channeller* in the BOOT AND SHOE MAKER section.

Channeller

A hand tool used for cutting a channel, usually near the edge of a piece of leather, in which stitches can be sunk to hide the sewing. (An English version of this tool is described under the entry *Martingale Groover*.)

(a) *American Channellers* Fig. 9:18 *a and b*
A diagrammatic view of one popular type is illustrated, and also a group of similar tools from the catalogue of C. S. Osborne & Co. (USA, *c.* 1883) who illustrate no less than seven distinct variations. It is possible that one or more of them may have produced an open groove like the *Race*, rather than a plain cut. Variants have different methods of adjusting the fence, or of changing the angle of the cut.

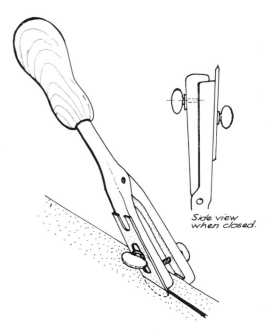

Fig. 9:18a

(b) *English Channellers* Fig. 9:45
It is strange that, apart from the *Martingale Groover*, the above American tools are not listed by English tool makers. Perhaps they were needed in America because their harness often contained more decorative stitching and grooving than was usual in England.

(c) *French Channellers* Fig. 9:14, Nos 428–33
A group is illustrated in the catalogue of G. Krempp (Paris, *c.* 1900). They may have served as models for some of the American Channellers.

Chape

This is the piece of leather by which a buckle is fastened to a strap (see Chape Punch under *Punch*).

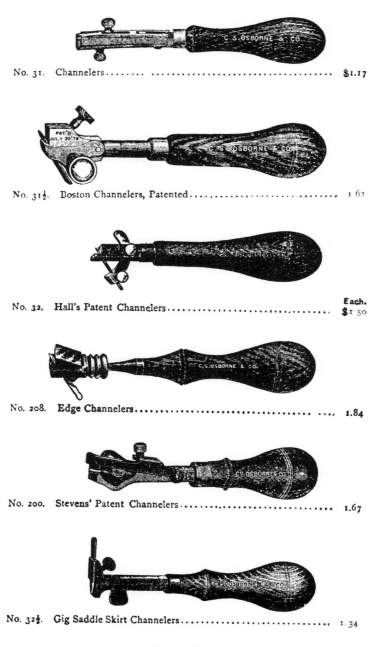

No. 31.   Channelers........ .... $1.17

No. 31½.   Boston Channelers, Patented............................ 1 67

No. 32.   Hall's Patent Channelers...................................
Each.
$1 50

No. 208.   Edge Channelers.. .... 1.84

No. 200.   Stevens' Patent Channelers............................... 1.67

No. 32½.   Gig Saddle Skirt Channelers.............................. 1.34

Fig. 9:18b

Clamp (Clam; Clamb; Clams. Scots: Clamish, Clam, Clooes or Glaum. The Oxford English Dictionary's entries for Clam and Clamp suggest that Clam may be the more correct word, or at least the earlier word for this tool. Examples of recent spelling include Devlin (1839): clam; Leno (1895): clam; Hasluck (1904): clamp; Hampson & Scott's catalogue (*c.* 1900): clamps or clamp; R. E. Thacker's catalogue (*c.* 1905): clambs.) *Figs 9:19–9:25*
Note: The following paragraphs relate to the use of the clamp in several leather-making trades including boot and shoe making. (See also *Stitching Horse*.)

The clamp consists of a pair of curved wooden jaws, 30–40 in. (76.2 cm–1.16 m) long × about 3 in. (7.6 cm) wide, described by Devlin (1839) as 'two tall nipping pieces of stave-like timber'. (They were often home-made, sometimes from the curved staves of a cask.) The top edges grip the leather and are kept together by pressure between the knees as well as by their own 'spring'. They are used for holding the work near the seam when sewing.

Present day clamps are made of springy wood, such as ash or oak, steamed and bent to a graceful curve. Hasluck (1904) expected saddlers to make their own. He writes (p. 24):

'A clamp can be made easily by the worker at home ... from two oak cask or barrel staves. The lower portion may be a sound piece of white deal, 20 in. by 3 in. by 3 in., and the only other requisites will be eight stout $2\frac{1}{4}$ in. screws. The staves should be cut 2 ft long by at least 3 in. wide, the points of greatest convexity being in the centre; the more bent the staves are the more useful the clamp will be. Clean up the outside with a spokeshave, leaving one end the full thickness of the staves, or about 1 in., and thinning off gradually to about $\frac{3}{4}$ in. towards the upper ends, which are to form the jaws of the clamp. The dovetail-shaped tenon in the lower part should be at least 6 in. in length, and will require careful cutting, the depth of the shoulders and the width of the upper end depending upon the amount of curve in the staves which are to be attached to it. It should be borne in mind that the object is to embed the staves so firmly that their upper ends, or the jaws of the tool, press tightly together.'

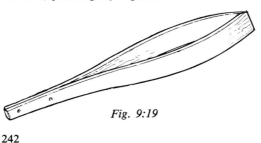

Fig. 9:19

242

Holding the Clamp
Harness makers and shoemakers hold the clamp differently. Hasluck (1904, p. 24) writing of the saddler explains this:

'Held between the knees in a slightly slanting position, the clamp keeps the work firmly in position while the stitching is being done; it lies against the left knee, and by throwing the right leg over it the work is held fast between the gripping points. Note that the saddler has the clamp between his legs in a slanting direction, and not as the shoemaker, who has them straight up, almost against his nose, when bending over the work. One reason for this is that the work done by the saddler with the clamp requires more force to press the awl through than the work done by the shoemaker; consequently the saddler must set his clamp against some firm object (his left knee) so that it will not yield under the pressure. Another reason is that the saddler stitches with needles, while the shoemaker uses bristles, and must see the hole made by the awl, as the bristles cannot force their way, as the needles, to some slight extent, are able to do.'

Fig. 9:20

The shoemaker's manner of holding the clamp is mentioned by the Scottish National Dictionary, quoting N. Macleod (1881): 'Ye ken John, I'm a shoemaker, and it's a dull trade, and squeezing the clams against the wame [the stomach] is ill for digestion.'

Edward Lawrence relates that when he worked in London the clamp was fixed in position to the end of a bench to form a sort of improvised *Stitching Horse*. It was held fast to the bench-end by means of a steel rod bent into a flat hook and known as a journeyman. 'One of the most characteristic sounds was the constant rattle of the journeyman as work proceeded at its usual high speed. The Stitching Horse, as such, did not need this device, being a complete piece of furniture in itself.'

Variants include:

(*a*) *Loop Clamp   Fig. 9:21*
Since the jaws of the ordinary clamp are too wide to grip loops (used for tucking in strap ends) a miniature clamp is set between the jaws of the parent clamp. This smaller clamp has jaws small enough to enter the loop.
Note: Loriners insert a similar device in the vice for holding small parts. They call it a 'Teddy Bear' (see the LORINER section).

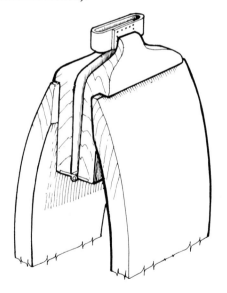

Fig. 9:21

(*b*) *Forked Jaw Clamp   Fig. 9:22*
This has a small piece taken out of the centre of the jaw to avoid contact with a stud or other obstacle

which may have been fitted to the leather before sewing began.

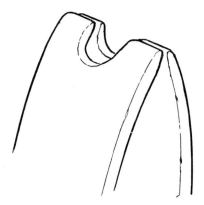

Fig. 9:22

(*c*) *French Clamp   Fig. 9:23*
Diderot (*c.* 1760) illustrates a clamp, under *Bourrelier* (Harness Maker), which is similar to the ordinary modern pattern except that one arm of the clamp is hinged at its base, and consequently there is no 'spring': knee pressure alone keeps the jaws tight on the work.

Diderot illustrates a similar clamp under Saddler and Trunk Maker, but not under Shoemaker. The hinged type survives in the catalogues of Blanchard, and Krempp (both of Paris, *c.* 1905).

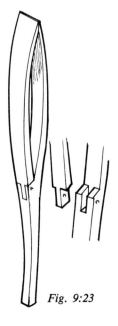

Fig. 9:23

243

(d) Chinese Clamp Fig. 9:24

Hommel (USA, 1937) describes clamps used by shoemakers in China. These consist of two wooden boards which are loosely mortised into a short wooden base, with which they form an isosceles triangle. The apex of the triangle, where the boards meet, provides the jaws for holding the work. These jaws are forced together either by a twisted rope tied between the upright boards, or by a wooden key which penetrates slots in both boards: when the key is pressed down, the boards are drawn together.

The Chinese shoemaker holds the clamp between his knees, and Hommel relates: 'Working in this position he is just as liable to become knock-kneed as his occidental brother.'

Fig. 9:24

(e) American Clamp (See illustration under *Stitching Horse*.)

Catalogues of harness and shoe tools, such as C. S. Osborne (USA, *c*. 1883) and Ross Moyer (USA, 1884), do not mention the ordinary 'knee-operated' clamp. Instead they illustrate a *Stitching Horse*. Knight (USA, 1877) also fails to include the ordinary clamp, but has several illustrations of the Stitching and Sewing Horses in various forms, including one which is hardly more than the ordinary clamp fitted with a treadle or foot strap to close it.

(f) Tug Clamp Fig. 9:9, No. 310

Listed by several English makers, this is an ordinary clamp but with narrower jaws. It is used for such work as gripping the heavy ring-shaped straps, known as shaft tugs, in which the shafts are supported. Like the Loop Clamp (described above) the jaws must be sufficiently small to enter the tug, and they are sometimes rounded inside to fit the curve of the tug.

(g) Clamp with strap for closing Fig. 9:9, No. 309

Horizontal slots about $1\frac{1}{2}$ in. (3.8 cm) wide are sometimes cut through each arm of the clamp a few inches below the point where the jaws meet. This is done to accommodate a foot strap which can be fitted if desired. It is fixed to one arm, passes freely through the other, and ends with a loop near the ground in which the foot is placed. The clamp is thus forcibly closed by pressing down the foot, instead of relying only on the pressure from the knees and the natural spring of the arms.

(h) Floor-Standing Clamp Fig. 9:25

This version, used in works making Driving Belts, is similar to the Chinese Clamp above, except that it is provided with a screw for forcing the jaws together.

Fig. 9:25

Collar-making Tools

Note: Information on the early development of the collar will be found in the introduction to this section. (See *Fig. 9:4* for the component parts of a typical heavy horse collar.)

Accounts of collar making are contained in works listed in the Bibliography under Dorothy Hartley (1939) and Paul Hasluck (1904).

For tools used in collar-making, see: *Awl* (Collar Awl); *Collar Measuring Tools*; *Collar Vice*; *Gouge, Buckle Tongue*; *Gouge, Collar Maker's*; *Knife, Saddler's and Harness Maker's* (Collar Knife); *Mallet, Collar Maker's*; *Needles*; *Palm*; *Smasher*; *Stuffing Iron* (Collar Rod and Collar Jemmie).

Collar Measuring Tools

Different methods of measuring a horse's neck for a collar include the following:

(*a*) *Collar Caliper Fig. 9:26*
A wooden caliper, often home-made, about 15 in. (37.5 cm) long, with the toes turned slightly inwards.

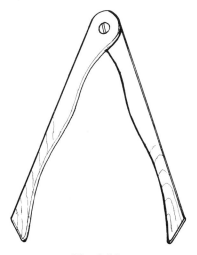

Fig. 9:26

(*b*) *Collar Measure Fig. 9:27*
The illustration comes from Hampson & Scott's *Equine Album* (*c.* 1900). A similar device illustrated by C. S. Osborne (USA, *c.* 1800) is described as 'Everet's Patent'.

This giant-sized caliper-gauge is *c.* 30 in. (76.2 cm) long. The stock is made of wood; the jaws are partly of metal, and are adjustable for measuring a horse's neck and the width across the breast and withers. The caption explains that measurements are taken by moving the arm *B* up or down the upright rule *E*; and

the width of the breast is taken by means of the sliding member *B* under the thumb-screw *C*. A measurement across the withers is taken with the movable joint at *S* and the brass rule *M*. The arrows *R* denote length and width. The joint *A* on the upright rule allows the measure to be folded to fit into a small leather case which makes it convenient to carry when away from home.

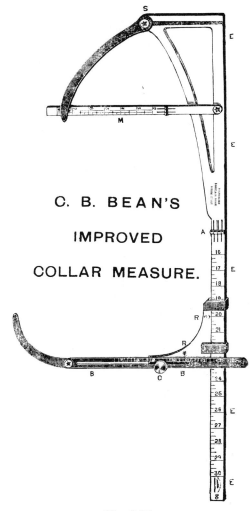

Fig. 9:27

(*c*) *Flexible Measuring Stick* (Trade names include Flexicurve and Akemblex.)
This is a modern device used for recording the contour of an irregular shape. Some consist of an articulated chain of metal links or beads, tightly

245

enclosed by a rubber or plastic tube. When bent to follow the contour of the object to be measured (such as a horse's neck) it retains its shape and will serve to transfer the contour to a sheet of paper, or to the material to be cut. (Before this device came on the market, saddlers often used a short length of lead-covered cable.)

Collar Vice (Collar Stretcher)
A tapered mandrel-like implement, oval in cross-section, on which a horse collar can be held tightly while being pounded and worked into shape; it can also be used as a stand on which to hang a collar while it is being stitched. (See also *Mallet, Collar Maker's*).

This tool has not been found in English tool-makers' catalogues, nor seen in the workshops. The examples described below come from abroad.

(a) American Collar Vice   Fig. 9:28
This example is in the San Joaquin County Historical Museum, USA (1976). The two sides of the vice are expanded to hold the collar securely by means of a screw set in the end of the table. The collar is released by forcing the two sides of the vice together again with the rope that is looped round it.

Fig. 9:28

(b) French Collar-Vice (Blanchard)   Fig. 9:29
A free-standing version of *(a)* above, without the table, but with a wood or metal screw joining the two halves near the top. This is illustrated by Blanchard (c. 1905).

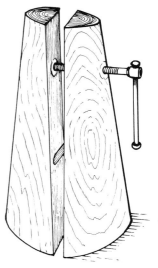

Fig. 9:29

(c) French Collar-Vice (Diderot)   Fig. 9:30
A simpler version is illustrated by Diderot (c. 1760) in the background of plate V of the section *Bourrelier, Bastier*. This appears to be a solid tapering block, oval in cross-section. A wedge-shaped piece is taken out of the top; this was probably done in order to make the block slightly compressible when the collar is forced down upon it.

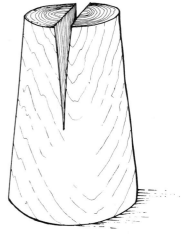

Fig. 9:30

Compass and Calipers

Those used by saddlers and harness makers include:

(*a*) *Collar Caliper*

A large caliper, usually made of wood, used for measuring a horse's neck. (See under *Collar Measuring Tools.*)

(*b*) *Race Compass*

A steel compass with one leg ending in the form of a Race Knife. (See under *Race Tools.*)

(*c*) *Saddler's Compass* *Fig. 9:7, Nos 69, 70 (p. 229)*

Ordinary steel compasses, about 7 in. (17.7 cm) long, used for marking the width of straps, position of stitching, crew hole etc., particularly on bridle work. Three or four pairs of compasses can be pre-set to hasten the work.

Winged, 'Lancashire'-type compasses, with a thumb-screw setting, as used in the metal and woodworking trades, are often found in saddlers' shops. They are usually ornamented with the traditional chamfers and serrations.

A harness-maker's caliper illustrated by Diderot (1760) is made of wood, with bowed legs.

(*d*) *Washer-Cutter Compass*

A steel compass with the foot of one leg made into a cutting blade. (See under *Washer Cutter.*)

(*e*) See also *Guider* below.

Corner Cutter

This tool is included in a price list of Joseph Dixon (1918).

Its appearance and purpose are not certain, but it may be similar to the Chisels. (See under *Punch* (*b*)4.)

Crease (Creasing Iron; Veining Iron. Randle Holme (1688) refers to a 'Cressa or Veining Stick'. For American terms see *American Crease Tools* below.)

Figs: see pp. 248–9 and *Figs 9:5, 9:8. 9:11 (pp. 227, 230, 233)*

Crease tools have many different shapes and are made of steel, wood or bone. The smaller ones have a gently curved shank set in a turned handle and measure 6–7 in. (15.2–17.7 cm) overall; the larger 'shoulder' creases may be as long as 14 in. (35.5 cm).

Though looking different from each other, all have one thing in common – a blunt blade (or blades) capable of imprinting lines on the surface of leather. This is done for decoration – for example, a line along the edge of straps – or as a guide or shallow channel for sewing.

When describing a wooden 'Cressa or Veining Stick', Randle Holme (1688) writes: 'It hath one end round with a nick therein, one side of the wood being broader than the other; the contrary end hath it round on one end, and sharp at the other: the name of this tool tell you the use of it, viz. to Vein and Score Leather, to adorn it for the sight of the Eye.' There does not appear to be an illustration of a crease in Diderot (c. 1760).

Many of these tools are provided with a fence, either fixed or adjustable, designed to regulate the distance between the edge of the leather and the line to be imprinted upon it. These fences are only just deep enough to hold the edge without touching the bench or other surface on which the leather is placed during this operation.

Steel creases are usually heated, and the leather previously dampened, to make the imprinted line more permanent; but if the dampened leather is light in colour, a steel crease can stain it: to avoid this, wood or bone creases are used. (See paragraph below on the *Wood or Bone Crease.*)

When heating a crease, the correct temperature can be judged by trial on a piece of waste leather; but some hold the tool near the cheek to judge the heat. Creases are not heated when used for marking out, nor for light work where deep lines are not required.

Examples of the crease family include:

(*a*) *Single Crease* *Fig. 9:32*

A flat, shield-shaped head, with a blunt edge. It is made in six different sizes according to the thickness of the line wanted.

These tools have no fence and can therefore be used in places where a fenced crease cannot go, for instance, in the centre of a large piece of leather or strap. They are not often heated except, for example, when creasing heavy loops or tug straps.

Edward Lawrence described their use as follows: 'I use the Single Crease, unheated, for marking round paper patterns on to the grain side of the leather; across straps before cutting; for marking the extent of stitching on all parts; for marking positions of turnbacks for buckles, etc.; after warming, to "tidy off" vein lines made by the Shoulder Vein, for instance, on the top of the cheek points on a bridle head.'

(*b*) *Double Crease* *Fig. 9:32*

Usually an 'axe-shaped' head, with two crease blades.

This tool produces two parallel lines at a fixed distance apart, and is used for all kinds of decoration, including cross-hatching, in which case one of the blades is made to follow along one of the two lines previously made. (See also *Checker Crease* below.)

HAME TUGS.

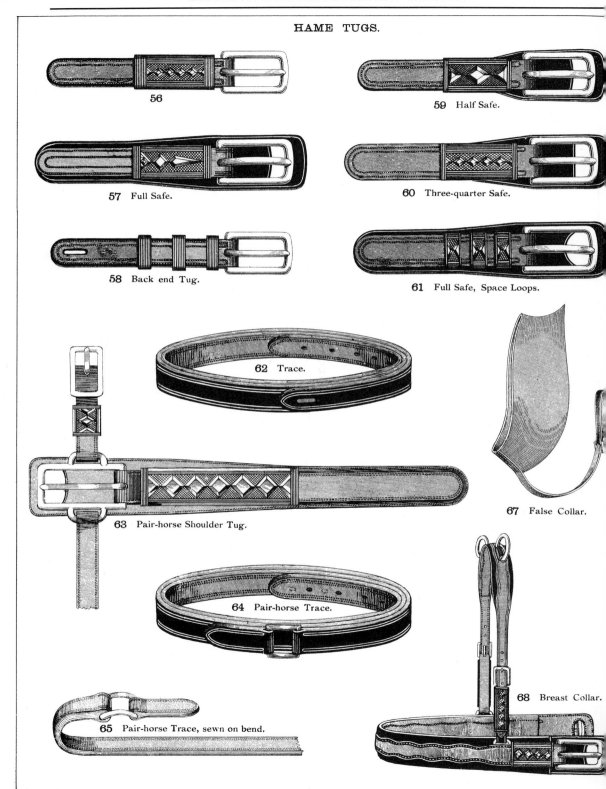

56

59 Half Safe.

57 Full Safe.

60 Three-quarter Safe.

58 Back end Tug.

61 Full Safe, Space Loops.

62 Trace.

63 Pair-horse Shoulder Tug.

67 False Collar.

64 Pair-horse Trace.

65 Pair-horse Trace, sewn on bend.

68 Breast Collar.

REGISTERED   TRADE MARK.

248   **Fig. 9:31** Examples of decoration made with Crease tools. (Hampson & Scott's catalogue, Walsall,

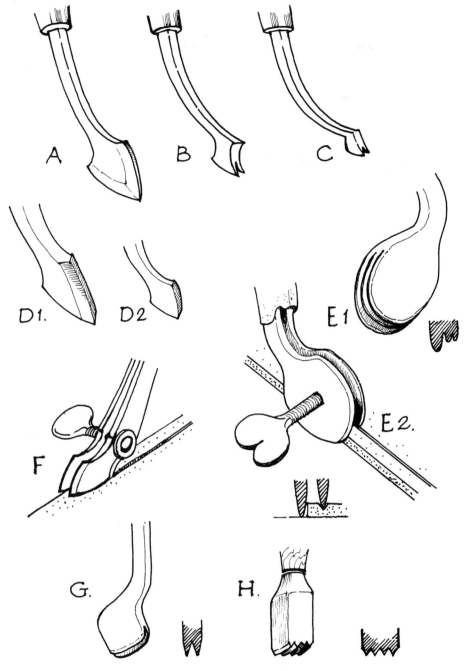

Fig. 9:32 Crease Irons: typical blades. (See also *Figs. 9:5, 9:8, 9:11*)

(A)	Single Crease	(E1)	Shoulder Vein (solid, double)
(B)	Double Crease	(E2)	Shoulder Vein (screw, single)
(C)	Checker Crease	(F)	Screw Crease
(D1)	Bevel Crease (double bevel)	(G)	Purse Crease
(D2)	Bevel Crease (single bevel)	(H)	American Cutting Crease

(c)　*Bevel Crease* (Beveller; R. Timmins, *c.* 1800: Bevelling Diamond Iron; USA: Bevel Tickler)　*Fig. 9:32*
A shield-shaped head, similar to the Single Crease, but thicker. The working edge may be bevelled on both sides, or ground to a single bevel. They are made in four different sizes.

This tool is used almost exclusively for creasing loops, winkers and other parts of the harness that are heavily ornamented. After heating, they are made to form deep, wide grooves, and are also used for smoothing up and deepening the edge of designs made by other crease tools.

(d)　*Checker Crease* (Checkering Iron; Double Crease; USA: Checking Tool)　*Figs 9:32c; 9:31*
This is a small version of the Double Crease, and is made in four sizes. The two parallel blades are used for making ornamental 'checker' lines on loops, and elsewhere if desired; one edge is run along the last line to be imprinted, and this line acts as a guide for keeping the lines parallel.

The effect of checkering is similar to that to be seen on gun stocks.

(e)　*Shoulder Vein Crease*　*Figs 9:32; 9:33*
(Randle Holme, 1688: Veining Stick Scoring Iron. The verb 'to vein' means to ornament with impressed lines suggestive of veins.)
This largest of the creases measures 12–14 in. (30.5–35.5 cm) overall, and may be either straight or cranked. The working head is rounded (except in the case of the Monkey Vein) and the head contains both fence and blade. The shank is often found covered by a leather sheath put on by the saddler himself to protect the hand when the tool is heated. (There is some evidence that the straight-shanked tool came before the cranked type: it is not included in the catalogue of the American maker of saddle and harness tools, C. S. Osborne & Co. *c.* 1880.)

The Shoulder Vein is designed for heavier work, mainly to make lines on the edge of large straps. Pressure is applied from the shoulder. It is heated before use, and when working the tool back and forth, it must not be left still for long, otherwise the leather may be scorched.

Randle Holme (1688, p. 297), who used the alternative names recorded above, writes as follows about the double-bladed version of this tool: ' . . . it is an Iron with three dents in the edge of it, having a long iron *Stail* . . . With this Iron being a little heated, they scoare and run Veines on the Leather which is about the Sadles, and also on bridle raines, and head-stalls, to make them look handsome, and pleasing to the eye.'

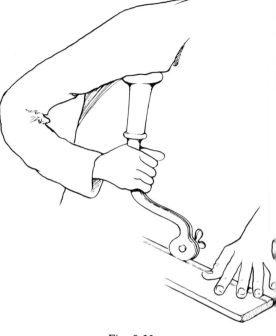

Fig. 9:33

Variants include:

(1)　*Single Shoulder Vein*
The Single Crease blade and fence are combined in a solid working head.
(2)　*Double Shoulder Vein*　*Fig. 9:32*
The same as (1) but with two crease blades instead of one.
(3)　*Triple Shoulder Vein*
The same as (1) but there are three crease blades. Used, for instance, for creasing the flesh side of saddle girth straps.
(4)　*Bevel Shoulder Vein*
Made with a head whose cross section is similar to the Bevel Crease.
(5)　*Screw Shoulder Vein*　*Fig. 9:32*
The shank is split, one leg ending with the head (made with Single, Double, Triple or Bevel Crease blades), the other ending with the fence. A thumb-screw sets the fence at different distances from the blade.
(6)　*Monkey (Shoulder) Vein*
The same as the ordinary Shoulder Vein (with the same variants) but the head is more rectangular than round, and so presents a flat working face to the leather. This tool may have been preferred for straight runs.

(f) Purse Crease Fig. 9:32
A name given by Joseph Dixon, tool makers, in their list of *c.* 1948, to a crease with a rather heavy rectangular head, made with single, double or bevel blades, each in two sizes.

These tools were designed for use on purses, wallets and note-cases. The term 'purse' was applied to all these goods which were often made by saddlers as a by-product to their main business.

(g) Screw Crease Figs. 9:32; 9:34
Similar to the Single Crease, and with the same shield-shaped head, but the head is split into two halves and their distance apart is controlled by a thumb-screw. The tool can therefore be used as a Single Crease with an adjustable fence to control the distance of the crease from the edge of the leather; or, on occasions, as a Double Crease with possibility of controlling the distance between the crease lines.

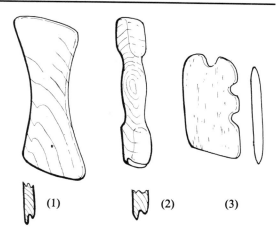

Fig. 9:35   Crease in wood or bone: (*1*) Home-made in hard wood; (*2*) Factory-made in boxwood; (*3*) Home-made in bone, and notched.

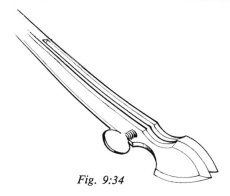

Fig. 9:34

(h) Wood or Bone Crease Fig. 9:35
These creases were made in many shapes, usually by the saddler himself, but a more standardised pattern was produced by the tool makers. There are many variants, though the majority were designed for making a single crease, and many were provided with a fixed fence.

The flat Bone Crease illustrated is a common shape, but horn-shaped creases, made from the tip of a cow-horn or from a piece of deer antler, are also used. An advantage of the flat bone was the addition of the notches cut on the edge that were used for rubbing down round reins, or the edges of leather straps.

Many saddlers prefer using bone (or hardwood) creases, but there are occasions when a wood or bone crease must be used. Owing to the interaction of iron with tanning materials, a steel crease is not used on dampened light-coloured leather, for fear of staining the leather.

(i) American Crease Tools
The following notes apply to the catalogue of C. S. Osborne & Co. (USA, *c.* 1880) and relate only to crease tools that appear to be different from the English crease tools in their purpose or nomenclature, or both.

1. *Tickler*
    This term is applied to Single, Double and Bevel Creases if they are made without a fence. They are similar in shape to their English counterparts, and are used in areas other than the edge of a strap.

2. *Edge Crease*
    This term is applied to a group of creases which are all provided with a fence. They have small 'cat's-paw'-shaped, solid, heads (rather like our Checker Crease) which contain both the crease blade(s) and a fixed (non-adjustable) fence. Each is made in five different sizes which vary in width from about $\frac{1}{8}-\frac{1}{4}$in. (0.4–0.7 cm). They are used for making creases parallel to the edge of the leather.

3. *Cutting Crease Fig. 9:32h*
    These have the blades cut on the end of a solid head which are ground to a cutting edge. They are used for Western American, Mexican and Spanish style of leather carving on saddles and harness.

4. *Mexican Spreading Tool*
    The head is formed like a Bevel Crease and is used for bevelling designs on carved leather.

5. *Sinking Tool*
   A solid three-sided head, ground to a bevel at one edge. Used as (4) above. No. 188 is intended for driving with a mallet.

Creasing Machine

This does the work of tools for creasing the edge of straps. The strap is pulled between two rollers turned with a cranked handle, like a mangle.

The rollers have a series of twin annular rings, placed at intervals along their length, which are known as 'passes'. These twin rings are fixed at different distances apart, to take different widths of straps. The strap is first dampened and then passed between the rings, guided by an adjustable fence; the rings imprint a crease along the edge of the strap.

Cutting Board

A wooden board or block, usually made with end-grain hardwood blocks; it is placed under the hide when cutting. (See entry in the BOOT AND SHOE MAKER section.)

Cutting Gauge (Slitting Gauge; USA: Draw Knife.)
Figs 9:5, No. 3088 (p. 227); 9:36

This tool is similar to a carpenter's Marking Gauge except that it has a cutting blade instead of a scratch-point. It is made of wood or iron and may be regarded as an ancestor of the *Plough Gauge*.

The tool consists of a square or oval stem *c.* 10 in. (25.4 cm) long, and often graduated; this stem penetrates the fence-block which can be set in any desired position along the stem with a set-screw or wedge. The stem carries a cutter knife at one end which can be adjusted for depth of cut by means of a wedge or thumb-screw.

It is used for cutting strips of leather, for example a strap or belt. In operation, the fence-block is made to bear on the edge of the bench or cutting block; it can be shifted to cut different widths of the leather. The tool can also be used for cutting a channel; as a substitute, for example, for the *Channeller* or the *Martingale Groover*.

The drawing of a home-made example is contributed by Mr D. A. Saguto (USA, 1980) and called by him a 'Draw Knife' — perhaps additional evidence that these adjustable cutting tools are ancestors to the factory-made *Plough Gauge* (USA 'Draw Gauge'). In this example the adjustable stock is graduated and contains a slot for a knife blade; an ordinary shoe knife was probably wedged into the slot with a skiving of leather.

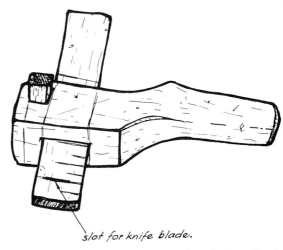

slot for knife blade.

Fig. 9:36 A home-made example of a Cutting Gauge (from USA).

Drawing Plate

A name given in C. S. Osborne's catalogue (USA, *c.* 1883) to a steel plate with five or six holes in it. They are used for rounding thongs. (See also *Rounding Tools* for rounding reins.)

Edge Trimming Tools
(See also *Spokeshave*)

This group includes tools designed for shaving and smoothing edges.

Elderly saddlers will tell how fifty years ago it was not unusual for a saddler to spend a whole day on trimming, polishing, and the general cleaning-up and finishing of a single saddle.

Edge Tools do not appear in Diderot (*c.* 1760). They begin to appear in English catalogues about 1850, and it may perhaps be presumed that before that time edges were bevelled or rounded with a piece of broken glass — a method still preferred by some tradesmen (see below).

(*a*) *Edge Shave* (Chamfering Tool; Edging Knife; Edge Stripper; Edge Trimmer. USA nomenclature: see below) *Figs 9:8, No. 68 (p. 230); 9:37 (opposite)*
A slender, curved shank, grooved on the upper side to form a fence on each side of a narrow, chisel-shaped cutting edge. It is used for running along the edges of straps and other parts of the harness to take off the sharp edge. It is listed in sizes Nos 1–12.

(*b*) *Hollow Edge Shave* (Round Edge Tool)
Similar to (*a*) above except that the blade is concave and is designed to produce a rounded edge instead of a bevel; the fences are often flattened and enlarged

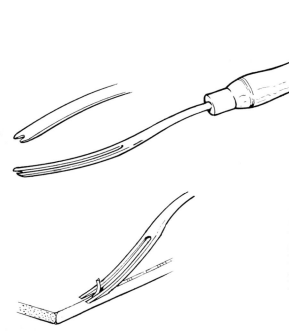

Fig. 9:37

('eared') to bear more securely on each side of the leather. It is listed in sizes Nos 1–12.

Edward Lawrence writes as follows about this tool:

'. . . with a concave cutting surface, this removes more leather than the usual edge shaving tool, and leaves a rounded edge, useful on heavy strapping next to the horse, and so less liable to cause chafing or hair loss. Used at Champion and Wilton for their famous "bevelled edge stirrup leathers", and (now by me) for the horse side of head collar noses and heads, etc.'

(c) Edge Rounding Iron   *Figs 9:8, No. 63 (p. 230); 9:38 (See also Seam Turner.)*
An egg-shaped head, at the end of a straight shank, *c.* $10\frac{1}{2}$ in. (26.7 cm) overall. The head has a concave groove on its periphery, and is listed with three different widths of this groove.

It is used for polishing edges, particularly the edges of saddle flaps. Edward Lawrence writes:

'After saddle flaps and skirts have been edged with the appropriate Edge Shave, the tool marks are blended into a neatly rounded edge using a piece of broken glass (old method – surely our cheapest tool!) or glasspaper, then stained and polished with a coarse linen cloth. The Edge Iron is then heated in a gas jet, pressed into a lump of beeswax sufficient to melt a quantity, which, adhering to the groove in the iron, is then carefully applied to the edge of the leather, the iron being run smoothly around until the melted wax has penetrated sufficiently. A very tricky operation: the iron must be the right heat, just sufficient wax used, and great care in handling lest the iron should leave the edge and skate over either surface leaving an indelible blemish. My Edge Iron has two grooves, one, the wider, for general use and a finer one used for race saddles which have thinner leather.'

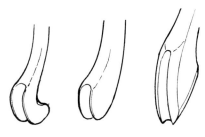

Fig. 9:38

(d) Skirt Shave (USA: French Edge Tool; Chamfering Tool) *Figs 9:39; 9:5, Nos 3103/4 (p. 227)*
This is a larger version of the *Edge Shave* described above, with a blade listed in several sizes up to $\frac{1}{2}$ in. (1.2 cm), and thereafter there is one of $\frac{5}{8}$ in. (1.6 cm) and one of $\frac{3}{4}$ in. (1.9 cm).

A variant, known as a Screw Skirt Shave, has a thicker fence on the right-hand side of the blade to take a small thumb-screw which impinges on a piece of spring steel riveted to the back of the tool; this tilts the blade up or down off the bench, thus regulating the angle of bevel to be cut.

This tool is used as an alternative to the Round Knife (see under *Knife*) for thinning down the upper edge of a saddle skirt ready for sewing in; it can also be used for paring down the edges of other parts.

Edward Lawrence writes as follows concerning its use:

'The skirt shave is used for the gradual edge-taper worked on the top (flesh) edge of a saddle skirt to achieve a similar thickness at this point to the adjacent pigskin. (Very difficult to use, I find, unless kept carefully ground and honed.) The work is usually finished off with a very sharp Head Knife, giving thus the desired "concave bevel" effect, perhaps the most difficult and crucial part of the work when making a saddle. Any over enthusiasm or, equally faint-heartedness, being at once obvious in the finished job.'

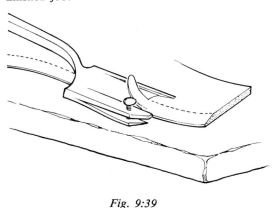

Fig. 9:39

(*e*)　*American Edge Tools*

(1)　*Edge Tool*

At least twelve different kinds of Edge Shave are illustrated in the catalogue of C. S. Osborne & Co. (USA, *c.* 1883). Most of them are named 'Edge Tool' but some have the prefix 'English' or 'French'. The 'French Edge Tool' appears to be the same as the English *Skirt Shave* (see above).

(2)　*The Bissonette Fig. 9:40* (The name may come from the French *biseau*, a bevel.)

C. S. Osborne gives this name to a tool that appears to be the same as one called a Cornering Tool by woodworkers. The blade is bent at the end, and contains a hole which is countersunk on the convex side. When this side of the blade is pushed or pulled along the edge of the leather, the sharp edge of the hole cuts a thin shaving from the leather.

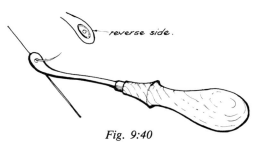

Fig. 9:40

Flap Block　*Fig. 9:41*

A square, wooden former, measuring *c.* 20 × 12 in. (50.8 × 30.5 cm) made up of wooden strips fixed to a curved base to produce a surface shaped in a gentle ogee.

Two of these blocks were found in 1954 in the workshop of Mr A. H. Marshall, a saddler at Kirton near Boston in Lincolnshire. It was stated that they were used for moulding and working saddle flaps.

Edward Lawrence writes that such blocks were used when flaps were covered with pigskin; this was pasted on to the solid backing and left overnight to dry tacked to the block. When dry, it was taken off the block, and the pigskin trimmed flush with the backing, and then stitched round.

Note: COSIRA (1973) illustrates a plastic block of similar shape to a knee-roll insert. It is used for blocking the front edge of the flaps to take the stuffing for the knee roll.

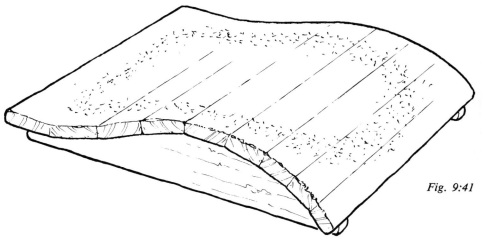

　　　　　　　　　　　　　　　　　　　　　　Fig. 9:41

Furniture

Furniture and equipment which may be found in the workshops are described under the following entries: *Bench*; *Collar Vice*; *Machines*; Punch Bench under *Punch*; *Saddle Fitting Block*; *Saddle Stand*; *Stitching Horse*; *Stool*; *Winker Press*.

Gauge: see *Cutting Gauge*; *Plough Gauge*.

Gouge, Buckle Tongue

A version of the ordinary wood-carver's spoon Bit Gouge was used by saddlers for recessing the holes in straps as a lead-in for heavier buckle tongues, as, for example, on stirrup leathers. (See also *Punch*.)

Gouge, Collar Maker's (USA: Round Edge Trimming Tool)

Illustrated by Joseph Dixon (*c.* 1948), this tool appears to be similar to a woodworker's gouge of *c.* $\frac{1}{2}$ in. (1.2 cm) width. Its purpose is not known to us.

Grooving Tools: see *Channeller*; *Crease*; *Martingale Groover*; *Race Tools*.

Guider (Fixed Compass) *Figs 9:8, No. 102; 9:15, No. 439 (pp. 230, 237)*

A hand tool with a two-pronged head, set in a wooden handle, *c.* $6\frac{1}{2}$ in. (16.5 cm) overall. The prongs have fine sharpened points. The tool was made in sets with the distance between the points rising by steps of $\frac{1}{8}$ (0.4 cm), from $\frac{1}{4}$ (0.7 cm) to $1\frac{1}{2}$ in. (3.8 cm).

The Guider is used for marking leather as a guide for the subsequent application of decorative lines by a Crease tool. (See, for instance, the Bevel Crease under the entry *Crease*.) These designs are frequently made on the back of strap loops; and for this purpose, the Guider is drawn across the loop from left to right, and again lower down if the length of loop requires it. Diagonal lines are then made with a Crease across the rectangular spaces marked off by the Guider.

Though illustrated in the catalogues of the tool merchants, the only examples known to us were those used by Mr David Barnes, a saddler working at Messrs Grant Barnes and Son in Malmesbury, Wiltshire (1981).

Hammer *Fig. 9:6 (p. 228)*

Hammers used by saddle and harness makers include the following:

(*a*) *Saddler's Hammer* *Fig. 9:6, No. 53a*

A light hammer with a long strapped head and a solid cross-pane; a claw is occasionally provided at the side of the pane, as on the Coach Trimmer's Hammer (below). The pane is tapered to a narrow edge and can thus be used for driving tacks into parts of the saddle tree that might otherwise be inaccessible.

Its use is described by Edward Lawrence as follows:

'... used for hammering tacks into saddle trees ... cross pane to start the tack, the face to hammer it home – allowing all day use without undue fatigue. This hammer, although intended purely as a "tack hammer", is also used for fixing plated nails, staples and heavy clout nails used in side saddle work. I have always been amazed at the amount of hard usage this tool stands up to, handles breaking occasionally but rarely the delicate head. A light Warrington hammer would have been more suitable on many jobs, but I never saw any other than the saddler's hammer used. Heavier ball-pane and riveting hammers are used for making and repairing saddle trees.'

The hammer illustrated in Diderot (*Bourrelier c.* 1760) is almost identical except that the head is eyed and not strapped, and, like the so-called French Coach Trimmer's Hammer, any sharp edges are well rounded.

(*b*) *Riveting Hammer* *Fig. 9:6, No. 55 (p. 228)*

Saddlers and saddle-tree makers use any suitable hammer of medium size for riveting provided it has a ball or cross-pane suitable for spreading the end of small rivets. That illustrated is of the 'London' or 'Exeter' pattern.

(*c*) *Harness Hammer* (Shoe Hammer; USA: Saddler's Snob Hammer)

This is an ordinary Shoemaker's Hammer, which is described and illustrated in the BOOT AND SHOE MAKER section. It has a mushroom-shaped face, and a flat down-turned cross-pane.

According to Edward Lawrence, when working at Messrs Champion & Wilton in London:

'... the harness department used a round faced (very carefully polished and cared for) shoemaker's hammer for hammering wet (or sometimes dry) leather to a shape, such as loops of all kinds; the convex face prevented damage to the leather surface, which would be cut by a normal flat-faced hammer. We also used this hammer to "level off" the reverse of a row of stitching on a trace; this was a "lazy" alternative to the more laborious rubbing of the work using a deer bone, or similar hard smooth object. When anyone was discovered hammering their stitching, one of the in-jokes was the loud good-humoured chorus of "Rub it down! rub it down!" which immediately followed.'

(*d*) *Coach Trimmer's Hammer*   *Fig. 9:6, No. 53b (p. 228)*

A long head with an octagonal or round face, a long tapering cross-pane (like the *Saddler's Hammer*) and a claw on one side of the pane. The head is normally eyed and not strapped.

There are two possible reasons why this hammer is sometimes found in saddlers' shops. One is that it could be exchanged with the saddler's hammer without inconvenience (some saddlers may have preferred it for the sake of the nail claw); and the other is that the two trades sometimes overlapped, for example when the saddler was called upon to make the suspension straps for the undercarriage, and the lighter straps inside the carriage itself.

Jemmie: see Collar Jemmie under *Stuffing Iron*.

Knife, Saddler's and Harness Maker's

These knives are used for cutting leather to shape, and, on occasions, for thinning down edges — an operation known in the shoemaking trade as skiving.

The most characteristic knife of the trade is the ancestral *Round Knife*, which is described below. The following variants are those most likely to be found in English saddlery and harness workshops:

(*a*) *Round Knife*   *Figs 9:5, No. 3095; 9:11, No. 301A (pp. 227, 233)*
Note: Similar knives, but sometimes with different names, will be found in the following sections: BOOT AND SHOE MAKER section: see *Knife, Half Moon*. LEATHER MANUFACTURE section II: see under *Knife, Moon* (a circular knife). GLOVE MAKER section: see *Knife, Doling*. MISCELLANEOUS TRADES section: see *Parchment and Vellum Maker*.

The saddler's Round Knife has a steel blade of roughly semi-circular shape, about 3 in. (7.6 cm) in diameter, with a handle protruding vertically from the top of the blade. After repeated sharpenings the blade tends to become slightly oval; and in some workshops the knife is ground to an almost triangular shape, which some workers prefer for long cuts.

The blade is often covered by a home-made leather sheath; indeed, a San Joaquin County Museum pamphlet (USA, 1976) illustrates a steel die for cutting out the sides of such sheaths.

A Round Knife of modern shape is depicted by the Egyptians in *c.* 500 BC being used by shoemakers. That illustrated by Diderot under *Bourrelier* (*c.* 1760)

has its tang bent round to bring the wooden handle parallel to the flat top of the blade.

The saddler's Round Knife is used for the general cutting of leather and especially for cutting strips that are too wide to be cut by the *Plough Gauge*; it can also be used for cutting irregular shapes, and, when held horizontally, for paring down edges. Some saddlers pare down the top edge of the saddle skirt with a Round Knife, rather than use the Skirt Shave (see *Edge Trimming Tools*). In operation the knife is pushed forward, but for short cuts it can be placed firmly on the cutting board and rolled (or rocked) forward over the leather to be cut.

The extraordinary adaptability and convenient shape of this knife explains its survival in face of competition with knives of more conventional shape.

(*b*) *Head Knife* (Heading Knife) *Figs 9:5, No. 3092/3; 9:11, No. 1144 (pp. 227, 233)*
A small knife made today in two forms:

(1) Single: with a quarter circle, hooked, blade.
(2) Double: with a semi-circular blade like a *Round Knife*, but only half the size.

Both knives are sometimes found with the curved edges straightened by grinding.

These knives are used like the *Round Knife*, but generally for lighter and shorter cuts, and also for such work as cutting holes for buckle tongues. Knight (1877) writes that it used 'to cut out holes in leather, too large for the application of punches, and smaller than are conveniently made by the *Round Knife* which is the ordinary cutting tool of the saddler'.

Mr Neil McGregor, an authority on leatherworking (1978), has pointed out that in Richard Timmins' catalogue (*c.* 1800, No. 1144, illustrated here) there is a Head Knife of unusual design. It has the usual rounded, hooked-shaped blade, but the inside edge of the blade is sharpened as well as the outside. It was thought at first that the sharpening on the inside edge was a mistake made by the engraver, but an actual example (with the same reeded handle) found on a London market stall proves that the engraving is correct.
Note: A Head Knife is illustrated by Krempp (1905) but not by Diderot.

(*c*) *Bridle Knife* *Fig. 9:5, No. 3094 (p. 227)*
This handsome-looking knife has the rather surprising profile of a medieval 'bearded' axe.

A saddler described it as a 'beautiful knife, and all that was needed for cutting a strap, trimming the end, and skiving the other end for the buckle — without reaching for any other tool'.

(d) Cap Knife
A name given by C. S. Osborne (USA, *c.* 1883) to an ordinary hand knife with a straight cutting edge and a pointed end. It is an all-purpose knife used for cutting and trimming threads, and for the fine cutting of harness parts.

(e) Collar Knife Fig. 9:5, No. 3091 (p. 227)
A heavy hand knife with the so-called 'broad' or 'square' point, and a straight edge.

A general purpose knife, but especially suitable for cutting the straw used for stuffing collars.

(f) French Pattern Knife Fig. 9:13, No. 394 (p. 235)
A name given by J. Dixon (1918) to a saddler's knife similar to the hollow-backed 'horned' knife illustrated by Krempp (*c.* 1905). It may be supposed that it was intended as an alternative to the conventional saddler's knives described in *(a)–(c)* above. (See also *Fig. 9:12* for other French Knives.)

(g) Paring Knife
Some saddlers use a shoemaker's Paring Knife (including the all-steel 'continental' type) instead of the saddler's knives described in *(a)–(c)* above.

(h) Press Knives
As in the boot and shoe trade, Press Knives, sometimes called Cutting Dies, were developed for the repeat-cutting of certain small parts of the harness. They consist of a steel strip forged to the shape of the piece of leather to be cut out, and sharpened on the lower edge. They are forced down on the leather in a hand or power press. (See also *Punch*.)

Leaping Head Wrench *Fig. 9:42*
A home-made iron wrench *c.* 18 in. (45.7 cm) long and $\frac{3}{8}$ in. (1 cm) thick, forged into a U-shape at one end.

The leaping head projects on the near side of a side-saddle. The rider's left knee is placed under the leaping head. Thus, with the left foot in the stirrup, and the knee braced against the leaping head, the rider can hold herself firmly in the saddle. The Leaping Head Wrench is used for screwing or unscrewing the head into the saddle tree.

Loop Stick *Fig. 9:43*
A loop (or 'keep') is the piece of leather placed crosswise on straps near a buckle to receive the point of the strap and hold it in position. The Loop Stick is a former on which the loop is moulded and hammered into shape.

Pieces of hardwood of rectangular cross-section, about 7–10 in. (17.7–25.4 cm) long and made in

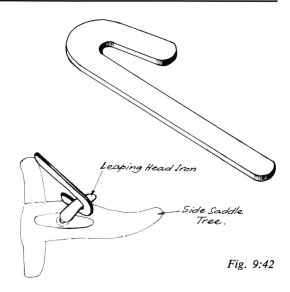

Leaping Head Iron

Side Saddle Tree.

Fig. 9:42

several sizes from $\frac{3}{8}$ in. (1 cm) to 2 in. (5 cm) in width. The smaller sizes, used for bridle loops and the like, are usually made of boxwood; the larger sizes, needed for heavier harness work, are often made in beech.

The sticks are tapered; the thinner end for fixed loops, to allow the passage of one thickness of strap; the thick end for slide loops, to take two thicknesses of strap. Some saddlers make their own Loop Sticks in lignum vitae, for this hardwood will stand a lot of hammering and compression, and it is not affected by wetting. For the same reason Iron Loop Sticks are made by the tool makers for heavy loops on which severe pressure must be applied when moulding.

There are two shapes of Loop Stick:

(a) Straight, for general work.
(b) Bent, for loops made for curved straps, such as tugs.

The ornamentation of loops is traditionally done with *Crease* tools, but under factory conditions by means of a die and press.

257

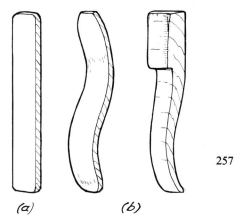

(a)   *(b)*

Fig. 9:43

Machines used by harness makers and saddlers
Hand-operated machines began to appear in the
workshops during the later years of the nineteenth
century.

The machine most commonly found is used for
thinning down strips of leather (see *Splitting
Machine*).

Other machines to be found occasionally in the
shops are described under *Creasing Machine* and
Bevelling Machine.

Mallet, Collar Maker's   *Fig. 9:9, Nos 302, 304
(p. 231)*
A heavy, rounded head about $5\frac{1}{2}$ in. (13.9 cm) in
diameter, but flattened on two sides like a Dutch
cheese. The head is usually made of lignum vitae, to
give weight and durability – indeed some were made
of iron. The head is mounted on a short ash handle
about 6 in. (15.2 cm) long.

This mallet is used for shaping the wale and body
of straw-stuffed horse collars; including the making
of a small hollow in the wale at the lower end of the
collar, to avoid any pressure on the horse's windpipe. This operation is done with the help of a 'shaping block' and, in some shops, a *Collar Vice*.

In use, the short handle is grasped close to the
head; when held in this position the butt of the
handle itself is sometimes used for beating down the
straw between the lacing.

A saddler described the above operation to us as
'heavy and mysterious work difficult to describe
without demonstration'. Anyone who has seen a
heavy-horse collar taken apart for repair will recognise the truth of these words. Few have described the
work, but a notable exception is the chapter on the
saddler in Dorothy Hartley's *Made in England*
(1939).

Mallet, Saddler's
Mallets of several kinds are used by saddlers, including the ordinary beechwood carpenter's mallet with
its flat-sided head. It is often found with a depression
on the face resulting from driving punches. Those
designed especially for saddles include:

(*a*)   *Punching Mallet Fig. 9:9, No. 300 (p. 231)*
This has a heavy, cylindrical, barrel-shaped head and
is made of lignum vitae, box or sometimes ash. It is
used for driving metal punches. C. S. Osborne
(USA, *c.* 1883) illustrates mallets of this sort: one
with an iron head and wooden faces, and one like a
mason's round mallet but with circular rawhide
inserts.

(*b*)   *Pricking Mallet*
A lighter version of (*a*) above, used for driving
Pricking Irons (see *Prickers*).

Mane Drag   *Fig. 9:44*
A forked implement with the tines turned back for
use on the pull stroke – hence the term 'drag'.

It is used by horsekeepers for trimming a horse's
mane. It is often kept in saddlers' shops for sale to
the stables; but sometimes it is used by the saddler
himself for combing out (carding) the flock for use
as stuffing in saddles (see *Carding Tools*).

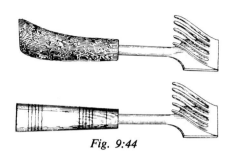

Fig. 9:44

Marlin Spike (Splicer)
A name given to a short, pointed deer horn, which,
like the rigger's Marlin Spike, is used for opening the
strands of a rope when splicing: for example, the
rope plough lines that serve the ploughman for reins,
and rope halters. A Suffolk saddler told us that he
used to pick up these deer horns in the woods.

Martingale Groover   *Fig. 9:45*
(See also *Channeller* and *Race Tools*.)
The name of this tool is a strange one, for there
seems to be no connection between the tool and that
part of the harness known as a martingale – the strap
that runs from the girth, between the forelegs, and
then upwards to the bridle or reins (see introduction
to this section). A possible connection is that some
martingale straps are round, and a Martingale
Groover is often used to cut a channel in round
straps in which to hide the stitches. The tool cuts a
knife slit rather than a groove.

The tool is *c.* 7 in. (17.7 cm) long overall with a
working head containing a small cutter and an
adjustable fence which regulates the distance of the
cutter from the edge of the leather. An ordinary
knife may be used for the same purpose, but this
requires considerable skill in controlling the depth of
cut and straightness of line. The cut is made on the
grain side and then eased open. After stitching, the
original cut is boned back into place.

The object of sinking the stitches is to prevent them from becoming worn by the carriage shafts or by the horse itself; or to improve the appearance of the stitching which looks neater when sunk in a shallow channel; or to hide the stitching altogether, as when making round reins (see above).

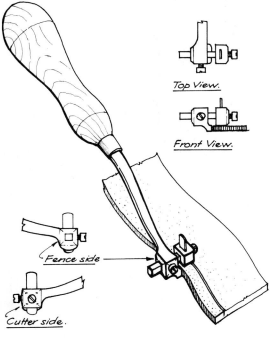

Top View.

Front View.

Fence side

Cutter side.

Fig. 9:45

Measuring Tools: see *Collar Measuring Tools; Compass and Caliper, Saddlers; Rule, Saddler's.*

Nail Claw (Claw Tool) *Fig. 9:8, No. 61 (p. 230)*
These tools are similar to the ordinary woodworker's Tack Lifter but are often more heavily made. This applies particularly to some which are like the heavy *Pig's Foot* – a type of Nail Claw used by shoemakers and cloggers. Some are made in steel throughout.

C. S. Osborne (USA, 1883) illustrates one of the heavier 'Pig's Foot' type but calls it a 'Boss Claw Tool'; and one called a 'French Claw Tool' has an anvil on the heel of the claw to act as a fulcrum.

Nail Claws are used for lifting tacks, e.g. those used for fixing leather and webbing to the wooden saddle tree.

Needles *Fig. 9:10 (p. 232)*
(See also *Awls; Stitching Tools; Palm.*)
Needles used in the harness and saddle trades are

outstanding examples of fine design and workmanship in steel. Those in general use in the trade include the following: (All are round in cross-section unless stated otherwise.)

(*a*) *Harness Needle* (Saddler's Needle)
There are two types:

(1) Blunt: A needle with a blunt point, made in eleven sizes from *c.* $1\frac{1}{2}$–$2\frac{3}{8}$ in. (3.8–6 cm) long. They are used when holes have been previously made with an *Awl.* In most cases the needles are used in pairs, one at each end of the thread for the 'saddle stitch' (see *Stitching Tools*).
(2) Pointed: An ordinary pointed needle made in eleven sizes *c.* 1–$1\frac{7}{8}$ in. (2.5–4.8 cm) long. These are used singly with a thimble on lighter work, such as the linings to saddle panels.

(*b*) *Quilting Needle* (Not illustrated)
A heavy version of the pointed Harness Needle, made in four sizes *c.* 2–$3\frac{1}{2}$ in. (5–8.8 cm) long. Used for quilting saddle panels, sewing girth straps etc.

(*c*) *Half-Round Needle* (Not illustrated)
Like the Quilting Needle, but bent into a half circle. The length along the curve varies in twelve sizes from $1\frac{1}{2}$–8 in. (3.8–20.3 cm). They are used for sewing linen or leather panel linings and other 'concealed' work.

(*d*) *Collar Needle*
These are heavy needles, with the point end diamond-shaped in cross-section, and made in eight sizes 3–8 in. (7.6–20.3 cm) long. Some of the large sizes have eyes large enough for sewing with leather thongs. There are two types:

(1) 'Straight' – with the pointed end slightly bent.
(2) 'Half Moon' – bent in a shallow curve from eye to point. It is used for stitching the edge of the body to the wale, across the straw.

(*e*) *Panel Needle*
A name given to a 'bent' needle similar to the so-called 'straight' Collar Needle, and used for sewing in the panel of a saddle.

Needle Case (Needle Box)
The following types are found in the workshops:
(*a*) *Tubular Boxes* *Figs 9:10, 9:15, No. 464 (pp. 232, 237)*
These are *c.* 7 in. (17.7 cm) long and $\frac{3}{4}$–$1\frac{1}{8}$ in. (1.9–2.84 cm) in diameter, made in wood or sheet metal.

(*b*) *Leather Pouches* *Fig. 9:46*
Usually home-made, and 8–10 in. (20.3–25.4 cm)

259

long, these needle pouches can take the large curved Collar Needles, as well as ordinary needles. They were part of the tool-kit of saddlers who travelled to farms and stables to do repair work; or, as one saddler put it, 'to take on journeys where some work had to be done to fit a difficult saddle'.

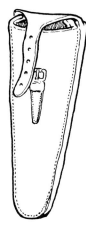

Fig. 9:46

Overstitch Wheel (False Stitch Wheel) See *Fig. 9:5, No. 3081 (p. 227)* for general appearance only.
A name given to a tool similar to a Pricker Wheel (see under *Prickers*), except that the space between teeth (the 'gullet') is a smooth, concave hollow like that to be seen on a chain-sprocket. Spare wheels with different numbers of teeth are provided for fitting into the frame at the head of the tool.

This tool was probably intended to serve two purposes:

(1) to 'set' the stitches; i.e. after choosing a wheel to match the number of stitches per inch, it was run over them to iron out minor irregularities. (Experienced saddlers declare that this is unnecessary if the sewing is done properly in the first place.)

(2) to simulate the stitching: this use is suggested by its alternative name, 'False Stitch Wheel'.

Palm
A tool used by saddlers and harness makers to force a needle through leather. For lighter sewing a *Thimble* is used. Palms are not illustrated by Diderot (1760), but they appear in English tool catalogues soon after that date, and were probably in use many years before.

There are two main types:

(*a*) *Collar Palm* (Hand Iron; Palm Iron) *Figs 9:6, Nos 97, 97b; 9:11, No. 389 (pp. 228, 233)*
This is used for collar making and for making cart saddles and heavy harness.

A pear-shaped implement, about 4 in. (10.1 cm) long, hollowed out on one side and with a round neck at the narrow end. The neck or 'stem' is made either straight or cranked, the latter being preferred by many for being less liable to slip through the hand. The hollow 'well' is given an indented honeycomb pattern designed to receive and hold the heel of the needle.

The neck has a single indentation at the end, intended to take the heel of the needle when all but the eye of the needle is left to push through. It can also be used for pulling a thread tight.

Some palms have a diamond-shaped hole bored transversely in the neck. This is used if the collar or harness needle gets stuck: the hole in the neck is fitted over the diamond-shaped end of the needle, so that the needle can then be turned from side to side and so loosened.

(*b*) *Sail Maker's Palm* *Fig. 9:10 (p. 232)*
Some saddlers prefer using a leather hand-palm of the kind used by sail makers and riggers. It consists of a ring of leather, worn round the hand, in which a dented metal plate of honeycomb design is mounted to take the heel of the needle when pushing it through the leather.

(*c*) *Plier-Palm* *Fig. 9:47*
This strange combination tool, made by J. Dixon of Walsall, is rarely seen in the workshops. It consists of a flat-nosed plier, with one of the handles made in the form of a Saddler's Palm. The hollow side of the handle could be used like the palm for pushing the needle; the jaws of the plier for pulling a light needle through.

Fig. 9:47

Patent-Leather Countersink
A name given by C. S. Osborne (USA, *c.* 1883) to a tool resembling a *Crease*. It is used for cutting a

narrow groove on the face of patent leather to hold the stitching.

Pincers and Pliers (For alternative names, see below.)
Note: For different shapes of pliers' jaws used in leather trades, see *Pincers* in the BOOT AND SHOE MAKER section.

Pincers used in the saddle and harness trades include the following:

(*a*) *Saddler's Pincers* (Bulldog Pliers) *Fig. 9:48*
Similar to a shoemaker's Lasting Pincer except that it has a short, blunt, 'bulldog' nose instead of a bent one. It was made in three sizes from *c.* $5\frac{1}{2}$–$6\frac{1}{2}$ in. (13.9–16.5 cm) in length. Like the shoemaker's version, the lower jaw carried a so-called 'anvil' which acts as a fulcrum when the pincers are used for straining leather over a saddle tree, for which purpose the surface of the jaws are heavily serrated. Inevitably the pincers are used on occasion for hammering in and drawing out tacks, when the anvil jaw acts most conveniently both as hammer and fulcrum.

Many of these pincers are made with the upper handle bent in a graceful curve, which incidentally transforms this simple tool into one of the best-looking in the saddler's kit.

The example illustrated by Diderot (*c.* 1760) has an anvil on both jaws.

Edward Lawrence writes as follows about the use of the tool. He calls it by its alternative name 'Bulldog'.

'The anvil, on the saddler's bulldogs, is used to slip over the edges of a saddle tree, giving a tremendous purchase (sufficient to split the seat or break the tree if not carefully applied). My first instructor said they are called bulldogs "because they grip and never let go". It is used in this way not only for blocking the wet pigskin seat, but also for straining on the webs, canvas, and seat cotton, sufficient to eliminate subsequent slackening in the future use of the saddle. The bulldog is rather a clumsy tool and some harness makers prefer to use the crocodiles [Blucher Pliers] for the lighter work of gig-saddle seating, etc.

'Our saddle makers used the bulldogs for blocking a seat, as follows: the saddle on the bench is gripped in left hand; a small section of the seat is gripped and strained into place by bulldogs in the right hand; the left thumb (the famous "saddler's thumb"!) is firmly pressed thereon, and the right hand (still holding the bulldogs) is simultaneously picking up and pressing a tack into position, with right thumb; the tack is then hammered in with the bulldog's anvil; thus following one of the basic trade principles, that of "only picking up each tool *once* for each job".'

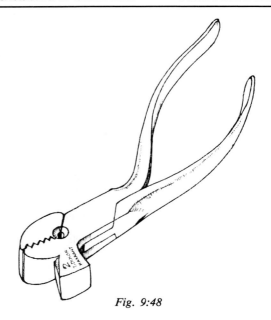

Fig. 9:48

(*b*) *Blucher Pliers* (Crocodile) *Fig. 9:7, No. 49 (p. 229)*
The jaws of these pliers are straight and serrated. They are used for gripping leather when straining it over a saddle tree in places where there is no room, or no necessity for an anvil to act as a fulcrum. They are about 5–6 in. (12.7–15.2 cm) long.

Nomenclature
There is some confusion in the alternative names given to both the Saddler's Pincers and Blucher Pliers: for the terms 'Bulldog' and 'Crocodile' are often interchanged. Why this particular saddler's plier, which is always listed by the makers as a saddler's tool, is given the name belonging to Field Marshal Prince Leberecht von Blücher (1742–1819) is a mystery. A note on this question will be found under *Blucher Boot* in the BOOT AND SHOE MAKER section; and there is some evidence, partly from America, that Blucher Pliers were also used by makers of heavy boots, including the army boot known as the Blucher.

The term 'Blucher Pliers' appears in catalogues issued by the following makers: Richard Timmins (*c.* 1800); R. E. Thacker, 'Four-in-Hand' catalogue (1905); Hampson & Scott, 'Equine Album' catalogue (*c.* 1900); and Joseph Dixon's Price List (*c.* 1918). The term has not been found in American tool-maker's catalogues.

Many saddlers consulted during the period 1965–80 had never heard of the term. Exceptions were Mr Edward Lawrence (1976) who called it a 'Blucher Crocodile' and related that Blucher Pliers were 'favoured in our shop by three Polish harness makers, who always called them "crocodiles" to distinguish them from the saddle-maker's version known as "Bulldogs"'; and Mr J. E. Rivers (1975) who remembered that when he was an apprentice, the older men would say, 'Pass me the Bluchers mate.'

(c)   Saddler's Pliers   Fig. 9:5, No. 3073 (p. 227)
A flat-nosed plier, *c.* 5½in. (13.9 cm) long, listed as a 'Saddler's Plier' by almost all makers of saddler's tools, although it appears to be no different from flat-nosed pliers used in many other trades except that the surface of the jaws are sometimes more heavily serrated.

They are used for such jobs as easing a piece of leather under the roller in a *Plough Gauge* (to avoid cutting the fingers); or for pulling through a 'lazy' needle (but see *Palm*).

(d)   Pad Screw Pliers   Fig. 9:7, No. 103 (p. 229)
A plier with both its jaws tapering to a point and curved towards each other like cow horns. The jaws can be fitted into two small holes on the head of the pad screw, and by this means the screws are turned.

The Pad is a light 'saddle' used on pair-horses, for supporting rein terrets and traces. Pad screws fasten the panel to the underside of the pad, and, at the same time, secure the girth to the upper surface of the pad.

(e)   Cutting·Pincers (Nipper)   *Fig. 9:7, No. 65 (p. 229)*
This is the name given by makers of saddler's tools to an ordinary 'carpenter's Pincer' used in the woodworking and other trades, and often described by the tool makers as a 'Tower-Pincer'. It has rounded jaws which meet with a blunt bevel for cutting, and rounded shoulders.

Used by saddlers for general purposes; and, like the boot and shoe makers, for pulling out any tacks that a Nail Claw is unable to cope with.

(f)   Punch Pliers   Fig. 9:7, No. 46 (p. 229)
These are pliers designed to punch holes. They are the same or similar to those described in the BOOT AND SHOE MAKER section under *Button Tools, Eyelet Tools, Punches.*

(g)   Cantle Pliers   Fig. 9:49
Illustrated in the catalogue of Henry G. Gomph (USA, *c.* 1875), a special feature of these pliers is the slight concavity at the nose.

The cantle is the upward curving rear part of a riding or harness saddle, but its connection with

these pliers, if there is any, is not certain. An experienced saddler has suggested that, since cantles are curved in more than one plane, these pliers might reduce possible damage to the wooden tree when straining the seats; and, since 'Western' saddle seats are made in two pieces stitched together round the top edge of the cantle, these pliers might be helpful at the blocking stage.

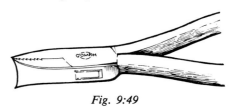

Fig. 9:49

(h)   Other USA types
C. S. Osborne (USA, 1883) offers the saddler four different sizes of 'Cutting Nippers' and nine other pliers with different shapes of jaw, including round, flat and duck-bill.

(i)   Plier Palm: see under *Palm.*

Pinking Tools: see under *Punch.*

Plane, Leather-Worker's   *Fig. 9:13, No. 389 (p. 235)*
A miniature Thumb Plane of the kind used by violin makers, illustrated by G. Krempp (Paris, *c.* 1905). It appears to have a flat sole, and is made in metal with a wooden core. It is engraved with the name G. LUTZ to whom Krempp were the successors. The caption suggests that it was used for jointing, and adds (but does not illustrate) a variant described as 'système américain'.

Plough Gauge (Plough Cutting Gauge. For American nomenclature see variants below.) *Figs 9:50; 9:51*
Used for cutting strips of leather for reins and straps, this tool is a development of the *Cutting Gauge.* It is made of metal, and is provided with a more elaborate means of adjustment for cutting different widths of leather. Judging by the tool-maker's catalogues, this tool appears to have been developed in the second half of the nineteenth century.

The term 'plough' is apt, for, like its namesake, the agricultural implement, it cuts when moving forward, and its knife is supported on a foot as the ploughshare is supported on a sole or 'land-slide'. The term 'gauge' is inherited from its immediate ancestor, the Cutting Gauge, which, like the carpenter's Mortice Gauge, is used for marking or cutting parallel to an edge.

The Plough Gauge consists of a foot which is tapered in front to travel under the hide being cut; a handled knife is mounted on the foot and sharpened on its forward end to cut when pushed (it is removable for sharpening by means of a set-screw). A graduated stem extends horizontally from the left side of the foot; a fence assembly is carried on this stem, which can be set at the desired distance from the knife to alter the width of the strip to be cut. A spring-loaded roller is mounted on one end of the fence, and is raised or lowered by a thumb-screw; this roller holds the hide down on the foot, just in front of the knife.

In use, the fence is set on the stem for the width of strip required; the hide is laid on the bench with one side cut straight, ready to bear on the fence; the roller is lowered on top of the hide to hold it down on the foot; a nick is cut in the edge of the hide where the plough knife is to enter; the near edge of the hide is grasped with pliers and drawn under the roller against the knife edge; then, with the left hand holding the hide, the Plough Gauge is pushed forward.

Fig. 9:51 A Plough Gauge in use

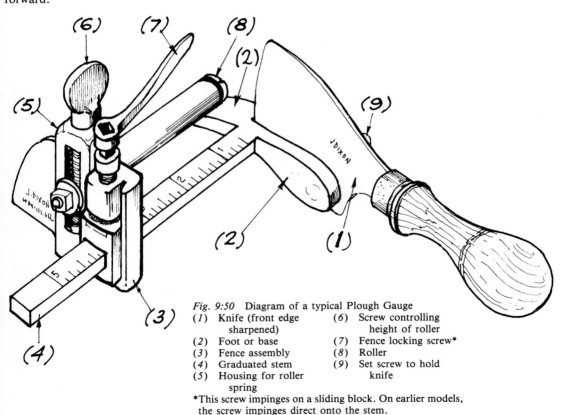

Fig. 9:50 Diagram of a typical Plough Gauge

(*1*) Knife (front edge sharpened)
(*2*) Foot or base
(*3*) Fence assembly
(*4*) Graduated stem
(*5*) Housing for roller spring
(*6*) Screw controlling height of roller
(*7*) Fence locking screw*
(*8*) Roller
(*9*) Set screw to hold knife

*This screw impinges on a sliding block. On earlier models, the screw impinges direct onto the stem.

Variants

There are many variations in the method of setting the fence on the stem, of unlocking the knife from the foot, and in the vertical adjustment of the roller. Below are listed only the more important variations in design:

(*a*) *American Draw Gage* (Draw Knife; Gage Knife; Slitting Gage. J. Dixon, 1918, calls this tool an 'American Draw Pistol') *Fig. 9:52*

This is a metal version of the *Cutting Gauge* rather than a variation of the *Plough Gauge*. Illustrated in Knight's Dictionary (USA, 1877), it is called a Slitting-Gage. The forward end of the grip acts as a fence, and is made to bear on the edge of the bench. A graduated stem penetrates the grip and is held in the desired position by means of a thumb-screw set in the head of the grip. In many cases, a locking-block is inserted between the set-screw and the edge of the stem. The cutting blade is housed in a slot on the left-hand end of the stem, secured by a thumb-screw.

In use the tool is pulled, and since the blade is mounted on the end of the stem, at some distance from the axis of the handle, the whole tool has a tendency to turn, and needs side pressure on the grip to hold it straight when drawing the knife through a heavy piece of leather.

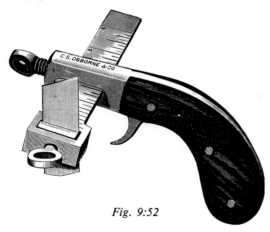

Fig. 9:52

(*b*) *'Long Screw' Plough Gauge Fig. 9:5, No. 3086 (p. 227)*

A name given to a Plough Gauge in which the position of the fence is controlled by a long square-threaded screw, turned by a thumb-screw at the end of the stem. It lies along the edge of the stem like the lead-screw on a lathe. The fence locking-screw is eliminated when the plough is fitted with this device.

(*c*) *Device for cutting close up to the knife Fig. 9:12, No. 367 (p. 234)*

Owing to the thickness of the foot, the knife is normally prevented from being set close enough to the fence to cut a very thin strip of leather such as a thong. To overcome this, a variant has a block about $\frac{1}{4}$ in. (0.7 cm) thick mounted on the side of the fence which brings the knife closer to the edge of the leather. The left-hand edge of the foot runs underneath the block.

Press

Special presses came on the market during the last century and after, for moulding certain parts of the harness. Some are screw presses, for instance see *Winker Press*. Another type of press is illustrated in Knight's Dictionary (USA, 1877), and is called a 'Pad-Crimp Press'. The piece of leather to be moulded is first dampened and then put between the two halves of a hand press. Made rather like a Victorian lemon squeezer, two bat-like pieces of wood are hinged at the blade end, and can be pressed forcibly together by their handles. The inside faces of the press are hollowed out to mould the leather to the desired shape, and are kept locked together over the damp leather until it is dry enough to keep shape.

Prickers (Stitch Marker; Tracing Wheel). See also *Stitching Tools*.

Note: For tools serving the same purpose but used by shoemakers, see *Pricker Tools* in that section.

These tools include the toothed punches or wheels used for marking and partly penetrating leather before sewing. They ease the path of the needle, and help to ensure a uniform distance between stitches. The teeth are mostly ground to a chisel point but, as will be seen below, some have round or triangular points.

Variants include:

(*a*) *Pricker Punch* (Pricking Iron) *Figs. 9:53; 9:11, No. 390 (p. 233)*

Steel punches, *c.* $4\frac{1}{2}$–5 in. (11.4–12.7 cm) long, with a flat (or occasionally curved) body, toothed at the foot. Each tooth is ground to a chisel-shaped edge and is set at an angle of *c.* 45° to the horizontal; the number of teeth varies from three to twenty-four, and they are spaced to mark from four to ten stitches per inch. Punches with as few as three teeth can be used to mark stitches round a curve, or at corners, though many saddlers would use an awl for this purpose. The teeth mark a stitch which slants downwards from left to right; but sometimes the teeth are slanted the other way, i.e. from right to left.

This may have been intended for the left-handed; or more probably for decorative purposes.

Care is needed when using these punches, for if driven too deeply, the leather between the stitches may be weakened.

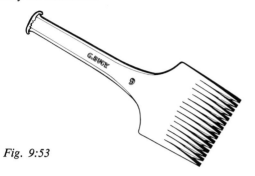

Fig. 9:53

(b)   Strap Pricker
A name given by Dixon (1918) to a Pricker Punch with pointed teeth instead of the usual chisel-shaped, slanting teeth. Its special purpose is not known.

(c)   Wheel Pricker (Rowel Pricker)
This is a toothed wheel, held on the end of a handle which is sometimes known as a 'frame'; the wheel can be changed, according to the number of stitches per inch required; the teeth are chisel-shaped and set at an angle like those of the *Pricker Punch* (above). Some are provided with a fixed or movable fence (or 'guide') to bear on the edge of the strap or other piece of harness to be marked. It can mark stitches along a curved path – an advantage over the Pricker Punch. (See also *Overstitch Wheel*.)

It is strange that while some saddlers regard the Pricker Wheel as 'new-fangled' and favour the Pricker Punch, Diderot (*c*. 1760, *Bourrelier*) illustrates a Pricker Wheel, but not a Pricker Punch.

There are a number of different designs including:

1.   Hand Pricker Wheel   *Fig. 9:8, Nos 87, 90 (p. 230)*
A toothed wheel is mounted on the end of a curved shank, *c*. 9 in. (22.8 cm) overall. It is sometimes found with a leather wrapping round the shank to provide a more comfortable grip. A change of wheel is usually made by releasing a wing nut and moving aside a part of the frame that carries the wheel.

2.   Shoulder Wheel   *Figs 9:5, No. 3082/3 (p. 227); 9:54*
A toothed wheel is mounted on the end of a cranked shaft, 12–14 in. (30.5–35.5 cm) long overall, similar in appearance to the Shoulder

Veins described under *Crease*. There is usually a fence, mounted on a stem and adjustable by a thumb-screw. A change of wheel is made by releasing the screw; but in another type, each size of wheel is mounted on the end of a flat metal 'slide' which fits into a socket on the shank of the tool.

Richard Timmins (*c*. 1800) illustrates Pricker heads with single or double wheels ('Rowels'), set to run near a crease-vein and a non-adjustable fence (see *Fig. 9:11, p. 233*).

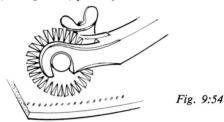

Fig. 9:54

3.   French Pricker Wheel   *Figs 9:55; 9:15, No. 454/5 (p. 237)*
This is similar to the Hand Pricker Wheel described above, made with or without an adjustable fence. It is often distinguished by the elegant chamfers cut on the shank; and, in some cases, by a hollow handle for holding a set of wheels.

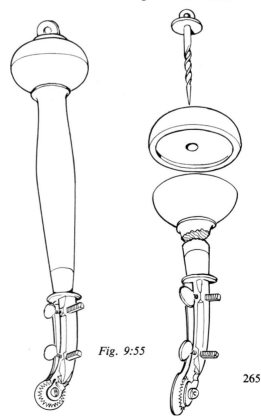

Fig. 9:55

4. A Pricker Wheel with triangular points
The teeth of the wheel are diamond-shaped so that the impression made on the leather is a slanting diamond shape which matches the cross-section of the Harness Awl (see under *Awl*).

Punch   *Fig. 9:56*
Note: Punches are also described in the BOOT AND SHOE MAKER section, and under *Backgrounding Tools* in the DECORATION OF LEATHER section. See also *Pricker Punch* in this section.

The punches used by saddlers and harness makers are those that cut holes and those that punch out small shapes or decorative edges.

Most of these punches are about 5 in. (12.7 cm) long, made in steel throughout with a squared shank. The cutting head usually consists of a hollowed taper or tube with a cutting edge of the desired shape at the foot. This 'tube' is also tapered internally so that the piece of leather punched out can escape at the top. One side of this cutting head is joined to the shank, leaving a side outlet or escape; or it is forged in a form known as 'arched', i.e. the shank is joined to the top of the cutting head on two sides, leaving the space between as an outlet. Fifteenth-century examples may be seen in the Museum of London.

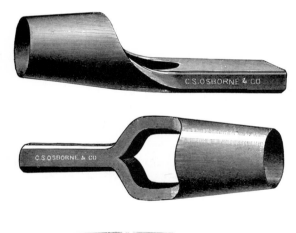

Fig. 9:56

Punching Bench
Some saddlers' shops have a separate bench set aside for punching. The equipment includes:

(1) A tool holder made from a block of wood with holes bored in the top.
(2) A 'cake' of lead (sometimes called a Lead Piece) on which to lay the leather to be punched. The lead, being soft, does no damage to the cutting edge of the punches. A piece of hardwood can be used instead, end-grain uppermost.
(3) Mallets and Hammers – see these entries.

Variants include:

(a) *Punches for making holes*

(1) Round Punches (Saddler's or Belt Punches) *Fig. 9:6 (p. 228)*
These punches cut round holes from $\frac{1}{16}-\frac{3}{4}$ in. (2 mm–1.9 cm) diameter.

(2) Oval Punch   *Fig. 9:6 (p. 228)*
Oval holes are usually preferred, for they are less weakening to the strap; and an oval hole, further recessed by using a *Buckle Tongue Gouge*, allows the buckle tongue to lie flat.

(3) Crew Punch (Buckle Tongue Punches) *Fig. 9:6 (p. 228)*
This cuts an oblong slot which can also be made by punching two holes at a distance from each other and cutting out the leather between them. Made in sizes 33–40 ($\frac{5}{16}-1\frac{1}{8}$ in. (0.8–2.8 cm) long). The term 'crew' is not included in the Oxford English Dictionary as a name for a Punch.

It is used to make the hole in the strap (or chape) which, when the strap is folded over the bar of the buckle, allows the heel of the buckle tongue to protrude and move freely.

(4) Band Punch   *Fig. 9:5, No. 3076 (p. 227)*
A name sometimes given to a strong punch for cutting round holes, often made in the form of a hollow tube. It was probably used for punching holes in machine bands (see the section DRIVING-BELT MAKER) – a task for which a saddler was called in, particularly when shortening or repairing very heavy belts such as those used on the old steam driven threshing machines.

(5) Trace Punch
This cuts a narrow triangular hole for dropping over a trace hook.
Note: Crew Punches (see (3) above) are used for punching a slot-shaped trace hole.

(6) Button Hole Punch   *Fig. 9:6, No. 45 (p. 228)*
This is used by saddlers for punching button holes in the end (billet) of a riding-bridle strap,

when studs are used for fastening instead of buckles. This punch is also used when making purses, holsters etc. (See *Button Tools* in the BOOT AND SHOE MAKER section.)

(7) Plier Punch   *Fig. 9:7, No. 46 (p. 229)*
Round punches mounted on a plier (see *Punch* in the BOOT AND SHOE MAKER section). This tool is useful for punching holes in narrow straps, and particularly while the strap is being worn by the horse. Hasluck (1904) remarks, 'Saddlers are sometimes called upon to do this, and without a hand (plier) punch the work is awkward, necessitating the use of mallet, punch and lead.'

(8) Round cutters for washers etc. see *Washer Cutter* and Wad Punch (below).

(*b*) *Punches for shaping small pieces of leather*
These punches have cutting edges designed to punch out specific shapes. In the shoemaking trades, much larger punches of this kind are made for the quantity production of shoe uppers and soles. An unusual example of such a punch used by saddlers is a leather-sheath die illustrated in a leaflet issued by San Joaquin County Historical Museum (USA, 1976). It was used to cut a crescent-shaped sheath for a saddler's Round Knife, to protect its sharpened edge.

The following are examples of smaller punches found in saddlers' shops:

(1) Chape Punch   *Fig. 9:6, No. 44 (p. 228)*
These punches cut out chapes which are pieces of leather by which a buckle or other fittings are fastened to a strap. One of the commonest Chape Punches cuts out chapes for attaching to the end of girth straps.

(2) Brace End Punch   *Fig. 9:6, No. 106 (p. 228)*
These punches cut out the leather button hole ends for ordinary men's braces. Braces were commonly made by saddlers, as well as other straps worn by horsemen, including wrist-straps, knee-bands, or 'grooms' belts.

(3) Square Punch   *Fig. 9:57*
Examples of these heavy punches, with 'arched' shanks, have been found among saddler's tools, but their purpose is uncertain. Sizes include $2\frac{3}{8} \times \frac{9}{16}$ in.   (6 × 1.5 cm), $1\frac{1}{2} \times \frac{1}{2}$ in. (3.8 × 1.2 cm), $2\frac{5}{8} \times 1\frac{5}{8}$ in. (5.7 × 4.2 cm).

(4) Strap-End Punch (Chisel; Point Cutter)
Used for shaping the end of a strap instead of using a knife. Among the punch shapes are round, pointed, 'egg point', and 'church window'.

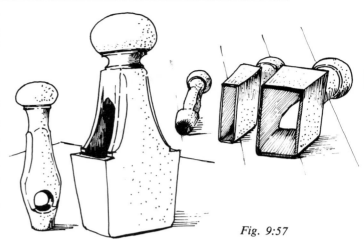

Fig. 9:57

(5) Mattress Tuft Punches
These punches produce the familiar small circular pieces of leather with 'pinked' edges, of $\frac{3}{4}$ or $\frac{7}{8}$ in. (1.9 or 2.3 cm) diameter, used for holding the thread that ties down the contents of a mattress at regular intervals over its surface. A chisel blade across the face of the punch makes a diametrical slit leaving the centre whole for attachment. Saddlers often made these tufts for the mattress makers.

(*c*) *Pinking-Iron Punches* (Pinking Punch; Rosette Punch; Scalloping Iron; Star Punch. USA: Diamond and Scallop Pinking Irons)   *Fig. 9:58*
This group of punches are used by saddlers and others for cutting ornamental designs in leather and other materials. They all produce shapes with serrated or scalloped edges and are made in the form of a circle, half moon, straight line, or Vandyke. (Vandyke is a term applied to indentations in the border to clothing depicted by Van Dyck, the seventeenth-century Flemish painter.)

The term 'pinking' was originally applied to the making of small ornamental holes; today, the term has come to mean an indented border. An example of the earlier meaning of the term is illustrated in the catalogue of Wynn, Timmins (1892) under the caption 'Pinking Punch'. The illustration shows an ordinary Round Punch except that the foot is shaped to cut out different small shapes including a crescent moon, a heart, triangle, square or semi-circle, star or diamond.

Decorative punches are mentioned by Randle Holme (*c.* 1688): on page 297 he describes a '*Scallop Iron* ... to cut leather Scallopwise, but more cornered'; and, 'for the adorning of Saddler's work',

267

he describes a '*Pegging Iron*, it is a kind of *Iron Punch* having five points all in straight line'.

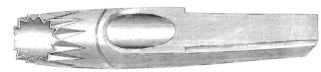

Fig. 9:58

(*d*) *Pinking Machine*
C. S. Osborne (USA, *c.* 1883) illustrates a hand-operated Pinking Machine made for clamping to a bench. Thirteen circular cutters are provided, each shaped to cut a different V-shaped or scalloped edge, or a combination of both. When the hand-wheel is turned, the leather is drawn between the revolving cutter and a roller beneath it.

(*e*) *Rivet Punch* (Setting Punch)
Similar to those used in many other trades, they are used for joining together two flat pieces of metal, wood or leather etc. One type combines a tube for forcing down the washer over the stem of the rivet; another provides a shallow indentation for spreading the stem of the rivet over the washer.

(*f*) *Washer Punch*
Round punches of relatively large size now occasionally used for making washers. (See also *Washer Cutter* in this section.)

(*g*) *Wad Punch*
A round punch usually made with an 'arched' shank and used for stamping out round pieces of leather. (See under *Punches* in the BOOT AND SHOE MAKER section.)

Race Tools
(See also *Channelling Tools*.)
These grooving tools have a blade made in the form of a U- or V-shaped cutter which excavates a groove ('race') when pulled over the surface of the leather.

They are similar to the Timber Scribe used for inscribing numbers on wood; they also resemble the *Binding Cutter* and *Crimper* described in the CLOGMAKER section.

Edward Lawrence describes their use as follows:

'. . . used in the saddle department for reducing from the flesh side a piece of thickish leather before sharp bending . . . also used in the harness department for cutting a fine shallow groove in patent leather to allow neater stitching – (very difficult unless this is done) – and for recessing a stitching line on the reverse of some harness parts to reduce friction-wear on stitching when in contact with horse or carriage shafts etc. Also used to enable concealed stitching on roundings such as bearing reins, to give, when finished, the appearance of a round piece of leather, with no join or stitching visible (a very fine art indeed). A Single Race is used around patterns or on irregular designs etc.; a Compass Race is used when cutting a groove parallel to an edge, or for a circle.'

Variants include:

(*a*) *Single or Double Race Fig. 9:5, No. 3105–6 (p. 227)*
A flat steel bar, 4–5 in. (10.1–12.7 cm) long, with a race cutter at one or both ends.

(*b*) *Screw Race Fig. 9:5, No. 3107 (p. 227)*
A steel tool 4–5 in. (10.1–12.7 cm) long when bent over on itself like a pair of sugar tongs, with a thumb-screw to regulate the distance of one leg, which acts as a fence, from the other which is turned up at the foot to form the race cutter. This tool is illustrated by Diderot (*c.* 1760) in the section *Sellier – Carrossier*.

(*c*) *Compass Race Figs 9:5, No. 3074 (p. 227); 9:59*
A wing compass, *c.* 6–7 in. (15.2–17.7 cm) long, usually of the 'Lancashire' type with one leg pointed at the foot (the pivot), the other foot made in the form of a race blade. A wing, which is either solid or slotted, enables the legs to be held in position by means of a turnscrew.

The leg with the pointed foot is normally bent out of line so that the point comes directly opposite the cutting edge of the race foot. This is an attempt to keep the pivot leg more vertical when cutting circles (see the forked foot version of this tool described below).

A variant has a brass thumb-plate fitted halfway down the 'race' leg to provide a flat surface on which to press the blade into the leather; another is provided with different sized race cutters which can be inserted into a socket provided at the foot.

The Compass Race is used for taking out a narrow strip on the grain side at a desired distance from an edge, or in a circle.

Fig. 9:59

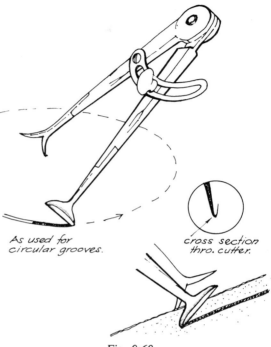

As used for circular grooves.

cross section thro. cutter.

Fig. 9:60

pivot-point foot tends to escape from the centre hole. When the fork-footed tool is used for the same purpose, one of the two pivot points remains almost vertical, and so rests firmly in the hole; and the race cutter still addresses the leather at a convenient angle for cutting.

(d) *Forked-Pivot Compass Race* (French Race Compass) *Figs 9:15, Nos 440–444 (p. 237); 9:60* This version of the Compass Race is illustrated in the catalogues of Blanchard (Paris, 1900) and Krempp (Paris, 1905). It is not certain whether the design originated in France.

Advantages given by this design are: (1) when cutting a circular groove its pivot point is less liable to escape from the centre hole; and (2) the race knife on the other foot, unlike the English version, will cut both ways – an added convenience for the user and especially for the left-handed.

One of the bent prongs on the pivot foot acts as a pivot when cutting circular gooves, and both together provide a fence when cutting a groove along the edge of a strap.

When an English Race Compass is used for cutting circular grooves, the tool is made to lean over to bring the leading edge of the race knife into contact with the leather for cutting. When this is done the

(e) *American Racer* Fig. 9:5, No. 3108 (p. 227) A slender blade, rather like an Edge Shave in appearance, but V-shaped in cross-section at the tip, so that, when pushed across the surface of the leather, it cuts a groove. The fact that it cuts when pushed, rather than when pulled like the race tool, is convenient for working free-hand, and especially when making curved grooves.

Rein Trimming Tool
A name given by C. S. Osborne (USA, *c.* 1883) to a hand tool with a forked head, like an Edge Tool. The head has a concave cutting edge and is used for rounding.

Rounding Tools
These tools are used for forming straps of round cross-section. Such straps are sometimes used for parts of bridles, martingales, the forepart of reins, and occasionally for other parts of the harness.

269

Making round reins is complicated; writers such as Fitz-Gerald (USA, 1875) devote several pages to the process which includes shaving, damping, rolling, channelling and sewing, and lastly the use of the tools described below.

(a)   Rounding Block (Fitz-Gerald, USA, 1875, calls it a 'Board Iron'.)
A block of wood or iron in which are cut a number of half-round grooves of different sizes. After preliminary rolling, the round straps are forced down in a groove of appropriate size, and then polished with a bone or stick. The block can also be used for shaping a strap to a semi-circular cross-section, e.g. for nose bands.

(b)   Rein Rounding Plate (Rounder) *Fig. 9:6, No. 111 (p. 228)*
Early examples are merely iron plates pierced by round holes of different sizes; but by the turn of the century, a more efficient tool was developed. This consists of a pair of long jaws with corresponding semi-circular notches along their length, which form, when closed, a series of smooth round openings. There are usually about nine of these openings, rising in diameter from $c.$ $\frac{3}{8}-\frac{7}{8}$ in. (1–2.3 cm). The edges of the holes are countersunk and well rounded to prevent injury to the rein.

The rein is first wetted and pulled through a larger hole, and then through smaller holes, one after another, until the rein becomes compressed and rounded.

Rubber Hand-Part Iron
A tool for drawing a rubber cover onto the hand-part end of reins. It is described by Mr Edward Lawrence, as follows:

'This is simply a three foot length of $\frac{1}{8}$ in. or $\frac{3}{16}$ in. wire, bent at one end into a small eye to take a piece of strong cord knotted to allow one long and one short end. The long end is first passed through the tongue hole at the handpart of one rein, and then through the crew hole at handpart of the other rein (of a pair); it is fastened so that the knot is clear of the rein. The rubber handpart is passed over the wire, and so eased onto the rein. This was a style of rein produced sometime in the 1920–30s (not noticed before the first war), so I guess this tool dates from then.'

Rubbing Stick: see *Bones and Sticks*.

Rule, Saddler's
Rules made for this trade are listed by several tool makers, including Edward Preston (1901). For

saddlers, a boxwood 2 ft (61 cm) rule is generally preferred, but for harness work, rules up to 6 ft (1.83 m) long are used. They are graduated in eighths (0.3 cm), are $1\frac{3}{4}$ in. (4.6 cm) wide and $\frac{3}{8}$ in. (1 cm) thick, and made of boxwood or beech with brass-plated ends; the edges are either square or bevelled. Folding rules of this type were also made.

The longer rules are similar to those used on the bench in other trades, except that they are thicker, i.e. $\frac{3}{8}$ in. (1 cm) thick rather than the more usual $\frac{1}{4}$ in. (0.6 cm) or less. Hampson & Scott (*Equine Album, c.* 1900, p. 254) ask their customers to use the ordinary thick saddler's rule when measuring a collar, but to inform them if a *thin* rule was used, because this would extend further inside the topmost point of the collar and give a slightly different measurement.

Saddle Bar Stretcher (Thomas Newton, 1865: Saddle-tree Bar Setter) *Fig. 9:61 opposite*
An appliance like a turnbuckle or wire-stainer, about 5 in. (12.7 cm) overall, illustrated in tool catalogues such as those issued by Thomas Newton (*c.* 1865), Bliss, Beauchamp & Bliss (*c.* 1883), and by Shattock Hunter (*c.* 1900).

In other trades, a turnbuckle is an adjustable screwed coupling used for regulating the length and tension of rods or wires. They are used for rigging on small boats, and for tensioning control wires or rods on vehicles and engines.

The purpose of this appliance in saddlery is not entirely certain, though the triangular shape of the buckles suggests an expanding action, rather than the reverse.

The most likely explanation is one given us by Mr O. Morton, Director of Beebee and Beebee, saddle-tree makers of Walsall (1982). He writes that he believes the tool was used on early Spring Trees to hold the steel springs in position while the saddler strained and set the seat. Without the use of the Saddle Bar Stretcher this operation might have distorted the tree. (Spring Trees were developed to give a saddle more resilience than the traditional rigid tree.) Mr Morton added that after 1930 a wood wedge was used instead to prevent the spring bars becoming distorted, and that 'today, the spring steel is such that the need for a holding device has gone'.

The tool may also have been used for opening the front arch of a saddle-tree. This could be done by placing the square ends of the buckles against the stirrup bars and then turning the screw.

Saddle Fitting Block
A piece of workshop furniture like the *Saddle Stand*, except that the top is shaped like a horse's back. It

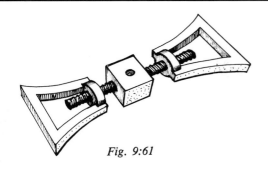

Fig. 9:61

is used for customers to mount and try out a saddle for fit and comfort.

Saddle Stand (Saddle Horse; Saddle Room Stand) *Fig. 9:62*
A framed or box-like piece of furniture with a pitched top. Used as a stand to support a saddle while it is being repaired or cleaned. Later examples are made in metal.

Fig. 9:62

Seam Turner *Figs 9:5, No. 3102; 9:11, Nos 1392, 386 (pp. 227, 233)*
This is a similar tool to the *Seam Sett*, described in the BOOT AND SHOE MAKER section, and used for the same purpose – to flatten and burnish a seam. The saddler's Seam Turner is usually a gently curved shank, mounted in a turned handle, and measures *c.* $6\frac{1}{2}$ in. (16.5 cm) in length overall. The small head has a shallow, concave depression. It is easily confused with an Edge Iron described under *Edge Trimming Tools*, or even with a Double Crease described under *Crease*.

Its chief use is to smooth down the underside of a welted seam, e.g. the seam between the skirt and seat of a riding saddle. These are sewn together on the inside with a piece of folded leather between them. The edges are then dampened, and are pressed out with the Seam Turner.

Sharpening Tools
Saddlers use the same tools for sharpening knives as other trades, including those described in the BOOT AND SHOE MAKER section under *Sharpening Bat* and *Sharpening Steel*.

Shaves: see *Edge Trimming Tools* (for Edge Shave, Skirt Shave, Buissonnette etc.) and also *Spokeshave*.

Smasher (Masher, USA: Bouncer, Bulley or Buller) *Fig. 9:9, No. 306 (p. 231)*
A wooden tool, made in lignum vitae or other hard-wood. It is shaped like a sock-darner, with a mushroom-shaped head. The length varies from 5–6 in. (12.7–15.2 cm) and the diameter of the head from *c.* $3–4\frac{1}{2}$ in. (7.6–11.4 cm).

Edward Lawrence writes:

'This tool is used in a similar manner to collar maker's mallet, for smoothing by light tapping the edges of a blocked saddle seat; for levelling and consolidating the stuffing in the seat with heavier blows; and for making heavy "smashing" blows to the modern stuffed leather panel, where the regulating awl cannot be used. I have a very fine lignum vitae smasher with one end of mushroom shape and the other end shaped to a quarter round profile, suitable for rubbing down stitching.'

What appears to be a Smasher is illustrated by Diderot (*c.* 1760) among the tools of the currier, but not in his harness and saddle sections. It does not appear in Tomlinson (1854), in Hasluck (1904), nor in Krempp (Paris, 1905). It is included in the catalogues of Hampson & Scott (*c.* 1900) and in Dixon (1918).

Splitting Machine (Skiving Machine; Slitting Machine) *Fig. 9:8, No. 92 (p. 230)*
This is one of the hand-operated machines often found in saddlers' workshops.
Note: The term 'Splitting Machine', or one of the alternatives mentioned above, is applied to two different machines. One is the hand-operated machine described below, used for thinning down a piece of leather; the other is a power-driven machine, described in the BOOT AND SHOE MAKER section which is used for splitting a hide into two separate layers.

The hand-operated machine (which is used by other leather-using trades besides the saddler) consists of a small cast-iron frame, designed for mounting on a bench. This contains a horizontal knife against which a strap can be pulled for thinning. A roller holds the strap against the knife; the level of the roller can be adjusted by means of a wheel at the base of the machine. A lever at the side, when depressed against a strong spring, moves the roller assembly to one side so that the strap can be inserted; when released, the spring presses the roller against the knife.

Edward Lawrence writes as follows about its use:

'Used for reducing the thickness of a strip of leather – a wasteful process sometimes necessary to obtain a constant thickness in a full length of leather when making doubled-and-stitched strapping, etc., or where a thinner piece of matching leather was needed for binding or for loops. We had a variety of these machines, all hand operated, including one which I found especially interesting: it not only split, but tapered the split, enabling splices, etc. to be accurately worked at the one setting – much easier than using a round knife.'

Spokeshave *Fig. 9:63*
(See also *Edge Trimming Tools*)
These Spokeshaves are the same as those used in many other trades. The stock is usually made of beech from *c.* $9\frac{1}{2}$–11 in. (24.1–27.9 cm) long; the steel cutter is $2\frac{1}{2}$–3 in. (6.4–7.6 cm) long; the sole is often plated to resist wear.

Spokeshaves have not been found in catalogues issued before *c.* 1816, but they must have been well established as a harness-maker's tool when Hasluck wrote about them at the turn of the century:

'It is suitable for thinning light straps, and not only takes less time to adjust, but does the work more quickly than the slitter [machine]. The chief use of the spokeshave, however, is to trim and finish traces, backbands, etc. After a trace or backband or other lined strap is stitched, the uneven edges require to be rounded and smoothed; this is done by clamping the strap between the knees, holding the clamp a little straighter than when stitching, and using the spokeshave.'

Variants used by harness makers include:

(*a*) *Common Pattern with 'knock-out' iron*
This is a pattern used by many trades. The blade is adjusted by tapping the ends of the tangs which penetrate the stock.

(*b*) *Screwed Pattern*
This type, with the blade adjusted by wing-nuts, is the one often found in saddlers' shops. The screwed tangs penetrate the wing-nuts which, held 'captive'

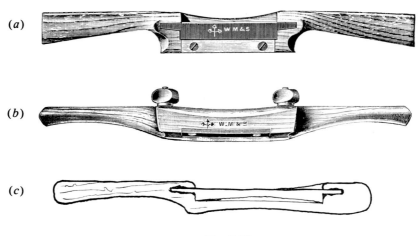

Fig. 9:63

272

on plates screwed to the stock, will push or pull the screwed tangs and so adjust the level of the cutting-iron. The overall length of the stock is $9\frac{1}{2}$–11 in. (24.1–27.9 cm).

(c) Single-Handed Spokeshave
This tool is made with a single handle. The only specimen we have seen was home-made: it does not appear to have been listed by English tool makers. But it is illustrated in the catalogue of C. S. Osborne in the USA (*c.* 1880). Used in some trades for working in otherwise inaccessible places, it is useful to harness makers for shaving a piece of leather (e.g. a trace) without holding it in the Clamp: instead, one can hold the work in one hand and shave it with the other.

Stirrup Bar Wrench (Saddle Bar Wrench)
A name given to a tubular bar used for straightening that part of the Stirrup Bar from which the stirrups are suspended.

Stirrup Bars, made to many different designs (including 'safety' patterns for releasing the stirrups in case of a fall), are riveted on each side of the saddle-tree. With wear, the bars can become bent, but if they were hand-forged when they were made, they can be straightened.

Stitching Horse (Horse Clamp; Sewing Horse; Sewing Clamp; Stitching Clamp; Stitching Seat) *Fig. 9:9, No. 313 (p. 231)*
The Stitching Horse was developed, probably in the mid-nineteenth century, as a less fatiguing method of holding two pieces of leather together than by pressing a *Clamp* between the knees. It consists of a pair of wooden jaws shaped like those of the clamp, but shortened for mounting on a stool – which was called a Horse because the workman sits astride it. One of the jaws is fixed, the other hinged, and they are operated by a foot treadle connected by a cord or strap. The cord passes through the fixed jaw and is attached to the hinged jaw; the work can be held without continuous pressure on the treadle by catching one edge of the treadle on the tooth of a rack that is fitted vertically on one leg of the Horse.

The Stitching Horse was used by other trades besides harness making: for instance by makers of machine driving belts. It seems to have been in greater demand in the USA than in England. It is not mentioned by Hasluck (1904) but Fitz-Gerald (USA, 1875) refers to it in his chapter on stitching harness, and it is described at some length by Knight (USA, 1897). It is illustrated in Hampson & Scott's catalogue (*c.* 1900) but it does not appear to have been included in other English tool catalogues of that time.

There are several variations, including:

(a) An addition of a thumb-screw to force the two jaws together with greater pressure than can be exerted by the treadle alone.

(b) Iron jaws instead of wood. (One of this kind is illustrated in a San Joaquin Museum Publication, USA, 1976.)

(c) Knight (USA, 1897) illustrates a Stitching Horse in which the jaws, instead of being fitted rigidly to the seat of the horse, is made 'vertically adjustable, to suit the varying stature of persons using it. A pin secures it at the required height to plates depending from the seat.'

(d) The jaws are sometimes set at an angle to the seated operator, thus simulating the position of a Clamp when held between the knees.

Stitching Tools (Sewing Tools) *Fig. 9:64*
(See also *Sewing and Stitching* in the BOOT AND SHOE MAKER section.)
Much has been written about the art of stitching harness – and rightly so, for the safety of rider or passenger depends so critically upon its strength. Its appearance was also important for, as in the boot and shoe trade (and especially when competition increased), makers vied with one another over the good looks of their products: and this depended to a considerable extent upon the elegance of the stitching. Though this elegance is apparent to anyone who looks at harness, it is mentioned by only a few of the authorities, notably by W. N. Fitz-Gerald (USA, 1875, p. 168) who writes:

'In stitching harness two objects are to be attained – strength and ornamentation. The first is secured by the use of thread of the required size to suit the work to be done, making it up properly, employing an awl that is neither too large nor too small and drawing the work well together. The second, by laying the stitches in an artistic manner so that, when the work is finished, the lines of the pattern are well maintained and the stitches of a uniform length and laid true.'

There are fashions in the lay of stitches, but one of the most handsome is that produced after using a Pricker Punch (or Wheel) in which the teeth are slanted, followed by an ordinary Harness Awl of diamond-shaped cross-section. This produces a diamond-shaped hole and an attractive diagonal slant to the stitch. This slant comes about because when the thread is pulled tight, it settles into a diagonal position between two points that are nearest to one another: these are the bottom left-hand corner of the hole it is leaving, and the top right-hand corner of the next hole.

An unusual but informative account of stitching is contained in Tim Severin's *The Brendan Voyage* (1978). He describes how a harness maker taught his crew to stitch together the heavy hides that covered the hull of the leather boat, in which, in the year 1976, the legendary voyage to North America by St Brendan was re-enacted.

The tools used for sewing and stitching are described under the following entries: *Awl; Channel Tools; Clamp; Needles; Needle Case; Palm; Pincers and Pliers (c); Prickers; Stitching Horse; Thimble.*

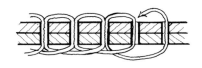

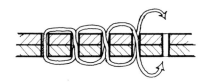

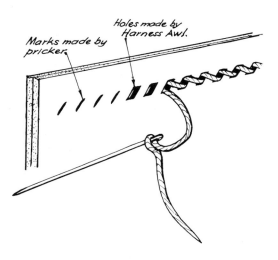

Fig. 9:64　Diagram of typical stitches used by saddlers and harness makers

Stitch Marker: see *Prickers.*

Stool　*Fig. 9:65*
Stools in saddlers' workshops are usually four-legged, and often roughly upholstered in leather by the saddler himself.

Fig. 9:65

Straight Edge
A wooden lath 6–8 ft (1.83–2.44 m) long, used for marking out a hide when making straps etc.

Strainer: see *Web Stretching Tools.*

Strap Holder　*Fig. 9:66*
A workshop aid illustrated by C. S. Osborne (USA, c. 1883) and captioned 'Meyer's Strap Holder'.

It consists of two jaws, one fixed, and one that can be released by a trigger. The jaws are 'float-cut' with opposing teeth, so that a strap pushed in between them cannot be pulled out again without lifting the trigger-handle. Its purpose is to hold the end of a strap while working upon it.

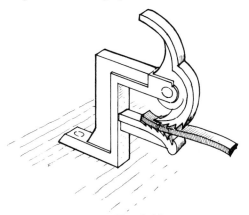

Fig. 9:66

Strap Marker (Girth Strap Marker)
A simple jig for the repetition marking of buckle tongue holes in sets of girth and other straps: it replaces the slower use of a compass. Its construction was thus described by Edward Lawrence:

'A strip of leather approximately $1\frac{1}{2}$ times the width of the strap to be marked, had, in the case of girth-straps, nine largish tacks driven in at 1 in. intervals, $2\frac{1}{2}$ in. from the point end. The tack points were cut off to $\frac{1}{8}$ in. of the surface, and a backing piece of leather was positioned to prevent the tacks being pushed out again in use. With the addition of a $\frac{1}{4}$ in. leather border, all was stitched together, the recess being just sufficient to hold each strap in turn; which, when placed face down, was pressed on to the blunt tack points by a rub with the Smasher.'

Stuffing Iron (Stuffer; Stuffing Stick. See other names below.) *Fig. 9:67 (overleaf)*
These rods or bars are mostly made of steel, but sometimes of wood, and they usually have a V-shaped notch or series of notches on the end.

Their purpose is to force hair, wool, flock, or in the case of collars, straw, into certain parts of the saddle and harness, in order to form cushions which prevent injury to the horse and which make the rider more comfortable.

These tools appear to have been commoner in continental Europe than in England: there are no less than nine varieties listed by Blanchard (Paris, *c.* 1900), while the English makers list only three or four. Diderot (*c.* 1760) illustrates three types. The following are the chief varieties:

(*a*) *Seat Iron* (Saddle Rod; Seat Steel; USA: Steel Stuffer; Stuffing Stick. Sometimes called a Belly Stuffer but see below.) See also Seat Iron under *Awl*.
There are two types, both handled:

(1) A flat, flexible steel blade, *c.* 15–16 in. (37.5–40.6 cm) long overall, tapering slightly towards the tip, which is serrated.
(2) A round steel rod *c.* $\frac{3}{16}$ in. (0.5 cm) thick, and 15–18 in. (37.5–45.7 cm) long overall. The rod is flattened at the tip and is serrated.

They are used for stuffing flock into cart-saddle panels and for stuffing the cantle and certain other parts of a riding saddle; also for re-stuffing when required. The tool with the flexible blade bends sufficiently to follow the curve of the saddle, and so avoids the risk of tearing or stretching the cover.

(*b*) *Belly Stuffer* (Dock Stuffer)
A round, steel shank, handled and bent to a shallow curve *c.* 6–11 in. (15.2–27.9 cm) overall. The tip is usually notched.

A small Stuffing Iron, often used as companion tool to the Seat Awl which is described under *Awl*. It is used for stuffing such parts as smaller cart-saddle panels, saddle knee-rolls, and also crupper docks – the padded loop that surrounds the root of the tail. The tool is illustrated by Diderot (*c.* 1760, *Bourrelier*, plate V, fig. 13) with a caption indicating that it is a stuffer for the crupper dock; and unlike the other tools of this family, it has an eye at the head of the tool, perhaps for inserting a wisp of the packing material.

(*c*) *Collar Rod* (Collar Iron; Straw Rod)
A long, round iron rod, about $\frac{3}{8}$ in. (1 cm) thick, made in lengths varying from 20–50 in. (50.8 cm–1.27 m). At one end there is a metal button which acts as a handle; the working end is often slightly thickened and is provided with a V-shaped notch.

The Collar Rod is used for stuffing straw into the fore-wale of the collar, and can also be used for stuffing the body itself. (The fore-wale is a tube of leather, filled with straw, which lies at the front of the collar.) The process is well described by Dorothy Hartley (1939, p. 197):

'The packing of the straw has to be done very skilfully, first to one side and then the other of the narrow tube. Never must the alternating wisps of straw end *level* in the tube; they must overlap and interlock, each separate strand blending down into the next, and each freshly inserted piece being pressed up into, not the preceding strand, but the strand furthest from it, so that there is a continuous "plaiting" going on inside the tube. The tube is barely 2 inches in diameter, and the whole job must be done rapidly, at one time, while the leather is still damp, so that it may shrink evenly upon the straw. ... Each strand is passed gently down into the wale and coaxed into its exact position. The whole is then inverted and the straw forced in tightly by banging the iron head of the rod forcibly on to a wooden block embedded in the ground.'

(*d*) *Collar Jemmie*
A round rod about $\frac{3}{16}$ in. (0.6 cm) thick, tanged into a ball-shaped wooden handle. The head of the tool is flattened, and the end shaped to the form of a shallow fork to hold the straw. Length overall *c.* 8–15 in. (20.3–38.1 cm).

It is often home-made, but if purchased from a tool maker it is customary to grind down the tines of the forked end to avoid the accidental piercing of the cover.

This tool is used for the 'sideways' adjustment of the straw in the body of the collar while the making proceeds. Longitudinal adjustments are made with the Collar Rod. As one collar maker explained, 'You keep the Jemmie always at hand – you can't work without it: and it's not only used for adjusting the straw, but also for taking a turn of thread when sewing, to tighten the stitches without cutting one's fingers.'

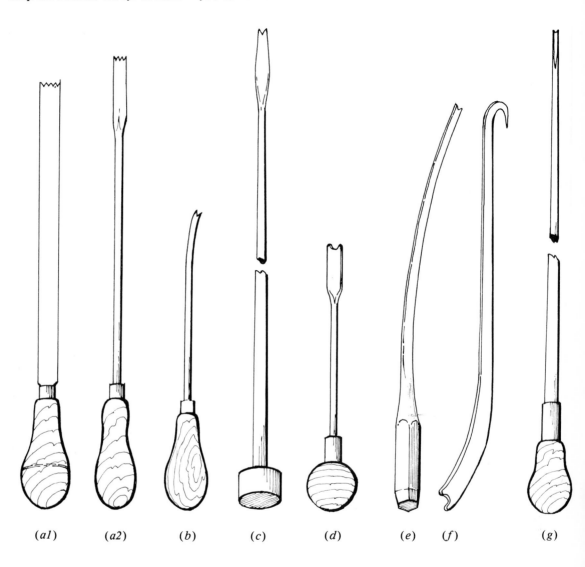

(*a1*)   (*a2*)   (*b*)   (*c*)   (*d*)   (*e*)   (*f*)   (*g*)

Fig. 9:67   Stuffing Irons

(*a1*)	Seat Iron (flat)	(*d*)	Collar Jemmie
(*a2*)	Seat Iron (round)	(*e*)	American Packing Iron
(*b*)	Belly or Dock Stuffer	(*f*)	Combined Stuffing and De-stuffing Iron
(*c*)	Collar Iron	(*g*)	French Stuffing Iron

(*e*) *American Packing Iron*
Illustrated by Osborne (USA, 1911), this appears to be a slightly bowed steel lath, with one end thickened to form a handle. It is interesting to note that this looks very much like the Stuffing Iron illustrated by Diderot (*c.* 1760, *Bourrelier*, Plate V, Fig. 10).

(*f*) *Combined Stuffing and De-Stuffing Iron*
In his *Academy of Armoury* (1688), Randle Holme describes a saddler's tool for removing as well as inserting material for stuffing parts of a saddle:

'*Hair hook or Stuffing Iron.* This is a long slender Iron, with a Hook at one end, and a kind of Fork at the other: As it hath two names, so it hath a double Imploy, the one to hook or draw out the old stuffing of a *Pannel*; and the other end to put Hair again into it or to any part of it.'

A tool of this kind is illustrated by Diderot under the caption *Tire-bourre* (*c.* 1760, *Bourrelier*, plate V, Fig. 9); and a similar tool is illustrated by both Blanchard and Krempp (Paris, *c.* 1900) under the caption *Debourroir*. (The French term for a Stuffing Iron is *Rembourroir*.)

This tool appears to be a slightly curved metal lath, forked at one end for stuffing, and tapering towards a hook at the other end for removing the stuffing.

(*g*) *French Stuffing Irons (opposite)*
As mentioned above, there are many varieties of the Stuffing Iron illustrated in French tool catalogues. They are of similar type to the English tools, but with one exception: all but the flat-bladed Seat Iron, and the De-Stuffing Iron, have a groove cut for a short distance down one side of the iron from the tip. This may be intended for pushing straw.

Thimble *Fig. 9:15, No. 463 (p. 237)*
Thimbles used by saddlers are similar to the domestic kind except that they are open at the top. This is probably done so that they will set well down on a man's finger; the side of the thimble is used to push the needle. (See also *Palm*.)

Tickler
An American term for a Crease, without fence, for use in areas other than the edge of a strap. The American term for the other members of this family is Crease, as in this country. (See *Crease*.)

Vein: see *Crease*.

Washer Cutter
Made like a small Beam Compass, but with a cross-handle mounted on the leg which acts as a pivot. A bar *c.* 5 in. (12.7 cm) long and often graduated slides through the foot of the pivot leg carrying a fixed cutter at one end, and sometimes, in addition, a movable cutter at the other.

Though saddlers need these tools for cutting circular pieces of leather for certain parts of the harness such as cheek guards, their main use in former times was in making leather washers for outside customers. For instance, wheelwrights and coach builders bought leather washers for fitting inside axle-boxes; and owners of pumps – commonly used for drawing water from a well or rainwater sump – would visit the saddler when a new pump-washer was needed.

Note: The larger sizes of Round Punch, described under *Punch*, are used for cutting out smaller washers.

Variants include:

(*a*) *Handled Washer Cutter Fig. 9:8, Nos 104, 104a (p. 230)* as described above.

(*b*) *Washer Cutter Bit*
The same as (*a*) but with a shank, instead of a handle, for fitting into the chuck of a brace.

(*c*) *Washer Cutter Compass Fig. 9:7, No. 71 (p. 229)*
A steel wing compass, with the foot of one leg made into a cutting blade.

Web Stretching Tools (Straining Tools; Web Strainers)
These are devices for stretching the strips of webbing that are fitted to a saddle-tree to provide a flexible support for the seat: pre-stretching prevents the seat from sagging in use. The process is familiar to upholsterers who stretch webbing across chair seats: but they use a bat-shaped wooden lever (equivalent to the straining fork described below) or a pincer rather like a shoemaker's *Lasting Pincer*, but with much wider jaws (see below).

Edward Lawrence writes: 'Web straining was one of the apprentice's perks, supposed to be done in one's lunch hour, and the webs "bought" by the men for 6d. each.'

Material can also be stretched over a saddle tree by means of a Straining Awl (see under *Awl*). In the absence of a stretching device, some saddlers secure the ends of the webbing strips across the bench, dampen them, and then gently force a block of wood between the bench and the webbing.

Randle Holme mentions the process in his *Academy of Armoury* (1688, Saddler, p. 396) but he illustrates the bat-shaped upholsterer's lever.

Web-strainers used by saddlers include:

(*a*) *Straining Fork* (Cross Straining Fork) *Fig. 9:68*

This is like a miniature garden hand-fork, with three to six prongs, and measuring about 7 in. (17.7 cm) overall. According to Osborne's list (USA, *c.* 1883) it is made with either straight or bent prongs. It is used, for instance, on webs stretched over the head of the tree after they have been secured with tacks at one end. The prongs are pushed through the damp web and caught on the edge of the tree; the fork is then used as a lever to strain the webbing over the tree. After this the other end of the web is tacked down.

Fig. 9:68

(*b*) *Web Straining Jack* (Straining Reel; Web Stretcher) *Fig. 9:69*

This is a miniature winch. There is a central spindle which is turned at one end by a lever or 'tommy-bar'; at the other end is a rack-and-pawl to prevent reverse motion. In the spindle there is a slot to take one end of the web. The Jack illustrated is fixed to a board on which webbing can be stretched separately from the tree. But other straining Jacks have forked legs to catch over the tree itself: one end of the webbing is secured to one side of the tree, and the other end is threaded through the spindle of the Jack.

(*c*) *Web   Stretching   Pincers* (Upholsterer's Pincers) *Fig. 9:70*

About 9 in. (22.8 cm) long with the jaws extended on both sides, and serrated for holding material securely. The projection at the centre of the jaws acts as a fulcrum.

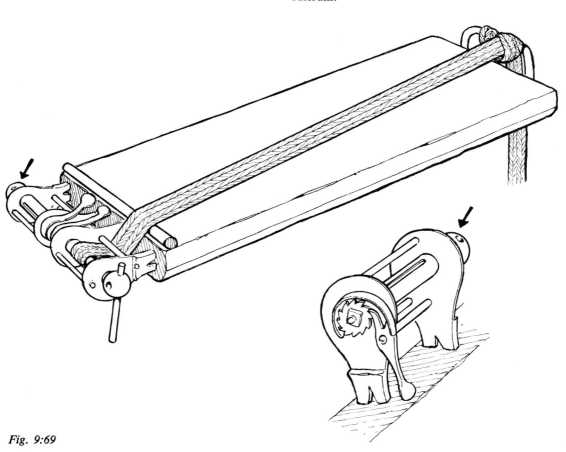

Fig. 9:69

Fig. 9:70

teen different dies are illustrated, with designs varying from a plain circle or rosette to a shield or scallop shells.

Wheel Tools (Rowel Tools): see *Overstitch Wheel*; *Prickers*.

Winker Press (Blinker Press) *Fig. 9:71*
A small screw press used for the ornamental embossing of winkers – the flaps attached to each side of a bridle at eye level. Winkers are intended to prevent a horse from seeing anything except what lies in front, so that he is not diverted by any happening to his left or right.

A base plate *c.* 6–8 in. (15.2–20.3 cm) square is surmounted by an iron frame, in which an upper plate is guided when forced downwards by a screw turned by a tommy-bar or 'fly' handle. The leather winker is inserted between the plates with an embossing die (or block) above it, and the two are pressed together.

The home-made example illustrated was found in 1954 in the saddler's shop of Mr A. H. Marshall of Kirton in Lincolnshire. It is now in the St Albans City Museum. A factory-made example is illustrated by Hampson & Scott (*c.* 1900) under the caption 'Reuben Sutcliffe's Saddler's Winker Dies'. Four-

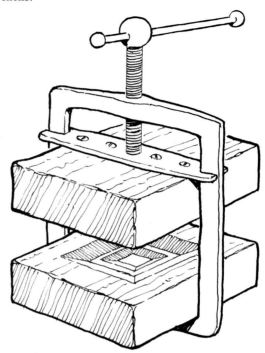

Fig. 9:71

— 10 —

Hat Maker

This section deals with leather and beaver hats. Since little appears to be known about the tools that were used at one time for making the legendary beaver hats, we have described the modern tools used for making top ('silk') hats in the belief that those formerly used for making the beaver hats were similar.

(a) Leather Hats Fig. 10:1
Protective leather hats were made for men working in certain occupations such as stevedores, firemen and policemen. The type worn by dustmen will be familiar to audiences of Bernard Shaw's 'Pygmalion' (and its musical version 'My Fair Lady') in which Alfred Doolittle, the dustman father of Eliza, wore such a hat. It has a long leather flap descending over the shoulders. This was done to protect the neck and shoulders when carrying a heavy and awkward-shaped load.

Protective hats made for other trades have now been mostly replaced by metal or reinforced plastic helmets. Brass helmets for firemen were introduced in about 1850.

The tools used for making leather hats are the Knife, Awl and Needle of the harness maker or shoemaker.

Another use of leather in hat-making is the all-important 'sweat band' sewn into the inside of the crown of all men's hats, and most of women's and children's hats. The purpose is to ensure a good and comfortable fit; indeed, as John Waterer has pointed out (1946), hat comfort is largely determined by the quality of the leather sweat band, and by its correct design and fit.

(b) Beaver Hats
The whole skin of the beaver, with its fur attached, was at one time used for making hats and caps. It

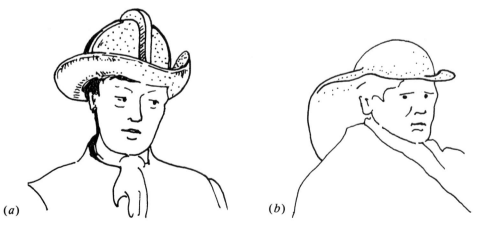

(a)   (b)

Fig. 10:1 Leather hats of the period *c.* 1750–1850: (*a*) Fireman (*b*) Stevedore and Dustman.

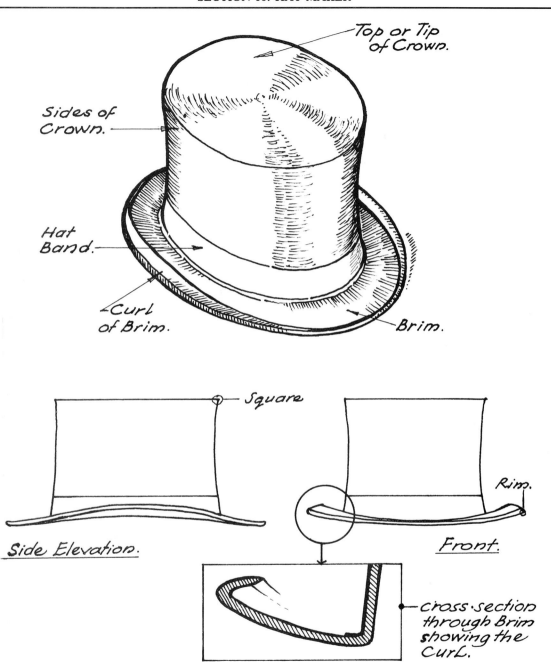

Top or Tip of Crown.

Sides of Crown.

Hat Band.

Curl of Brim.

Brim.

Square

Side Elevation.

Rim.

Front.

cross·section through Brim showing the Curl.

Fig. 10:2 Parts of a typical top hat

owed much of its popularity to its handsome appearance. But as early as the sixteenth century it became apparent that it would be more economical, and result in an equally good-looking and possibly a more comfortable that, to remove the fur, sell the shorn skin to the glue makers, and to employ the art of combining beaver fur with wool and other fibres to make a felt suitable for hats. (See *Felt Maker* in the section MISCELLANEOUS TRADES AND TOOLS.)

There were two common types of beaver hat:

(1) The soft beaver-felt hats to be seen in those popular paintings of 'The Trial of Charles I' (1649), in which members of the House of Commons are wearing beaver-felt hats with enormous brims.

(2) The beaver 'top' hats made from a beaver-felt 'hood' stuck on a built-up textile crown and brim. There are two kinds: the tall 'stove pipe' hat, and the less tall topper as worn by Johnnie Walker in the whisky advertisements.

After it became apparent that the beaver was near extinction through over-hunting (it is related that a musket held upright on the ground was given to North American Indians in exchange for a pile of beaver skins of equal height), a mixture of cheaper fibres were used for making the felt. Finally came the replacement of the beaver hat by the modern 'silk' top hat.

(c) The Modern Top Hat Fig. 10:2
The origin of the silk 'topper' is not certain. Some writers say that it became fashionable in the nineteenth century to wrap silk round the crown of a beaver 'topper'. However, during the later years of the eighteenth century the 'silk' hat offered a cheaper alternative to the beaver. This hat was made of cloth stiffened with varnish, and covered with silk or other materials. In W. P. Frith's painting of 'Derby Day' (*c.* 1870), both the silk top hat and the 'furry' beaver top hat can be seen in the same picture.

In recent years the silk hat is no longer covered in silk: it is in fact made in much the same way as the former beaver top hat except that the felt hood (or 'pullover') is now often made from rabbit fur.

(d) Process of making a top hat Fig. 10:3
The following notes are intended only to indicate the main steps in the process. The tools illustrated (drawn by Mr Norman Purnell) were seen in the workshop of the hat makers S. Patey (1979), and at the Luton Museum.

(1) The Body Maker builds the foundation of the hat from calico impregnated with shellac. Andrew

Lawson, describing Patey's hat factory (*Handmade in London*, 1978), writes:

'The substance secreted by an insect to make its protective cocoon is the basis for the hard hat that protects a man's head when he falls from his horse. The substance is shellac, and it is imported by Patey's at a huge price from India. The body of a hat is made from stretched cotton dipped into melted shellac and then dried. The shellac-impregnated cotton, known as "gossamer" in the trade, is a stiff material of great strength. It is ideal for making hats because it can be pressed and moulded into any shape with a hot iron, and it keeps its shape when it cools. Also the hot iron melts the shellac which then acts as a glue, and will hold any material that is pressed on to it.'

A Hat Block (of a size determined by the *Conform Brow*) is used as a mould when building up the sides and top of the crown; it is placed on a *Spinner* to enable the crown to be revolved during the process of building up, varnishing and ironing. When the sides and top are complete, a square of 'gossamer' material (known as the 'brim square') is cut and built up to form the brim. After being cut away at the centre, the brim square is pulled down over the crown so that there is a turn-up of about $\frac{1}{2}$ in. (1.2 cm) all round the crown. The crown and brim are then 'married together' with more varnishing and ironing, and the joint between the two parts masked by a muslin strip called a 'robin'. The tools used include *Hat Irons* and *Dummies*, and also the *Brim Gauge* (see under *Hat Gauges*) for marking the brim square before cutting.

(2) The Finisher covers the calico foundation with a 'hood' or 'pullover' of silk, felt or other material. As in the days of beaver 'top' hats, the body is covered in adhesive (e.g. shellac) before the hood material is pulled down over it.

When dry, the hat is placed on a *Half Block* and worked with *Hat Irons* and *Dummies* as in the process of body-making.

(3) The Shaper goes to work on the brim to give it the stylish curl that distinguishes the fashionable top hat. This is done on the *Setting Frame* with a *Brim Shaping Tool*, *Dummies* and *Hat Plane*. He also shapes the brow of a hat to fit the customer's head.

(4) The Trimmer covers the edge of the brim with braid, and sews the bands with or without buckles round the base of the crown. A paper or cork lining is fitted inside the crown and covered by silk stamped with the firm's name and trade mark. Finally a

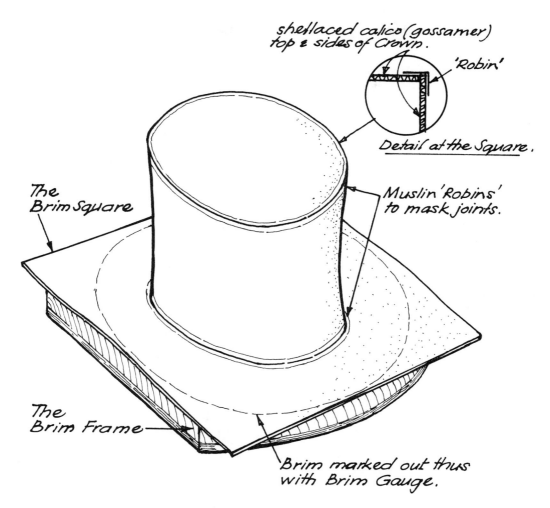

shellaced calico (gossamer)
top & sides of Crown.

'Robin'

Detail at the Square.

Muslin 'Robins'
to mask joints.

The
Brim Square

The
Brim Frame

Brim marked out thus
with Brim Gauge.

'Bodymaking'

The Brim is married to the Crown & the joints
are masked by muslin 'robins.'

Fig. 10:3

283

leather sweat band is sewn in around the inside of the crown. Its purpose is to ensure a good and comfortable fit.

Band Robin   *Fig. 10:3a*

A wooden block, square in cross-section, *c.* $1\frac{5}{8} \times 3\frac{3}{8}$ in. (2.9 × 8.6 cm) with curved grooves of different widths cut on three sides of the block.

This tool was seen among the Christy Collection of hat tools at the Luton Museum (1980). A robin is a strip of cloth used for masking the joint between the crown and the brim of the hat. The purpose of this wooden block is not clear, but it may have been used to shape the robin strips after they had been impregnated with shellac.

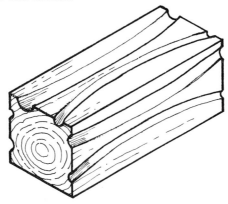

Fig. 10:3(a)

Brim Frame (Body Maker's Sunk Frame)   *Fig. 10:4*

This is used when joining ('marrying') the brim to the crown, and also when ironing the brim. It is similar to the *Plate* but larger, *c.* 16 in. (40.6 cm) across, and tapering from the centre towards the front. The centre of the Brim Frame is hollowed out to receive the *Hat Block*; the remaining surface is covered with zinc sheeting to provide a base for cutting the brim to the correct size and contour. (An example seen at the Luton Museum was marked on top 'W. Safe'.)

Fig. 10:4

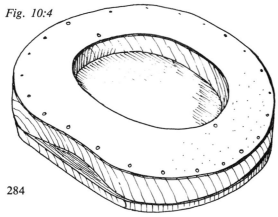

Brim Shaping Tool (Curler; Hand Brimmer; Plough; Shaping Tool. Sometimes called a 'Curling Dummy', but see *Dummies*)   *Fig. 10:5*

A tool used to 'bring up the curl' of the brim. It is a handled wood or metal block *c.* 5 × 2 in. (12.7 × 5 cm), with metal strips of L-shaped cross-section fitted by means of adjustable screws to one edge of the sole. The brim is thrust between the metal strip and the block, and a turning movement of the hand produces the required curl. Two examples are illustrated, one in wood and the other metal.

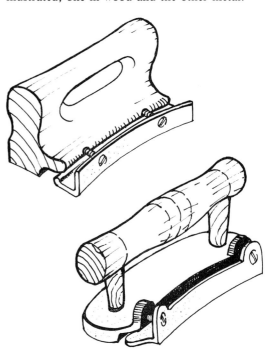

Fig. 10:5

Conformature   *Fig. 10:6*

This tool is used for measuring the profile of a person's head and brow. It is a hat-shaped contraption consisting of about forty-eight wood or ebonite fins attached by springs to a buttressed crown and capped by a card-making device.

When it is placed on a client's head and the fins adjusted to conform to the head and brow, the profile is indicated by a series of perforations on the card which is used later to regulate the size and contour of the inside brow of the hat. The Conformature in Mr Patey's factory was stamped with the name of Allsé Maillard of Paris (Brevete SGDG).

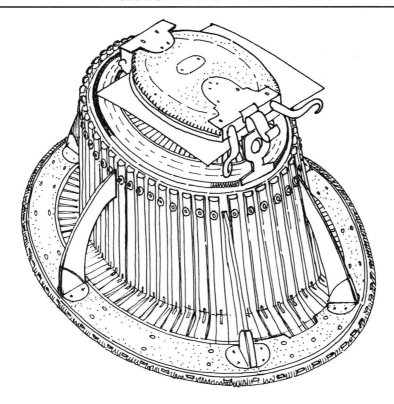

Fig. 10:6

Conform Brow *Fig. 10:7*

This is used in conjunction with the *Plate* to determine the right size of *Hat Block*.

It consists of two oval brass plates *c.* $5\frac{1}{4} \times 4\frac{1}{2}$ in. (13.2 × 11.4 cm) separated by a leather gasket. The two plates are held together by eight wing nuts; and between the lower plate and the leather gasket there are about forty-eight adjustable tapered formers made of hardwood.

When the Conform Brow is placed on the *Plate*, these tapered formers are adjusted so that their inner pointed ends coincide with the perforations on the Conformature card. The screws are then tightened and the external hardwood formers will then provide the exact profile of the hat crown required – as measured at the brow. This profile is then compared with the *Hat Blocks* in stock, and the nearest size is selected for use.

Fig. 10:7

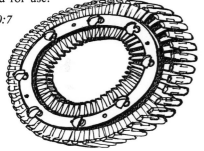

Curling Strap *Fig. 10:8*

This is a thin, bowed, felt-covered lath about 11 in. (27.9 cm) long, and tapering towards each end.

It serves as a former when placed inside the curl of the brim during the process of ironing with the *Flooster* (see under *Dummies*).

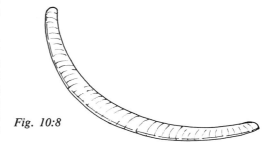

Fig. 10:8

Dummies

These are cast-iron, brass, or wooden tools with heads shaped to serve as smoothing or shaping irons or blocks. As a general rule, metal dummies are pre-heated and used for smoothing and shaping the body

285

and brim of the hat; wooden dummies are used in the finishing process.

Variants include:

(*a*) *Curling Dummy* (Thumb Brimmer; Thumb Dummy) *Fig. 10:9*

A concave smoothing tool with a foot-shaped handle made in iron or wood, about 5 in. (12.7 cm) long, and used to shape the outside of the curl of the brim. The iron tool is generally used before the wood. (See also *Brim Shaping Tool*.)

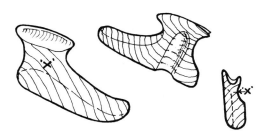

Fig. 10:9

(*b*) *Foot Dummy* *Fig. 10:10*

A shaped smoothing tool, made in brass or iron, *c.* $3\frac{1}{2}$ in. (8.8 cm) long, and attached to a wooden handle. Used for shaping the inside curl of the brim.

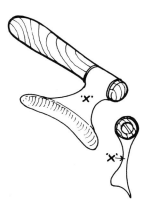

Fig. 10:10

(*c*) *Concave Dummy* *Fig. 10:11*

A handled metal plate with a concave sole *c.* $5 \times 2\frac{1}{2}$ in. (12.7 × 6.4 cm) and usually round in front and square behind. Used for ironing the side of the crown.

Fig. 10:11

(*d*) *Flat Dummy* (Tip Dummy; called a 'Multer' in *The Boy's Book of Trades*, *c.* 1866) *Fig. 10:12*

Similar to (*c*) above, but with a flat sole and used for ironing the top of the crown.

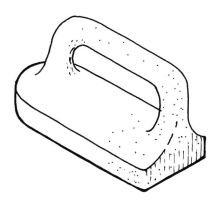

Fig. 10:12

(*e*) *Blistering Iron* *Fig. 10:13*

An oblong iron head with a rounded end, tanged into a wooden handle, and *c.* 13 in. (33 cm) overall. Sometimes made with an L-shaped cross-section on one edge. It is used on the brim and curl.

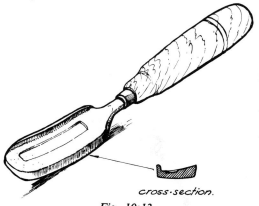

cross-section.

Fig. 10:13

(*f*) *Flooster* (Fluster; Weasel) *Fig. 10:14*
A boat-shaped iron head mounted in a wooden handle *c.* 12 in. (30.5 cm) long overall. It is used in conjunction with the *Curling Strap* for ironing the inside of the brim.

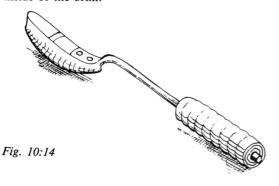

Fig. 10:14

(*g*) *Wooden Finishing Dummies* (Flatteners) *Fig. 10:15*
Shaped like the *Concave* or *Flat Dummy* (above) but made of wood, often of polished boxwood, and used for final smoothing.

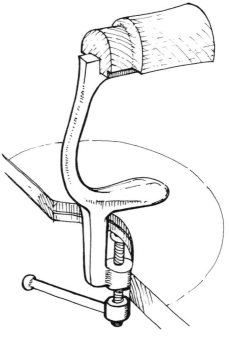

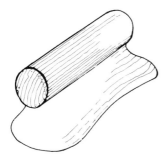

Fig. 10:15

Felter's Bow: see *Felt Maker* in the section MISCELLANEOUS TRADES AND TOOLS.

Half Block (Polishing Block) *Fig. 10:16*
This is used during the process of brushing and polishing hats.

  The arm is about 14 in. (35.5 cm) high, and is clamped to a cut-away section of the work bench; the Half Block, semi-circular in cross-section, is fitted to the top of the arm. The crown of a hat fits over the block and can then be rotated as required. (An example at the Luton Museum is marked W. Plant, Manchester.)

Fig. 10:16

Hat Block *Fig. 10:17*
This forms the mould for the crown of a hat. It is made up of five separate hardwood components and each set of components represents a different size of hat, and is marked accordingly. The block is normally kept in a felt cover, but when the components are removed for use, their correct assembly is guided by a series of location marks. (The blocks in Messrs Patey's works were stamped with the name of William Plant.)

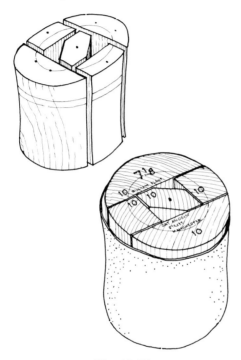

Fig. 10:17

Hat Gauges

(*a*) *Brim Gauge   Fig. 10:18*
This is used for measuring and marking out the size of the brim. When the crown and brim have been joined on the *Brim Frame*, the gauge is set to mark the sheet of the brim material to the width of the brim required.

It is made in mahogany and brass. The pin underneath that marks the contour of the brim is carried by a sliding arm, and can be secured at the required distance from the crown by means of a thumb-screw mounted on a metal bridge across the back of the gauge.

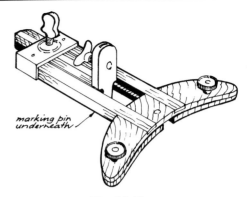

Fig. 10:18

(*b*) *Rounding Card*
A name given to a tool illustrated in the *Boy's Book of Trades* (1866) which appears to be a metal gauge similar to the Brim Gauge above, but which is described, probably in error, as being used for 'pressing'. It has a turned wooden handle at the back.

(*c*) *Rounding-Brass* (Rounding Gauge) *Fig. 10:19*
A Y-shaped metal tool illustrated in Tomlinson's Cyclopaedia (1853, Vol. 5, p. 6) and described as follows: '. . .the proper width is given to the brim by means of a *rounding-brass*, or gauge, with notches, into one of which a knife is fitted, and in passing round the brim cuts off the superfluous portion.'

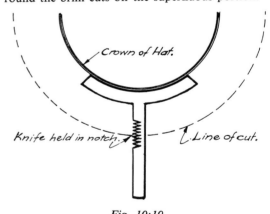

Fig. 10:19

Hat Iron (Finishing Iron) *Fig. 10:20*
Used for all the heavier ironing processes, e.g. the hat body when mounted on the block. The 10 lb size is about 6 in. (15.2 cm) long, 3 in. (7.6 cm) deep, and $2\frac{1}{2}$ in. (6.4 cm) wide, – with one end rounded and the

other square. The irons are lifted from the stove by iron hooks about 16 in. (40.6 cm) long, and then transferred to an L-shaped stirrup which allows the iron to be inverted so that the handle can be cooled in a pail of water.

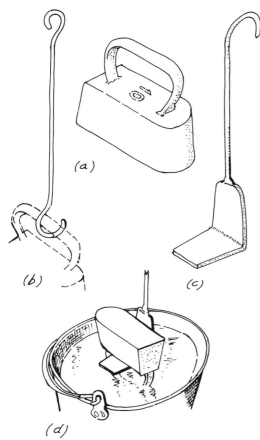

Fig. 10:20 Hat Iron. (*a*) A 10 lb size Iron. (*b*) Hook for lifting the Iron off the stove. (*c*) Stirrup for holding the Iron when dipping. (*d*) Cooling the handle of the Iron in a pail of water.

Hat Plane *Fig. 10:21*

This remarkable tool is a member of the Thumb Plane family. It is used for 'cutting the curl' – for shaving down the shellac-impregnated calico where it forms the curl of the brim.

Examples seen are made in steel or gun-metal. The sole is $1\frac{3}{4}$ in. (4.4 cm) long and about $\frac{5}{8}$ in. (1.6 cm) wide at the heel, tapering to *c.* $\frac{1}{4}$ in. (0.7 cm) at the toe. The sole is flat, but rebated along the right-hand edge, which has a gentle convex curve. The iron is $\frac{3}{8}$ in. (1 cm) wide, has a skewed cutting edge, and is

bedded under a wooden wedge through an opening at the back of the plane, emerging at a mouth on the vertical edge of the rebate. This unusual arrangement enables the upper part of the plane to be tapered down in a graceful curve to serve as a handle.

An opening on the left-hand side of the stock, just forward of the wedge, serves as the outlet for shavings. As will be apparent from the illustration, the iron is bedded with its width set at right angles to the sole, instead of the usual horizontal position.

Note: The example illustrated was used by Messrs Horace Slade, a firm of hat makers at St Albans, Hertfordshire. The number stamped on the sole belonged to the hat body maker who had the use of the plane, and enabled him to identify and reclaim the plane from the pawnshop where, according to Mr Patey, the London hat maker, the men were in the habit of pawning their tools before payday.

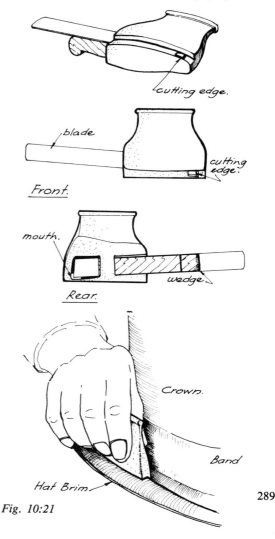

Fig. 10:21

Hatter's Rule   *Fig. 10:22*
Made from boxwood with brass mounts at both
ends, *c.* 5 in. (12.7 cm) long, and with an extension
slide on one side. The face is graduated in inches and
quarters of an inch; the reverse displays a table which
relates the length and width of the crown to the hat
size. (This rule is illustrated in the catalogue of
Edward Preston & Sons, Birmingham, 1901.)

Picker and Tweezers   *Fig. 10:24*
These small tools, 4–5 in. (10.1–12.7 cm) long, are
used for locating and extracting isolated long hairs
which may have been left in the cover material.
(These hairs are known in the trade as 'kemps' – a
term deriving from old Norse *kamp* – whisker.)

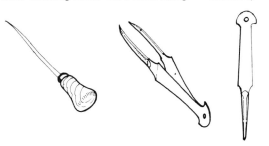

Fig. 10:24

Plate (Brow-Piece)   *Fig. 10:25*
This is used with the *Conform Brow* to establish the
requisite size of *Hat Block* to be used. It is an oval
wooden plate *c.* 9½ in. (24.2 cm) across and slightly
tapering in thickness from the centre to the front and
back. On the face there are two pins to hold the card
from the *Conformature*. The *Conform Brow* is
placed on this card.

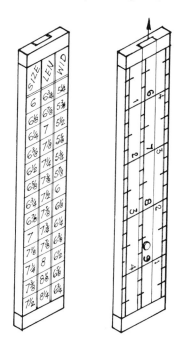

Fig. 10:22

Lure (Looer; Lewer. The term comes from the old
French *velour* – velvet)   *Fig. 10:23*
A velvet-covered pad used for final polishing. It is
generally about 6 × 3½ in. (15.2 ×·8.8 cm) and 1½ in.
(3.8 cm) thick.

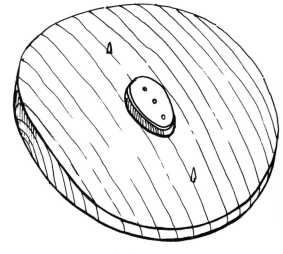

Fig. 10:25

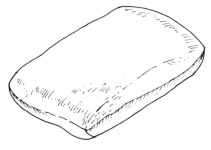

Fig. 10:23

Puller-In (Stirrup)   *Fig. 10:26*
A wire loop joining the forked end of a leather strap
which is 3 ft (91.4 cm) long. It is used to hold a silk
cover close to the sides of the crown while ironing.

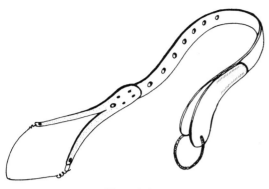

Fig. 10:26

Scissors (Scissors with cranked blades as illustrated are known in the trade as 'Crooks'.) *Fig. 10:27*
These scissors are used for general purposes. The cranked shape enables the user to cut material lying flat on the bench.

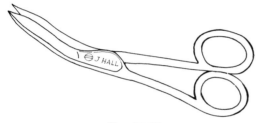

Fig. 10:27

Setting Frame *Fig. 10:28*
This is another method of supporting the hat during the brushing and polishing process. It consists of an oval-shaped wooden block *c.* $14\frac{1}{2}$ in. (36.7 cm) from front to back, and $2\frac{1}{2}$ in. (6.4 cm) thick at the centre, tapering down at both ends. The top face is covered in moleskin.

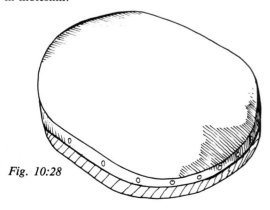

Fig. 10:28

Shaping Screw (Hat Stretcher) *Fig. 10:29*
Made in hardwood, this tool has a screwed sleeve loosely attached to one of its semi-circular heads. The tool is held inside the crown of the hat and expanded by turning the sleeve. It is used for shaping and stretching hats during manufacture; or, by the hat shop when fitting a customer.

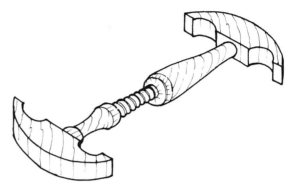

Fig. 10:29

Spinner *Fig. 10:30*
A circular wooden block used when varnishing, ironing or brushing hats. It is about $6\frac{1}{4}$ in. (15.9 cm) in diameter and $1\frac{1}{2}$ in. (3.8 cm) thick and is provided with a central spike. The Hat Block is placed centrally on this spike so that the hat can then be turned during the process.

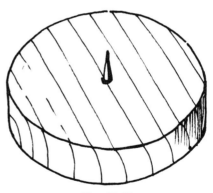

Fig. 10:30

Tipstand *Fig. 10:31 (overleaf)*
A stand for supporting hats, particularly the top of the crown during the finishing process. It consists of a circular iron base of *c.* $6\frac{1}{2}$ in. (16.5 cm) diameter, supporting a turned stem *c.* 9 in. (22.8 cm) high with a circular table at the top. The table is felt covered.

291

Fig. 10:31

Wire Card (Brim Carder) *Fig. 10:32*
A wire brush used for 'beavering-up'. A hat maker described it as a 'persuader for straightening the nap of the tougher felts'. It consists of a wooden block about $4\frac{1}{2} \times 2\frac{1}{2}$ in. (11.4 × 6.4 cm) with a slightly convex face covered in moleskin (now felt) through which the wire bristles protrude.

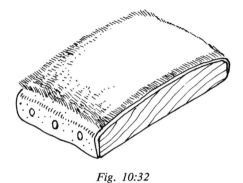

Fig. 10:32

— 11 —

Leather Manufacture

Note: The outer covering of an animal is generally known as a pelt, hide or skin. Trade usage confines the term 'skin' to that of smaller animals such as goat, pig, sheep or calf; and it applies the term 'hide' to the skin of larger animals such as horses and cattle.

1. The structure of skin Fig. 11:1
A diagrammatic cross-section of a typical skin is illustrated. The central part, known as the corium or dermis, is the substance that is converted into leather after the outer layer of hair and epidermis and the subcutaneous flesh and fat have been removed. (The surface of the leather from which the hair was removed is known as the grain side; the other surface is known as the flesh side.)

2. Some definitions
(a) *Leather* may be defined as an animal skin that has been made incorruptible by tanning.

(b) *Tanning* is a general term applied to treatments which render an animal skin indigestible to bacteria, and consequently no longer liable to putrefaction. (*Curing* is the temporary preservation of a skin by drying, salting or by other means.)

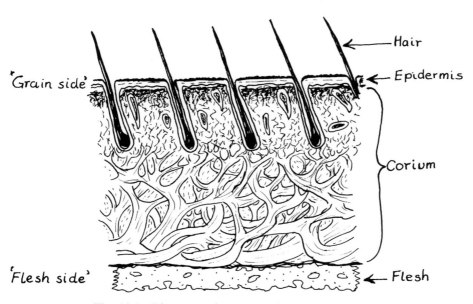

Fig. 11:1 Diagrammatic cross-section through a skin

(*c*) *Currying* was a term originally applied only to the impregnation of tanned leather with grease to give it increased flexibility and resistance to damp. Today the term has come to be applied to all the processes that improve the quality and appearance of leather after the tanning process has been completed.

3. *Historical Note*

The discovery of stone-scraped pelts of over 100,000 years old suggests that the skins underwent some form of preservation – possibly by unplanned smoking in caves or huts. By the time 'modern' man emerged, some 40,000 years ago, good leather was being produced, tanned by the rubbing in of fats. Tanning by immersion in a solution of alum (possibly mistaken for salt) was known in Egypt in *c.* 4000 BC.

Vegetable tanning appeared in Neolithic times (*c.* 8–10,000 years ago). J. Waterer (1954) suggested that this may have resulted from skins being accidentally immersed in forest pools containing a tanning agent such as oak bark, or from attempts to colour skins with vegetable matter.

Vegetable-tanned material is fairly stable, particularly in moist, mildly acid soils, and remains of leather artifacts from those times have been discovered all over Europe.

The Egyptians used all the tanning methods mentioned above. A wall painting of *c.* 1500 BC in a noble's tomb at Thebes illustrates the processes of unhairing, fleshing and tanning. The picture also shows men engaged in the process of staking – a method of softening and stretching leather still in use today. (See *Staking and Perching Tools* described in the section LEATHER MANUFACTURE, II. Currier's Tools.) In later centuries leather was also 'worked' by pummelling with wooden mallets, and kneaded by trampling underfoot.

Tanning tools of the modern type were already fully developed by the first century AD. Roy Thomson (1978) thus describes the tools discovered in Pompeii that had lain buried there since the city was overwhelmed by the eruption of Vesuvius in AD 79:

'The tools discovered included curved blunt-edged unhairing knives, curriers' knives with their sharpening steels, and half moon knives. These tools and the lay-out of the plant suggest that a Roman tanner would have felt completely at home in the tanneries depicted by the eighteenth century French encyclopaedists. Indeed, there appear to have been few fundamental advances in the technology of leather manufacture between the classical Greco-Roman period and the Industrial Revolution.'

It may be added that the Roman tanner would not have felt a stranger in the great tanneries which, until about fifty years ago, were still flourishing in many English towns. (See 6. *The Tannery* below.)

Work in the tanneries was arduous, noisome and long: the process of tanning a skin often took more than a year to complete. Today much of the work is done by machine, and modern mineral tanning agents have shortened (and sweetened) the tanning process out of all recognition.

4. *Methods*

Anyone who wants to understand the process of leather manufacture may well be daunted by the diversity of method, the confusing use of ancient terms for the many alternative processes involved, and the vast literature on the subject of leather tanning and dressing.

Brief notes of three traditional methods are given below. (For a more detailed account of the process the reader may refer to the books listed at the beginning of the Bibliography.)

Before tanning begins, the hair and subcutaneous flesh are removed from the skin, leaving the central layer exposed: this layer will be converted into leather by the tanning process. If the hair or wool is to be retained, a modified tannage is applied.

(*a*) *Vegetable tanning*
This was the commonest method employed during recent centuries. It involved soaking the skins for 9–15 months in a solution of oak bark in water. The process is still carried out in its traditional form by a few well-known tanners who produce leather for the makers of high-quality leather goods.

(*b*) *Oil tanning* ('*Chamoising*')
In this ancient process the skins are impregnated with fish oils and then left in a warm atmosphere for the oils to oxidise, i.e. react with the surrounding air. This method is still used for making the soft 'chamois' leathers.

(*c*) *Mineral tanning* ('*Tawing*')
This method, like that using oils, was known in the Stone Age. Alum is applied to the raw skin, either as crystals or in solution. This produces a white leather that was much used for making harness and gloves. Alum is used in one of the many mineral processes that have shortened and simplified the tanning operation in modern times.

When the tanned skins are delivered to the currier they are rough, stiff, and uneven in thickness. The function of the currier is to give this rough leather an even thickness, the degree of flexibility demanded by the future use of the leather, and, not least, a pleasing 'feel' and appearance.

It is the art of the currier to vary the properties of his final product according to the requirements of his customer. Leather can be hard, soft, flexible, resilient, stretchy or rigid, depending on the nature of the skin and the currying process employed. Flexibility and softness is brought about by first impregnating the leather with grease (this coats the leather fibres and allows them to slip over each other), and then by physically 'working' the leather with various implements: see the entries *Sleeker*; *Mace*; and *Staking and Perching*, in the section LEATHER MANUFACTURE, II. Currier's Tools.

The following are examples of specific properties that the currier is required to impart to the leather: shoe uppers must be soft and mould to the foot, but retain the shape of the shoe; shoe sole leathers must be reasonably flexible yet resist abrasion and penetration by sharp stones; harness leather must be flexible yet very strong and long-wearing; leathers for industrial driving belts have to be flexible, and able to withstand sudden tension without stretching; gloving leathers must stretch and mould to the hand.

5. *How tanning works*

The aim of the following paragraphs is to explain in non-technical language how a raw, putrescent animal skin is transformed into the incorruptible, water-resistant and highly useful substance we know as leather. What follows is based on material kindly put at our disposal by Mr Roy Thomson, a chemist engaged in the manufacture of leather and a writer on the history of tanning.

'If we look at a cross-section of skin under the microscope, it is seen to be made up of three layers: The outer epidermis and hair-root structure; the central dermis or corium; and the inner sub-cutaneous or flesh layer.

'The tanner first removes the epidermis and flesh layers, and cleans up the central corium layer to reveal a complex three-dimensional interwoven network of tough fibre bundles made of protein known as collagen. These fibre bundles are subdivided into fibres, and then to minute, thread-like fibrils, until you get down to the collagen molecules themselves. These protein molecules are long and rod-like in shape, and they are joined together by short cross-linking chains made of other protein-based materials. These collagen molecules may be compared to the uprights of a scaffolding structure, and the cross-linking chains are analogous to the cross-ties holding the structure together.

'When an animal dies, biochemical reactions begin to break down these cross-links. If a scaffold struc-ture has its cross-ties taken out it will collapse, and this is analogous to the process of putrefaction. What tanning does is to replace the natural cross-links with chemical cross-links that are indigestible to bacteria and consequently resistant to the breakdown mechanisms of putrefaction.

'How are these chemical cross-links implanted in the substance of an animal skin? A prehistoric method was the application of fats, or by exposing the skin to wood smoke. Some naturally occurring oils and fats, when exposed to the air, produce reactive chemicals called aldehydes — similar chemicals present in wood smoke are responsible for the stinging of the eyes. It is these aldehydes that provide the cross-links which perform the action of tanning. The ancient method of oil-tannage is still used in the modern chamois tanning process.

'Another ancient method was a mineral process using alum and salt. This, and certain other mineral tanning materials, such as Chromium, or Zirconium, have the ability to provide cross-links in the collagen network. Most of the leather produced today is tanned by using commercial chrome tanning mixtures.

'Vegetable tannins (e.g. oak bark solutions) contain mixtures of large complex molecules known as polyphenols, and it is these that form the cross-links when they react with the collagen network.'

6. *The Tannery*

Very few of the old 'outdoor' tanneries remain today. A reconstructed example — re-erected from its original site — can be seen in the Welsh Folk Museum at St Fagans, near Cardiff.

The older tanneries were often built on the bank of a river to ensure a supply of water. The tannery yards contained the pits used for the processes of liming and tanning: these measured about 10×8 ft. (3.04×2.43 m) in area and about 6–8 ft (1.82–2.43 m) deep, and were often roofed over; they were given special names according to their purpose — see *Pit Tools* (below) under LEATHER MANUFACTURE, I. Tanner's Tools.

Buildings provided for the tannery usually include a Beam Shed where the skins are unhaired and fleshed; a Bark Mill shed where the oak bark is broken and then ground; and a Drying Room where the skins are hung to dry out.

The site sometimes contained the owner's or manager's dwelling house and stable. An advertisement of 1881 (belonging to the Hitchin Museum) describes a 'Valuable Property known as the Whitwell Tan yard Estate'. After listing a number of sheds, buildings and tan pits, the advertisement adds that there is also a 'Timber and slated Nag Stable, a lean-to Piggery and Day Yard; Timber and Thatched Cart-Horse Stable with Chaff Loft; ... a 3-Bayed waggon and Cart Shed; ... Seven Lime Pits ... Horn and Ash Stores, Weigh House; together with Two Enclosed Gardens well stacked with thriving trees ... bounded on the South Side partly by the River Mimram.'

Tanning required a team of work-people, working outdoors in the tan yard, or in the sheds where the skilled job of unhairing and fleshing was carried out. Much of the work was arduous, dirty, and gave off evil smells which clung to the worker's clothes to such an extent that in some towns separate seats are said to have been reserved for tanners in the horse-buses or trams serving the area where they worked.

The tanner's conditions of work in the nineteenth century are described by Henry Mayhew in his *London Labour and London Poor* (1851): see References and Bibliography.

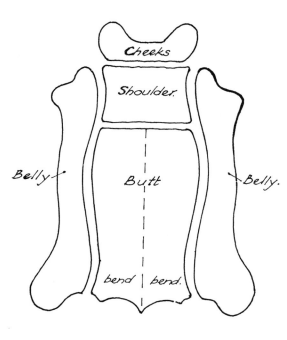

Fig. 11:1(a)   Parts of a typical hide (diagrammatic)

7. *Tools of the Trade*

I THE TANNER

	See tool entries:
Removing unwanted pieces, and taking off certain extremities, such as shoulders and bellies, for lighter tannage	*Knife, Trimming* *Knife, Rounding*
Handling the skins in the yard and pits generally	*Pit Tools*
Scraping off the hair and epidermis (after loosening the hair in a solution of lime)	*Beam, Tanner's* *Knife, Unhairing*
Removing fatty substances remaining on the flesh side of the skin	*Knife, Fleshing*
Removing any remaining hair and other debris ('skud') after the above treatment	*Knife, Scudding*
Preparing the oak bark and other materials for tanning	*Bark Breaking Tools*
Suspending or laying skins in pits containing the tanning liquids	*Pit Tools*
After tanning, cleaning up the skin before drying	*Striking Pin*

II THE CURRIER

For softening the leather and making it flexible	*Mace* *Pin Block* *Staking and Perching Tools*
For paring down to the required thickness	*Knife, Currier's* *Beam, Currier's*
For smoothing, stretching, and working in dubbin	*Sleeker*
For softening and 'bringing up the grain'	*Graining Board* (including *Pommel*)
For consolidating the heavy leather	*Roller*
For the final cleaning and paring down of the flesh surface after currying	*Whitening Knife*

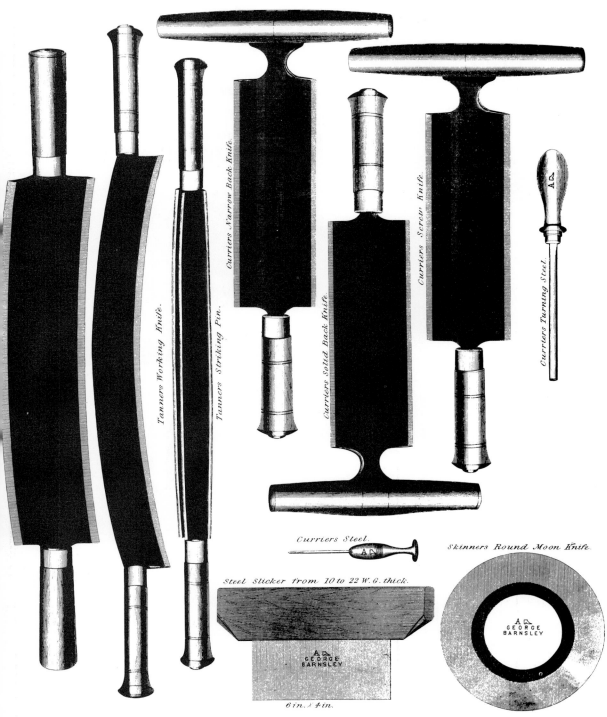

Tanners Working Knife.

Tanners Striking Pin.

Curriers Narrow Back Knife.

Curriers Solid Back Knife.

Curriers Screw Knife.

Curriers Turning Steel.

Curriers Steel.

Steel Slicker from 10 to 22 W.G. thick.

GEORGE BARNSLEY

6 in. × 4 in.

Skinners Round Moon Knife.

GEORGE BARNSLEY

Fig. 11:2 Tanner's & Currier's Tools. (George Barnsley and Son's Catalogue, Sheffield, 1898)   297

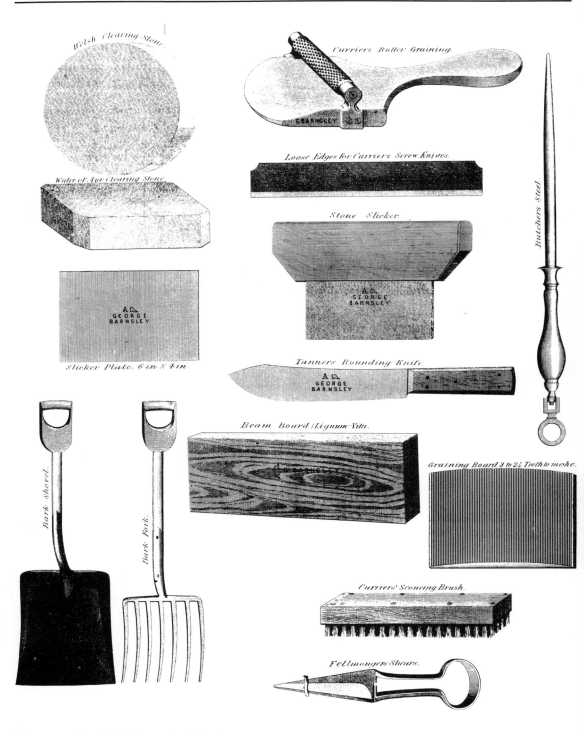

Fig. 11:3 Tanner's & Currier's Tools. (George Barnsley and Son's Catalogue, Sheffield, 1898)

I. Tanner's Tools

Bark Breaking Tools

The oak bark from which tannin was extracted by soaking ('leeching') was first broken up by various tools, including:

(a) *'Hewing Knife'*

A term used by Randle Holme (1688) for a hatchet which, he writes, is 'for Hewing the Bark small, and to prepare it for the Mill'

(b) *'Scutching Knife'*

A name given by Randle Holme (1688) to a tool like a cooper's Drawing Knife of the jigger-type with one handle in line with the blade and the other at right angles to it. He writes that 'by it all the roughness and exorbitances and filthy excrescenses growing on the outside of the bark are cut away.' (In America, this process is called 'rossing', from 'ross', the exterior part of the bark which contains little tannin.)

(c) *Bark Mills*

Since medieval times, different sorts of mill, both hand- and power-driven, have been developed for breaking up bark. Randle Holme (1688) describes an edge-runner mill – a stone set with knives leaded into the stone and running in a trough, which 'causeth the Irons to cut the Bark very small'.

In many of the bark-breaking machines of the nineteenth century, the bark was first broken up between toothed rollers, and then poured into the hopper of a toothed conical drum running vertically rather like a giant pepper mill.

Bark Fork and Shovel *Fig. 11:3*

(a) *Bark Fork*

A type of fork known in the tool trade as a 'Stone Fork' or a 'Potato Fork'. This has seven flat tines which are slightly scoop shaped. It is used for handling both bark and hair.

(b) *Bark Shovel*

A wide, metal shovel with a square blade.

Barking Iron (Wrong Iron; Bark Spud; Peeling Iron; Piping Bar; Rinding Iron; Ripping Iron; Tan Spud) *Fig. 11:4*

A blade, some two inches across, and either round or semi-circular, spade-shaped, or shield-shaped. In section it is wedge-shaped, rounded on the upper side to prise off the bark. It is quite blunt. The length varies from 10 to 30 inches (25.4–76.2 cm), the smaller one sometimes called a Wrong Iron since it is used to remove the bark from the 'wrongs', i.e.

smaller branches or crooks. The handle of these smaller socketed irons is often a piece of naturally forked branch which gives a good grip. The longer tools have a plain knob, T-handle or plain iron ring. In correspondence (1975) about this type Mr Stephen Price of the Birmingham City Museum states that this heavier and longer Barking Iron is called a Piping Bar at Alton in Hampshire, and was used for preliminary heavy work on larger oaks. Animal bones, with an edge filed down, are sometimes used for the same purpose.

Barking Irons are used for removing bark which is sold to the tanners to make the liquor for tanning.

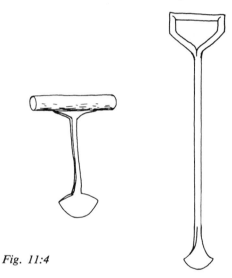

Fig. 11:4

Beam, Tanner's

(See also *Beam, Currier's* in the section LEATHER MANUFACTURE II; and Tanner's Beam Tongs under *Pit Tools*.)

(a) *Unhairing and Fleshing Beam* *Fig. 11:5*

A sloping board with a convex surface, made of wood, stone or cast-iron and *c.* 3 ft 9 in. (1.37 m) long by 20 in. (50.8 cm) or more wide. The work done on the beam is described under the following entries:

Unhairing: see *Knife, Unhairing*
Fleshing: see *Knife, Fleshing*
Scudding: see *Knife, Scudding*

When pushing the knives downwards over the hide the worker, known as a 'beamsman', prevents the hide slipping downwards by leaning against the edge of the hide which overhangs the top edge of the beam.

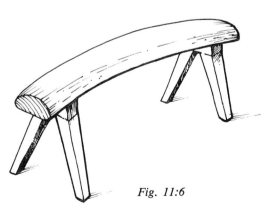

Fig. 11:5

(b)   Striking Beam   Fig. 11:6

A long beam, slightly bowed in its length, with a convex working surface. It is about 6 ft 6 in. (1.98 m) long and 2 ft 6 in. (76.2 cm) high. (An example in the Castle Museum in York is made of whalebone.) The use of the beam is described under *Striking Pin*.

Fig. 11:6

Beater (Mallet; Walloper)   *Fig. 11:7*

A beechwood maul seen in the Croggan tannery at Grampound, Cornwall (1975). About 14 in. (35.5 cm) long, with a head rounded on one side, it was used for beating out 'bumps' on the whole hide when still hanging to dry, and about half dried out.

A similar process is described in *The Art of Tanning and Currying Leather* (Dublin Society, 1774): 'Those hides that are puckered are malotted, that is, they are beaten with a mallet on a smooth block of wood: the beating helps to stiffen, to draw out and smooth them; some tanners beat all their hides.'

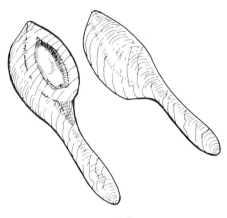

Fig. 11:7

Bramskin

An obsolete Scots term for a leather apron worn by tanners and curriers.

Knife

(See also *Beam, Tanner's*)

Tanners and curriers apply the term 'knife' to a number of rather different tools:

(a)   Handled Knives of the kind used by butchers.

(b)   The two-handed instruments that look rather like woodworker's drawing knives, but are worked by pushing forward instead of being pulled towards the user, and have handles in line with the blade instead of being set at right angles. They are used by beamsmen on a *Beam* over which the hide is laid.

(c)   Tools which are scrapers rather than knives (see nos. 5 and 6 below).

Roy Thomson, an authority on leather, writes (1982):

'I am sure that many of the two-handed tools were interchangeable. A sharp Unhairing Knife could be used for fleshing, and a blunt Fleshing Knife could be used for unhairing and scudding. I have seen Fleshing Knives used for trimming and even rounding; and I feel certain that a Striking Pin was occasionally used for scudding and vice-versa.'

Tanner's and currier's knives are described under the following entries:

	See entry in the section LEATHER MANUFACTURE, I. Tanner's Tools unless otherwise stated.
(1) Hand knives for trimming away unwanted edges of the pelt before tanning.	*Knife, Trimming* *Knife, Piercing*
(2) Hand knife for removing certain outer parts of the hide that are to be tanned separately.	*Knife, Rounding*
(3) Two-handed tool for removing hair.	*Knife, Unhairing*
(4) Two-handed tool for removing any remains of fat or flesh.	*Knife, Fleshing*
(5) Two-handed tool, with a slate blade used for removing any remaining 'debris'. It is also used for pressing out fluid after liming.	*Knife, Scudding*
(6) Two-handed tool of roughly triangular cross-section used for scrapping off any remaining impurities after tanning. Also used by curriers for removing wrinkles.	*Striking Pin*
(7) Two-handed tool used by curriers for levelling and reducing the thickness of the hide.	*Currier's Knife* (See LEATHER MANUFACTURE II)
(8) Circular knife used for paring and perching.	*Knife, Moon* (See LEATHER MANUFACTURE II)
	See entry in the section LEATHER MANUFACTURE, I. Tanner's Tools unless otherwise stated.
(9) Two-handed tools similar to the *Unhairing Knife*, used for processes known as 'breaking' and 'frizzing'.	*Knife, Breaking* *Knife, Frizzing*
(10) A Sleeker type of tool with its edge turned for paring.	*Whitening Knife* (Buffing Sleeker)

Knife, Breaking
A name sometimes given to a blunt, two-handed knife similar to an *Unhairing Knife*. It was used on a beam for a process known as breaking-over or knocking-up. Its purpose was to break down the fibres of hides that remained hard even after soaking; and also for working the flesh side of finer skins to allow the liming and other agents to penetrate.

Knife, Fleshing *Figs 11:2 (p. 297); 11:8*
There are three kinds:

(*a*) The most usual type is a two-handed knife (as illustrated) with a double-edged blade which is about 4 in. (10.1 cm) wide and is made in five sizes from *c.* 15–18 in. (37.5–45.7 cm) long. The blade is either riveted on to separate iron tangs, or the tangs are forged as part of the blade. The tangs penetrate wooden handles (which are mounted in line with the blade) and are normally riveted over washers at the handle ends.
The blade is curved both ways, that is, both longitudinally and across its width. The convex longitudinal edge (known as the leading edge) does the cutting; the concave edge (known as the trailing edge) is less sharp and may be used for pulling the hide into place on the beam as the work proceeds, without having to put the knife down and use one's hands.
However, there are deviations from the normal as exemplified by the following paragraph from the catalogue of Edward Wilson & Son Ltd (*c.* 1950):
'We can supply either the British or the American type of knife, the latter being narrower and having the back uniformly radiused. Fleshing Knives can be fitted with safety guards to reduce the risk of accidental cuts to the hides, and if desired the inner

or concave edge can be saw-toothed for use in moving the hide on the beam.' (See (*b*) and (*c*) below.)

(*b*)　A variant is the *Spring-Back Flexible Knife*. This is usually imported and is often known as a German Fleshing Knife. They have straight blades, from 16–25 in. (40.6–63.5 cm) in length, with edges bevelled on one or both sides. It is said that, being flexible, these knives are useful for lighter work when they will bend to follow the contour of the beam.

(*c*)　Another variant is the *Saw-toothed Fleshing Knife*. Sometimes used for rough, dry skins, this had a serrated edge. (See *Taxidermist* in the section MISCELLANEOUS TRADES AND TOOLS.)

Purpose and operation　Fig. 11:8
The purpose of the Fleshing Knife was expressed thus by Randle Holme (1688): he refers to a Shaving Knife like a drawshave 'by which tanned skins are shaved and cleaned from their filthy excrescences of flesh, hair and end of skins'.

The beamsman throws the hide over the beam and standing behind it he bends forward over the hide, pushing the knife away from himself, down the beam. The concave (hollow) side of the blade lies nearest the work, and he moves the knife in a slicing

Fig. 11:8

action, swinging the blade diagonally across the hide; because of the curvature of the beam he cuts away the unwanted flesh and fat in strips.

The beamsman holds the trailing edge of the knife slightly lifted, and at this angle the leading (cutting) edge is pushed under the flesh to be removed. If the leading edge is kept well sharpened, the effort of cutting will be reduced, and with less danger of cutting the hide itself. On this question, an experienced beamsman working at J. & F. J. Baker (1979) said that he 'turned up' the leading edge of the knife with a steel and that this upwards burr helped to prevent 'digging in' and the accidental cutting of the hide.

Another method
J. Geraint Jenkins (1965) has recorded a different method of fleshing. He relates that:

'In many Welsh tanneries it was customary to keep one or two large mastiff dogs, and it is said that as soon as market hides were delivered to the tanyard, each one was pegged to the ground so that the dogs could bite off any fats and flesh that adhered to the skins. The mastiffs were, of course, useful to guard the premises and to keep control of the vast number of rats that always infested tanneries. In addition the dogs' excreta when mixed with hot water was essential for treating certain types of soft leather before tanning.'

Knife, Frizzing (Frezing Knife)
A name given to a two-handed knife of the same shape as the *Unhairing Knife* but with a sharp edge.

It was used for the process known as frizzing, i.e. the cutting away of the grain layer of hides and skins intended for the manufacture of buff or chamois leathers by oil tannage. The grain layer would have made the leather too firm, and its removal also facilitated the penetration by oils. A similar operation was at one time done by rubbing away the grain side of the hide with pumice stone. (See also *Parchment Knife* in section MISCELLANEOUS TRADES.)

Frizzing was replaced by splitting when machines for this purpose were developed.

Knife, Moon (or Perching Knife): see the section LEATHER MANUFACTURE, II. Currier's Tools.

Knife, Piecing　*Fig. 11:9*
A narrow, curved blade, *c.* 16 in. (40.6 cm) long. This knife is used on the beam for scraping off any remaining wool from sheepskins and also for trimming the edges of the skin.

Fig. 11:9

Knife, Rounding   *Figs 11:10; 11:1a*

A heavy hand knife of various types including one with a deep blade which Randle Holme (1688) describes as 'a short broad blade like a Turkish scimitar, a thick back and a short handle'.

It is used for the operation known as 'rounding': this is the removal of the outer parts of the hide that are less durable, including parts of the neck, shoulders and belly, leaving, after their removal, the central butt which makes the best leather for heavy work. The rejected parts ('offal') are not thrown away but are tanned for use where resistance to wear is less important.

Fig. 11:10

Knife, Scudding   (Scudder; Scouring Knife; Scudding Slate; Scudding Stone. Knight, 1877: Stock Stone)   *Fig. 11:11*

A two-handed wooden stock *c.* 16–24 in. (40.6–60.9 cm) long overall, in which is secured a blade of slate with a concave, blunt working edge 9–12 in. (22.8–30.5 cm) long. Later examples have metal or vulcanite blades. Slate blades are liked because they are said to be less harsh in operation than metal.

The Scudding Knife is used for pressing out the lime solution in which the hides were soaked for unhairing, and for the removal of degraded tissue and fat. At the same time it scrapes off any remaining 'scud', i.e. short hairs and dirt. This work is done on the beam by pushing the knife over the hide (see *Beam, Tanner's*).

Fig. 11:11

Knife, Trimming   (Tanner's Hand Knife)

A name given by tanners to a number of different hand knives such as the sickle-shaped *Butt Knife* (see BOOT AND SHOE MAKER section), and to several kinds of butcher's knives including one of narrow triangular shape with a very sharp point.

These knives are used for cutting off unwanted scraps from the edge of the skin before tanning.

Knife, Unhairing   (Dehairing Knife; Working Knife. Randle Holme, 1688: Pilling Knife.)   *Fig. 11:2* over the caption 'Tanner's Working Knife', and *Fig. 11:12* overleaf.

A two-handed knife with a blunt, slightly concave working edge, made in four sizes from 16–19 in. (40.6–48.2 cm) long, tanged into wooden handles at each end. It is used for removing the hair after it has been loosened by steeping the hide in a lime solution. The hair must 'slip' off quite easily before beginning this operation.

A variant has a straight or convex working edge, but the blade is slightly bowed in its length.

At Messrs Josiah Croggon (1979) the beamsman pushed the hairs out on the forward stroke, and 'wiped' the hairs aside with the back of the blade on the return stroke.

There are few, if any, tanneries where this work is still done by hand. The following description appears to be an eye-witness account and is quoted for that reason (Gresham, I, 97, 1920):

'Practically every method of disintegrating the epidermis and loosening the hair leaves the cutis still covered with its outer coatings, which must be forcibly removed. For this purpose the hide is thrown, hair side upwards, over a slanted beam, thick and convexly rounded. Taking a blunt two-handled knife the blade of which is slightly concave, and, bending over the head of the beam, you push off the epidermis and hair. If the lime-pits or other depilatory agents have done their work, the job is very easy, calling for nothing more than consistent and regular pressure of the blunt edge downwards on the surface of the hide. The pressure of the body upon the part folded over the top of the beam holds the hide steady, and resists the pull of the knife. Inequalities on the inner side of the hide give some trouble, causing the knife to skip at times; but the main difficulty arises from ineffective action of the depilatory agent. Young hairs and hard places in the epidermis resist the blunt knife. Though contrary to regulations, and risky in itself, the common practice is to take a sharp knife to these parts, cutting and scraping the cutis clear. If carefully done, no harm need accrue, though a slip of the knife or too deep scraping may injure the hide seriously.'

Fig. 11:12

Marking Hammer (Hide-marking Hammer; Pricking Hammer)
An ordinary hammer but with letters or figures cut on one or both faces designed for marking by imprint, or by perforation.

Used for marking hides. At some tanneries each man is allotted his own Marking Hammer, so that if the hide is damaged — for example in the fleshing process — it can be traced to the man who did it. (A modern Marking Hammer of the perforating type is illustrated in the FURRIER section under *Furrier's Tools*.)

Pit Tools *Fig. 11:13*
A general term for the hand tools used in and about the pits in a tanner's yard. These pits include the following:

Lime Pit, filled with water and lime in suspension into which skins are soaked to loosen the hair.

Leech Pit (Mashing Vat; Latch Pit in Cornwall; Leck in Scotland) in which tan liquors (or 'oozes') are prepared.

Handler Pit (Floater Pit) in which the hides are laid flat in a tan liquor of medium strength in order to give a uniform surface colour. The skins are regularly 'handled' to prevent adhesion and to accelerate the process.

Layer Pit (Bloomer Pit; Layaways) in which skins are laid with oak bark sprinkled between them.

TAN-YARD.

Fig. 11:13

The Pit Tools used include the following:

(*a*) *Filter*
Described by Randle Holme (1688) as a 'nett-work' scoop to take bark out of the water.

(*b*) *Handler Hook* (Crook; Handling Hook; Hauling Hook; Hide Hook; Plunger Hook; Tanner's Hook.) *Fig. 11:14*
These are either all metal, with a T-handle, *c.* 10–15 in. (25.4–38.1 cm) long, or socketed and mounted on the end of a wooden pole *c.* 6 ft (1.82 cm) long.
These hooks are used for handling, and for removing skins from the pits. The points are of various designs:

(i) A single blunt point for general use.
(ii) A sharp forked point, used for pulling hides from the lime pits before unhairing. (The points must be applied to the flesh side of the hide, *not* to the grain side.)

(iii) A single 'duck-bill' end which may be used on the grain side with less risk of damage to the hide.

(c) Jet Fig. 11:14
A bucket or scoop, at one time coopered in wood, mounted on the end of a 6 ft (1.82 m) wooden handle. Used for applying tan liquors.

(d) Plunger Fig. 11:14
A wooden plate or block on the end of a long handle, used for mixing oak bark in a leeching pit, or for stirring the tan liquor before immersing the skins. One of those illustrated here ends with a device that looks like a giant 'whisk'.

(e) Pooler (Poker)
A name given by Randle Holme (1688), and also by Knight (1877) for a long stick used to stir the liquid in the vats or pits.

(f) Runge or Soe
Randle Holme (1688) writes: 'This is a vessel (like a large tub) with two ears or Stouks, (as some call them) having a round hole in each, through which a long *Weigh* or *Pole* is thrust, and so it is born between two Men. It is to carry Water in for the Benefit of their Washing, and filling their Pits.'

(g) Tongs
Those used by tanners include:

(1) Tanner's Tongs (Pit Tongs) *Fig. 11:14*
Like blacksmith's tongs, but about 6 ft (1.82 m) in length, and usually provided with knobs or rings on the ends of the handles to stop the hands slipping off. They are used for removing the hides from the tanning pits.

(2) Tanner's Beam Tongs *Fig. 11:15*
A pincer *c.* 14 in. (35.5 cm) overall, with serrated jaws. The hooked handle is useful when lifting a heavy hide. Used also by beamsmen for dragging skins over the beam.

Fig. 11:15

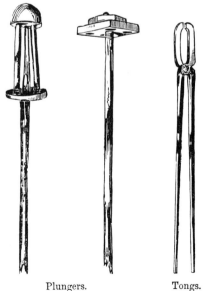

Fig. 11:14   Plungers.   Tongs.   Jet.   Hook.

305

Roller *Fig. 11:16*

Heavy leather, such as that used for soles, is rolled in order to compact the fibres. Before the introduction of mechanical rollers, a 'hand-cart' filled with stones or metal weights, mounted on a roller, was used for this purpose. Formerly leather had been beaten with hammers – a process still performed by shoemakers to improve the wearing quality of the sole leathers they purchase from the merchants (see *Lap Stone or Lap Iron* in the BOOT AND SHOE MAKER section).

Mr J. Snell, formerly employed at Messrs J. & F. J. Baker & Co., the tanners and curriers at Colyton in Devon, used the 'hand-cart' type of roller some sixty years ago. He described the operation as follows (1979):

'We had a brass roller surmounted by a heavy iron box, a long wooden shaft being attached to it. For the first rolling (rolling on) the box would have two or three iron plates placed in it, but the second time (rolling off) it would be fully loaded to give maximum pressure.

'The roller was hoisted on to the Butt by placing small pieces of thinner leather between the roller and the Butt. As the plates were about 20 lbs. in weight and there were ten or twelve of them, and the Box being of heavy cast iron, the work was very laborious, and required considerable strength. Battens of wood were nailed across the floor to give the man a good foothold.'

Fig. 11:16 Rolling hides

Sharpening Tools: see entry in LEATHER MANUFACTURE, II. Currier's Tools.

Striking Pin (Setting Pin; Striking Knife; Stripping Pin; Fluted Pin) *Figs 11:2 (p. 297); 11:17*

A blade about 20 in. (50.8 cm) long of triangular section. This provides three scraper edges, and three faces in between which are slightly hollowed to leave the edges in contact with the hide. Longitudinally, the tool may have a gentle fusiform contour. The ends of the blade are tanged into wooden handles which are mounted in line with the blade.

This tool is used by other tanners and curriers: by tanners for smoothing and cleaning the skin before drying; by curriers for removing the bloom (caused by the tannage) and sometimes for smoothing and stretching, instead of using a sleeker – especially on rougher and thicker hides.

In operation, the hide is placed grain side up over a long, horizontal beam and the 'pinner' works from the left side of the beam, holding the Striking Pin flat on the leather while making forward strokes (see *Beam, Tanner's*).

Fig. 11:17 Striking hides

II. Currier's Tools

Beam, Currier's (Shaving Beam; Horse; Shaving Peg). See also *Beam, Tanner's* in the section LEATHER MANUFACTURE, I.   *Fig. 11:18*
A thick, flat wooden board *c.* 3 ft 9 in. (1.37 m) high and 8–10 in. (20.3–25.4 cm) wide, set in a substantial wooden base, either vertically or at a slight angle. The working surface of the beam is usually covered with a separate 'Shaving Block' or 'Beam Board' made of lignum vitae, or by a piece of wood that can be replaced when worn. The angle of the board is sometimes adjustable by hinge or other means, with stays for holding it at the required angle.

It is used as a support for the skin while being shaved to reduce its thickness (see *Knife, Currier's*).

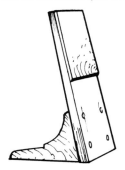

Fig. 11:18

Brush, Currier's   *Fig. 11:3 (p. 298)*
A number of different brushes were made specially for the various processes of scouring, applying dubbing and other currying materials, and for colouring, finishing and polishing. Most of them were similar in appearance to domestic brushes, but some had a leather strap on the back to hold the hand. They were usually named after the process in which they were used, e.g.

Blacking or Colouring Brushes: sometimes of circular shape.

Oiling-Off Brush: about the size and shape of a clothes brush, for applying oils.

Pasting Brush: a wide, flat brush of the paper hanger's type.

Pigment, Staining and Tinting Brushes.

Scouring Brushes: about $8\frac{1}{2} \times 3\frac{1}{2}$ in. (21.5 × 8.89 cm) with very strong bristles.   *Fig. 11:3*

Stuffing or Drumming Brush: with soft bristles for applying dubbing.

Sueding Brush: with wire bristles.

Dubbing (Dubbin)
A mixture of tallow and certain fish oils, used by curriers for 'stuffing', i.e. to make certain skins more flexible and waterproof.

Fluffing Tool   *Fig. 11:19*
Similar in appearance to a *Graining Board* but having an extension on the back to serve as a handle. The face of the tool is covered with emery grit, fine sand or pumice.

It was most probably used for the process known as fluffing – the raising of a nap on the flesh side of the leather, to give a suede effect.

The example illustrated comes from the tannery of Webb & Sons (Combs) of Stowmarket in Suffolk. Similar abrading tools are mentioned by several writers, though often under different names. They include:

(*a*) *Grounding Tool.* 'An emery covered crescent of wood with a cross handle was worked over the back of the leather in order to remove the rough surface.' (Leyland & Troughton, 1974.)

(*b*) *Buffing Tool.* A scraper for the removal of deeper scars and scratches.

(*c*) *Snuffing Tool* for the same purpose as buffing (above), but for removing only slight grain defects.

Fig. 11:19

Glove, Currier's
Described by Knight (1877) as a 'heavy glove having a pile of coir woven into the hempen fabric, and shaped to the hand. Back and palm are alike, and either may be used for currying'.

Coir is the fibre made from the husk of the coconut which would give the gloves a rough fibrous surface. It is probable that the gloves were used instead of a brush for hand-stuffing with dubbing etc. (see *Brush, Currier's*.)

Graining Boards (Armboard; Arm Grainer; Cork-board; Creasing Board; Handboard; Hand Grainer; Pommel; Raising Board) *Fig. 11:20*
These wooden tools are usually flat on the back and convex on the face. A leather strap is fixed to the back of the tool to hold the hand or arm.

They are used for graining or boarding. This is a process applied to soft dressed leathers for bringing back the pleasant-looking grain on the hair side which tends to become flattened during tanning. The process also helps to make the leather supple, and can also be used to give a final polish.

The leather is folded over on itself, grain inwards, and laid flat on the bench. The Graining Board is then moved forwards and backwards upon it so that the fold is pushed forwards and backwards as well — thus 'opening' the grain.

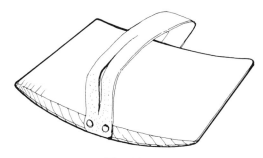

Fig. 11:21

(*b*) *Arm Graining Board Fig. 11:22*
About 15×6 in. (37.5×15.2 cm), with peg-handle and arm-strap, and a flat or slightly convex sole. The sole is covered in various materials such as those described under (*a*) above. It is used for the same general purpose.

In recent years this tool has been made of aluminium with a rubber-covered face.

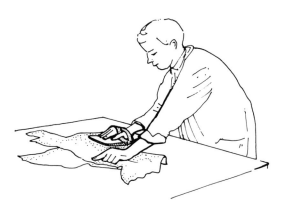

Fig. 11:20

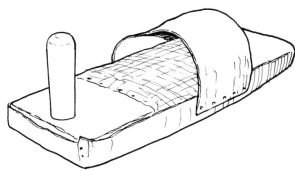

A century ago it was common practice to use the naked forearm for graining and polishing. Jenkins writes (1976, p. 115), 'It is said that in the past a good currier was often recognisable by the fact that his forearm was coloured a near-black.'
Variants include:

(*a*) *Hand Graining Board Fig. 11:21*
Measuring about 10×6 in. (25.4×15.2 cm) with a flat back and convex sole, rather like an Edwardian desk blotter. A leather strap for the hand is usually provided on the back, sometimes cut with a hole for the thumb.

For leather such as calf or goatskin the sole of the Graining Board is covered in cork; for shoe upper-leathers the Graining Board is often made of mahogany without a special covering.

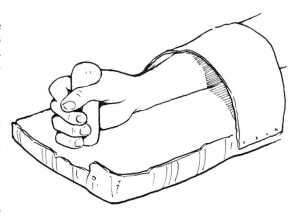

Fig. 11:22

(c) Crippler

An alternative name for the *Pommel* (below) but the term is also applied to a graining tool with a flat sole on which are cut a number of latitudinal grooves about $\frac{1}{2}$ in. (1.2 cm) wide.

(d) Fluffing Tool (Sometimes called a Buffing, Grounding or Snuffing Tool.)

This looks like a Graining Board but is used for a different purpose. (See separate entry under *Fluffing Tool*.)

(e) Gripper

A name given to a Graining Board faced with a sheet of perforated tin like a household nutmeg grater. Purpose uncertain.

(f) Pommel (Crippler; Dublin Society, 1774: Paumelle) *Figs 11:23; 11:3 (p. 298)*

Shaped like a Hand Graining Board (above), with a corrugated working face. It is often made in boxwood. Randle Holme wrote in 1688:

'This is a Board with Nicks in after the manner of a Saw, if you look sideways at it, but turn it up and you will perceive the Nicks, Teeth, or Riggers (call them what you will) run quite athwart the Board; it hath a Leather fastened on the top to put the hand through, thereby to hold it more steady, and to work it the more easie.'

A variant is a block of wood with a flat sole about 4–5 in. (10.1–12.7 cm) square, furrowed across the working surface.

Pommels were used for boarding heavier leathers: the corrugations help to prevent the tool slipping over the folded surface.

Fig. 11:23

Horse (Trolley)

A piece of currier's furniture on which hides and skins are carried. It is a framed stand, triangular in end elevation, with wheels mounted on the base.

Jigger, Hand

A name given to a hand-operated machine used for polishing leather. It consists of a roller made of some hard material, such as boxwood, mounted at the foot of a frame which is suspended from the ceiling. This frame is swung backwards and forwards by hand with the roller bearing on the surface of the leather.

Knife, Currier's (Beam Knife, Shaving Knife. Randle Holme, 1688: 'Paring or Shaving Knife'). *Figs 11:2 (p. 297); 11:24*

A two-handed, two-edged rectangular knife, with handles at both ends, one in line with the blade, the other at right angles to it: as Randle Holme puts it (1688, p. 351), 'the handles stand one contrary, or cross to the other'. The overall length is 19–23 in. (48.2–58.4 cm), the blade itself 10–14 in. (25.4–35.5 cm) long and 5 in. (12.7 cm) wide.

There are several patterns of this tool, including:

(1) A solid forged blade tanged into both handles (sometimes called 'solid back').

(2) A central iron bar, forked and bolted through the cross handle, but tanged to the other ('narrow back'). This bar is either split to hold the steel blade (which is riveted to it), or made in the form of two plates holding the blade on each side along its centre by means of screws so that a new blade can be inserted when required.

The purpose of this tool is to level and shave down the leather to the desired thickness. The work is done on a flat, almost vertical beam, over which the dampened leather is laid, with the blade of the knife held nearly at right angles to the surface of the leather. The cross handle is provided so that the blade can be held firmly at this angle (see *Beam, Currier's*). Though called a knife, the sharpened edges of the tool are turned with a steel like a cabinetmaker's scraper, transferring the process from a paring cut to a scraper cut. (See also *Sharpening Tools*.)

Levelling and reducing was done in this way until the invention of the splitting machine which saved a great deal of leather that previously was shaved off and thrown away.

The method of operation is well described by H. G. Crockett (Gresham, 1920, Vol. II, p.29):

' ... the workman, firmly grasping the straight handle in his right hand, and holding the cross handle in the palm of his left, begins to shave with long, steady, equal strokes, sending the knife farther and farther down on the hide, which he holds firm by the weight of his body as he bends over the beam. The excrescences on the leather are sometimes hard, and resist the blade of the knife; but by force of muscle the worker must keep straight on, shearing through all obstructions.

'With such work, the edge of the knife is not long in losing its keenness. To remedy this without continual recourse to grinding, we have a small instrument called a "steel", shaped like a blunt bodkin, with the point of which the turned edge is worked up. At intervals during shaving this action is repeated, till the hide has been shaved or the knife needs grinding, or "rubbing" as the currier prefers to call it.'

Fig. 11:24 Diagrammatic section of a Currier's Knife showing the edges turned with a Currier's Steel. *Below*: the Currier's Knife in use.

Variants include:

(a) Flattening Knife
A name sometimes given to a Currier's Knife that has been ground and sharpened until both cutting edges are worn down almost to the central bar. It is then sometimes used for the initial cutting off of the ridges that may have been caused by the *Fleshing Knife*: the tanner's *Beam* is convex and this may lead to the *Fleshing Knife* leaving ridges on the surface of the hide.

(b) 'Patent' Currier's Knife Fig. 11:25
Many attempts were made to simplify the work of shaving, for instance by providing an adjustable fence to control the angle at which the blade is applied to the work. One such, illustrated here, from the currier's shop of W. J. Francis & Son, Falmouth, 1962, is inscribed 'J. J. Bryant's No. 14061 Patent'.

Knife, Moon (Circular Knife; Lunette; Paring Knife; Perching Knife; Skinner's Knife) *Figs 11:2 (p. 297); 11:26; 11:27.* (See also *Pincers, Stretching*.)
Note: This circular knife should not be confused with the semi-circular type of knife used by shoe makers, saddlers and parchment makers, which is described as 'round' or 'half-moon'.
The Moon Knife is a steel disc, *c.* 6–12in. (15.2–30.5 cm) in diameter, saucer-shaped, with a hole cut in the centre across which is clamped (or wedged) a wooden bar that serves as a handle. The circumference is ground to a sharp edge for paring, or a blunt edge for staking.
The Moon Knife has three purposes:

(a)   For Paring – i.e. for reducing the leather to a uniform thickness, an operation known as 'grounding'. This was done, for instance, by

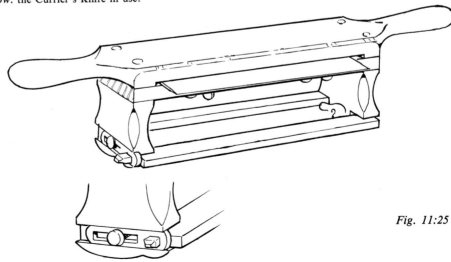

Fig. 11:25

chamois dressers and for the glovers. An advantage of a circular knife was that it could be rotated slightly from time to time, thus presenting a sharp edge for a longer period before regrinding was necessary.

(*b*) For Perching – a staking process for more delicate leather – see the entry under *Staking and Perching Tools* which also describes the *Perch*, a device for holding the skin during this operation.

(*c*) For Scraping – there is some evidence that the Moon Knife was sometimes used to pare leather by scraping. In this case the edge could be 'turned' with a steel.

Fig. 11:26 A Moon Knife used for paring leather held horizontally. (After B. Ellis 1921)

Fig. 11:27 A Moon Knife used for paring leather while hanging vertically. The strap-and-pincer holding device is described under *Pincer, Stretching* below. (After Diderot's Encyclopaedia, *Corroyeur*, Paris, *c.* 1760)

Knife, Striking: see *Striking Pin* in the section LEATHER MANUFACTURE, I. Tanner's Tools.

Mace (Currier's Mallet) *Fig. 11:28*
A wooden mallet named after the medieval spiked club of the same name. It is described by Knight (USA, 1877) as follows: 'A currier's mallet with a knobbed face, made by the insertion of pins with egg-shaped heads. It is used in leather-dressing to soften and supple the tanned hides, and to enable them to absorb the oil, etc. It is analogous to the fulling-hammer.' This tool is illustrated by Diderot (*c.* 1760, *Corroyeur*) who calls it a *Bigorne* (reproduced here). He also mentions the trampling of leather on a hurdle. (See also *Pin Block* – a tool serving the same purpose.)

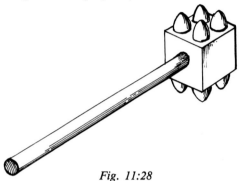

Fig. 11:28

Pin Block (Owler Head)
Randle Holme (1688, p. 351) describes and illustrates this tool, which appears to be a cylindrical wooden block on three short legs, with knobs fixed to the upper surface: 'This is a Block set full of Wooden Pins, about 2 or 3 inches high, upon which they beat their leather to make it pliable and gentle, being rouled up.' (See also *Mace* – a tool serving a similar purpose.)

Pincers, Pulling (Named Tanner's Pincers in the catalogue of the American tool makers C. S. Osborne, *c.* 1930). *Fig. 11:29*
Pincers measuring 8–9 in. (20.3–22.8 cm) overall, with rounded nose and serrated jaws. It is used for pulling hides out of a splitting machine. The handles are bent so that the action of pulling tends to increase the pressure on the jaws.
  Roy Thomson writes (1982):

'These plier-type tools could be used to grip limed hides when they are put through a splitting machine. The limed hides are rather rubbery and very slippery, and when cattle hides are split it is not unusual to have a team of two men feeding the machine, and three or four men and boys pulling the hide out from the other side. I have only seen men using rubber gauntlets dipped in sawdust or wood flour for this pulling out operation, but I can imagine that pliers or pincers could help.'

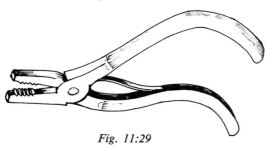

Fig. 11:29

Pincers, Stretching   *Fig. 11:30*
A name given to pincers of various types that are provided with a sliding ring surrounding both handles. When this ring is moved downwards it holds the jaws securely closed – like the Sliding Tongs used in clock-making and other trades for holding objects being worked upon. Judging by the illustration in Diderot's Encyclopaedia (1760) (*Chamoisseur et Megissier*, plate II and *Corroyeur*, plate I), these pincers were used for gripping the lower edge of a skin hanging from a *Perch* and being pared with a Moon Knife. The worker is wearing a belt which is attached to the sliding ring on the handles of the pincers. By leaning forwards slightly to apply the knife, the belt round the hips is pulled outwards, so stretching and holding the skin ready for the paring operation. (See illustration in *Knife, Moon*.)

These pincers are also used to stretch skins while nailing them on boards for drying. (The nailing is done to prevent the skin from shrinking while being dried. To avoid tears, special thick nails, or nails provided with wooden collars, are used.) By attaching the pincers to the waist, both hands are left free for nailing.

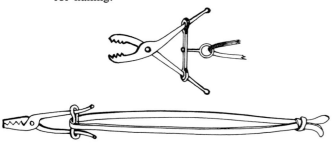

Fig. 11:30   Stretching Pincers: *above*, an example illustrated in an English catalogue *c.* 1920; *below*: after Diderot's Encyclopaedia *Corroyeur*, Paris, *c.* 1760.

Roller Grainer   *Fig. 11:3 (p. 298)*
A metal, glass or stone roller, engraved with the pattern of natural grain, is mounted on a bat-shaped board with one end serving as a handle. Another type had a longer handle with a crutch to fit under the arm. Metal rollers are sometimes heated before use.

This tool is used to hand-emboss a pattern to simulate the natural grain when, for example, the grain has been previously shaved off to remove blemishes. Such work was later performed by an embossing machine of the roller or plate type.

Sharpening Tools   *Figs 11:2; 11:3 (pp. 297, 298)*
Sharpening tools used by tanners and curriers are similar to those used by other trades. The following are typical:

(*a*)   *Rub-Stone* (Grinding Brick)
A block of fine sandstone used for the initial grinding of the bevel.

(*b*)   *Clearing-Stone*   *Fig. 11:3 (p. 298)*
A stone with finer grain is used for removing scratches on the bevel and fining down.

(*c*)   *Steel* (Randle Holme, 1688: Whetting Steel)   *Fig. 11:2 (p. 297)*
A steel is used for 'turning' the edge to form a burr for shaving the leather. It consists of a short length of hardened steel rod set in a wooden handle, *c.* 5 in. (12.7 cm) overall. Those found in curriers' shops include:

(1)   *Turning Steel*. Round or triangular in cross-section, used for general edge-turning.
(2)   *Currier's Small Steel* (Finger Steel). A name given to a smaller version of (1) with a narrow neck in the handle which enables the beamsman to carry the steel between his fingers like a cigarette, ready for renewing the 'burr' on his knife when this is necessary (see *Knife, Currier's*).
(3)   *Two-handed Steel*. A steel rod of about $\frac{1}{4}$ in. (0.7 cm) diameter with a handle at both ends. The double handle helps the user to apply a greater pressure when turning an edge.

Sleeker (Slick; Slicker; Stretching Iron; Dolly Stone: see (1) below. Knight, USA: Stock Stone; Leather-Dicing Tool)   *Figs 11:2 (p. 297); 11:31*
A flat rectangular plate made of metal or stone, 4–6 in. (10.1–15.2 cm) along the working edge, and usually set in a wooden handle.

Sleekers are used for stretching, flattening, squeezing out liquids, working in Dubbing, removing creases and wrinkles, and for polishing. The operation is known as sleeking, slicking, or, occasionally, striking out. The *Striking Pin* performs a similar function, but is used for heavier skins. (See also *Whitening Knife* and *Staking and Perching Tools*.)

The action of sleeking is described by H. G. Crockett (Gresham, *c*. 1920, pp. 31–2):

'Preparatory to either currying or dyeing, leathers have to be thoroughly cleared from all incrustations or remains of tanning matters which may not have become completely absorbed in the fibre. Typical of those matters, though not inclusive of them all, is the powdery yellow deposit which occurs on goods tanned by vegetable agents, and called "bloom". . . . Having laid the hide evenly down, the workman takes up his sleeker – a flat piece of square steel with a round edge and broad wooden holder and firmly strikes along the back, then outwards towards the belly and shoulders, making firm, sweeping strokes, which flatten out the fibres. When this is done, the other half of the hide is treated in the same way . . . Having been thoroughly slicked, or sleeked, on the flesh side, the hide or skin is thrown back into the soaking-tub. It is soaked well once more, and lifted out and laid grain side upwards on the table. The tool used now is a smooth stone, which is generally set in a holder like the sleeker, and blunt on the face. The movement of stoning is similar to that of sleeking, though it partakes more of the rubbing action, because the object is to smooth the grain as well as work up the fibres of the skin.'

(1) *Sleeker blade materials*
These include steel or brass for general work; slate or marble for 'stoning', i.e. pressing out moisture after soaking; and glass, which is sometimes used for final polishing. A stone blade used without a wooden handle is known as a *Dolly Stone*.

Evidence from the workshops suggests, however, that difference in the blade material does not necessarily imply a special or exclusive purpose for the Sleeker concerned. In practice, the currier seems to have selected the Sleeker he considered most convenient for the work in hand.

(2) *Historical note*
The Sleeker is mentioned by several early writers, including:

Diderot (*c*. 1760): 'The stretching implement made of iron or copper.'

Randle Holme (1688, p. 351): 'Smoother with which all their leather is *slickened*, as they call it, that is made bright and shining; it is all of iron . . .'

Cotgrave (1611): The Oxford English Dictionary quotes from his *Dictionary of the French and English tongues*: '*Estire* the yron toole wherewith a Currier draynes the skin he receives from the Tanpit; some call it a Sleeker.'

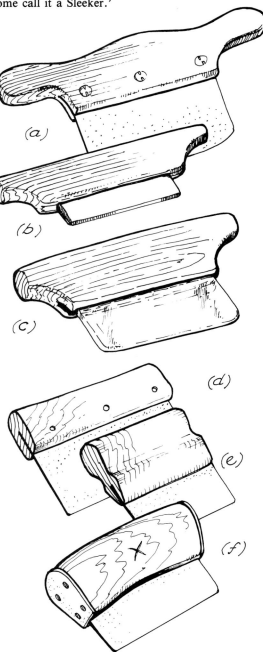

Fig. 11:31 Sleekers: examples with blades made of (*a*) steel; (*b*) slate; (*c*) glass; (*d*)–(*f*) steel.

Staking and Perching Tools
(See also *Mace*)
The terms 'staking' and 'perching' are applied to
processes by which a skin is stretched, softened and
made more flexible. In staking, the leather is drawn
over a blunt, horizontal blade mounted on a vertical
Stake; in perching, a blunt blade is drawn over a skin
suspended from a *Perch*.

The staking process was known in ancient Egypt,
and only recently have machines superseded the hand
operation. Even today the hand method is preferred
for certain very light leathers. Tools and methods are
described below:

(*a*) *Post Stake Figs 11:32; 11:33*
A stout post *c.* 3 ft (91.4 cm) high, with a blunt,
convex blade, *c.* 7 in. (17.7 cm) across, set on top of
it. The worker grasps the dampened leather in each
hand, lays it over the stake, flesh side downwards,
and draws it back and forth over the blade, working
the fibres against the blunt edge.

'Knee staking' is a term applied to a method of
staking stouter leathers, in which the workman uses
his knee as well as his hand to exert additional
pressure on the leather while pulling it over the stake.

Fig. 11:33 The Post Stake in use. (After B. Ellis, London 1921)

(*b*) *Shoulder Stake* (Crutch stake) *Fig. 11:34*
This tool may be described as a portable version of
the Post Stake (above), in which a stake blade is
drawn over the leather instead of the leather being
drawn over the blade.

It looks like a short spade, *c.* 24 in. (60.9 cm) long
overall, with blades of various shapes and materials,
but usually iron. It is held with one hand on the
crossbar or 'crutch' at the top, the other on a handhold near the blade itself. The leather to be worked
was hung from a *Perch* (see below).

This tool was used mainly for leathers requiring
less harsh treatment than that given by the *Post
Stake*, but which needed stronger treatment than that
given by the *Moon Knife* (below).

A retired Devon currier (J. Snell, 1980) describes
how he used this tool:

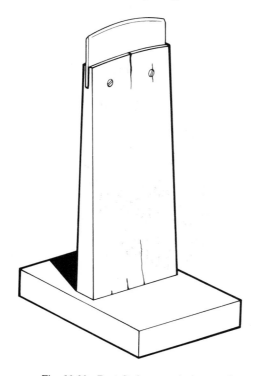

Fig. 11:32 Post Stake: a typical example

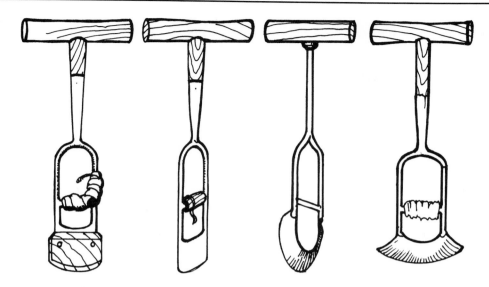

Fig. 11:34 Shoulder Stakes: the left-hand example has a wooden blade, the rest are iron

'A hard working tool this! Its purpose was to break down the hard crust of the hide and also take the stretch out of it. The hide was placed over a beam of wood and kept in place with a rope. The crutch was put under the armpit and the hand gripped the middle bar. The man then took hold of some of the hide with the other hand, placed the blade against the leather higher up and made a downward lunge. This being repeated until the whole had been stretched.'

(c) Withe Iron
Withe was a name given to a band or tie made of tough flexible twigs; but the term is also applied to a ring made of twisted iron which is used as a Stake. The twisting produces a spiral, voluted surface, over which the leather was pulled back and forth. It is illustrated by Pyne (1822) and is described as follows by Randle Holme (1688):

'A Glovers With ... is a square Iron, writhen (as it wear) like a Wreath. ... Upon this they do use to rub and fret their Leather Skins to make them soft and plump; which kind of work from the name of the Instrument, they term Withing.'

Note: There is evidence that a ram's horn was sometimes used for the above purpose.

(d) Moon Knife Figs 11:26; 11:27
This is the circular knife used in several leather trades for paring (see *Knife, Moon*). It was also used for softening more delicate leathers for which the staking operation would have been too severe. This less

severe process is known as perching and is done with a Moon Knife with a blunt edge on skins suspended from the perch. The process is thus described by H. G. Crocket (Gresham, 1920, p. 45):

'The aim of the percher is to reduce the hardness of the fine leathers to a velvety softness, by breaking down all the stiffness in the fibres. The goods are fixed, flesh side upwards, in the clamp of the perch, and hang down the front of the stand. Taking up his moon knife, he inserts his fingers through the opening and grasps the handle, holding the convex side of the knife downwards. Gripping the edge of the skin with his left hand he pulls it out taut, and brings the turned edge of his knife firmly down against the leather. Stroke by stroke, the percher works over the whole skin, breaking down the stiffness of its fibres. ... 'In the case of very stubborn skins, the percher fastens the edge of the skin to his girdle by a wooden clip and a cord. Some attach the cord to their knee, and use it as a lever to obtain extra purchase.' (See *Pincers, Stretching*.)

(e) Chinese 'body' stake Fig. 11:35
In his *China at Work* (1937) Hommel describes and illustrates a type of Shoulder Stake that has a yoke-shaped handle for holding against the stomach, while the other hand holds the tool near the blade. Hommel calls it a 'Hide-Softening Knife' and explains that the edge of the blade is dull. He describes a similar tool, but with a sharpened edge, which he

315

calls a 'Leather Maker's Trimming Knife': this is used to 'even the inside surface of the hide'.

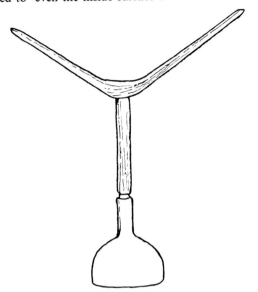

Fig. 11:35

A note on the Perch
This is a clamping device designed to hold one end of a skin while it is being 'staked' or pared. The device may be compared with the woodland worker's Brake used for holding a piece of wood while it is being trimmed. (Similar devices are illustrated under *Knife, Moon* above.)

The two most common types of perch are:

(1)　*The Pole Perch.* Two horizontal poles mounted about five feet off the ground, the lower one fixed, the upper one free to rise and fall in guides. The top edge of the leather was placed over the top pole, and then folded back between the two; thus a downward pull on the lower edge of the leather caused the perch to grip the top edge more tightly.

(2)　*The Rope Perch.* This device uses a rope instead of the moving pole described above. The rope method is illustrated by Diderot (*c.* 1760, *Corroyeur*).

Steel: see *Sharpening Tools*.

Striking Pin: see under the section LEATHER MANUFACTURE I.

Toggle Hook (Toggle; Toggle Clip; Toggle Grip)
Fig. 11:36
A device used for gripping the edge of a hide or skin when suspended from a rack, or when being held by cords from a frame for drying or stretching.

The name 'toggle' is given to various holding devices from screw-grips to a piece of bent wire. That illustrated is taken from the catalogues of B. & J. Wright (1920) and is intended for suspending heavy hides. The edge of the hide is pushed up into the jaws of the toggle where it is held by the toothed pawl. To remove the hide, the pawl must be pushed upwards.

Today, most toggles are designed to fit into the metal toggle-frames which can be placed bodily into drying stoves. Before toggle-drying developed in the early twentieth century, the skins were dried after being nailed out onto boards. The nails were made of brass or galvanised iron, and were thickened with short wooden sleeves under their heads to prevent tearing the skin.

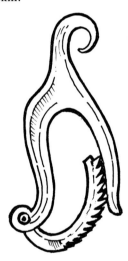

Fig. 11:36

Whitening Knife (Buffing Sleeker)
Similar in appearance to a *Sleeker*, but intended for paring. For this purpose, the edge (about 5 in. or 12.7 cm long) is 'turned' with a steel to produce a burr.

It is used for a final cleaning-up of the flesh side after the currying process (including the paring down with a *Currier's Knife*) has been completed.

— 12 —

Loriner

Historical Note

The term 'loriner', sometimes spelt 'lorimer', derives from the Latin *lorum* – a thong. (*Fig. 12:1, p. 318*)

The loriner is a highly skilled smith who makes horse-bits, spurs, stirrups, and sometimes harness buckles.

A bit is a metal bar which is placed across a horse's mouth. Each end of this bar is connected by reins to the rider's hands, enabling the rider to control the horse in two ways: by exerting a pressure on the left or right side of the mouth which the horse is taught to recognise as a signal to turn; and by pulling the horse's head towards the direction in which he is to go.

The design of horse-bits has not altered much during the last four or five thousand years; those that have survived from the ancient world look much like the snaffle or bradoon bits of today.

Before the coming of the motor car, the loriner, like the harness maker and saddler, served a vast public. Many worked in small workshops in the Walsall district. In forging bits they matched the skills of the 'little masters' of Sheffield and elsewhere who forged the metal tools, gun-locks or kitchen implements of that time; and like these beautifully made objects, the bits were also finished by a long process of filing and burnishing by hand. The material used was wrought iron; today most ordinary bits are cast in steel, thereby avoiding work in the forge, but still requiring hand-finishing.

Catalogues of the nineteenth and twentieth century often list as many as 250 varieties of horse-bits. There was a saying in the trade that there is a key to every horse's mouth. This adage originates from a paragraph in a remarkable book written by Benjamin Latchford, *Bridle, Bit, Stirrup and Spur Maker* (London, 1871). The author was a humane man who strongly opposed cruelty in the training of horses; he maintained that if the right bit could be found, a difficult horse became a manageable one.

'I have always found in my long experience that the horse's mouth and temper may be compared to a lock, so made, that only one key will fit it; and to find the right Bit – patience and perseverance are necessary in so doing. On no account punish the horse; on no account hurt his mouth. When my friends have come to me concerning their unmanageable horses, I invariably find the poor animal has been over bitted, or wrongly bitted, and recommend the easiest kind of bit, which, in nine cases out of ten, succeeds.'

Most of the tools used by loriners are the same smith's tools as those to be found in the small forges mentioned above. But certain special tools have been developed by the loriners, some of which are described below.

Bit Gauge *Fig. 12:2*

A metal gauge with side-gates, usually home-made. It was used by loriners, and by saddlers who sold bits, to measure the thickness of the pieces of the mouthpiece, known as the hefts. The gates were calibrated from $\frac{5}{16}-\frac{12}{16}$ in. (0.75–1.80 cm) rising by sixteenths. For example, customers could obtain bradoon bits with $\frac{7}{16}$, $\frac{1}{2}$ or $\frac{9}{16}$ in. (1.05 cm, 1.27 cm, 1.35 cm) thickness of heft.

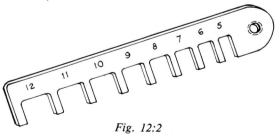

Fig. 12:2

RIDING BITS

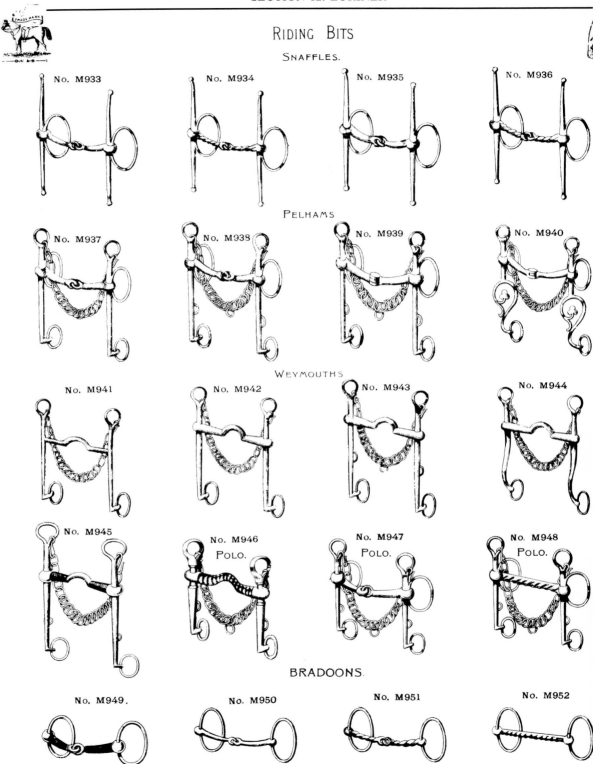

318   **Fig. 12:1**   Typical Riding Bits from the catalogue of D. Mason & Sons, Walsall (*c.* 1900)

Forge Tools

Before the coming of the modern cast metal bits, the anvil, hammer and file were the chief tools of the loriner's forge. Mr William T. Stone, a retired loriner (1979), writes:

'For the forger to be happy in his work he must be at ease and comfortable; the anvil and block should be very close to the hearth so that there is hardly any need for him to take a stride; this is important, for when welding his rings he must not lose the heat. The anvil block and side irons should be a little lower than the hearth, so that when he starts to use the hammer he can direct the full force of it on the work. He must also have a "bosh" of water close by him. His leg vice must be very strong, and should be mounted on a low bench so that he can get on top of the work. In other words – all his fixtures and tools must be at his fingertips.'

The forging process Fig. 12:3

The steps taken when forging the mouth of a typical bit (shown in the diagram) are as follows:

A.   Two lengths of round iron of $\frac{1}{2}$ in. diameter are prepared. If a twisted mouth is required, square iron is used and twisted with a wrench.

B.   The 'outer' end of each rod is 'jumped up' on the anvil. This thickens the end to form the butt.

C.   The swollen ends are 'jumped-up' further, and rounded.

D.   The ends are shaped in a die and a hole punched through each to form the butts.

E.   The other ends of the rods are now tapered down to form the central hinge of the mouth. The end of the upper-side is forged to form a hook.

F.   The end of the pierced side is 'jumped-up' and pierced in a die to form the ring. Finally the hook end of the upper side is threaded through the pierced side and welded up.

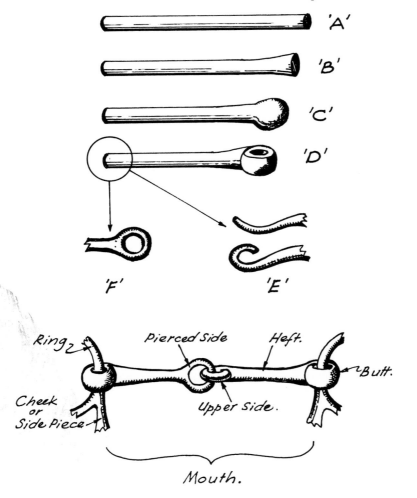

Fig. 12:3

319

Jagging Block (Jagging Clamp; Notching Clamp)
Fig. 12:4
A block of iron on which a stirrup is stood while the tread is being 'jagged' to prevent the rider's boot slipping out. Jagging is the raising of 'pock marks' on the tread of the stirrup by means of a punch. The stirrup is held down on the block by a bow-shaped cramp. The face of the block at one end is flat for jagging flat-bottomed stirrups; it is slightly concave at the other end for jagging round-bottomed stirrups such as racing or Hussar stirrups.

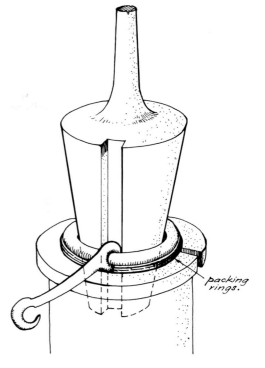

Fig. 12:5

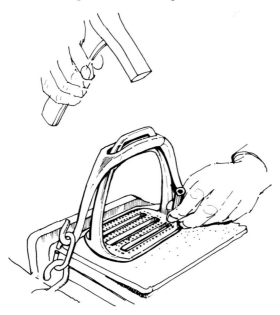

Fig. 12:4

Mandril *Fig. 12:5*
An iron, cone-shaped mandril used for trueing-up rings after they have been joined to the mouth of the bit. The mandril can also be used for trueing other rings on harness, for instance, hame-rings. The ring is placed on the head of a heavy cylindrical block, and the mandril is driven through the ring to round it. The mandril is grooved down its length to accommodate the mouth joint of the bit; flat packing rings are used as washers to support larger bit-rings on the block.

Pitch Bowl *Fig. 12:6*
A device used when punching, chasing or engraving metal ornaments, rosettes, monograms or horse brasses.

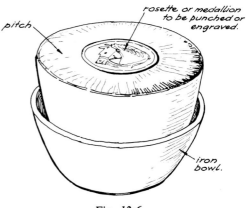

Fig. 12:6

A bowl, filled with melted pitch, is placed in a loosely fitting iron basin. The object to be engraved is pressed into the pitch which is then allowed to set. Bedded firmly in the pitch, the piece is conveniently held for working upon; and the bowl can be turned round inside the outer basin for access to any part of the work.

Plane and Hank (What the term 'hank' implies is not clear, but an OED entry suggests that a hank is something secured by a loop over a hook. This meaning may perhaps apply to the hooked arm that carries the burnishing head.) *Fig. 12:7*

Loriners give this name to a burnishing tool operated like the levered blade of a woodworker's Bench Knife. Diderot (*c.* 1760) illustrates this tool, and calls it a *Polissoir* (Polisher), but it should be pointed out that the process of burnishing differs from metal polishing in that no part of the material being burnished is removed: the process 'closes the pores' of the metal and smooths down any scratches left after filing.

The tool consists of a bowed iron arm hinged at one end to an iron base. The arm is *c.* 30 in. (76.2 cm) long, with a handle at one end and a hook at the other. The hook end acts as a hinge with a ring welded to the front of the base. The burnishing head is held by push-fit into a tapered hole about halfway along the arm. A number of differently shaped heads are kept to be used according to the shape of the object to be burnished: for example, a narrow boat-shaped head is used for 'inside work' such as the burnishing of smaller rings. The base, which is held in a vice, has a grooved upper face on which to rest the work to be burnished; a piece of rag can be placed underneath the work to prevent it from slipping or becoming scratched.

In operation, the hinged arm is lowered until the burnishing head makes contact with work, after which the work is burnished by vigorous movements from the wrist, using the hinged arm to increase the pressure applied. A little oil and a few iron filings are put on the work. The filer keeps the burnishing head bright by rubbing it up and down on the bench near his vice.

It should be added that loriners also used conventional burnishing irons (round and half-round hard steel rods) for burnishing the inside of very small rings etc.

When burnishing the inside of stirrups, the hinged arm is unhooked from the base, and passed through the stirrup, which is held in a *Stirrup Frame*. The handle is held in the right hand while the hooked end, covered with a piece of felt, is supported just above the elbow of the left arm, thus providing the tool with a fulcrum when it is pressed down on the work.

Note: A miniature portrait of this tool, but without its base, is displayed as a trademark in Hampson & Scott's catalogue (*c.* 1900) *See Figs 9:6–9:10.*

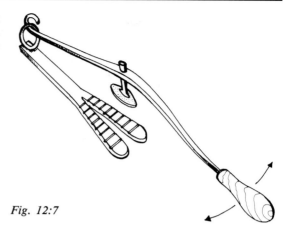

Fig. 12:7

Ring Peg *Fig. 12:8*
A device which, when held in the vice, is used for holding rings when filing down the weld. A short cross-piece, about 4 in. (10.1 cm) long, is welded to the back of an iron stem which has a hook on the top. Any sharp edges on the inside of the hook are removed to avoid marking the work.

In use, the Ring Peg is held in the vice with the hook towards the filer. The ring is slipped under the hook and lies on the crossbar away from the filer. With the ring in this position, the filer pushes a half-round file downwards inside the ring.

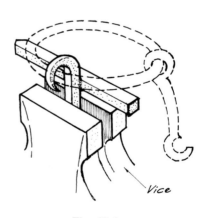

Vice

Fig. 12:8

Spur Block *Fig. 12:9 overleaf*
A semi-circular, cast-iron block, with a lug at the foot for holding in the vice. Two sizes are kept on which to shape the bow for men's or women's spurs.

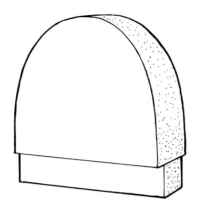

Fig. 12:9

Stirrup Frame *Fig. 12:10*

A metal frame with a lug at the bottom for holding in the vice. The stirrup is held down by a screw at the top. Used when filing-up newly forged stirrups, and also when burnishing with a *Plane and Hank*.

Teddy-Bear Clamp (The origin of this quaint name is not known. In the metal trades it is called a Riveting Stock, Dog-vice, or Spring Stock). *Fig. 12:11* (See also *Clamp* in the HARNESS MAKER AND SADDLER section.)

This all-iron tool belongs to the family of small clams or clamps used for holding objects that are too small or delicate to be held conveniently in a full-size vice. It is jointed at the foot like a hand vice, and shouldered to rest between the jaws of the parent vice. It is made in different sizes from *c.* 4 in. (10.1 cm) overall upwards.

Loriners and brass-dressers use this tool for holding the work when filing buckles, D-rings and other small harness mountings.

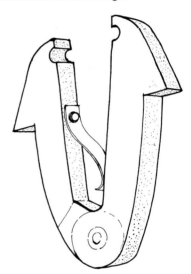

Fig. 12:11

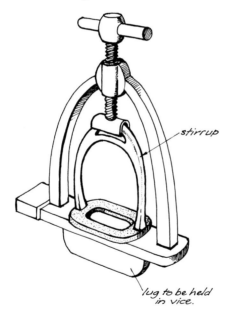

stirrup

lug to be held
in vice.

Fig. 12:10

13

Miscellaneous
Trades and Tools

Ball Maker

The ball appears in the literary and graphic records of ancient Egypt, Greece, Persia and Rome. Early balls consisted of leather strips or sections sewn together to cover various materials, or an air-filled bladder. The precise origins of present day ball games have not been established, but it is evident that some early forms of cricket and football were popular in Western Europe in the fifteenth and sixteenth centuries.

Perhaps those who look with dismay at the football supporters of today may take some comfort from reading how the game was conducted in the sixteenth century. Sir Robert Eliot, writing of football in 1531, describes it as being 'nothyng but beastely fury and extreme violence wherefrom proceedeth hurt and consequently rancour and malice to remayne with them that be wounded. ...'

A few years later, Shakespeare wrote in 'The Comedy of Errors' (Act II, Scene 1):

'Am I so round with you, as you with me
That like a football you doe spurne me thus
You spurne me hence, and he will spurne me hither,
If I last in this service, you must case me in leather.'

(1) CRICKET BALL TOOLS

Manufacture involves the following main processes:

(a) Making the quilt

The centre of the ball, known as the quilt, is a cube of cork round which are wound alternate layers of woollen yarn and further strips of cork. After each layer is wound, the quilt is put into a metal mould and hammered into shape. The yarn is worked wet:

when it dries out it shrinks and tightens the centre cube and strips of cork. This helps to give the ball its bounce.

(b) Making the quarters Fig. 13:1

The leather is cut into 'quarters', i.e. the segments that form the cover. The edges of these quarters are bevelled to prevent the seam from 'standing proud' when they are subsequently lapped and sewn together. The quarters are placed on a Holing Board and each one marked out for stitching.

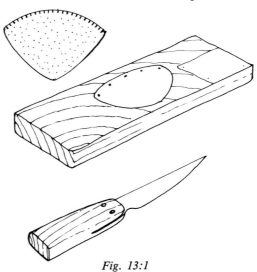

Fig. 13:1

(c) Making the half-cover Fig. 13:2

Two quarters are then placed in a Ball Vice which is a hollowed-out block set on the workbench. Using a finished quilt as a mould, the maker holds the work in position by pressing his foot on the stirrup under the bench while he stitches the two quarters together. When completed, the two quarters are turned inside out to form a half-cover.

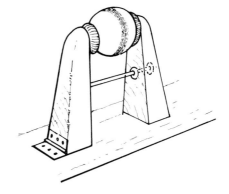

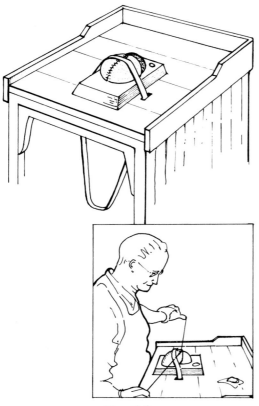

Fig. 13:2

Fig. 13:3

(d) Sewing the half-covers over the quilt
Fig. 13:3
The half-covers are fitted round the finished quilt, and the whole is squeezed together in a powerful vice with cup-like jaws so that the edges of the two parts of the cover overlap slightly as the quilt is temporarily compressed. This allows the first seam to be stitched.

The ball is then placed in a Horn (illustrated below) for the final stitching along each side of the first seam. J. Waterer (1946) writes:

'All good balls thus have triple seams. In cheaper ones the second and third are but dummies, the cover being held by one row of stitching only. This savours of the noxious practice of imitation, but, actually, the three rows of stitching are necessary to provide a good grip for the bowler.'

(2) FOOTBALL TOOLS
The modern round football owes its design to a London maker, Joseph W. Pracy, who, in 1903, hit upon the idea of dividing the ball into six equal-sided panels of similar shape so that any tendency to stretch would be equalised and so avoid a misshapen ball.

At Rugby School a football game was developed in which hands were used as well as feet, and came to be called Rugby football. It is not known why the Rugby football is oval rather than round, but a possible reason is that it makes for easier handling.

In making, the sections are stretched and then assembled to be sewn inside out. Many of the best balls are sewn by hand, leaving a gap through which the ball is turned the right way out; and a tongue is sewn in at this point to cover the bladder where the ball is laced.

The tools used are mainly the knives and awls of the harness makers and shoemakers. But the user of the ball is provided with the following tools for lacing:

(a) Lacing Needle Fig. 13:4
A steel shank with an eye near the blunt 'point'.

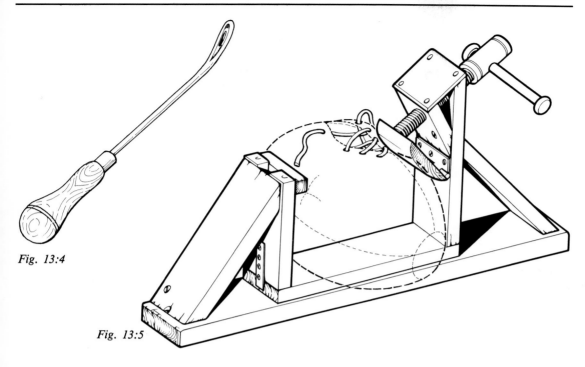

Fig. 13:4

Fig. 13:5

(b) Ball Squeezer Fig. 13:5
A wooden frame incorporating a screw press. It is
used for compressing an inflated ball to close the
opening before lacing up. (The home-made example
illustrated was used by the Harpenden Rugby Football Club *c.* 1950.)

Coach Trimmer

Coach trimmers were responsible for the upholstery
and internal furnishing of the coach. Their work is
described by J. Philipson (1897) as follows:

'...we would like to bespeak for the work of the
coach-trimmer a somewhat higher place than it
usually occupies in the estimation of those engaged
in other branches of the trade. It has been truly said
that the trimmer must quilt like an upholsterer, stitch
like a harness-maker, and sew like a tailor, and it is
just as necessary that he should have good taste and
a knowledge of design, proportion and colour. The
materials which he uses are the most costly of those
employed in the carriage-factory and require great
care in storage and in working, to avoid waste.'

Coach trimmer's tools include the awls, creases,
needles, knives, and pliers of the harness maker, and
many of the tools of the upholsterer. Special tools
include the following:

(a) Cramp, Carriage Trimmer's Fig. 13:6
This is made from two pieces of wood, hinged across
the top with a piece of leather. The two jaws are
drawn together by a nut and bolt; layers of leather
were often sewn together to serve as the nut. The
coach trimmer would have a dozen or more of these
cramps to hold the leather or other covering material
(often black 'patent' leather) while it was being
stitched onto the frames of the mudguards and
elsewhere.

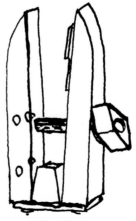

Fig. 13:6

(*b*)   *Hammer, Coach Trimmer's*

These were lightweight hammers listed under names such as coach trimmer's or upholsterer's hammers. They had long, light heads and were designed for driving and extracting small tacks. The English coach trimmer's hammer head is the only one of this group that is not strapped; and it is also unique in having a claw at the side, so leaving a long, flat, cross-pane for driving tacks in confined spaces.

Two main types of coach trimmer's hammer were listed by the tool makers:

1.   English type   *Fig. 13:7*

A long, eyed head with an octagonal or round face, a flat tapered cross-pane, and a side-claw.

Octagon Coach Trimmers Hammer Head.

Round Coach Trimmers Hammer Head.

Fig. 13:7

2.   French 'Cabriolet' type   *Fig. 13:8*

A long, strapped head with a round face and a clawed cross-pane. Special features of this pattern are the overall polished roundness of the head, and the smallness of the face – useful for driving tacks on very fine work.

Fig. 13:8

(*c*)   *Needle, Coach Trimmer's* (Half-Moon Needle; Half-Round Needle) *Fig. 13:9*

These are semi-circular eyed needles measuring around the circumference from $1\frac{1}{2}$–8 in. (3.8–20.3 cm). Messrs John James (1948) illustrates two types, differing in cross-section: one with a round-section body and triangular point; the other with a flat-section body and flat-oval point.

Fig. 13:9

(*d*)   *Yard-Wand*

A name given by coach trimmers to an ebony stick of round section used as a yard measure.

Felt Maker

(*a*)   *A note on felt making*

Felt requires neither spinning nor weaving and is one of the oldest fabrics known to man. Tradition gives the credit for its invention to St Clement, the fourth Bishop of Rome, who was later made the patron saint of the felt makers. It is told that when St Clement was forced to flee from persecutors, his feet became so blistered by long travel that he put a little wool between his sandals and the soles of his feet. On continuing his journey the motion and pressure of his feet worked the wool into a compact substance. St Clement saw that he had made a useful discovery, and he is said to have told a local cloth maker about it.

This old tale gives quite a good insight into the process. Many fibres have minute barbs or scales on their outer surfaces which have the power to interlock; the tiny barbs spread out from the main fibre, catch hold of other barbs and cling fast, uniting to form a dense, compact cloth, which cannot easily be torn.

Felt is used in the Near East and beyond for making clothes, hats, footwear, floor covering, bedding, tents, saddle-cloths, and, when specially processed to resist water, for pots and jugs. In the West felt is now chiefly used only for hats and slippers and, in a cheaper quality, for lining roofs and carpets.

(*b*)   *The Bow* (Hatter's Bow; Stang) *Fig. 13:10*
(See also the HAT MAKER section.)
The Felter's Bow looks like a giant cello bow. It

consists of an ashen or pine staff, from 5–7 ft (1.52–2.13 m) long, with a hardwood bridge at both ends. It carries a single string, usually made of catgut.

Its purpose is to separate individual fibres of hair or wool, shake out any dust or dirt, and to spread them in an even layer ready for felting. The Felter's Bow is still used in countries such as Egypt and Ceylon for unravelling the stuffing of mattresses and pillows: itinerant bowers take up a position in the village where the inhabitants can bring their bedding. The contents are spread out for the bowman to disentangle.

The following description of the process comes from *The Penny Magazine* (Jan. 1841, p. 44):

'A bench extends along the front of the room beneath a range of windows, and each "bower" has a little compartment appropriated to himself. ... The bow is suspended in the middle by a string from the ceiling, whereby it hangs nearly on a level with the work-bench, and the workman thus proceeds: the wool and coarse fur, first separately and afterwards together, are layed on the bench, and the bower, grasping the staff of the bow with his left hand, and plucking the cord with his right by means of a small piece of wood, causes the cord to vibrate rapidly against the wool and fur. By repeating this process for a certain time, all the original clots or assemblages of filaments are perfectly opened and dilated, and the fibres, flying upwards when struck, are by the dexterity of the workmen made to fall in nearly equable thickness on the bench, presenting a very light and soft layer of material. Simple as this operation appears to a stranger, years of practice are required for the attainment of proficiency in it.'

The above account is similar to several to be found in encyclopaedias and other publications of the nineteenth century. The writers appear to have copied from one another without, one suspects, having seen the process with their own eyes. And neither enquiries among museum staff who have studied felt, nor some elementary experiments with a vibrating gut and a handful of fur, have so far explained to the author's satisfaction how this seeming miracle is actually performed.

Today, the preparation and spreading of the fibres is a machine operation in which a current of air distributes the fibres evenly over a metal surface of the required shape. Thus, for making a hat, the surface over which the fibres are spread is a metal block shaped to the contours of the hat being made. The subsequent making-up process has also been partly mechanised.

Fig. 13:10

Gut String Maker (Though gut is often called catgut, the intestines of a cat are not used for making gut strings. The etymology is doubtful.)

The making of strings for bows from animal intestines can be traced back to c. 500 BC, and the making of gut strings for musical instruments to only a slightly later date. From the mid-sixteenth century until modern times gut strings have been used in sports rackets, for clock cords, driving belts, the binding of whip stocks, and for many other purposes where a smooth, hardwearing, high-tensile string is required. In a more recent application very fine gut strings are used for uniting the edges of a wound or of incisions made in surgical operations. The fine strings gradually dissolve but remain intact long enough for the wound to heal.

The process of making gut strings has remained fundamentally unchanged except for recent innovations brought about by chemical technology and the development of machines. The basic material is still by preference sheep intestines, but those of pigs and cattle are also used.

After an initial cleaning process, the gut is split into strips, called strands or ribbons. This is done by pulling the intestines over a wooden *'Splitting Horn'*

327

(see below). The strands are then cleaned individually by passing each one across a *Seeker*, a metal thimble designed for scraping. These cleaning and scraping processes, and subsequent drying, prevent putrefaction.

The strands are then assembled for spinning. The number of strips to be spun together depends on the type of gut string required: for example, there are eleven different diameters required for racket strings alone. The spinning was done until recently on a wooden *Spinning Wheel* which was turned by hand. The strings are then given a period of at least six months to mature, during which time the individual strips in the string unite and become translucent.

Hand tools used in gut-making include the following:

(a) Splitting Horn *Fig. 13:11*

A piece of horn-shaped wood supported on the blade of a vertical knife, with a small blade set into its side. The knife stands blade uppermost, with its handle fitted into a hole made in the surface of the bench.

The horn varies in size according to the type of intestine used and it is slightly curved to correspond to the natural curve or 'bias' of the intestine. The intestine is pulled over the horn across the blades, so splitting it into the required number of strips.

(b) Seeker (Thimble) *Fig. 13:12*

This is made in the form of an open-ended thimble of copper or brass (or now stainless steel). It is placed on the workman's thumb, and the gut strip is pulled between its open end and the workman's forefinger which is protected during the process by a piece of rubber tube. This scraping process cleanses the gut of unwanted matter.

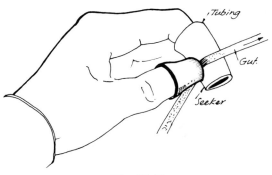

Fig. 13:12

(c) Spinning Wheel *Fig. 13:13*

A hand-driven wheel supported on two uprights which, when turned, drives a smaller wheel whose axle extends to form a hook to which the strips of intestines are attached for spinning. Mr C. Meinel, of Bow Brand British Ltd. (1980), the gut string makers, writes as follows about this machine:

'We used wooden spinning machines until 1953. Similar machines have been used since early times. A twenty-two foot gut string requires over 800 turns in

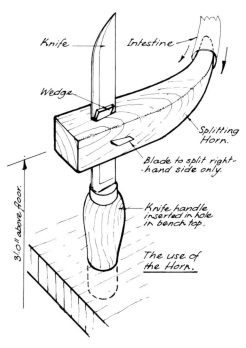

Fig. 13:11

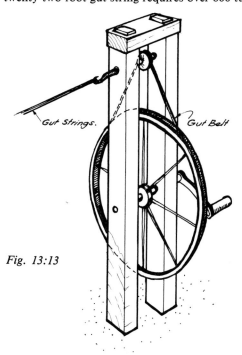

Fig. 13:13

its drying process – too many spins to do without the help of a device of this kind. We still use these machines, but now we have small geared machines with fibreglass tables. We put about 16 strips of beef gut on a loop and put this on one hook; we take all the strips down the bench together, and put them over a hook or bar and then continue back to the spinner.'

Hydraulic Pump-Leather Maker (Packing Maker)
Fig. 13:14
These leathers still play an indispensable part in industry, for in many cases there is no satisfactory substitute. Hydraulic leathers are found in petroleum pumps 3,000 feet below the surface of the earth and in the hydraulic mechanisms of space craft as many miles above it.

Hydraulic or pneumatic leathers are used for packing the glands surrounding shafts, pistons or rams to prevent the escape of liquid or air. Most of them are made from oxhide leather: oaktanned for air or water; chrome-tanned for mineral oils; rubber impregnated leather for oil or water at high temperatures. An advantage of leather for these packings is its ability to conform to any wear on the surface of ram or cylinder; and, unlike some of its substitutes, it is not so liable to sudden collapse if damaged.

the hide with a hand knife and moulded in an hydraulic press. A short maul, with a leather-covered head, is used for knocking the metal moulds apart to release the packing inside.

Plain leather washers can be cut out with a tool called a Washer Cutter. This is usually made in the form of an adjustable bit for use in a Brace. The stem of the bit ends in a spike which acts as a pivot to a spur cutter carried on a bar held in the stem of the bit. The cutter can be set at different distances from the pivot by moving the bar in and out of the stem. This enables the tool to cut washers of different sizes. A home-made version is also illustrated.

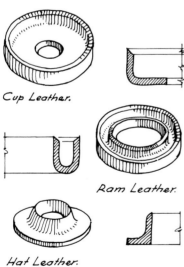

Cup Leather.

Ram Leather.

Hat Leather.

Fig. 13:14

Fig. 13:15

Tools involved *Fig. 13:15*
Small leather packings are stamped out with dies in a hand or machine press; the larger sizes are cut from

Last and Boot Tree Maker

Note: Boot trees are made by a process similar to Lasts; see the entries *Last* and *Boot Tree* in the BOOT AND SHOE MAKER section for illustrations.

A Last is a model of a foot on which a boot or shoe is moulded and constructed.

The traditional material for lasts is beech, or occasionally maple, but in recent years wood is being replaced by plastic. One of the advantages of the wooden last is that it can be built up to match any peculiarities of the foot, and later modifications can be introduced to some extent either by the use of 'fittings' or 'runners' − as described in the BOOT AND SHOE MAKER entry *Last*.

Lasts for mass produced shoes have to follow a compromise on fit, although the inclusion of half sizes in some ranges helps to ensure comfort.

Except in the case of a few bespoke shoemaking firms, last making is a separate trade distinct from shoemaking, although obviously there is close co-operation between them. Eighteenth-century advertisements show that this division is not new.

Last makers can still be seen at work (1980) in the London showrooms of Messrs John Lobb, the bespoke shoemakers. They use tools which are almost identical to those illustrated in Diderot's Encyclopaedia of *c.* 1770. Gresham (1920, Vol. II, p. 263) points out that '. . . the last maker's tools are of the simplest character, and have varied little for generations, affording room for wonder how work so beautiful and accurate can be produced with appliances so primitive.'

Some writers complain about badly made lasts. For instance, H. W. Mobbs (1947), when remembering his younger days, writes, 'There was little accuracy or precision observed in last making at this time, the tools being few and primitive. The beech wood was seldom seasoned, and often shrunk after the lasts were made.' Leno (1895, chap. V) writes that a 'good last maker is worth his weight in gold'. This is not a gross exaggeration when one realises that a last must shape a shoe to cover the peculiarities of the human foot without losing that elegance of appearance that every customer expects.

Process

The logs of beech are sawn into lengths sufficient for two or three lasts, and then split into triangular sections which are called 'spokes'. These spokes are then sawn into last lengths, roughly shaped with an axe, with the narrow angle of the spoke forming the instep of the last. After being left to dry, the spokes are trimmed to shape with a so-called Bench or Stock Knife: this includes the hollowing of the waist, rounding of the heel and forming the toe-spring. The last is then given its final shape with spokeshave, rasp, and scraper. (Today the Surform Tool has taken much of the work from the rasp and file.) Finally the last is smoothed with glass paper.

In some workshops, the roughing out with an axe and Stock Knife has been replaced by the ingenious copying lathe. But the final shaping and finishing is done by hand. Tools used include:

A post-vice
Axe for preliminary shaping.
Bench Knife: this is the same as the *Clog Knife* which is described and illustrated in the CLOGMAKER section.
Rasps, files, scraper and glass paper.
Size Stick: see *Measuring Tools* in the BOOT AND SHOE MAKER section.
Sharkskin: see (*h*) Sharkskin Rasp under *Other Uses of Leather*.

Parchment and Vellum Maker

The term parchment is connected with the Latin name Pergamum, a city in Asia Minor, where, in *c.* 400 BC, parchment is said to have replaced the papyrus reed formerly used by the Egyptians as a substance for writing on. The term 'vellum' comes from the Latin word *vitellus* − a calf.

Parchment is made from the flesh side of a sheepskin after the grain surface has been scraped off. It is used as a writing material. Vellum is usually made from unsplit calfskin and, being stronger than parchment, can be used for bookbinding, drum heads etc.

Until recent years, parchment was much used for legal documents. Today, the demand comes mainly from universities and other institutions who require a durable material upon which to inscribe degrees and diplomas, or for illuminated addresses and the like. It is still used when repairing old manuscripts, and for the handwritten Scrolls of the Law read in synagogues throughout the world.

Process

The skins are not tanned, but are preserved from decay by a process of cleaning, degreasing, and subsequent drying. Today, the skins are provided ready-dressed by the chamois leather makers; formerly they came direct from the fellmongers. The parchment and vellum makers suspend the skins on a *Stretching Frame* and remove unwanted material by scraping down the skin with a *Filling Knife*, using long sweeping strokes, and carefully paring the surface surrounding the 'pippins' with the upper corners of the knife. Hot water is thrown over the skin at intervals during this operation to facilitate the work.

Next, a *Shaving Knife* is used to pare down the skin to a uniform thickness.

The skins are then painted with a thick cream of whiting containing washing soda which, during the time it is left to dry in the heated drying room, dissolves any grease still remaining in the skin. The whiting acts like blotting paper, absorbing and holding the grease.

When dry, the skins are washed free of the whiting, and rubbed with pumice, and the *Scalding Knife* is used for a final smoothing.

Note: The above knives are described under *Parchment Knives* below.

Tools used:

(*a*) *Stretching Frame* (Herse) *Fig. 13:16*

A stout wooden framework *c.* 3 × 4 ft (0.91–1.21 m) on which skins are stretched by cords running from points around the skin to an adjacent peg on the frame. This is done so that the skin can be exposed for scraping and cleaning, and subsequently for drying. Diderot (1760) illustrates a rectangular Stretching Frame like that of today, and also a circular hoop used for the same purpose.

For suspending the skin, small balls of skin peelings, known as pippins, are pushed into the edge of the skin and a cord is tied round them with the pippins held inside. The other end of the cord is tied round a peg, so that when the peg is turned by a wrench (see *Wrist* below) the skin is pulled tight on the frame. The pegs are tapered to fit tightly in the frame like the tuning pegs of a violin.

See detail Fig 13:18

Fig. 13:16

(*b*) *Parchment Knife* (Half-Moon Knife. Hartley, 1939: Strickle. Names for variants: see below) *Fig. 13:17*

The alternative name Half-Moon Knife is confusing, for that term is sometimes applied to the traditional semi-circular knife of the shoemaker and harness maker. In their trades the tool is used as a conventional knife, i.e. to make a slicing cut in line with the edge of the blade. But the parchment maker uses the tool as a scraper; and for this purpose he moves the knife at right angles to the plane of the blade.

The Parchment Knife has a semi-circular blade *c.* 12 in. (30.5 cm) across the chord, from which extends a central tang which is secured in the handle by a wedge. The handle (or 'stock') is barrel-shaped with a peg-handle on each end, *c.* 14 in. (35.5 cm) overall. The blade fits into a kerf cut at right angles to, and in the centre of, the stock, so that the tool can be held with hands on both ends.

The mounting of the blade closely resembles that of the appliance known as a 'box' which serves as the lower handle of a Pit Saw.

The Parchment Knife is used to scrape the surface of a skin stretched on a frame (see *Stretching Frame* above). It is held in both hands and moved at right angles to the plane of the blade in a sweeping action. This type of knife is also used to scrape down chamois leathers: see *Knife, Frizzing* in the section LEATHER MANUFACTURE, I. Tanner's Tools.

Three different Parchment Knives are used, each with its own name. Though similar in appearance, each has its edge prepared for a particular function as described below:

(1) *Filling Knife*. A Parchment Knife with a sharp bevelled edge used, after applying hot water, for scraping off any remaining flesh or fat.

(2) *Shaving Knife*. A Parchment Knife with its sharpened edge 'turned' with a steel, used to pare off the grain, and to pare down the skin to the correct thickness.

(3) *Scalding Knife*. A Parchment Knife with a blunt edge, used for the final smoothing of the skin. Hot water is thrown over the skin during this operation.

Note: In her remarkable book *Made in England* (1939), the late Dorothy Hartley describes and illustrates a Parchment Knife which is similar to that described above, except that the blade is circular. She calls it a Strickle — a country term applied to a rod used for scraping off surplus grain from a heaped vessel used as a measure.

Miss Hartley informed us (1980) that she saw this knife being used in 1930 by parchment makers in Sawston near Cambridge. Enquiries made in

Sawston recently have so far failed to confirm the use of this round knife.

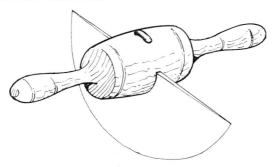

Fig. 13:17

(c)   *Wrist*   *Fig. 13:18*

A wrought iron bar about 8 in. (20.3 cm) long, with a 2 in. (5 cm) slot at one end, and a V-shaped 'fish tail' at the other.

It is used for turning the pegs on the *Stretching Frame*. The slotted end of the Wrist is dropped over the head of the peg which, when turned, winds the cord and so stretches the skin within the frame.

The fish-tail end of the Wrist is used for pushing the pippin towards the edge of the frame before attaching the cord to the peg.

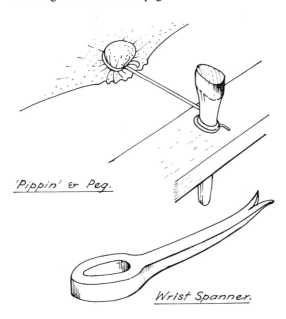

'Pippin' & Peg.

Wrist Spanner.

Fig. 13:18

Taxidermist

The art of the taxidermist is to preserve the skin of an animal, to sew this skin over a modelled replica, and to mount this in a lifelike posture. The process requires both zoological knowledge and the artistic and manipulative skill of a sculptor.

The skins of smaller mammals are treated with a comparatively short mineral tannage; the larger, by the vegetable-tanning method (see the section LEATHER MANUFACTURE).

After tanning, the skin must be made sufficiently flexible to mould over the shape of the model. This process, known as 'relaxing the skin', is described under one of the tools used in the process (see *Skin Scraper* below).

Smaller animals are stuffed with various fillings. For the larger animals, the taxidermist constructs a frame on which a replica of the skinned carcass is modelled in clay, over which the skin is then fitted and stitched into position. In another technique the carcass, or a replica of it, is used for making a plaster mould from which the final figure or 'manikin' is cast to support the skin.

Special skill is needed to select and fit glass eyes, and in some cases the muzzle; and to model gums and tongue in clay or wax, and to colour them with an oil paint to give a natural and lifelike appearance.

TOOLS OF THE TAXIDERMIST   *Fig. 13:19*

These include some of the ordinary tools of the woodworker, wire-worker and sculptor, some of the knives used by the shoemaker, as well as the specialised scalpels and scissors of the surgeon. The following are the more specialised implements:

(1)   *Hooks and chain*
This is used for hanging up a bird while skinning.

(2)   *Drill*
A spike made in several sizes, used for penetrating the bones of animals through which supporting wires may be passed when setting up a skeleton.

(3)   *Stuffing Tools* (*Crowder; Stuffer*)
These are used for inserting the filling into narrow parts of the skin such as the neck of a bird. Those illustrated are forceps of the surgical type with serrated jaws, and about 12 in. (30.5 cm) long. Another stuffing tool is a brass rod with a fork-shaped end, similar to the saddler's *Stuffing Iron*.

(4)   *Dissecting Saw*
A handsaw of surgical type with a $4\frac{1}{2}$ in. (11.4 cm) blade. The 'back' of the saw is removable to permit the blade to pass freely through thicker bones.

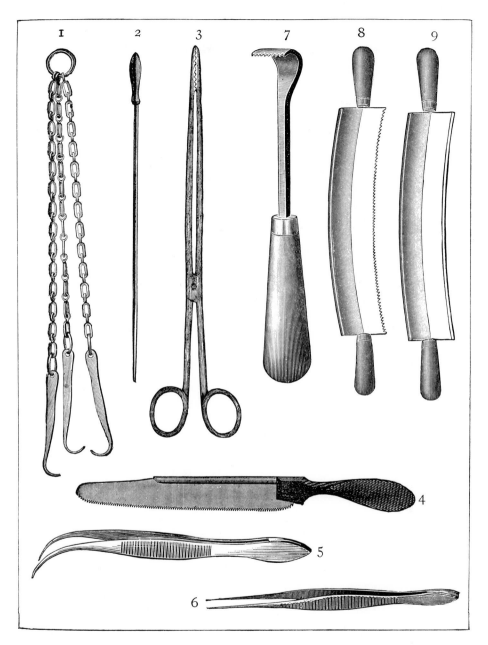

Fig. 13:19 Tools of the taxidermist. (Reproduced from *Methods in the Art of Taxidermy* by Oliver Davie, USA, 1894)

(5,6) *Spring Forceps*
Tweezers with curved or straight points for arranging delicate parts of the skin, e.g. eye-lids or feathers. Curved Shoe-Awls are also used for such work.

(7) *Skin Scraper*
A scraper with a toothed edge used for shaving down the flesh side of the tough skins of larger mammals. This was part of the process mentioned above for making the skin pliable for fitting round the replica of the animal. Skins were sometimes delivered to the taxidermist in a very dry state, for instance, after previous storage or long sea voyages. O. Davie (1894) writes as follows about the process:

'I shall here describe the method I have always employed in relaxing the dry skins of mammals, whether they be the size of a mouse, or from that upward to the size of an elephant. To relax an old, dry skin of a deer, elk, moose, horse, or anything larger, the best plan is to place it in clear, lukewarm water. ... It will soon become pliable, especially if worked vigorously with the hands. The next step is to take it out of the water bath, throw it over a beam, as the tanners do, and either scrape it with a skin-scraper or toothed currier's knife, or thin the skin down with a sharp, common carpenter's draw-shave, or a keen-edged currier's knife. Do not be afraid of cutting the skin too thin; do not trim down below the roots of the hair, for the hair will come out. ... Work at the skin with the determination to make it as soft and elastic as possible, and this can be done only by hard work. ...

'I once spent three days' labor on a horse's skin which was two years and a half old, and at the end of the third day the skin was almost as soft as a kid glove. If there were any faults in the shapes which I afterward gave to the various parts of the skin on the clay model, they could not be attributed to the condition of the skin, for its pliability was all that could be desired. You cannot give the proper form to a skin that is hard and thick.'

(8) *Toothed Fleshing Knife*
A two-handed knife of the type used by tanners for unhairing, but with a serrated edge. It is used for the same purpose as the *Skin Scraper* described above.

(9) *Sharp-edged Fleshing Knife*
As (8) above, but with the cutting edge sharpened. It is used for thinning down the skin of larger animals on the flesh side.

Other tools used:

Knives
Those used for skinning are of the handled type used by shoemakers, including their narrow, pointed Clicking Knife. Surgeon's scalpels — the delicate knives that are held like a pen, are also used.

Pliers
Much used by taxidermists, including those with side cutters for wire cutting, and those with long jaws used for fitting adjustments to claws etc.

Skin Needles
These are mainly three-cornered needles of the type used by glovers and sail makers. They are pushed through heavier skins with a sail-maker's or saddler's palm (see HARNESS MAKER AND SADDLER section). They are used when sewing the skin over the plaster figure.

Modelling Tools
Tools of the sculptor's and plasterer's type are used when making the original clay replica.

Whip Maker *Fig. 13:20*
Ever since animals were first harnessed to provide the motive power for transport and farming, whips have been used to control them. The useful characteristics of a whip are that it can strike a blow at a distance from the user; and that it can make a sound when 'flicked' which working animals can be taught to recognise.

The two basic types are straight-out whips and lash whips. Straight-out whips have a long resilient stock and a short thong, and are used mainly for driving carriages and waggons; lash whips (e.g. hunting crops) have a shorter, stiff stock and a long, heavy thong — sometimes as long as 25 feet (7.62 m). The whip can be 'cracked' by flicking the thong.

In agricultural use, convenience of carrying was important: whips were designed to be slung over the ploughman's shoulder or round his neck — or slung on the horse-collar.

Many whips from the nineteenth century are beautifully designed, and evidently made with specialised skill. The tapering thongs were made from many different leathers including horse-hide; finer thongs were made from foal or calfskins; kangaroo leather was particularly suitable for the fine plaited thongs for which Australian whips were famous.

The handle, known as the whip stock, was made in woods such as holly, yew or cane and was often provided with ivory, brass or silver mounts. Others were composed of split cane, with whalebone (later glassfibre) centres, glued together and bound, usually by threads of gut.

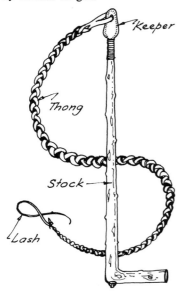

Fig. 13:20 A typical hunting crop, with the names for the parts of a whip

(1) WHIP-STOCK TOOLS

Ordinary woodworking tools were used for cutting and trimming whip-stocks made in such woods as holly and yew. Basket-maker's tools were employed when whip-stocks were made from strips of cane; these included the Basket-maker's Cleaver, and the Basket-maker's Shave. The following tools were also used:

(a) *Whip Plane Fig. 13:21*

A short wooden plane with a sole measuring *c.* $3\frac{1}{4} \times 2$ in. (8.2 × 5 cm), sometimes plated, and with a single cutting iron set at 45°. The example illustrated here was used by Messrs Crawley & Sons, Whip Makers, Peterborough (established 1806) for paring down tapering cane strips.

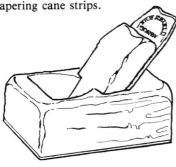

Fig. 13:21

(b) *Whip Braiding Machine Fig. 13:22*

This ingenious, hand-operated machine is used for covering the handles of whips with gut, flax and other threads. It is adapted from a machine used in the textile trades. The whip-stock is suspended in the centre of a horizontal wooden wheel of about 4 ft 6 in. (1.37 m) diameter which is mounted on a platform. Beneath are fitted the bobbins that hold the thread, and the keys and other mechanisms that regulate the plaiting operation. When the wheel is turned the threads are plaited maypole-fashion round the whip handle. One of these machines, formerly used by the whip makers G. & J. Zair, is now in the Birmingham City Museum.

Fig. 13:22 A whip braiding machine. Reproduced by courtesy of *Country Life* (August 1948)

(2) WHIP-THONG TOOLS

Before cutting the thongs, the leather is usually drawn back and forth over a blunt blade, known as a *Stake*, to take the stretch out of it, and to make it more supple. (The Stake is described under *Staking and Perching Tools* in the section LEATHER MANUFACTURE II.)

The leather is then cut into strips, tapered and plaited with the tools described below.

The basic cutting tool is a sharp knife used with the thong-maker's thumb nail acting as a guide to regulate the width. In addition to the cutting tools described here, reference may be made to tools borrowed from other trades that are sometimes used by whip makers for cutting thongs. See:

Lace-Making Tools } in the BOOT AND
Welt Tools   } SHOE MAKER section

335

Welting Strip Cutter, in the CLOG MAKER section

Cutting Gauge ⎫
⎬ in the HARNESS MAKER AND
Plough Gauge ⎭ SADDLER section

(*a*)　*Gang Cutters Fig. 13:23; 13:24*
This tool consists of .a group of cutting blades mounted on a base with provision for adjusting the number of blades and the distance between them. The leather is pulled against the blades and this produces a group of parallel thongs. Two types are illustrated:

(1)　An American pattern:　*Fig. 13:23*
The cutters are mounted on the front of a bench. (From D. W. Morgan, USA, 1976)

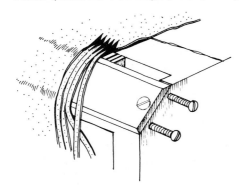

Fig. 13:23

(2)　A home-made pattern:　*Fig. 13:24*
Neil McGregor (Tetbury, 1980) describes a home-made gang cutter used by a whip maker in Cheltenham:

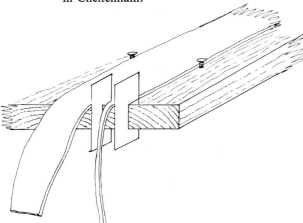

Fig. 13:24

'. . . his method of cutting whip thongs was first to cut from the alum-tawed horse hide a strip $1\frac{1}{8}$ to $1\frac{1}{2}$ in. width depending on the number of thongs to be plaited. This was done with a harness-maker's Plough Gauge. He had driven into the end-grain of a flat piece of hardwood three or four very thin blades. One blade was used as a guide for the edge of the leather to run against. The blade to the right of it was set at the width required, but the blade was inclined inwards by a degree or so to keep the strip "set" to the width. When the thongs were cut to the length and width required, they were transferred to two more blades, set at a smaller width, and part of their length was reduced in width again. The individual thongs were thus tapered from about $\frac{3}{16}$ in. or $\frac{1}{4}$ in. at top to as fine as you could make them.'

(*b*)　*An American Lace Cutter Fig. 13:25*
A blade held in a kerf cut in a wooden block, with an adjustable fence to control the width of the leather being cut. (The illustration is taken from *Whips and Whipmaking* by D. W. Morgan, 1976. It is presumably a home-made tool.)

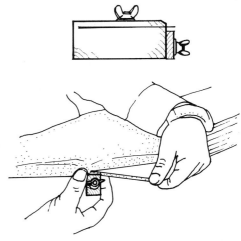

Fig. 13:25

(*c*)　*Fid*
A name borrowed from the sail makers and applied to a smooth, round, bodkin-like spike set in a wooden handle, 3–5 in. (7.6–12.7 cm) long. Used when plaiting for making an opening or holding open a gap in the thongs to allow another thong to pass.

(*d*)　*Rounding Board*
A flat board *c.* 14 × 9 in. (35.5 × 22.8 cm) and 1 in. (2.5 cm) thick, with a thin leather covering on the

bottom, and a leather loop on the top for a handhold.

After the whip has been plaited, it is dampened and laid on a clean flat surface. The board is then used to roll the plaited thong back and forth, working along the whip in sections, but lessening the pressure as the thong tapers. The purpose of this operation is to make the individual thongs lie evenly.

(e) Thonging Bowler

A tool described by H. Lloyd-Johnes (1948): '. . . a cylindrical piece of solid wood is used for shaping and bowing the plaited thongs with their whalebone centres.'

Other Uses of Leather

The following are examples of equipment in which certain parts are made in leather. Most of the tools used are those of the harness maker's; but those developed for particular products are described below.

(a) Bellows

Known to have been in use over 5,000 years ago, leather-sided bellows are still made for both industrial and domestic purposes. Bellows with pear-shaped boards joined by flexible leather sides, were used in innumerable blacksmiths' forges throughout the country; a much smaller version is still in use in the home to brighten up the fire, and in industry for blowing dust out of delicate mechanisms, such as clocks or pianos.

(1) The Blacksmith's Bellows Fig. 13:26

The traditional pear-shaped blacksmith's bellows, referred to above, were being made from 16 to 50 inches (40.6 cm–1.27 m) in length. They were replaced in recent years first by the cylindrical-shaped bellows, and today by electric fans.

Fig. 13:26

(2) Organ-Builder's Bellows and the Leather Stick Fig. 13:26a

Bellows were also made for pipe organs. The name *Leather Stick* was given to a simple spatular-type of wooden tool used for spreading

Scotch glue on the leather when joining seams and when attaching the bellows to surrounding woodwork. Joining by means of rivets (as in blacksmiths' bellows) was not suitable for organ bellows because rivets do not provide a completely airtight joint.

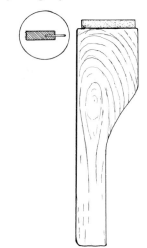

Fig. 13:26a

(b) Boats Fig. 13:27a; 13:27b overleaf

Curraghs and coracles are still used by salmon fishermen on the rivers of Ireland and Wales. Their split willow frames were in earlier times covered with leather; today they are covered with calico impregnated with pitch.

These boats are described by J. Geraint Jenkins (1965) and E. Estyn Evans (1967). For a remarkable account of building a leather boat and its journey across the Atlantic, see Tim Severin (1978).

Fig. 13:27a A Welsh Teifi Coracle

337

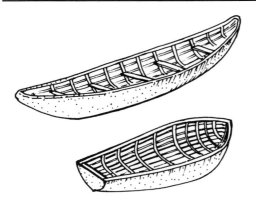

Fig.13:27b Irish curraghs (after *Ships Through the Ages* by D. Lobley, London 1972)

(*c*) *Leather Fillets for Pattern-Making Fig. 13:28*
A Fillet Plane is used to cut leather strips for filling sharp interior angles in wooden patterns and coreboxes used for sand-casting in the foundry. A pattern is the wooden counterpart of the metal casting to be produced. It is used for moulding a shape in the sand into which molten metal is subsequently poured.

The filling of sharp internal corners with a leather fillet is done to avoid the sand breaking away at those points, and to encourage 'free delivery' of the pattern from the sand without damaging the mould. There are several variants of this plane, but all have a V-shaped cutting iron with a 90° included angle.

The plane cuts a triangular strip from the surface of the leather and this is glued into an internal corner of the pattern.

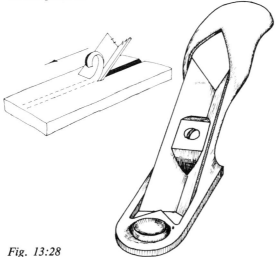

Fig. 13:28

(*d*) *Moulded Leather*
Leather can be made plastic by wetting and then moulded into almost any shape desired by working it into hollow moulds, by forcing it over wood or metal formers, or by pressing it between dies. When dry, the leather sets and keeps its shape.

This process was known to the ancient makers of shields and armour; and from the Middle Ages until the early nineteenth century the process was used for making the leather jugs known as bombards and black jacks; and for making utensils such as leather flasks, fire buckets and drinking mugs.

(*e*) *Protective Clothing Figs 13:29; 10:1 (p. 280)*
This includes the following leather garments designed to protect the wearer at work:

(1) Leather gloves reinforced with metal plates and leather boots reinforced with metal-covered toe-caps are worn in the foundry (e.g. by fettlers), and in other occupations where the hands or feet are liable to injury.

(2) Protective leather hats were made for men working in certain occupations, such as miners, firemen, and policemen. The type worn by stevedores and dustmen will be familiar to audiences of Bernard Shaw's 'Pygmalion' (and its musical version 'My Fair Lady') in which Alfred Doolittle, Eliza's father, wears a hat with a leather flap falling over his shoulders to protect him from the load being carried. Brass helmets for firemen were introduced about 1850. Today, protective leather hats have been mostly replaced by metal or plastic helmets.

(3) Leather aprons are worn by such tradesmen as blacksmiths, coopers and farriers. Farriers in particular need some tough material to protect them when holding a horse's hoof between their legs for shoeing.

The tools used are mainly the Knife, Awl and Needle of the harness maker or shoemaker. Some of the helmets were moulded: after cutting to shape, the leather was dampened and then shaped by forcing it into a wood or metal mould. (See *Moulded Leather* above.)

Fig. 13:29 A seaman's leather hat as worn aboard Brunel's *Great Eastern* (c. 1866)

(f) Rawhide Gears and Hammers

Rawhide is made from hide freed from hair and flesh, and then dried but not tanned.

The meshing of a pinion and spur-gear was made less noisy if the pinion was made of rawhide. Rawhide is also used for facing hammers: this makes it possible to strike hard without leaving hammer marks — an essential tool to the millwright when repairing or re-assembling a machine.

(g) Safety Belts Fig. 13:30

Steeplejacks, linesmen and window cleaners depend on these leather belts for their lives when working high above ground. The example illustrated was made for the GPO by Barrow, Hepburn & Gale, the London makers of safety equipment, *c.* 1970.

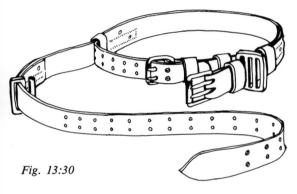

Fig. 13:30

(h) Sharkskin Rasp Fig. 13:31

A name given to a wooden tool rather like a rolling pin round which is nailed a piece of skin from a shark or dogfish. The example illustrated is in the Northampton Leather Museum and is dated *c.* 1850. The skin has been nailed over a cloth lining.

The scales of the skin are hard and pointed, and stand up obliquely, so that they abrade in one direction and not in the other.

This type of abrasive tool was in common use for smoothing wood before the sand or glass papers came into general use. It is related that the skin, when bent round the finger, could be used as a file. There is evidence that last makers continued to use these abrasive skins until recent times.

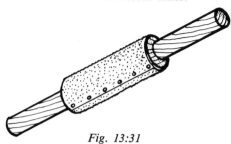

Fig. 13:31

(i) Textile-Machine Leathers

Leather is still used in textile machinery where resistance to wear and reduction of noise is important: for instance, for making Pickers. These are leather 'hammers' used to knock the shuttle back and forth in mechanical looms. A number of special leather parts were used in other textile machines, and until recently many northern tanneries specialised in their manufacture.

(j) Upholstery and Furniture Leather

Leather was used in ancient Egypt for covering stools, chairs and beds. Recently, chairs with buttoned leather upholstery, popular in Victorian times, have come back into fashion. The work is done with both upholsterer's and harness-maker's tools.

Cabinetmakers have used dyed leather from the eighteenth century onwards for the tops of desks and library tables. The table top is bordered with veneer, and leather is cut to fit within it. The edge of the leather is decorated by gilding with *Rolls* and other tools described in the BOOKBINDER section.

References and Bibliography

1. Abbreviations

J Article from a journal.
P Printed book or pamphlet.
T Trade catalogue, price list, or directory.
V Visit to, or correspondence with, the person or firm named. These entries also signify the author's thanks for help and information given.

2. Books on particular trades

Books on particular trades are included in the Bibliography under the following authors:

Bookbinding
Burdett, E.
Clements, J.
Cockerell, D.
Middleton, B. C.

Boot and Shoe making
Devlin, J.
Garsault, M. de
Golding, F. Y.
Leno, J. B.
Modern Boot and Shoe Maker
Plucknett, F.
Rees, J. F.
Swaysland, E. F. C.
Thornton, J. H.

Clog making
Liège Museum
Vigeon, E.

Decoration of Leather
Ellin-Carter, E.
Francis-Lewis, C.

Furrier
Bachrach, M.
Grover, F.
Links, J. G.
Rosenberg, C. J.

Glove making
Ellis, B. E.
Leyland, N. L. and Troughton, J. E.

Handbag and Purse making
Moseley, G. C.

Harness making and Saddle making
Council for Small Industries in Rural Areas (COSIRA)
Fitz-Gerald, W. N.
Grant, B.
Hasluck, P. N.
Rice, Lee M.
Shields, J. H. L.

Hat making (Beaver)
Penny Magazine
Tomlinson's Encyclopaedia

Leather Manufacture
Dublin Society
Jenkins, G. J. (1973)
Lamb, M. C.
Proctor, H. R.
Sharphouse, T. H.
Thomson, R. S.
Watts, A.

Leather-working Trades (General)
Diderot's Encyclopaedia
Hartley, D.
Hill, J.
Jenkins, J. G.
Knight's Practical Dictionary
Waterer, J. W.
Woods, K. S.

Loriner
Latchford, B.
Tuke, D. R.

Miscellaneous Trades
Cricket Ball making: Barty-King, H.
Coracle making: Jenkins, G. J. (1966); Hornel, J.
Coach Trimming: Philipson, J.
Felt making: Burkett, M. E.
Gut-String making: Tomlinson's Encyclopaedia
Last making: Mobbs, H. W. and Russel, S. H.
Leather Bottles: Baker, O.

340

Parchment Maker: Hartley, D.
  Tomlinson's Encyclopaedia
Taxidermy: Browne, M.; Davie, O.
Whip making: Morgan, D. W.

3. Museums

A list of museums and other institutions consulted will be found in the Acknowledgements at the front of the book.

4. References and Bibliography

V Aaron, Benjamin, & Sons (Halifax, 1977). Clog maker.

P Adcock, K. J. *Leather*. Pitman, London. *c.* 1915.

V Adelman, M. (London). Technical executive, Marks & Spencer.

V Aldous, Leonard (Debenham, Suffolk. 1974). Saddler.

P *Amateur Mechanic* Bernard Jones (ed.). Waverley Book Co., London. *c.* 1910. Chapters on shoemaking and repairing by D. Lawrence Lord in Vols. I–IV.

P Amman, Jost and Sachs, Hans. *Book of Trades*. Frankfurt am Maine. 1568. (Reproduced by Dover Publications, New York. 1973.)

PV Arnold, J. *The Shell Book of Country Crafts*. Baker, London. 1968.

T Arthur, Henry. USA, 1874. Catalogue of Leather and Findings. (Reproduced by Alexander Farnham. USA, 1980).

P Ashford, W. G. *Whips and Whip-making*. First published in 1893. Reproduced in *Whips and Whipmaking* by David W. Morgan. Cornell Maritime Press, USA. 1972.

PV Avitsur, Prof. Shmuel. Authority on trades of the Near East. Author of *Historical Atlas of Tools and Workshops in the Holy Land*. Jerusalem, 1976.

P Bachrach, Max. *Fur*. Prentice-Hall, New York. 1930.

V Baker, J. & F. J., & Co. (Colyton, Devon). Tanners and curriers. See also Bishop, R. W., and Snell, J.

P Baker, Oliver. *Black Jacks and Leather Bottels*. 1921.

V Bamforth, J. H. (Golcar, York). Authority on clog making.

V Band, H., & Co. Ltd (London, 1981). Tanners and vellum makers.

V Barnes, David (Malmesbury). Harness maker and saddler.

T Barnsley, George, & Sons. Sheffield. 1890, 1927 & 1970. Makers of shoemaking, tanner's and currier's tools.

V Barnsley, George. Director, George Barnsley & Sons Ltd (Sheffield).

V Barrow Hepburn Equipment Ltd (London). Makers of hydraulic leathers, safety belts etc.

P Barty-King, Hugh. *Quilt Winders and Pod Shavers*. (History of cricket bat and ball manufacture.) Macdonald Jane, London. 1979.

V Basing and Mathews (Newbury). Saddlers.

V Beitler, A. M. (USA). Writer on trade tools.

V Bell, G. H. (Northampton). Shoe repairer.

T Berg, E. A. Manufacturing Co. Ltd. Sweden, 1939. Shoemaker's and other tools.

P Bertrand, J. E. *Description des Arts et Métiers*. Neuchâtel. 1775.

V Bigelow, Russel (USA). Retired saddler and harness maker.

V Bigg, H. R. (Harpenden). Shoe repairer.

V Bishop, R. W., Works Manager, J. & F. J. Baker & Co. (Colyton, Devon). Tanners and curriers.

T Blanchard, Simonin. Paris, *c.* 1900. (Founded 1823.) Makers of tools for harness-making, saddlery, curriers and other leather-working trades. See also Krempp, G., who makes use of same illustrations.

T Bliss, Beauchamp & Bliss. London, *c.* 1883. Saddler's tools.

V Booth & Co. (International) Ltd (Nottingham). Tanners etc.

V Botting, K. (Harpenden, Herts. 1960). Shoe repairer.

V Bowles, E. W. (Cambridge). Saddler and harness maker.

P *Boy's Book of Trades* and the tools used in them. Geo. Routledge, London. 1866.

V Bradnell, William (Besses O'th Barn, Lancs, 1953). Clog makers.

V Brewer, A. (Redbourn, Herts, *c.* 1948). Saddler.

V Brierley, H. (Rochdale, 1960). Clog and patten makers.

V British Leather Manufacturers' Research Association (Northampton). London, 1972.

P British Standards Institution. *Glossary of Leather Terms*.

V Britter, R. D. (London). Director of Leather Institute.

P Bronowsky, J. *The Ascent of Man*. BBC Publications, London. 1973.

P Browne, M. *Artistic and Scientific Taxidermy and Modelling*. Adam & Charles Black, London. 1896.

V Brownlee & Son (Bathgate). Saddlers.

T Buck & Hickman Ltd, London, 1935. Tools for many trades.

P Burdett, Eric. *The Craft of Book Binding.* David & Charles, Newton Abbot. 1975.

P Burkett, M. E., OBE. *Art of the Felt Maker.* Abbot Hall Art Gallery, Kendal. 1979.

V Byrne, Richard O. National Museum of Canada.

V Calman Links (London). Furriers.

V Campfield Press (St Albans). Bookbinders.

P Carman, W. Y. *Dictionary of Military Uniforms.* Batsford, London. 1977.

V Chalwin, B. D. (London). Shoemaker and maker of riding boots.

V Champion & Wilton (London, 1935). Successors: see Gidden, W. & H.

T Cheney, Edward & Sons. Kettering, *c.* 1960. Makers of shoemaker's tools.

P Childe, Gordon. *What Happened in History.* Penguin, Harmondsworth. 1942.

V Clark, Alfred (Ipswich, 1949). Saddler.

V Clayton, Joseph & Sons (Chesterfield). Tanners.

P Clements, Jeff. *Bookbinding.* Arco Publication, London. 1963.

V Clothier, L. E., & Co. (Woodstock). Glove makers.

V Coburn, Mr & Mrs L. G. (Harpenden).

P Cockerell, Douglas. *Bookbinding and the Care of Books.* Pitman, London. 1901.

V Collier (late), Arthur. Tool maker and tool merchant in London. Authority on tools and trades.

V Connolly Bros (London). Curriers.

V Cook, Percy (Luton). Shoemaker.

J Cook, Rupert. 'The Shoemaker's Tools and Craft in Antiquity'. Unpublished thesis. 1977.

V Cordwainers' College (London).

P (COSIRA): Council for Small Industries in Rural Areas. *Making a Saddle.* London. 1973.

V Cowley, William & Son (Newport Pagnell). Parchment makers. Director: Mr J. Visscher.

V Cox, Herbert (Chesham). Saddlers.

VT Crawley & Sons (Peterborough, 1958). Whipmakers, established 1806.

P Crocket, H. G. See *Modern Boot and Shoe Maker.*

V Croggon, Josiah, & Sons (Grampound, Cornwall). Tanners.

P Davie, O. *Methods in the Art of Taxidermy.* David McKay, USA, 1894.

V Deard, W. (Welwyn, Herts.). Saddlers.

P Dekker, Thomas. *The Shoemaker's holiday or the gentle craft.* 1600.

V Delf, W. (Cirencester). Harness maker and saddler.

P Deloney, Thomas. *The Gentle Craft.* 1597.

V Dent-Fownes Ltd (Warminster). Glove makers.

T Derrick & Hosegood Ltd. Bristol, 1962. Grindery merchants.

P Devlin, James. Part I: *The Shoemaker.* Part II: *The Guide to the Trade.* London. 1839–41.

V Dew, H. (Middlesbrough, 1951). Shoe repairer.

P Dictionaries, Directories and Encyclopaedias, see:

British Standards Institution. *Glossary of Leather Terms.*
Carman, W. Y. *Dictionary of Military Uniforms.*
Dictionary of Occupational Terms. HMSO, 1927.
Diderot, D. *Encyclopaedia.* Paris, *c.* 1751.
Halliwell. *Dictionary of Archaic and Provincial Words.*
Freudenberg, W. *International Dictionary of Leather.*
Kelly & Co. *Directory of Leather Trades.*
Orton, H. & Dieth, E. *Survey of English Dialects.*
Oxford English Dictionary.
Rees, Abraham. *Encyclopaedia and Universal Dictionary of Arts, Science and Literature.*
Scottish National Dictionary.

P *Dictionary of Occupational Terms.* HMSO, London. 1927.

P Diderot, D. and D'Alembert, J. le R. (eds) *Encyclopédie ou dictionnaire raisonné des sciences, des arts, et des métiers.* Paris. 1751–72. (Reproduced by Readex Microprint, New York. 1981).

TV Dixon, Joseph, Tool Co. Ltd (Walsall, *c.* 1950). Makers of saddler's tools.

P Dobbs, Brian. *The Last shall be first.* (Story of John Lobb the bootmakers). Hamish Hamilton, London. 1972.

V Downes, W. (USA, 1975). Writer on trade tools.

P Dublin Society. *The Art of Tanning and Currying Leather.* London. 1774.

V Easey, G., & Son (Saxmundham, Suffolk). Saddler.

V Eastern Counties Leather Co. (Cambridge). Leather merchants and tanners.

P Edwards, E. Hartley. *Saddlery.* J. A. Allen, London. 1963.

V Edwards, Henry. Writer on early Christian saints.

P Ellin-Carter, E. *Artistic Leather work.* Spon, London. 1926.

P Ellis, B. Eldred. *Gloves and the Glove Trade.* Pitman, London. 1921.

V Emmerson, M. J. (Boston, 1950). Saddler.

T *Equine Album see* Hampson & Scott.

P Evan, E. Estyn. *Irish Folk Ways*. Routledge & Kegan Paul, London. 1967.

PV Evans, George Ewart. *Ask the Fellows who Cut the Hay*. Faber, London. 1956.
  — *The Pattern under the Plough*. 1966.
  — *The Farm and the Village*. 1969.
  — *Where Beards Wag All*. 1970.
  — *The Days that We have Seen*. 1975.
  — *From the mouths of men*. 1976.

V Evans, Norman (Princes Risborough). Saddler.

V Fellowes, A. (Harpenden). Shoe repairer.

P Fitz-Gerald, W. N. *The Harness Makers Illustrated Manual*. New York. 1875. (Reprinted by North River Press 1977).

P Fowler, Eric. *A Hundred Years in the Shoe Trade 1862–1962*. J. Buckingham, Norwich. 1962.

T Fralick & Sherman. USA, ·c. 1882. Retailers of leather and findings.

V Francis, W. J., & Son (Falmouth, 1962). Curriers & saddlers.

P Francis-Lewis, Cecile. *A Practical Handbook on Leatherwork*. Francis-Lewis Studio, London. 1928.

P Frazer, James George. *The Golden Bough*. Abridged edn. Macmillan, London. 1932.

PV Freeman, Charles. Luton and the Hat Industry. Luton Museum. 1953.

P Freudenberg, Walter. *International Dictionary of the Leather and Allied Trades*. Berlin. 1951.

V Fudge, W. E. (London, 1935). Millwright, Albany Engineering Co., Lydney.

P Garsault, M. de. *L'Art du Cordonnier*. 1767. (Forthcoming translation with notes by D. A. Saguto. USA).

V Gibbons, W. K. (Harpenden). Shoemaker.

V Gidden, W. & H. (London). Saddlers.

V Gilbert, D., & Sons (Newmarket). Saddler.

V Glasow, W. B. (Porlock). Formerly boot & shoemaker at Messrs John Lobb, London.

T Goldenberg & Co., Alsace, France. 1875, 1901, 1904, and 1950. Tools for many trades.

P Golding, F. Y. (ed.). *Boots and Shoes, their making, manufacture and selling*. 8 Vols. New Era and Pitman. 1934.

T Gomph, Henry G. USA, 1875. Makers of tools for saddlers and harness makers.

V Goodfellow, A V. (Northampton, 1973). Shoemaking instructor, Northampton College of Technology.

VP Goodman, W. L. (Bristol). Authority on the history of woodworking and other tools. Author of *The History of Woodworking Tools*. Bell, London. 1964.

P Grant, Bruce. *How to make Cowboy Horse Gear*. Cornell Maritime Press, USA. 1953.

P Grant, I. F. *Highland Folk Ways*. Routledge & Kegan Paul, London. 1961.

V Graysmark, W. (London). Shoemaker. Formerly at J. Lobb, Bootmakers, London.

P Gresham Publishing Company: see *Modern Boot & Shoe Maker*. This book, which is written by various authors, is referred to in the text as 'Gresham 1920'.

P Grover, Frank. *Practical Fur Cutting*. Technical Press, Oxford. 1936.

V Hacker Furs Ltd (London). Furriers.

T Haley, Thomas, & Co. Leeds, 1898. Leatherworking tools and machinery, including tools for makers of driving belts.

P Halford Publishing Co. *Shoemaker's Guide*. Leicester. 1969.

P Halliwell, J. O. *A Dictionary of Archaic and Provincial Words*. London. 1847.

T Hampson & Scott. *Equine Album*. Walsall *c*. 1900. Established 1794. Catalogue of saddle and harness requisites and tools.

V Handord Greatorex & Co. (Walsall, 1955). Curriers.

T Harrild & Sons, London, 1903. Catalogue of bookbinder's tools.

V Hartenberg, Richard S. Professor of Mechanical Engineering, Northwestern University, USA.

P Hartley, Dorothy. *Made in England*. Methuen, London. 1939.

J Hartley, V. A. 'The St Giles shoe school: an incident in thé history of shoe manufacturing in Northampton'. *Journal of the British Boot and Shoe Institution*. Vol 9, No. 14, September 1961.

P Hasluck, Paul N. (ed.). *Saddlery and Harness Making*. London, 1904. Reprinted by J. Allen & Co. London. 1962.
  — *Boot making and mending*. Cassell, London. 1898.

V Hawley, Kenneth (Sheffield). Tool merchant and authority on tools and tool makers.

V Hayward, Charles H. Authority on woodworking and other trades. Author of books on woodworking, upholstery and furniture design.

V Healy, Chris (Nottingham). Worker in leather.

T Hill, James R., & Co. USA, *c*. 1912. Catalogue of harness maker's and saddler's tools. (Reproduced by W. C. Cavallini, 1974.)

P Hill, Jack. *The Complete Practical Book of Country Crafts*. David & Charles, Newton Abbot. 1979.

T Hirth & Krause. USA, 1890. Catalogue of leather, findings and shoemaker's tools. (Reproduced by Early American Industries Association. 1980.)

V Holden, Edward Thomas, & Son. (Walsall, 1955). Curriers.

P Holme, Randle. *The Academy of Armoury, or a storehouse of armoury and blazon.* 1688.

P Hommel, R. P. *China at Work.* John Day, New York. 1937.

P Hornel, J. *British Coracles and Irish Curraghs.* 1938.

V Huline Dickens, A. M. (London). Instructor in saddlery, Cordwainers' Technical College, London.

V Humphrey, G. F. (Royston, Herts. 1951). Saddler.

V Huskisson, G. T., & Son (Walsall). Harness and collar maker.

V Ibberson, W. G., OBE (Sheffield). Director of George Ibberson, Cutlers. Makers of industrial and other knives.

T Jackson, Isaac, & Son Ltd. Glossop, *c.* 1909. Tools for making driving belts.

T James, John, & Sons. Redditch, 1948. Needles, awls etc.

PV Jenkins, J. Geraint.
— *Traditional Country Craftsmen.* Routledge & Kegan Paul. London. 1965.
— *Life and Tradition in Rural Wales.* Dent, London. 1976.
— *The Rhaeadr Tannery.* Welsh Folk Museum, 1973.

PV Jobson, Allan. *Household and Country Crafts.* Elek, London. 1953.

V Jones, A. Oris (USA). Writer on trade tools.

V Jones, Prof. Joseph. (University of Texas, USA.).

V Jones, Tristan (St Nicholas-at-Wade). Authority on certain trades and tools.

J Jope, E. M. 'Vehicles and Harness'. *A History of Technology.* Vol II. Oxford. 1954.

T Joseph, Marcel. Dijon, *c.* 1920. Shoemaker's tools.

V Kebabian, John S. (USA). Editor of *The Chronicle of the Early American Industries Association.*

VP Kebabian, Paul B. (USA). Author of *American Woodworking Tools.* 1978.

P Kelly & Co. *Directory of the Leather Trades for England, Scotland, Wales & Ireland.* 1896. (Earlier editions in the Guildhall Library, London.)

V Ketteringham, A. (Royston). Upholsterer.

V Kilby, Kenneth (Luton). Authority on the cooper's trade.

P Knight, Edward H. *Practical Dictionary of Mechanics.* Published in the USA in 1877 and afterwards by Cassell, Petter and Galpin in London. (Reproduced in 1980 by the Early American Industries Association.)

V Knight, Dr Richard (Birmingham). Expert on trade tools.

T Krempp, G. (Successeur Georges Lutz). Paris, 1905. Makers of tools for harness, saddlery and other leather-working trades. See also Blanchard, who makes use of the same illustrations.

P Lamb, M. C. *Leather Dressing.* Anglo-American Technical Co., London. 1925.

P Latchford, Benjamin. *The Loriner.* London. 1871.

V Launer, S., & Co. (London). Handbag makers.

V Lawrence, Edward (Canterbury). Saddler and harness maker. Formerly at Champion & Wilton in London.

P Lawson, Andrew. *Handmade in London.* Cassell, London. 1978.

P Lebrun, M. *Bourrelier-Sellier.* France. 1833. (Reprinted by Roret, *c.* 1978.)

P Leno, J. B. *Art of Boot and Shoe making*, 1895. Reprinted by Technical Press, London. 1949.

P Leyland, N. L. and Troughton, J. E. *Glovemaking in West Oxfordshire, the craft and its history.* Oxford City and County Museum Publication No. 4, 1974. See also Troughton, J. E.

P Liège Museum, Belgium. 'La Fabrication de Sabots'. *Enquêtes du Musée de la Vie Wallonne.* Nos 11 & 12. 1926.

P Lilley, S. *Men, Machines and History.* Cobbett Press, London. 1948.

P Links, J. G. *The Book of Fur.* Barrie. 1956.

V Linney, C. (Leighton Buzzard). Saddlers.

V Liverpool Tanning Co. (Liverpool, 1954). Tanners.

J Lloyd-Johnes, Herbert. 'The Making of Whips and Thongs', *Country Life.* Aug. 27, 1948.

V Lobb, John (London). Bootmaker.

P Lord, D. Lawrence. Articles on bootmaking and repairing in *The Amateur Mechanic* (q.v.).

P Lyes, D. C. *The Leather Glove Industry of Worcester in the Nineteenth Century.* Worcester City Museum. 1973.

V McGregor, Neil (Tetbury, Glos.). Authority on the working and decoration of leather.

V Maddie, J. G. (Harpenden, 1946). Saddler.

V Mallinson, Anne (Selbourne). Bookseller.

V Mann, G. (Northampton). Orthopaedic shoemaker.

V Marks, H. W. (Enfield). Retired Shoemaker's Clicker.

V Marlow, C. (Northampton). Shoemaker instructor.

V Marshall, A. H. (Kirton, Lincs., 1954). Saddler.

V Martin, William (Barley, Herts., 1877–1950). Shoe repairer, barber and postman.

V Martin-Rice Ltd (London). Fur dressers.

T Mason & Son Ltd. Walsall, *c.* 1900. Catalogue of saddlery.

PV Massingham, H. J. *Country Relics*. Cambridge University Press. 1939.

P Mayhew, Henry. *London Labour and the London Poor*. London. 1851. (See also *The Unknown Mayhew* under Thompson, E. P.)

V Maxwell, Henry & Co. Ltd (London). Shoemakers.

V Meinel, C. (Bow Brand, Kings Lynn). Gut string makers.

T Melhuish, Richard & Sons Ltd. London, 1885, 1912, 1913. Tools for many trades.

P Middleton, Bernard C. *A History of English Craft Bookbinding Technique*. Hafner, London. 1963.

V Miles, J., & Son (Dorchester). Saddlers.

V Milner, S., & Son (Leicester). Saddler.

J Mobbs, H. W. 'The Development of Last-Making from a Hand Craft to the Modern Industry'. *Journal of the British Boot and Shoe Institution*, 1947, p. 238.

P *Modern Boot and Shoe Maker*. 4 Vol. Gresham Publishing Company, London. 1920. This book is by various authors and is referred to in the text as *Gresham, 1920*.

P Morgan, David W. *Whips and Whipmaking*. Cornell Maritime Press, USA. 1976.

P Moseley, G. C. *Leather Goods Manufacture*. London. 1939.

T Moseman, C. M., & Brother, New York, *c.* 1890. Catalogue of saddlery, stable requisites, tools etc.

V Mullane, John (Caddington, Beds.) Shoemaker and repairer.

V Munt, K. S. (Harpenden, 1968). Shoe repairer.

V Murga-Candler Ltd (London). Table liners and gilders.

V Murison, David (Edinburgh). Editor, *The Scottish National Dictionary*.

V Museums: see list in the Acknowledgements at the front of the book.

V National Union of Boot & Shoe Operators (London).

PV Needham, Joseph, and Wang Ling. *Science and Civilisation in China*. 7 Vols. Cambridge University Press, 1954–65.

JV Needham, Joseph, and Lu Gwei-Djen. 'Efficient Equine Harness; The Chinese Inventions'. *Physis*, Vol. II, 1960, pp. 121–62.

T Newton, Thomas. Walsall, *c.* 1865. Catalogue of saddlery and harness.

P Northampton Museums and Art Gallery. *Catalogue of Shoe and Shoemaker Pictures and Works of Art*. 1975.

P Norwood, John. *Craftsmen at Work*. John Baker, London. 1977.

P Orton, H., and Dieth, E. *Survey of English Dialects*. 4 Vols. Leeds. 1963–.

T Osborne, C. S. New Jersey, USA, *c.* 1883. (A later edition is reprinted by the Early American Industries Association, 1975.) Tools for saddlers and harness makers.

P *Oxford English Dictionary*. 12 Vols. The Clarendon Press, Oxford. 1933.

V Pangbourne, W. R. & Sons (London). Leather Merchants.

P Parker, Rowland. *The Common Stream*. Collins, London. 1975.

V Patey, S. (London). Hat makers.

J *The Penny Magazine*. 'A Day at a Hat-Factory'. No. 567. Vol. X,G (Supplement). Jan. 1841. pp. 4–48.

P Petrie, Sir W. M. Flinders. *Tools and Weapons*. Constable, London. 1917.

T Pfannstiel, Gebr. Germany, 1950. Catalogue of shoemaker's tools.

P Philipson, John. *The Art and Craft of Coachbuilding*. Bell, London. 1897.

V Pickup (Burnley, 1953). Clogmaker.

PV Pinto, Edward H. *Treen and other wooden bygones*. Bell, London. 1969.

P Plucknett, Frank. *Boot and Shoe Manufacture*. Pitman, London. 1916, 1922, 1931.

T Pocock Brothers Ltd (Incorporating Ullathorne & Co.). London. *c.* 1920. Grindery.

V Pond, R. C. (Norwich, 1973). Shoemaker.

V Portway, Nicholas W. (Stowmarket, Suffolk). Director of Webb & Son (Combs) Ltd. Makers of sueded shearlings. Until recent years this firm were also tanners and curriers and makers of leather driving belts.

V Powell, Cyril (Salford). Clog maker.

V Powell, Roger, OBE, and Rita G. (Froxfield, Hampshire). Bookbinders.

T Preston, Edward & Sons Ltd. Birmingham, 1914. Rules, levels and other tools.

P Proctor, Henry R. *A Text-Book of Tanning*. Spon, London. 1885.

P Pyne, W. H. *Pictorial Groups for the Embellishment of Landscape*. 1822.

P Randle Holme, *see* Holme, Randle.

V Reader, Alfred & Co. (Maidstone). Maker of cricket balls.

P Rees, Abraham. *Cyclopaedia or Universal Dictionary of Arts, Sciences, and Literature*. 1802–20.

P Rees, John F. *The Art and Mystery of a Cordwainer*. London. 1813.

V Reichman, Charles (USA). Writer on trades and tools.

P Rice, Lee M. *How to make a Western Saddle*. Cornell Maritime Press, USA. 1956.

V Richardson, W. & J. (Derby). Tanners and curriers.

T Richter, L. & Son, Northampton, *c.* 1890. Catalogue of shoe tools.

V Risley, Ivan (Kansas City, USA). Writer on trades and tools.

V Rivers, J. E. (Petersfield, Hants.). Saddler and harness maker.

V Roberts, Kenneth D. (Fitzwilliam, USA). Author and publisher of books on tools and trades.

J Roberts, Warren E. (Indiana University, USA). 'Folklore in the Novels of Thomas Deloney', from *Studies in Folklore*. Indiana University Press, Bloomington. 1957.

P Rosenberg, Cyril J. *Furs and Furriery*. New Era Publishing Co. Ltd. 1927.

T Ross Moyer Manufacturing Co. Cincinnatti, USA, 1884. Machinery and tools for boot and shoemaking.

V Russel, G. W. & Son (Hitchin, Herts.). Leather manufacturers.

J Russel, S. H. 'The Making of Cast-Iron Lasts... A Forgotten Craft'. *Foundry Trade Journal*, p. 227, August 1967.

T Russell Bookcrafts, Hitchin, Hertfordshire. 1930–70. Bookbinding tools and materials.

V The Saddlers' Company (London).

P Saguto, D. A. *Translation of The Art of the Cordwainer by M. de Garsault, 1767*. (A forthcoming publication, USA.)

V Saguto, D. A. (Kensington, Maryland, USA). Shoemaker and authority on eighteenth-century shoemaking methods. Correspondence with the author, 1980–3.

P Salaman, R. A. 'Tradesmen's Tools *c.* 1500–1850', in *A History of Technology*, Vol. III. Oxford, 1954.

— *Dictionary of Tools used in the Woodworking and Allied Trades, c. 1700–1970*. Allen & Unwin, London. 1975.

P San Joaquin Historical Museum. *The Harness Maker and his Tools*. (USA, 1976.)

V Saunders, James (London). Shoe closer.

V Savva, T. (London). Hand-sewn shoemakers.

P *Scottish National Dictionary*. Edinburgh. 1974–6.

P Severin, Tim. *The Brendan Voyage*. Book Club, London. 1978.

J Sexton, H. J. 'Fifty years in the shoe trade'. *Journal of the Norfolk Industrial Archaeology Society*, Vol. I, No. 7. July, 1974.

P Sharphouse, T. H. *Leather Technician's Handbook*. Leather Producers' Association, London. 1971.

T Shattock, Hunter & Co. (Bristol, *c.* 1890). Catalogue of harness and saddler's tools.

T *Sheffield Illustrated List, The*. Pawson and Brailsford, Sheffield. 1888.

V Sheldrake, G. (Hunstanton, Norfolk). Shoe repairer.

P Shields, J. H. L. *To Handmake a Saddle*. J. A. Allen. 1975.

V Siegal, Robert H. M. Writer on sabot making etc. USA, 1970.

P Singer, Holmyard and Singer, Hall. *A History of Technology*. 5 Vols. The Clarendon Press, Oxford. 1954.

P Sloane, Eric. *A Museum of Early American Tools*. Wilfred Funk, New York. 1964.

V Snell, Jack. Retired leather worker and beamsman, at J. & F. J. Baker (Colyton, Devon), tanners and curriers.

V Society of Master Saddlers (London).

V Southall, Jas., & Co. Ltd (Norwich). Shoe manufacturers.

V Stace, George (Birchington, Kent). Retired collar maker.

V Stack, F. (London). Boot and shoemaker at Messrs James Lobb.

T Stahlschmidt Tool Co. Germany, 1911. Tools for many trades.

V Stanley Tools (New Britain, USA and Sheffield, England). Makers of tools for many trades.

V Stiff, Sydney (London). Retired coach trimmer.

V Stone, William T. (Walsall). Retired loriner, and authority on the forging of bits and stirrups.

V Street Shoe Museum (Street, Somerset).

V Swann, Miss J. M. (Keeper, Northampton Shoe Collection). Authority on the history and making of boots and shoes.

P Swaysland, Edward F. C. *Boot and Shoe Design and Manufacture*. Jos. Tebbut, Northampton. 1905.

V Szulikowski, Georges. (London). Boot and shoemaker at Messrs J. Lobb.

V Tarrant, Tom (Monewden, Suffolk). Shoe repairer.

T Taylor & Co. Tools Ltd. London, *c.* 1960. Tools for leather-working.

V Texas Folklore Society (Texas University, USA).

T Thacker, R. E., Walsall. 1905. Catalogue of harness, saddles, and bits etc.

P Thompson, E. P. and Yeo, E. (eds). *The Unknown Mayhew*. Merlin Press, London. 1971. (Selections from Mayhew's letters about nineteenth-century trades and tradesmen. See also Mayhew, Henry.)

V Thomson, Roy S. Leather chemist; writer on the history of leather manufacture. Author of:

J — 'The industrial archaeology of leather', *Leather*, Sept. 1978.

J — 'Leather manufacture in the post-medieval period with special reference to Northamptonshire', *Journal of the Society of Post-Medieval Archaeology*, Vol. 15. 1980.

J — 'Tanning. Man's first manufacturing process?' *Transactions*, Newcomen Society, Vol. 53, 1981–2.

PV Thornton, J. H. Formerly Head of the Department of Boot and Shoe Manufacture, Northampton College of Technology.

P — *Textbook of Footwear Manufacture*. Butterworth, London. 1970.

V — Correspondence with the author, 1978–82.

J — 'The English Shoe-Size Scale', *Journal of British Boot & Shoe Institution*. Vol. 4, No. 10, June 1951, p. 514.

J — 'From Cottage to Factory', an article published by the Craft's Council for the *Shoe Show: British Shoes since 1790*, held in London 1979.

T Timmins, Richard & Sons. Birmingham, *c.* 1850. Tools for many trades. (See also Wynn, Timmins).

P Tomlinson, Charles. *Cyclopaedia of Useful Arts and Manufactures*. 9 Vols. George Virtue, London. 1853.

   — *Illustrations of Trades*. London. 1860. (Reprinted by Early American Industries Association, 1972.)

V Townsend, Raymond R. (Willamsburg, USA). Writer on the history and making of boots and shoes.

V Troughton, J. E. (Woodstock, Oxon.). Retired glove maker and writer on glove making: see Leyland and Troughton.

P Tuke, Diana R. *Bit by Bit*. Allen, London. 1965.
   — *Stitch by Stitch. A Guide to Equine Saddles*. Allen, London. 1970.

P Utley, M. C. *Practical Painter and Decorator*. (Includes chapter on gilding.) Odhams Press, *c.* 1945.

PV Vigeon, Evelyn. 'Clogs or Wooden Soled Shoes', *Journal of the Costume Society*. 1977. (Reprinted for the Ordsall Hall Museum, Salford, Manchester.)

V Walker, Philip (Debenham, Suffolk). Authority on woodworking and other trades, and their history.

V Walkley, F. (Clogs) Ltd (Huddersfield). Clog makers.

P Walloon Museum publication: see under Liège Museum.

V Walton Bros (Halifax). Clog makers.

P Ward, F. G. *Boot and Shoe Repairing*. Foyle, London. 1953.

V Ward, H. E. (Holme, Norfolk. 1964). Shoemaker.

V Ward, W. (Dover, 1954). Shoe repairer.

T Ward & Payne Ltd. Sheffield, *c.* 1900 and 1911. Tools for many trades.

V Waterer, J. W. Authority and writer on the leather trades and their history.

P — *Leather in Life, Art and Industry*. London. 1946.
   — *Leather Craftsmanship*. Bell, London. 1968.
   — *Leather,* History of Technology, Vol. II: see Singer, Holmyard and Singer, Hall.
   — *Leather and the Warrior*. Museum of Leathercraft, Northampton. 1944.

P Watts, Alexander. *The Art of Leather Manufacture*. Crosby Lockwood. 1885.

V Webb, Clifford (1978), Beamsman at Messrs Josiah Croggan, Tanners, Grampound, Cornwall.

V Webb & Son (Combs) Ltd (Stowmarket). Tanners etc: see Portway, Nicholas.

V Weiss, Francis (London). Authority on the fur trade.

J Weiss, Francis. 'The Fur Coat Turn-about', *Worckelmann Fur Bulletin*. April, 1977.

V Whitcher, Jack (Aldeburgh, 1950). Army shoemaker.

V Whitcomb, W. (Street, Somerset). Shoemaker.

V White, James W. (Chelmsford). Writer on loriner's work.

P White, Lyn, Jr. *Medieval Technology and Social Change*. Oxford University Press. 1962.

V Wilkerson, Jack. (Barley, Herts.). Farmer and archaeologist.

V Wilkinson, Martin (Redbourn, Herts.). Saddler.

V Williams, J. C. (Canterbury). Worker in leather.

V Willinson, D., & Son (Northampton, 1952). Saddlers.

T Wilson, Edward & Son. Bootle, *c.* 1950. Tanner's and currier's hand tools.

P Wilson, Eunice. *A History of Shoe Fashions.* Pitman, London. 1969.

P Woods, K. S. *Rural Crafts of England.* Harrap, London, 1949.

T Wright, B. & J., & Sons, Leeds, *c.* 1920. Catalogue of tanner's and currier's tools and accessories.

V Wright & Son (St Albans). Furriers.

P Wright, Thomas. *The Romance of the Shoe.* Farncombe, London. 1922.

P Wymer, Norman. *English Country Crafts.* 1946.
— *English Town Crafts.* Batsford, London. 1949.

TV Wynn, Timmins & Co. Ltd. Birmingham, 1890, 1892. (See also Timmins, Richard). Tools for many trades.

GENERAL INDEX

ABBREVIATIONS

Abbreviation	*Section*
Bk	= Bookbinder
B/S	= Boot and Shoe Maker
Clog	= Clog Maker
Dec	= Decoration of Leather
Driv	= Driving-Belt Maker
Fur	= Furrier
Glov	= Glove Maker
H/bag	= Handbag and Purse Maker
H/S	= Harness Maker and Saddler
Hat	= Hat Maker
L/Mf	= Leather Manufacturer
Lor	= Loriner
Misc	= Miscellaneous Trades and Tools

A

B

C

D

E

F

G

H

I

J

K

Knife: note on nomenclature.
Knives described as 'round', 'circular' or 'semi-circular' are sometimes also given one of the following names:

If circular: Lunette; Moon; Paring; Perching; Skinner's; Round.

If semi-circular: Cheese; Cutting Out; Half-Circle; Half-Moon; Head; Round.

Knives with one of the above names will be found in one or more of the following Trade Sections: Boot and Shoe Maker; Harness Maker and Saddler; Leather Manufacture, II. Currier; and under *Parchment Maker* in the Miscellaneous Section.

L

M

N

O

P

Q

R

S

T

U

V

W

Y